1.15 miles	$\cong$ 1 minute (1′) of latit~~ude~~
1.6449	= coefficient fo
3.141 592 654	= π
*6 miles	= length, width
*10 sq. chains (ch²)	= (Gunter's) 1 a
*15° longitude	= width of one t
15°F	changes length ~~of~~ ~~100~~-ft steel tape by 0.01 ft
*16½ ft	= 1 rod = 1 pole = 1 perch = ¼ ch (Gunter's)
*20°C	= standard temperature (Celsius) in taping = 68°F
23°26½′	= maximum declination of sun at solstices
23ʰ56ᵐ04.091ˢ	= length of sidereal day in mean solar time, and 3ᵐ55.909ˢ solar time short of mean solar day; also 3ᵐ56.555ˢ sidereal time short of mean solar day
*24 hr	= 360° of longitude
*25.4 mm	= 1 in. (U.S. standard foot of 1959)
*36	= number of sections in normal township
*50	= Beaman arc reading for 0° vertical angle (30 in old arcs)
57°17′44.8″	= 1 radian (rad) = 57.295 779 51°
*66 ft	= length of Gunter's chain = 100 links (lk)
69.1 miles	$\cong$ 1° latitude
*80 ch	= (Gunter's) 1 mile
100	= usual stadia ratio
101 ft	$\cong$ 1 second (1″) of latitude
300	$\cong$ stadia ratio in some precise levels
333⅓	$\cong$ stadia ratio in some precise levels, for yard rods
*400 grads	= 360°
*480 ch	= width and length of normal township
490 lb/ft³	= density of steel for tape computations
*640 acres	= one normal section of 1 mile²
6076.10 ft	= 1 nautical mile
*3600/3937	= ratio U.S. yd/m for old legal (1866) and surveyor's foot
4,046.9 m²	= 1 acre
*6400 mils	= 360°
5,729.577 951 ft	= radius of 1° curve, arc definition
5,729.650 686 ft	= radius of 1° curve, chord definition
10,000 km	= distance from equator to pole (basis for length of meter)
*43,560 ft²	= 1 acre
206,264.806 25 sec	= 1 radian = cot 1 sec = 180°/π in sec
299,792.5 km/sec	= speed of light, and other electromagnetic waves, in vacuum
1,650,763.73	= wave lengths of krypton gas in vacuum, 1960 meter length
6,356,583.8 m	= earth's polar semi-axis (Clarke ellipsoid 1866)
6,378,206.4 m	= earth's equatorial semi-axis (Clarke ellipsoid 1866)
20,906,000 ft	= mean radius of earth = 3960 miles
29,000,000 lb/in.²	= Young's modulus of elasticity for steel

* Denotes exact value. All others correct to figures shown.

ELEMENTARY SURVEYING

THE IEP SERIES IN CIVIL ENGINEERING
Series Editor
Russell C. Brinker
New Mexico State University

Brinker and Wolf   *ELEMENTARY SURVEYING*, 6th Edition
Clark, Viessman, and Hammer   *WATER SUPPLY AND POLLUTION CONTROL*, 3rd Edition
Hill   *FUNDAMENTALS OF STRUCTURAL DESIGN: STEEL, CONCRETE, AND TIMBER*
Jumikis   *FOUNDATION ENGINEERING*
McCormac   *STRUCTURAL ANALYSIS*, 3rd Edition
McCormac   *STRUCTURAL STEEL DESIGN*, 2nd Edition
Meyer   *ROUTE SURVEYING AND DESIGN*, 4th Edition
Moffitt   *PHOTOGRAMMETRY*, 2nd Edition
Moffitt and Bouchard   *SURVEYING*, 6th Edition
Salmon and Johnson   *STEEL STRUCTURES: DESIGN AND BEHAVIOR*
Spangler and Handy   *SOIL ENGINEERING*, 3rd Edition
Ural   *FINITE ELEMENT METHOD: Basic Concepts and Applications*
Viessman, Harbaugh, Knapp, and Lewis   *INTRODUCTION TO HYDROLOGY*, 2nd Edition
Wang   *COMPUTER METHODS IN ADVANCED STRUCTURAL ANALYSIS*
Wang and Salmon   *REINFORCED CONCRETE DESIGN*, 2nd Edition

ELEMENTARY SURVEYING

SIXTH EDITION

RUSSELL C. BRINKER

New Mexico State University

PAUL R. WOLF

University of Wisconsin, Madison

THOMAS Y. CROWELL COMPANY
New York   Established 1834

ELEMENTARY SURVEYING, Sixth Edition

Library of Congress Cataloging in Publication Data

Brinker, Russell Charles.
    Elementary surveying.
    (IEP series in civil engineering)
    Bibliography: p.
    Includes index.
    1. Surveying. I. Wolf, Paul R., joint author.

II. Title.
TA545.B86 1977   526.9   77-23334
ISBN 0-7002-2493-9

CONTENTS

Computation of latitudes and departures. Methods for traverse adjustment. Traverse computation using electronic devices. Latitudes and departures by traverse tables. Rectangular coordinates. Lengths and bearings from latitudes and departures, or coordinates (inversion). Coordinate computations in boundary measurements. Traverse orientation by coordinates. State plane coordinate systems. Sources of error in traverse computations. Mistakes. Problems.

PART B

PREFACE

The Sixth Edition of *Elementary Surveying* continues the approach of previous editions, which emphasized fundamental theory and procedures, while offering practical hints and illustrations not covered generally, or at all, elsewhere.

A new chapter, Control Surveys, has been added and another, Industrial Applications, deleted. The chapter on Adjustment of Instruments is now in Appendix A, and the previous appendix on State Plane Coordinates has been expanded and placed in the text. The longest chapters—Linear Measurements, Leveling, and The Transit and Theodolite—have been divided into three parts for ease of reading. SI units are discussed and used in many problems and examples throughout the text.

Other changes and additions include:

1. A list of some important numbers in surveying with formulas for metric conversions inside the front cover, and commonly used abbreviations of surveying terms with a list of mapping symbols on the inside back cover.

2. Expanded information on government agencies, discussions of new uses for surveying, and a brief description of early determination of the earth's size and shape.

3. More suggestions and examples for notekeeping, with completely relettered noteforms.

4. New material on EDM instruments. The HP 3800 is discussed as representative, and a generalized sketch of its operating characteristics

provided. Photos show other instruments. Updated tables of the devices, which are split into three categores—electro-optical, microwave, and long-radio wave—list radiation sources, ranges, and weights.

5. Examination of the laser and its applications in several chapters.

6. A brief comparison of the original U.S. "official" foot and the U.S. "survey" foot.

7. Enlarged coverage of the differences between transits and theodolites, with more illustrations of theodolite reading systems, and description and direction readings with a set of notes.

8. A 1975.0 chart showing distribution of magnetic declinations, with a discussion of a second method for computing bearings.

9. A different arrangement for calculating areas by coordinates, and a photo of an electronic planimeter.

10. Some additional properties of contours, and a new section on computer mapping.

11. Updated sample observation computations in field astronomy, and an earth's orbit figure plus a sketch relating vertical and horizontal angles to time in solar shots. The mean polar distance table is continued through 1984.

12. Expansion of the Boundary Surveys chapter with new metes-and-bounds, coordinate, and combined metes-and-bounds-coordinate descriptions, figures, subdivisions with a plat, and a land-partitioning example.

13. Revision of the Survey of Quadrangles in the U.S. Public Lands System Figure.

14. Substantial enlargement of the Construction Surveys chapter with new sections on horizontal and vertical control, other surveys, figures, noteforms, and practical points.

15. Topics on intersection of a circular curve and straight line, and on passing a circular curve through a fixed point.

16. Introduction of the general equation for a parabolic curve and an illustrative example having the curve start at a plus station as a supplement to the "arithmetic" solutions previously offered.

17. Revision of the method used in computing cross-sectional areas by coordinates.

18. Current data on the National Geodetic Survey's five classes of leveling, accuracy standards for horizontal control, and error limits for geodetic survey control azimuths; and diagrams showing the National Geodetic Network of horizontal and vertical control in Florida.

19. Discussion of Satellite Geodesy and Doppler surveying methods, plus a short section on inertial surveying systems.

20. A revision of the Photogrammetry chapter to bring in a consideration of orthophotos and some new instruments.

21. The deletion of descriptions of adjustments for the Beaman Arc and planetable alidade, but an addition of those for the optical plummet and bull's-eye level bubble.

22. Elimination of the natural functions table and the sample traverse table, and a reduction of the stadia tables from eight to four pages (but retaining data for vertical angles up to 16°) to make room for new text material. Low-cost pocket electronic calculators permit this change.

23. Over 1000 total homework problems are at the ends of chapters, sufficient for many semesters without repeating assignments. Some problems are carried through several chapters so progressive steps in their solutions can be followed; these problems are marked with asterisks so students can refer to their solutions for later use. For the first time, answers are given in Appendix A for some typical problems. A solutions manual is available to teachers adopting the Sixth Edition.

Stress in the text and problems is placed upon the theory of errors, correlation of theory and practical field methods, significant figures, and the interdependence of field, computation, and mapping requirements.

Engineers, architects, geologists, and foresters must be able to make measurements and analyze the precision and accuracy of results obtained by other people. They should be qualified to properly locate and set machinery; lay out houses, buildings, and other common structures; and understand and prepare simple topographic maps. Each of these areas is discussed and proper field procedures to obtain a desired precision noted.

A few cost figures are introduced so that students will learn early in their college work to associate the three bases of engineering practice—theory, application, and costs. All surveying is a constant fight to reduce or isolate errors and mistakes. In each chapter the student is reminded of this point through lists of typical errors and mistakes.

Although all six editions retain the title *Elementary Surveying*, the material goes beyond the elementary stage in length and scope. The large number of chapters, however, permits inclusion or omission of subjects to correspond with the class time available for students in civil engineering, other engineering curricula, architecture, geology, agriculture, and forestry.

Chapters are arranged in the order found most convenient at numerous colleges. Fundamental material is collected in the first fourteen chapters. Theory and use of the fundamental ground surveying instruments—the tape, EDMs, level, transit, theodolite, and planetable—are described in detail, and new types of equipment noted. Any chapter following Chapter 11 can be omitted without loss of continuity, although several are short enough to be suitable for a single assignment.

Limited coverage of such subjects as photogrammetry, field astronomy and boundary surveys, is given to fit various programs offered. For example, the brief chapter on boundary surveys is intended to make students aware of a few problems involved in the survey and transfer of property, and the legal requirements of professional registration. Some instructors give broad survey-type courses and want their students to get an overall view of the many surveying functions. It is believed that the arrangement in scope of material presented herein will meet that need, also.

Taping, EDM, leveling, the transit and theodolite are taken up in order because students find it easier to acquire some facility with the equipment in this sequence. Also, this arrangement permits the start and continuation of field work with a minimum of preliminary lecture time. The arrangement of field assignments at the beginning of Appendix A makes it possible to begin effective computation and drafting-room problems after just a few periods in the field if bad weather is encountered.

The difficulty in getting through all of the background material (basic concepts of the profession, history, theory of errors, and methods of note-keeping) before commencing field work during the first week is recognized. Nevertheless the authors feel that these topics should precede the theory and use of instruments.

The subject of notes and noteforms—an important part of surveying and engineering—is discussed in a separate chapter. Most sample noteforms are collected in Appendix A, rather than being scattered throughout the book, to assist in finding them quickly.

ACKNOWLEDGMENTS

The authors wish to acknowledge the use of helpful suggestions, assistance, or pertinent material for this or previous editions, or both, given by Professors A. S. Cutler, O. S. Zelner, and L. F. Boon; C. B. Andrews; P. P. Rice; D. F. Griffin; A. S. Chase; L. Perez; Lt. Col. W. L. Baxter; E. G. Rich; J. P. Rastroni; D. V. Smith; E. C. Wagner, H. E. Kallsen, J. L. Clapp, R. B. Buckner, and S. Johnson; G. Lyon; W. A. Wintz, Jr.; D. C. McKee; J. M. DeMarche; C. F. Meyer; C. H. Drown; J. R. Coltharp; P. W. McDonnell, Jr.; J. O. Eichler; D. C. McNeese; D. A. Tyler; D. S. Turner; J. O. Meadows; E. F. Kuhlan; R. E. Hauck; K. S. Curtis; P. E. Borgo; and P. Newlin. Also, Mr. W. C. Wattles, R. B. Irwin, T. Henderson, F. Sieker, F. Thomack, R. Holdridge, R. Minnick, and J. Kessler.

Illustrative material and other help has been freely supplied by the U. S. Bureau of Land Management, U. S. Geological Survey, National Geodetic Survey, U. S. Soil Conservation Service, and the Defense Mapping Agency. Manufacturers of surveying equipment who provided photographs include the Keuffel & Esser Company; W. & L. E. Gurley; Kern Instruments, Inc.; Wild Heerbrugg Instruments, Inc.; Zena Company; Hewlett-Packard; Cubic Industrial Corporation; Laser Systems and Electronics, Inc.; AGA Corporation; Tellurometer, U.S.A.; Construction Laser Division of Blount Industries, Inc.; Carl Zeiss, Oberkochen; Alster and Associates, Inc.; Bausch & Lomb, Inc.; Danko Arlington, Inc.; Wallace and Tiernan; Lenker Manufacturing Company; Lietz Company; California Computer Products, Inc.; and Numonics Corporation.

ELEMENTARY
SURVEYING

PART A

1
INTRODUCTION

1-1. DEFINITION OF SURVEYING. Surveying has traditionally been defined as the science and art of determining relative positions of points above, on, or beneath the surface of the earth, or establishing such points. In a more general sense, however, surveying can be regarded as that discipline which encompasses all methods for gathering and processing information about the physical earth and the environment. Conventional ground systems are most frequently used, but aerial and satellite surveying methods, which evolved through the defense and space programs, are also common.

In general, the work of a surveyor can be divided into five parts:

1. *Decision making.* Selecting the survey method, equipment, most likely corner locations, etc.
2. *Field work or data acquisition.* Making measurements and recording data in the field.
3. *Computing or data processing.* Preparing calculations based upon the recorded data to determine locations, areas, volumes, and so on.
4. *Mapping or data representation.* Plotting measurements to produce a map, plat, or chart, or portraying the data in a numerical or computer format.
5. *Stakeout.* Setting monuments and stakes to delineate boundaries or guide construction operations.

1-2. IMPORTANCE OF SURVEYING. Surveying is one of the oldest and most important arts practiced by man because from the earliest times it has been found necessary to mark boundaries and divide land. Surveying

3

has now become indispensable to our modern way of life. The results of today's surveys are being used to (a) map the earth above and below sea level; (b) prepare navigational charts for use in the air, on land, and at sea; (c) establish property boundaries of private and public lands; (d) develop data banks of land-use and natural-resource information which aid in managing our environment; (e) determine facts on the size, shape, gravity, and magnetic fields of the earth; and (f) prepare charts of our moon and planets.

Surveying continues to play an extremely important role in many branches of engineering. For example, surveys are required prior to, during, and after planning and constructing highways, railroads, rapid-transit systems, buildings, bridges, missile ranges, launching sites and tracking stations, tunnels, canals, irrigation ditches, dams, drainage works, urban land subdivisions, water supply and sewerage systems, pipelines, and mine shafts. Surveying or surveying methods are commonly employed in laying out assembly lines and jigs, fabricating and placing large equipment, providing control for aerial photography, and in many related tasks in geology, forestry, landscape architecture, and archeology, but particularly in military and civil engineering. Optical alignment represents an application of surveying in shop practice.

All engineers must know the limits of accuracy possible in construction, plant design and layout, and manufacturing processes, even though someone else may do the actual surveying. In particular, civil engineers who are called upon to design and plan surveys must have a thorough understanding of the methods and instruments used, including their capabilities and limitations. This knowledge is best obtained by making measurements with the kinds of equipment used in practice to get a true concept of the theory of errors, and the small but recognizable differences which occur in observed quantities.

In addition to stressing the need for reasonable limits of accuracy, surveying emphasizes the value of significant figures. An engineer must know when to work to hundredths of a foot instead of to tenths or thousandths, or perhaps the nearest foot, and what precision in field data is necessary to justify carrying out computations to the desired number of decimal places. With experience, he learns how available equipment and personnel govern procedures and results.

Neat sketches and computations are the mark of an orderly mind, which in turn is an index of sound engineering background and competence. Taking field notes under all sorts of conditions is excellent preparation for the kind of recording and sketching expected of engineers. Additional training having a carry-over value is obtained in arranging computations properly.

Engineers designing buildings, bridges, equipment, and so on, are fortunate if their estimates of loads to be carried are correct within 5 per cent. Then a factor of safety of two or more is applied. But except for topographic work, only exceedingly small errors can be tolerated in surveying, and there is no factor of safety. Traditionally, therefore, surveying stresses both manual and computational precision.

1-3. HISTORY OF SURVEYING.   The oldest historical records in existence today which bear directly on the subject of surveying state that this science had its beginning in Egypt. Herodotus says Sesostris (about 1400 BC) divided the land of Egypt into plots for the purpose of taxation. The annual floods of the Nile River swept away portions of these plots, and surveyors were appointed to replace the bounds. These early surveyors were called *rope-stretchers* since their measurements were made with ropes having markers at unit distances.

As a consequence of this work the early Greek thinkers developed the science of geometry. Their advance, however, was chiefly along the lines of pure science. Heron stands out prominently for applying science to surveying, about 120 BC. He was the author of several important treatises of interest to engineers, including one called *The Dioptra*, which related the methods of surveying a field, drawing a plan, and making calculations. It also described one of the first pieces of surveying equipment recorded, the *diopter* (Fig. 1-1). For many years Heron's work was the most authoritative among Greek and Egyptian surveyors.

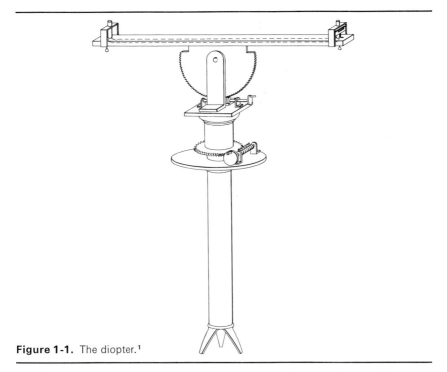

Figure 1-1. The diopter.[1]

---

[1] Figures 1–1 and 2 are shown through the courtesy of Professor Edward Noble Stone.

Real development in the art of surveying came through the practical-minded Romans, whose best-known writing on surveying was by Frontinus. Although the original manuscript disappeared, copied portions have been preserved. This noted Roman engineer and surveyor, who lived in the first century, was a pioneer in the field and his essay remained the standard for many years.

The engineering ability of the Romans was demonstrated by their extensive construction work throughout the Empire. The surveying necessary for this construction resulted in organization of a surveyors' guild. Ingenious instruments were developed and used. Among these were the *groma* used for sighting; the *libella*, an A frame with a plumb bob, for leveling; and the *chorobates* (Fig. 1-2), a horizontal straightedge about 20 ft long, with supporting legs and a groove on top for water to serve as a level.

One of the oldest Latin manuscripts in existence is the *Codex Acerianus*, written in about the sixth century. It contains an account of surveying as practiced by the Romans and includes several pages from Frontinus' treatise. The manuscript was found in the tenth century by Gerbert and served as the basis for his text on geometry, which was largely devoted to surveying.

During the Middle Ages, Greek and Roman science was kept alive by the Arabs. Little progress was made in the art of surveying, and the only writings pertaining to it were called "practical geometry."

In the thirteenth century Von Piso wrote *Practica Geometria*, which contained instructions on surveying. He also wrote *Liber Quadratorum*, dealing chiefly with the *quadrans*, a square brass frame having a 90° angle and other graduated scales. A movable pointer was used for sighting. Other instruments of the period were the *astrolabe*, a metal circle with a pointer hinged at its center and held by a ring at the top, and the *cross staff*, a wooden rod about 4 ft long with an adjustable crossarm at right angles to it. The known

Figure 1-2. The chorobates.

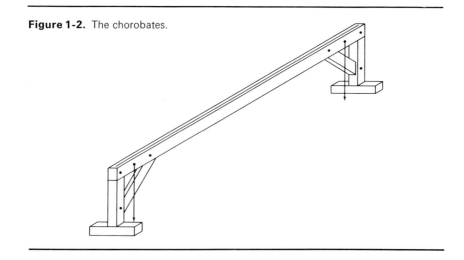

lengths of the arms of the cross staff permitted distances to be measured by proportion and angles.

Early civilizations assumed the earth to be a flat surface, but by noting the earth's circular shadow on the moon during lunar eclipses, and watching ships gradually disappear as they sailed toward the horizon, man slowly deduced that his planet actually curved in all directions.

Determining the true size and shape of the earth has intrigued man for centuries. History records that a Greek named Eratosthenes, about 220 BC, first attempted to compute its dimensions. He ascertained the angle subtending the meridian arc between Syene and Alexandria in Egypt by measuring shadows cast by the sun at these cities. The arc length was found by multiplying the number of caravan days between Syene and Alexandria by the average daily distance traveled. From the angle and arc measurements, applying elementary geometry, Eratosthenes calculated the earth's circumference to be about 25,000 miles. Subsequent precise geodetic measurements using better instruments and a technique equivalent geometrically to Eratosthenes' have shown his value, although slightly too large, to be amazingly close to the current accepted one. Actually, of course, the earth approximates an oblate spheroid having an equatorial radius about $13\frac{1}{2}$ miles longer than the polar radius.

In the eighteenth and nineteenth centuries the art of surveying advanced more rapidly. The need for maps and location of national boundaries caused England and France to make extensive surveys requiring accurate triangulation. Thus geodetic surveying began. The United States Coast and Geodetic Survey (now the National Geodetic Survey, National Ocean Survey, National Oceanic and Atmospheric Administration (NOAA) of the U.S. Department of Commerce) was established by an act of Congress in 1807.

Increased land values and the importance of exact boundaries, along with the demand for public improvements in the canal, turnpike, and railroad eras, brought surveying into a prominent position. More recently, the large volume of general construction, the numerous land subdivisions and better records required, and the demands posed by the fields of exploration and ecology have entailed an augmented surveying program. Surveying is still the sign of progress in the development and use of the earth's resources.

During World Wars I and II, and the Korean and Viet Nam conflicts, surveying in its many phases played an important part because of the stimulus provided to improve instruments and methods used to make measurements and maps. Progress continued into the space program where new equipment and systems were needed to supply precise control for missile alignment and moon mapping of proposed landing sites. Electronic distance-measuring (EDM) equipment, laser devices, north-seeking gyroscopes, improved aerial cameras, helicopters, inertial surveying systems, remote sensors, and various-size computers are examples of but a few products of modern technology now being directly applied in modern surveying with terrific impact.

Figure 1-3. Wild T-2 theodolite (left), Zena NI 025 self-leveling level, and Hewlett-Packard 3810 EDM. (Courtesy Wild Heerbrugg Instruments Inc., Zena Company, and Hewlett-Packard.)

Traditional surveying instruments—transit, level, and steel tape—are now frequently supplanted by the theodolite, the self-leveling level, electronic distance-measuring equipment (Fig. 1-3), and the aerial camera (see Fig. 25-1). In the mapping field, except for small areas, photogrammetry has generally replaced ground surveying on many kinds of projects but conventional ground surveys still are essential for establishing locations of horizontal and vertical control points, property corners, construction layout, and so on. For planning purposes with regard to land-use and natural-resource mapping, new remote sensing systems carried in satellites make possible the acquisition of voluminous data heretofore physically impossible to obtain.

1-4. TYPES OF SURVEYS.   There are many types of surveys, each so specialized that someone proficient in a particular area may have little contact with other areas. Anyone seeking a career in surveying and mapping, however, should be knowledgeable in every phase, as all are closely interrelated in modern practice. The more important classifications are described briefly.

Plane surveying. In plane surveying, except for leveling, the reference base for field work and computations is assumed to be a flat horizontal surface. The direction of a plumb line (and thus gravity) is considered parallel throughout the survey region, and all measured angles are presumed to be plane angles. For areas of limited size the surface of our vast spheroid is actually very nearly flat. On a line 5 miles long, the spheroid arc and chord lengths differ by only about 0.02 ft. A plane surface tangent to the spheroid has departed only about 8 in. at 1 mile from the point of tangency. In a triangle having an area of 75 miles^2, the difference between the sum of the three spheroidal angles and three plane angles is about 1″ (one second). It is evident, therefore, that except in surveys covering extensive areas, the earth's surface can be approximated as a plane, thus simplifying computations and techniques. In general, algebra, plane and analytical geometry, and trigonometry are employed. Even for very large areas, such as those involved in state plane coordinate systems described in Chapter 17, plane surveying can be used, with some allowances being made in computations. Use of state plane coordinates is not plane surveying but a shortcut to accomplishing geodetic surveying.

Geodetic surveying. Geodetic surveying is the technique to determine relative positions of widely spaced points and lengths and azimuths of long lines which require consideration of the size and shape of the earth.

Photogrammetric surveying. Photogrammetric surveying involves the use of data obtained by camera or other sensors most often carried in airplanes or satellites. Maps and data from such surveys embody the principles of photogrammetry or remote sensing.

Control surveys. Control surveys establish a network of horizontal and vertical monuments that serves as a reference framework for other surveys.

When the control survey is of small extent, plane surveying methods may be used, but generally geodetic methods are employed.

Construction surveys. Construction surveys provide points and elevations for building civil engineering projects; they are often called *engineering surveys*.

Property surveys. Property surveys establish property corners, boundaries, and areas of land parcels. They are also termed *land surveys, cadastral surveys*, and *boundary surveys*. All states now require professional registration to do property surveys.

Topographic surveys. Topographic surveys are used to prepare maps showing locations of natural and man-made features and elevations of points on the ground.

Route surveys. Route surveys are surveys of and for highways, railroads, pipelines, transmission lines, canals, and other projects of long linear extent.

Hydrographic surveys. Hydrographic surveys are made to map shorelines and bottom depths of lakes, streams, reservoirs, and other larger bodies of water. Sometimes the combination of topographic and hydrographic surveying is designated *cartographic surveying*.

1-5. PRESENT STATUS OF SURVEYING. There is an increasing demand for good maps in the United States, and various governmental agencies are attempting to provide them although handicapped by insufficient funds and personnel. A common misconception is that the entire country has been adequately mapped by now. Actually, about 95% of the United States is covered by mapping at scales of 1 mile to the inch or larger. At the present rate of new map production and periodic revision of satisfactorily mapped areas, complete coverage should be attained in the early 1980s. The primary basic map series is on a $\frac{1}{24,000}$ scale.

Accurate mapping cannot be done without good *basic control*. National survey nets for geodetic horizontal and vertical control are continually being extended over the country, primarily by the United States National Geodetic Survey, for the control of nautical charts and topographic maps, and to provide coordinated position data for all surveyors. The horizontal-control survey net consists of arcs of first-order and second-order triangulation, lines of first-order and second-order traverse, and first- and second-order trilateration (see Chapter 18). The data from this net are coordinated and correlated on the North American datum of 1927 extending through Alaska and Central America. The vertical-control survey net of the conterminous United States consists of over 168,000 km of first-order and 329,000 km of second-order leveling which determine the elevations of over 400,000 bench marks on the National Vertical Geodetic Datum (NVGD), which replaces the North American Datum of 1929. The advent of missiles, satellites, and space craft has caused a resurgence in geodesy and the control data they provide.

Three U.S. government agencies do surveying and mapping on a large scale:

1. The Coast and Geodetic Survey (now National Geodetic Survey) was organized to map the coast. Its activities now include triangulation, traverse, trilateration, precise leveling, preparation of nautical and aeronautical charts, photogrammetric surveys, tide and current studies, collection of magnetic data, gravimetric surveys, and worldwide control surveying activities which involve satellites. The basic control points established by this organization are the foundation for all large-area surveying.

2. The General Land Office, established in 1812, directed the public-lands surveys. Lines and corners have been set for most of the public lands in the conterminous United States, but much work remains in Alaska and is proceeding with " modern techniques." The Bureau of Land Management now has jurisdiction over the survey and sale of these lands.

3. The Geological Survey, established in 1879, will ultimately map the entire country. Its standard $7\frac{1}{2}'$ (minute) and $15'$ quadrangle maps show topographic and cultural features, and are suitable for general use and a variety of engineering and scientific purposes. Over 10,000,000 copies are distributed each year.[1]

In addition, units of the Corps of Engineers, U.S. Army, have made extensive surveys for emergency and military purposes. Some of these surveys provide data for engineering projects, such as those connected with flood control.

The mission of the Defense Mapping Agency is to provide map and associated products and services for the Department of Defense and all land combat forces. It has been reorganized into the following military mapping groups: Aerospace Center, Defense Mapping School, Hydrographic Center, Inter-American Geodetic Survey, and Topographic Center. The groups accomplish their assignment by furnishing identification and accurate positioning of features on the earth's surface in the form of geodetic data, digital information, and topographic maps in various forms.

Extensive surveys have also been conducted for special purposes by the Forest Service, National Park Service, International Boundary Commission, Bureau of Reclamation, Tennessee Valley Authority, Mississippi River Commission, United States Lake Survey, Department of Transportation, and so on.

Many states are also involved in surveying and mapping activities, particularly within departments of natural resources, highways, and transportation.

---

[1] As of this writing, mail orders for maps covering areas east of the Mississippi River should be addressed to the Branch of Distribution, U.S. Geological Survey, 1200 South Eads Street, Arlington, Virginia 22202, and for locations west of the Mississippi River to Branch of Distribution, U.S.G.S., Federal Center, Denver, Colorado 80225.

1-6. THE SURVEYING PROFESSION. Surveying is classified as a learned profession because the modern practitioner needs a wide background of technical training and experience, and must exercise independent judgement. A registered (licensed) professional surveyor must have a thorough knowledge of mathematics—particularly geometry and trigonometry with some calculus; a solid understanding of surveying theory, instruments, and methods in the areas of geodesy, photogrammetry, remote sensing, cartography and computers; some competency in economics, geography, geology, astronomy and dendrology; and be familiar with laws pertaining to land and boundaries. He should be accurate in computations and field operations, and able to do neat drafting. Above all, he is governed by a professional code of ethics, and is expected to charge reasonable fees for his work.

The personal qualifications of a surveyor are as important as his technical ability. He must be patient and tactful in dealing with clients and their sometimes hostile neighbors. Few people are aware of the painstaking search of old records that is required before field work is done. Diligent, time-consuming effort may be needed to locate corners on nearby tracts for checking purposes as well as to find corners for the property in question.

Permission to trespass on private property or to cut obstructing tree branches and shrubbery must be obtained through a proper approach. Such privileges are not conveyed by employment in a state highway department (but a court order can be obtained if a land owner objects to necessary surveys) or by a surveying license.

All 50 states, Guam, and Puerto Rico have registration laws for professional engineers and land surveyors (as do the provinces of Canada). Ten states presently have separate licensing boards for surveyors. In general, a surveyor's license is required to make property surveys, but not for construction, topographic, and route work unless boundary corners are set. To qualify for registration as either a professional engineer or land surveyor, it is necessary to have an appropriate college degree (or usually a longer equivalent number of years of experience), plus 4 years of acceptable practical experience, and then pass a 2-day written examination. Within a few years a technical degree will doubtless be mandated, and a truly national uniform examination in the fundamentals, principles, and practice of land surveying will make transfer of registration from one state to another easier.

The standard registration law makes it a misdemeanor "to practice or offer to practice land surveying" without a license and provides for certain penalties. Technical considerations, and lack of professional liability insurance (costly but vital), should discourage anyone other than an experienced surveyor from setting property corners, even for a friend, relative, or unwary client. As in all professions, scholastic training is merely the first step toward the goal of every aspiring surveyor and engineer—true professional status denoted by registration.

1-7. FUTURE CHALLENGES IN SURVEYING. Many important tasks involving measurements and mapping lie ahead to challenge surveyors. The National Geodetic Control network must be maintained and readjusted to meet the requirements of high-order future surveys; new topographic maps with larger scales are necessary for future planning and design; existing topographic maps of our rapidly expanding urban areas need revision and updating to reflect changes; long-range planning and assessment of environmental impacts of proposed construction projects call for maps of natural resources and land usage; cadastral surveys of the yet unsurveyed public lands are essential; monuments set many years ago by the original land surveyors have to be recovered and remonumented for preservation of property boundaries; appropriate surveys having very demanding accuracy are prerequisites for positioning drilling rigs as mineral and oil exploration press farther offshore; and in the space program, the desire for maps of neighboring planets will continue.

These and other opportunities offer a professional rewarding indoor or outdoor life, or both, for numerous people with suitable training in the various branches of surveying.

PROBLEMS

NOTE : Answers for these problems and some in later chapters can be obtained by consulting a dictionary, the references in Appendix B, general experience, other chapters, or by visiting the office of a surveyor, engineer, or land recorder.

1–1. List 10 uses for surveying in areas other than land surveying.
1–2. How is surveying used in the layout of radio station facilities ?
1–3. List some applications of surveying in geology, forestry, and mining.
1–4. Why is it necessary to make accurate surveys of underground mines ?
1–5. What are patent surveys ?
1–6. Name some equipment used in leveling huge farms and ranches for row irrigation, and to control contour plowing.
1–7. What astronomical observations are made by surveyors ?
1–8. Why should a surveyor have a knowledge of geology ?
1–9. Name two uses for lasers you have read about (other than in surveying).
1–10. In what other contexts is the term "survey" employed ?
1–11. What surveying measurements does a contractor need to lay a 30-in. sewer line that are not required for an 8-in. water main ?
1–12. How are surveying methods applied in fabrication of huge ships and planes ?
1–13. Explain how weather conditions affect the accuracy of surveys.
1–14. Devise a simple instrument which could be used for leveling a garage floor 22 × 24 ft prior to placing a concrete slab.
1–15. Describe a method for laying out a right angle to set a foundation for a U-shaped ranch-type house 50 × 25 ft overall, if a transit is not available.

1–16. Which organization in your state will furnish maps and surveying reference data to surveyors and engineers ?

1–17. How do you think the early Romans controlled elevations for the huge aqueducts they built to bring water to their cities ?

1–18. What kinds of surveys in Section 1-4 would be classified as "engineering" surveys ?

1–19. Is a vertical aerial photograph a map ? Explain.

1–20. Why should the purchaser of a farm, city lot, or home demand a survey before making final payment ?

1–21. Do the subdivision laws of your community specify the accuracy required for surveys made to lay out a subdivision ? Why or why not ?

1–22. What methods are employed to control the locations of offshore oil drilling leases and platforms ?

1–23. Can mechanics' liens be used by surveyors and civil engineers ? Explain.

1–24. Describe the purpose of the horizontal lines in some binoculars—for example, those used in field artillery operations.

1–25. List the legal requirements for registration as a land surveyor in your state.

2
THEORY OF MEASUREMENTS AND ERRORS

2-1. MEASUREMENTS IN GENERAL. The process of making measurements in surveying requires a combination of human skill and mechanical equipment applied with the utmost judgment. Experience and good physical conditions improve the human factor; superior equipment enables good operators to do better work with more consistent results and in less time. The design of measurement programs, comparable with other engineering design, is now practiced. Matrix algebra and the electronic computer are two of the newer tools used to set up measurement projects and to investigate and distribute errors after the results have been obtained.

2-2. TYPES OF MEASUREMENTS MADE IN SURVEYING. Five kinds of measurements illustrated in Fig. 2-1 form the basis of plane surveying:

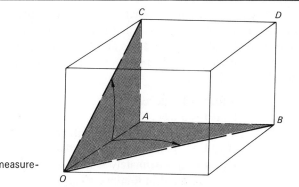

Figure 2-1. Kinds of measurements in surveying.

(1) horizontal angles, (2) horizontal distances, (3) vertical angles, (4) vertical distances, and (5) slope distances. Horizontal angles, as angle AOB, and horizontal distances, OA and OB, are measured in horizontal planes; vertical angles, as AOC, in vertical planes. Vertical lines, AC and DB, are measured in the direction of gravity; slope distances, OC, determined along inclined planes. Using combinations of these basic measurements, relative positions between any points can be computed.

2-3. UNITS OF MEASUREMENT. The units of measurement in surveying are those for *length, angle, area,* and *volume.* The *English system* length unit of *foot* has been most commonly used in the United States. It bears a definite relation to the *meter,* the basis of the *metric system.* Originally the meter was defined as $\frac{1}{10,000,000}$ of the earth's meridional quadrant. When the metric system was legalized for use in the United States in 1866, the meter was defined as the interval under certain physical conditions between lines on an International Prototype bar made of 90% platinum and 10% iridium, and accepted as equal to 39.37 in. A copy of the bar is held by the United States Bureau of Standards and compared periodically with the international standard stored in France.

In October 1960, at the General Conference on Weights and Measures (CGPM) the United States and 35 other nations agreed to redefine the meter in terms of the wavelength of a certain kind of light. Now one meter is equal to the length of 1,650,763.73 waves of the orange-red light produced by burning of the element krypton (Kr 86). The inch, foot, yard, and other units of length, like the meter, should not actually change since the wavelength standard and the metal standard are in satisfactory agreement, but some apparently discrepant measurements are still being checked. The new definition will permit industries to make more accurate measurements and to check their own instruments without recourse to the standard meter-bar in Washington. The wavelength of orange-red krypton light is a true constant, whereas there is a risk of instability in the metal meter-bar. If the CGPM had been held one year later, the laser might well have become the standard instead of krypton light.

In plane surveying, decimals of a foot are used extensively. Carpenters and builders employ inches and fractions in their work. The surveyor must be careful in making conversions and labeling all measurements properly.

Units of length used in past and present surveys in the United States include the following:

1 foot = 12 inches
1 yard = 3 feet
1 meter = 39.37 inches (see footnote 1, next page) = 3.2808 feet
1 rod = 1 pole = 1 perch = 16½ feet
1 vara = approximately 33 in. (an old Spanish unit often encountered in southwest U.S.)

1 Gunter's chain = 66 feet = 100 links (lk) = 4 rods
1 engineer's chain = 100 feet = 100 links (lk)
1 mile = 5280 feet = 80 Gunter's chains (ch)
1 nautical mile = 6076.10 feet

A common unit of area is the *acre*. Ten square chains (Gunter's) equal one acre. Thus an acre contains 43,560 ft^2. In the metric system, area is commonly given in *hectares*. One hectare is equal to 10,000 m^2 or 2.471 acres. The *arpent* (equal approximately to 0.85 acre but varies somewhat in different states), was used in land grants of the French crown; when employed as a linear term, it refers to the length of a side of 1 arpent^2.

The unit of angle used in surveying is the *degree*, defined as 1/360th of a circle. One degree (1°) equals 60′, and one minute equals 60″. Divisions of seconds are given in tenths, hundredths, and thousandths. Other methods have also been used to subdivide a circle, for example, 400 *grads* and with 100 *centesimal minutes/grad* and 100 *centesimal seconds/minute*; and 6400 *mils*. In the future, some instruments may be graduated to read angles in degrees and decimals.

The radian is an angle subtended by an arc of a circle having a length equal to the radius of the circle. Obviously 2π rad = 360°, 1 rad = 57°17′ 44.8″ = 57.2958°, and 0.01745 rad = 1°.

2-4. INTERNATIONAL SYSTEM OF UNITS (SI).[2]   A worldwide movement is now under way toward adoption of the *International System of Units*, generally known as *SI*. The system, which involves no changes in dimensions or values, is being advocated as a means of standardizing and simplifying units of measurement throughout the world. Units in the SI system of major concern to surveyors (standard symbols given in parentheses) are the *meter* (m) for distances, *radian* (rad) for plane angles, *square meter* (m^2) for areas, and *cubic meter* (m^3) for volumes.

Subdivisions of the meter are the *millimeter* (mm), *centimeter* (cm), and *decimeter* (dm), equal to 0.001 m, 0.01 m, and 0.1 m, respectively. A *kilometer* (km) equals 1000 m, or approximately five-eighths of a mile. Degrees, minutes, and seconds are also acceptable subdivisions of the radian for plane angle measure in SI.

---

[1] The foot originally adopted in the United States was based on 39.37 in. being equal exactly to 1 m, and thus 1 ft equal to 0.3048006 m. In 1959, however, the United States officially adopted the inch as equal to exactly 2.54 cm, so under this standard 1 ft equals 0.3048000 m. This difference in standards amounts to one part in 500,000, or 1 ft in 99.6969 . . . miles. Since all surveying prior to 1959 was done on the original standard, it would have been confusing to change. Therefore the original basis, now called the *U.S. Survey Foot*, has been officially adopted for surveying.

[2] A pamphlet entitled "International Standard ISO 1000," which describes the SI system in detail, is available at nominal cost from the American National Standards Institute, 1430 Broadway, New York, N.Y. 10018.

Although Congress has not yet officially adopted SI units, this action seems inevitable. Transition from English to SI units has already begun in the United States, but will require a gradual and lengthy process to complete because the public must be educated to the system and become accustomed to it. The English system can never be completely replaced because our archives will always contain volumes of valuable data recorded in these units. Original land descriptions for title insurance investigations must continue giving lengths in feet, just as some still carry distances in chains and links.

For surveyors the transition will likewise be a long one because many surveying instruments are graduated in English units, and changes must be made at a pace equal to the acceptance rate by the profession, clients, and general public. Although conversion will be difficult, and at times confusing, surveyors presently burdened with theory and computations in the archaic and awkward yard, foot, and inch units should welcome the change.

This book, prepared in the midst of the transition, uses both English and SI units in discussion and example problems.

2-5. SIGNIFICANT FIGURES.   In recording measurements, an indication of the accuracy attained is the number of digits (significant figures) recorded. By definition, the number of significant figures in any value includes the positive (certain) digits plus one (*only one*) digit which is estimated, and therefore questionable. For example, a distance recorded as 873.52 ft is said to have five significant figures; in this case the first four digits are certain and the last digit is questionable. In order to be consistent with the theory of errors, it is essential that data be recorded with the correct number of significant figures. If a significant figure is dropped off in recording a value, the time spent in acquiring certain accuracy has been wasted. On the other hand if data are recorded with more figures than those which are significant, false accuracy will be implied and time may be wasted in making computations.

The number of significant figures is often confused with the number of decimal places. Decimal places may have to be used to maintain the correct number of significant figures, but in themselves they do not indicate significant figures. Some examples follow:

Two significant figures: 24, 2.4, 0.24, 0.0024, 0.020
Three significant figures: 364, 36.4, 0.000364, 0.0240
Four significant figures: 7621, 76.21, 0.0007621, 24.00

Zeros at the end of an integral value may cause difficulty because they may or may not indicate significant figures. In the value 2400 it is not known how many figures are significant; there may be two, three, or four. One method of eliminating this uncertainty is to place a bar over the last significant figure, as in $240\bar{0}$, $24\bar{0}0$, or $2\bar{4}00$. Another method is to express the value in terms of powers of ten; the significant figures in the measurement are then written as a number between 1 and 10, including the correct number of zeros at the end, and the decimal point is placed by annexing a power of 10. As an example, 2400 becomes $2.400 \times (10)^3$ if both zeros are significant, $2.40 \times (10)^3$ if one is, and $2.4 \times (10)^3$ if there are only two significant figures.

In engineering computations it is imperative that calculations be consistent with the measured values. For addition or subtraction, round off the answer, retaining as the last significant figure the digit found in the *rightmost column full* of significant figures. Two examples are shown.

46.4012	57.301
1.02	1.48
375.0	629.
———	———
422.4	688.

In multiplication the percentage error of the product is equal to the sum of the percentage errors of the factors. This percentage error can be maintained by having the number of significant figures in the answer the same as the least number of significant figures in any of the factors. For example, 362.56×2.13 will give 772.2528 when multipled out; but there should be only three significant figures in the answer, which becomes 772.

In surveying, three types of problems relating to significant figures are encountered.

1. The field measurements are given to some specific number of significant figures, thus dictating that a corresponding number should be shown in a computed value. In an intermediate calculation it is common practice to carry at least one more digit than required, and then round off the answer to the correct number of significant figures. If logarithms or natural trigonometric functions are used, they should always have one more place than the number of significant figures desired held in the answer.

2. There may be an implied number of significant figures. For instance, the length of a football field might be specified as 100 yards. But in laying out the field, such a distance would probably be measured to the nearest hundredth of a foot, not the nearest half-yard.

3. Each factor may not cause an equal variation. For example, if a steel tape 100.00 ft long is to be corrected for a change in temperature of 15°F, one of these numbers has five significant figures while the other has only two. A 15° variation in temperature changes the tape length by only 0.01 ft, however. Therefore an adjusted tape length to five significant figures is warranted for this type of data. Another example is the computation of a slope distance from horizontal and vertical distances, as in Fig. 2-2. The vertical distance V is given to two significant figures, and the horizontal distance H measured to five significant figures. From these data the slope distance S can be computed to five significant figures. For small angles of slope, a considerable change in the vertical distance

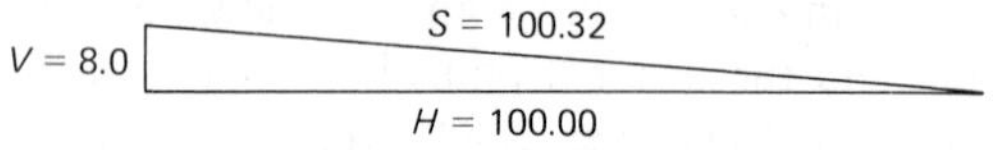

Figure 2-2. Slope correction.

$V = 8.0$ $S = 100.32$ $H = 100.00$

produces a relatively small increment in the difference between the slope and horizontal distances.

2-6. ROUNDING OFF NUMBERS.   Rounding off a number is the process of dropping one or more digits so that the answer contains only those digits which are significant or necessary in subsequent computations. In rounding off numbers to any required degree of accuracy in this text, the following procedure will be observed:

1. When the digit to be dropped is less than 5, the number is written *without* the digit. Thus 78.374 becomes 78.37.
2. When the digit to be dropped is exactly 5, the nearest *even* number is used for the preceding digit. Thus 78.375 becomes 78.38, and 78.385 is also rounded to 78.38.
3. When the digit to be dropped is greater than 5, the number is written with the preceding digit *increased* by one. Thus 78.376 becomes 78.38.

The procedures in (1) and (3) are standard practice. When rounding off the value 78.375 in (2), however, some computers always take the next-higher hundredth, whereas others invariably use the next-lower hundredth. Using the nearest even digit, however, produces better balanced results in a series of computations.

2-7. METHODS OF COMPUTATION.   Elementary surveying computations require only arithmetic, plane and analytical geometry, and trigonometry. Logarithms were universally used as a means of hand computation some years ago but have limited application now. Slide rules could be utilized only sparingly (mostly for checking purposes) because the number of significant figures needed could not be secured from the scales. Mechanical calculators were employed extensively in the past for surveying calculations. These methods, however, have now almost completely given way to electronic computing devices.

A wide variety of electronic computers and calculators is in current use for surveying calculations. In general the different types may be classified into one of three categories: (1) large-capacity computers, (2) programmable desk-top calculators, and (3) pocket calculators.

Large-capacity computers have huge memories and can solve the biggest surveying problems in a fraction of a second. Input is usually by magnetic tape, punched cards, or punched paper tape. Output is most often printed on paper. Large-capacity computers normally operate on standard program languages such as FORTRAN.

Programmable desk-top calculators having rather sizable memories and capable of executing programs requiring many steps fill the gap between large computers and pocket calculators. Input is usually made on the keyboard of the unit with output visually displayed or printed on paper. Specially developed programs to perform standard surveying problems such as traverse calculations and curve and earthwork computations are available from the manufacturers of these calculators.

Pocket calculators have become an indispensable tool of the surveyor. Most are able to perform diverse functions such as extracting square roots and computing trigonometric functions almost instantaneously. Some have memories, others provide limited programming capabilities. These small instruments are moderately priced and ideal for carrying into the field. They have been improved in capability so rapidly during the past few years it is difficult to imagine what models of the future will accomplish. One fact is certain, however; they have vastly simplified surveying computations and all but eliminated the need for surveying textbooks to carry tables of logarithms and trigonometric functions.

In spite of electronic devices, longhand calculations are frequently necessary. When used, they should be arranged, if possible, to take advantage of the process which normally produces the fewest mistakes. The preferable order is addition, subtraction, multiplication, and division.

2-8. DIRECT AND INDIRECT MEASUREMENTS. Measurements may be made directly or indirectly. Examples of *direct measurements* are applying a tape to a line, fitting a protractor to an angle, or turning an angle with a transit.

An *indirect measurement* is secured when it is not possible to apply the measuring instrument directly to the distance or angle to be measured. The answer is therefore determined by its relation to some other known value. Thus the distance across a river can be found by measuring the length of a line on one side, the angle at each end of this line to a point on the other side, and then computing by one of the standard trigonometric formulas. Since many indirect measurements are made in surveying, a thorough knowledge of geometry and trigonometry is essential.

2-9. ERRORS IN MEASUREMENTS. It can be unconditionally stated that (1) *no measurement is exact*, (2) *every measurement contains errors*, (3) *the true value of a measurement is never known*, and therefore (4) *the exact error present is always unknown*. These facts are demonstrated by the following: when a distance is scaled with a rule divided into tenths of an inch, the distance can be read only to hundredths (by interpolation). If a better rule graduated in hundredths of an inch is available, however, the same distance might be estimated to thousandths of an inch. And with a rule graduated in thousandths of an inch, a reading to ten-thousandths is possible. Obviously, accuracy of measurements depends upon the division size, the reliability of the equipment used, and the human limitations in interpolating closer than about one-tenth of a scale division. As better equipment is developed, measurements will more closely approach their true values. Note that *measurements*, not *counts* (of cars, bolts, buildings, or other objects), are under consideration herein.

Mistakes are caused by a misunderstanding of the problem, carelessness, or poor judgment. Large mistakes are often referred to as *blunders* and are not considered in the succeeding discussion of errors.They are detected by systematic checking of all work, and eliminated by redoing part of the job or even all of it. It is very difficult to detect small mistakes because they merge with errors. When not exposed, these little mistakes must therefore be treated as errors and will contaminate the various types of errors.

2-10. SOURCES OF ERRORS IN MAKING MEASUREMENTS.
Errors in measurements fall into three classes:

Natural errors. These are caused by variations in wind, temperature, humidity, refraction, gravity, and magnetic declination. For example, the length of a steel tape varies with changes in temperature.

Instrumental errors. These result from any imperfection in the construction or adjustment of instruments, and from the movement of individual parts. For example, the painted graduations on a rod may not be perfectly spaced, or the rod may be warped. The effect of most instrumental errors can be reduced by adopting proper surveying procedures and applying computed corrections.

Personal errors. These arise from limitations of the human senses of sight, touch, and hearing. For example, there is a small error in the measured value of an angle when the vertical cross hair in a transit is not aligned perfectly on a target, or the top of a rod is out of plumb when sighted.

2-11. TYPES OF ERRORS.
Errors in measurements are of two types: systematic errors and random errors.

Systematic errors. These errors conform to mathematical and physical laws. Their magnitude may be constant or variable, depending upon conditions. Systematic errors, also known as *cumulative errors*, can be computed and their effects eliminated by applying corrections. For example, a 100-ft steel tape which is 0.02 ft too long introduces a plus 0.02-ft error each time it is used. The change in length of a steel tape resulting from a given temperature differential can be computed by a simple formula, and the correction easily made.

Random errors. These are the errors which remain after mistakes and systematic errors have been eliminated. They are caused by factors beyond the control of the observer, obey the law of probability, and are sometimes called *accidental errors*. They are present in all surveying measurements.

The magnitudes and algebraic signs of random errors are matters of chance. There is no absolute way to compute or eliminate them. Random errors are also known as *compensating errors*, since they tend to partially cancel themselves in a series of measurements. For example, a person interpolating to hundredths of a foot on a tape graduated only to tenths, or reading a level rod marked in hundredths, will presumably estimate too high on some lengths and too low on others. Individual personal characteristics may nullify such partial compensation, however, since some people are inclined to interpolate high, others interpolate low, and many favor certain digits, for example, 7 instead of 6 or 8, 3 instead of 2 or 4, and particularly 0 instead of 9 or 1. It will be shown later in the discussion on probability that *the number of random errors remaining after cancellation of some of the plus and minus values is the square root of the number of opportunities for error.*

2-12. MAGNITUDE OF ERRORS.   *Discrepancy* is the difference between two measured values of the same quantity. It is also the difference between the measured value and the known value of a quantity. A small discrepancy between two measured values indicates that probably there are no mistakes, and random errors are small. It does not reveal the magnitude of systematic errors, however.

Precision denotes the degree of repeatability among various measurements of the same quantity and is based upon the refinement of measurements and size of discrepancies. The degree of precision attainable is dependent upon the sensitiveness of the equipment and skill of the observer. In surveying, precision should not be confused with *accuracy*, which denotes absolute nearness to the truth. A survey may be precise without being accurate. To illustrate, if refined methods are employed and readings taken carefully, say to 0.001 ft, but there are errors in the measuring device (or in the procedures), the survey cannot be accurate. Also, a survey may appear to be accurate when rough measurements have been taken. For example, the angles of a traverse (p. 211) may be read with a compass to only the nearest $\frac{1}{4}°$ and yet produce a zero error of closure. On good surveys, precision and accuracy are consistent throughout.

Agreement between two measured values of the same quantity implies precision but does not assure accuracy. Thus two measurements of a distance with a tape assumed to be 100.000 ft long but actually 100.020 ft might give results of 453.270 and 453.272 ft. These values are precise but they are not accurate since there is an error of approximately 0.090 ft in each of them. The *apparent precision* obtained would be expressed as $0.002/453.271 = 1/220,000$, which is excellent, but accuracy of the distance is only $0.09/453.71 = 1$ part in 5000.

2-13. MINIMIZING ERRORS. All field operations and office computations are governed by the constant fight to reduce errors to a minimum.

Mistakes can be corrected only if discovered. Comparing several measurements of the same quantity is one of the best ways to isolate mistakes. Making a commonsense estimate and analysis is another. Assume that five measurements of a line are recorded as follows: 567.91, 576.95, 567.88, 567.90, and 567.93. The second value disagrees with the others, apparently because of a transposition of figures in reading or recording. This mistake can be eradicated by (a) repeating the measurement or (b) casting out the doubtful value.

When a mistake is detected it is usually best to repeat the measurement. If, however, a sufficient number of other measurements of the quantity are available and in agreement, as in the foregoing example, the widely divergent result may be discarded. Serious consideration must be given to the effect on an average before discarding a value. It is seldom safe to change a recorded number, even though there appears to be a simple transposition of figures. Tampering with physical data is always bad practice and will certainly cause trouble, even though done infrequently.

Systematic errors can be calculated and proper corrections applied to the measurements, or a field procedure used which automatically eliminates the errors. For example, the error due to sag of a tape supported at the ends only can be computed and subtracted from each measurement. If, however, the tape is supported throughout its length or at short intervals, the sag error is zero or negligible. A leveling instrument out of adjustment causes incorrect readings, but if all sights are made the same length, the errors cancel in differential leveling.

2-14. SCOPE OF PROBABILITY. At one time or another, everyone has had an experience with games of chance, such as coin flipping, card games, or dice, which involve probability. In basic mathematics courses, laws of combinations and permutations are introduced. It is shown that things which happen randomly or by chance are governed by mathematical principles referred to as probability. These theories are applicable in many sociological and scientific measurements. In Section 2-11 it was pointed out that random errors exist in all surveying work. Their frequency and magnitude are governed by the same general principles of probability.

For convenience, the term *error* will be used to mean only random error for the remainder of this chapter. Ways to compute and correct for systematic errors are discussed later. It will be assumed that all systematic errors have been eliminated before random errors are considered.

2-15. OCCURRENCE OF RANDOM ERRORS. When making physical measurements, it is necessary to record values read from scales, dials, gauges, or similar equipment. It is characteristic of a measurement that *it cannot be* *made exactly* and so will always contain random error. The size of that error can be reduced by refining the equipment and procedures used.

To develop the principle of how random errors occur, suppose that a distance measurement of 10.46 in. is made with a scale on which a reading can be estimated to 0.01 and is correct to ± 0.05. In this case the true value of the measurement is between 10.41 and 10.51; and to the nearest hundredth, it may be 10.41, 10.42, 10.43, 10.44, 10.45, 10.46, 10.47, 10.48, 10.49, 10.50, or 10.51. Thus there are 11 possible values for the correct answer. For this discussion it can be assumed that all these readings have the same possibility of being correct. The probability of any one answer being correct is therefore $\frac{1}{11}$ or 0.0909.

Consider a line requiring two adjacent measurements made with this scale, each having the same possible error. The answer, a sum of two measurements, can be the total of any pair of 11 possibilities for each separate measurement, all having an equal chance of being correct. From mathematics, if one event can happen n ways and another can occur r ways, the two events together can happen nr ways. For the assumed conditions, there are $(11)(11) = 121$ possibilities. The difference between the sum of the measurements and the true value will be between -0.10 and $+0.10$. Only one pair of possible values can give a difference of -0.10; that is the pair for which the difference in each measurement is -0.05. An error of -0.09 can be obtained in two ways; there may be a difference of -0.05 in the first reading and a difference of -0.04 in the second, or a difference of -0.04 in the first reading and a difference of -0.05 in the second. This analysis can be continued to obtain the results shown in Table 2-1.

If three adjacent measurements are taken in the same manner, with a maximum difference of -0.05 (and $+0.05$), all three would have to be off by -0.05 (or $+0.05$) to get a range of error from -0.15 to $+0.15$. Also, by the principles of mathematics, the total number of chances is $(11)(11)(11) = (11)^3 = 1331$. The complete development is listed in Table 2-2.

The values in columns 1 and 3 of Table 2-2 are plotted as a bar graph called a *histogram* in Fig. 2-3 and show graphically how the errors are distributed. By connecting centers of the tops of plotted bars, a smooth and continuous *probability curve* is obtained. The bell shape of this curve is characteristic of a *normally distributed* group of errors, and thus often referred to as the *normal error distribution curve*. Statisticians frequently call it the *normal density curve*, since it shows the densities of errors of various sizes. In surveying, normal or very nearly normal error distributions almost always occur, and henceforth in this book that condition will be assumed.

Each bar of the histogram of Fig. 2-3 has a width equal to an error increment of 0.01 and a height which represents the probability of the error corresponding to the value at its abscissa. Therefore the area under the entire probability curve represents the sum of all the probabilities in column 3 of Table 2-2, or *one*. Also, the total area between any two ordinates is equal to the sum of the partial areas or probabilities between them.

TABLE 2-1. PROBABILITY FOR TWO MEASUREMENTS

Value of Error	Number of Possibilities	Probability	Probability, as Decimal
−0.10	1	$\frac{1}{121}$	0.0083
−0.09	2	$\frac{2}{121}$	0.0165
−0.08	3	$\frac{3}{121}$	0.0248
−0.07	4	$\frac{4}{121}$	0.0331
−0.06	5	$\frac{5}{121}$	0.0413
−0.05	6	$\frac{6}{121}$	0.0496
−0.04	7	$\frac{7}{121}$	0.0579
−0.03	8	$\frac{8}{121}$	0.0661
−0.02	9	$\frac{9}{121}$	0.0744
−0.01	10	$\frac{10}{121}$	0.0826
0.00	11	$\frac{11}{121}$	0.0909
0.01	10	$\frac{10}{121}$	0.0826
0.02	9	$\frac{9}{121}$	0.0744
0.03	8	$\frac{8}{121}$	0.0661
0.04	7	$\frac{7}{121}$	0.0579
0.05	6	$\frac{6}{121}$	0.0496
0.06	5	$\frac{5}{121}$	0.0413
0.07	4	$\frac{4}{121}$	0.0331
0.08	3	$\frac{3}{121}$	0.0248
0.09	2	$\frac{2}{121}$	0.0165
0.10	1	$\frac{1}{121}$	0.0083

Total: 1.000

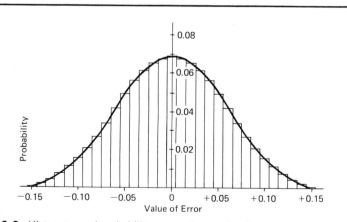

Figure 2-3. Histogram and probability curve of errors for three measurements, with maximum error of ±0.05 units in each.

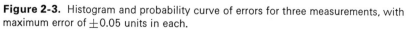

TABLE 2-2. PROBABILITY FOR THREE MEASUREMENTS

Value of Error	Number of Possibilities	Probability
±0.15	1 each, or 2	0.0008
±0.14	3 each, or 6	0.0023
±0.13	6 each, or 12	0.0045
±0.12	10 each, or 20	0.0075
±0.11	15 each, or 30	0.0113
±0.10	21 each, or 42	0.0158
±0.09	28 each, or 56	0.0210
±0.08	36 each, or 72	0.0270
±0.07	45 each, or 90	0.0338
±0.06	55 each, or 110	0.0413
±0.05	66 each, or 132	0.0496
±0.04	75 each, or 150	0.0563
±0.03	82 each, or 164	0.0616
±0.02	87 each, or 174	0.0654
±0.01	90 each, or 180	0.0676
0.00	91 91	0.0684
	Sum: 1331	1.0000

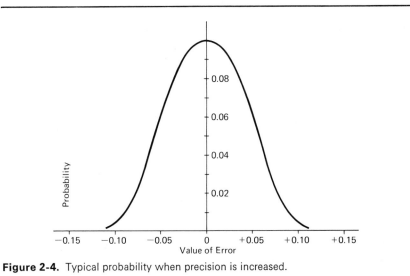

Figure 2-4. Typical probability when precision is increased.

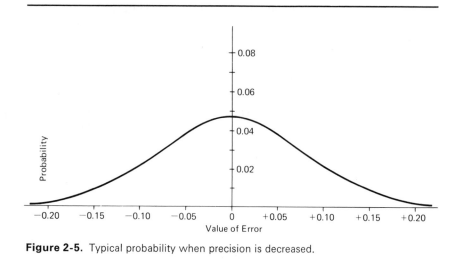

Figure 2-5. Typical probability when precision is decreased.

If the same measurements of the preceding example had been taken with a smaller possible error (that is, more precisely), the probability curve would be similar to Fig. 2-4. This curve shows that a greater percentage of values have small errors, and fewer measurements contain big ones. For readings taken less precisely, the opposite effect is produced in Fig. 2-5, which shows that a considerable percentage have large errors. In all three cases, however, the curve maintained its bell-shaped characteristic.

In this section, it was assumed that random errors occurred in only three readings. Also, it was implied that the equipment used was simple and the errors were primarily due to lack of precision in estimating the readings. With more elaborate equipment there are many additional sources of random errors, but the probability curve remains fundamentally the same.

2-16. GENERAL LAWS OF PROBABILITY. From an analysis of the data in the preceding section and curves in Figs. 2-3, 2-4, and 2-5, some general laws of probability can be stated:

1. Small errors occur more often than large ones; that is, they are more probable.
2. Large errors happen infrequently and are therefore less probable; for normally distributed errors, unusually large ones may be *mistakes* rather than random errors.
3. Positive and negative errors of the same size happen with equal frequency; that is, they are equally probable.

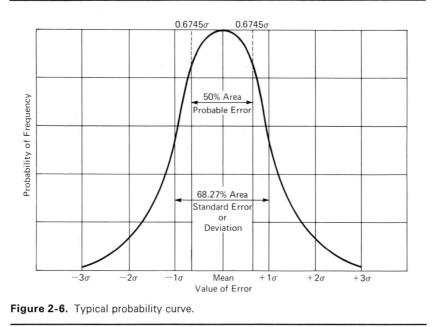

Figure 2-6. Typical probability curve.

2-17. PROBABILITY EQUATION FOR NORMAL DISTRIBUTION.
An equation for the typical normal distribution probability curve shown in
Fig. 2-6 is

$$y = \frac{1}{\sigma\sqrt{2\pi}} e^{-x^2/2\sigma^2} \tag{2-1}$$

where y is the probability or frequency of a certain error; x the error, or
deviation from the mean; e is 2.718, the base of natural logarithms to three
places; and σ the standard deviation (to be covered in Section 2-19).

Equation (2-1) is based on the following assumptions:

1. Random errors are infinite in number.
2. Increment of error of measurements is infinitesimal.

2-18. THE MOST PROBABLE VALUE: THE MEAN.
In physical mea-
surements the true value of any measurement is never known, and therefore
it is not possible to say what error does exist in any measurement. According
to one of the general laws of probability stated in Section 2-16, positive and
negative errors of a certain magnitude happen with equal frequency so that
the most probable value of a group of repeated measurements is the average

(*arithmetic mean*). The detectable error of any particular measurement is the amount by which it deviates from the mean. This error, or deviation, is known as the *residual*.

It is not to be assumed that the mean is without error. The error of the mean will be discussed in Section 2-25.

2-19. MEASURES OF PRECISION.   Referring again to Figs. 2-3, 2-4, and 2-5, although the curves have similar shapes, there are significant differences in their error spreads or *dispersions*; that is, their abscissa widths differ. The magnitude of dispersion is an indication of the precision of the measurements. *Standard deviation* (often interchangeably called *standard error*) and *variance* are statistical terms commonly used for expressing precisions of groups of measurements. The equation for standard deviation is

$$\sigma = \pm \sqrt{\frac{\sum v^2}{n-1}} \qquad (2\text{-}2)$$

where σ is the standard deviation of a group of measurements of the same quantity, v is the residual of an individual observation, $\sum v^2$ the sum of the squares of the individual residuals, and n the number of observations.

Variance is equal to σ^2, *the square of standard deviation*. When the mean is an exact value, as it may be for some data other than physical measurements, then n is substituted for the term $(n-1)$. This also may be done when n is very large. Since neither of these conditions tends to exist in surveying, the term $(n-1)$ is used.

In surveying, a deviation is thought of as an error, and therefore the term *standard error* will be used instead of standard deviation in this book.

Figure 2-7 is a graph showing the percentage of the area of a probability curve corresponding to the range of error between equal positive and negative values. Thus the area between errors of $+\sigma$ and $-\sigma$ represents 68.27% of the total area under the probability curve, and hence gives the limits of errors which can be expected to occur 68.27% of the time. This relation is shown more clearly on the typical probability curve in Fig. 2-6. In a corresponding manner the percentage of error for any proportion of the probability curve can be obtained from Fig. 2-7. Once the standard error has been found, the entire probability curve can be evaluated.

2-20. INTERPRETATION OF STANDARD ERROR.   It has been shown that the standard error establishes the limits within which measurements are expected to fall 68.27% of the time. In other words, if a measurement was repeated 10 times, it would be expected that approximately 7 of the results would fall within the limits established by the standard error, and conversely about 3 of them would fall anywhere outside these limits. Another interpretation is that one additional measurement would have a 68.27% chance of falling within the limits set by the standard error. A third deduction is that the true value has a 68.27% probability of falling within the limits of the standard error.

2-21. THE 50, 90, AND 95% ERRORS.   From the data given in Fig. 2-7, the probability of an error of any percentage likelihood can be determined. The general equation is

$$E_p = C_p \sigma \tag{2-3}$$

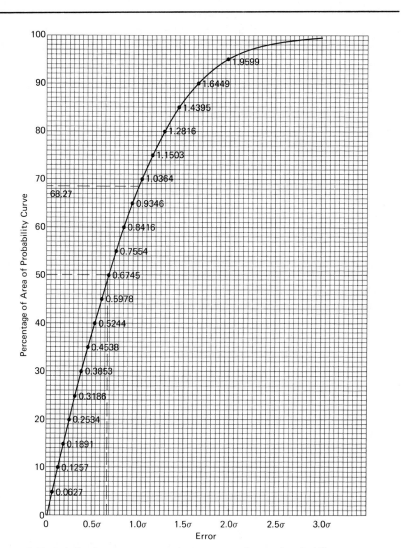

Figure 2-7. Relation between error and percentage of area of probability curve.

where E_p is the percentage error and C_p the numerical factor taken from Fig. 2-7.

Using Eq. (2-3), the following are expressions for errors which have a 50, 90, and 95% chance of occurring:

$$E_{50} = 0.6745\sigma \tag{2-4}$$

$$E_{90} = 1.6449\sigma \tag{2-5}$$

$$E_{95} = 1.9599\sigma \tag{2-6}$$

The 50% error, or E_{50}, is the so-called *probable error*. It establishes the limits within which the measurements will fall 50% of the time. In other words, a measurement will have the same chance of coming within these limits as it will have of falling outside of them. The 50% limits are shown graphically on Fig. 2-6. In the past, probable error was employed extensively in discussing random errors, but now it is seldom used.

The x axis is an asymptote of the probability curve, so the 100% error cannot be evaluated. This means that no matter what error is found, a larger one is possible. For this reason either the 90 or 95% error is often considered to be the maximum practical value.

2-22. EXAMPLE PROBLEM.   As an example problem to clarify definitions and use the equations given in Sections 2-19, 2-20, and 2-21, suppose that a line has been measured 10 times with the results shown in the first column of Illustration 2-1. It is assumed that these measurements have already been corrected for all systematic errors. The following conclusions can be drawn:

1. The most probable length is 1000.45 ft.
2. The standard error of a single measurement is ±0.08 ft.
3. The normal expectation is that 68% of the time, a recorded length would lie between 1000.37 and 1000.53 ft; that is, about seven of the values would lie within these limits. (Actually seven of them do.)
4. The probable error (E_{50}) is ±0.05 ft. Therefore it can be anticipated that half, or five, of the measurements will fall in the interval 1000.40 to 1000.50 ft. (Four values do.)
5. Ninety percent of the time a measured length would not contain an error larger than ±0.13 ft, and its value would be within the range 1000.32 to 1000.58 ft.
6. The 95% error would be ±0.15 ft, and the length would lie between 1000.30 and 1000.60 ft 95% of the time. (Note that all measurements indeed are within the limits of both the 90 and 95% errors.)

2-23. ERROR OF A SUM.   Analyzing the equation for standard error [Eq. (2-2)], it is observed that random errors are a function of the square root

ILLUSTRATION 2-1 STANDARD ERROR

Length (ft)	Residual v (ft)	v^2
1000.57	+0.12	0.0144
1000.39	−0.06	0.0036
1000.37	−0.08	0.0064
1000.39	−0.06	0.0036
1000.48	+0.03	0.0009
1000.49	+0.04	0.0016
1000.32	−0.13	0.0169
1000.46	+0.01	0.0001
1000.47	+0.02	0.0004
1000.55	+0.10	0.0100
1000.45 (average)	$\Sigma = -0.01$	$\Sigma v^2 = 0.0579$

Eq. (2-2), $\sigma = \pm \sqrt{\dfrac{\Sigma v^2}{n-1}} = \pm \sqrt{\dfrac{0.0579}{9}} = \pm 0.08 \text{ ft}$

Eq. (2-4), $E_{50} = \pm 0.6745\sigma = \pm 0.6745\,(0.08) = \pm 0.05 \text{ ft}$

Eq. (2-5), $E_{90} = \pm 1.6449\,(0.08) = \pm 0.13 \text{ ft}$

Eq. (2-6), $E_{95} = \pm 1.9599\,(0.08) = \pm 0.15 \text{ ft}$

of the sum of the squares of the individual errors. Correspondingly, the equation for the error of a sum of independently observed quantities is

$$E_{\text{sum}} = \sqrt{E_a^2 + E_b^2 + E_c^2 + \cdots} \qquad (2\text{-}7)$$

where E represents any specified error, and a, b, and c are the separate measurements.

As an example, assume that a line is measured in three sections, with errors in the individual parts equal to ± 0.012, ± 0.028, and ± 0.020 ft, respectively, Then the error of the total length is

$$E_{\text{sum}} = \pm \sqrt{0.012^2 + 0.028^2 + 0.020^2} = \pm 0.036 \text{ ft}$$

A similar computation applies to the error of any product and, thus, to the error of an area.

In Fig. 2-8 the error in one direction (side A) is E_a, in the other (side B) it is E_b. Therefore, the error in area caused by E_a is BE_a, and that due to E_b is AE_b. Then the equation for the error in the area (product AB) is

$$E_{\text{prod}} = \sqrt{A^2 E_b^2 + B^2 E_a^2} \qquad (2\text{-}8)$$

As an example, for a rectangular lot $50.00 \pm 0.01 \times 100.00 \pm 0.02$ ft, the error in area is

$$\pm \sqrt{50^2(0.02)^2 + 100^2(0.01)^2} = \pm 1.41 \text{ ft}^2$$

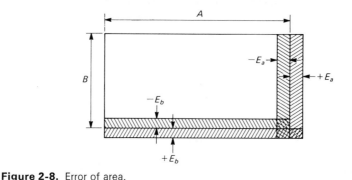

Figure 2-8. Error of area.

The area as computed might be $(50.00)(100.00) = 5000.0000$ ft². How-ever, the rule for significant figures (Section 2-5) states that there cannot be more significant figures in the answer than in any of the individual factors used. Accordingly, the area should be rounded off to $500\bar{0}$ ft² (four signi-ficant figures). From the calculation above, the error is ± 1.41 ft², the last digit in 5000 is questionable, and the number of significant figures to be used in the answer (four) is verified.

2-24. ERROR OF A SERIES. Sometimes a series of similar quantities, such as the angles of a traverse, are read with each measurement being in error by about the same amount. The total error in the sum of all measured quantities of such a series is called the *error of the series*, designated as E_{series}. If the same error E in each measurement is assumed and Eq. (2-7) applied, the series error is

$$E_{\text{series}} = \sqrt{E^2 + E^2 + E^2 + \cdots} = E\sqrt{n} \qquad (2-9)$$

where E represents the error in any individual measurement, and n is the number of measurements.

This equation shows that when the same operation is repeated, the random errors tend to balance out and the remaining error of the series is proportional to the square root of the number of observations. The equation has extensive use—for instance, to determine the allowable error of closure for the angles of a traverse, to be discussed in Chapter 9.

As an example involving the application of Eq. (2-9), assume that any distance of 100 ft can be taped with an error of ± 0.02 ft if certain techniques are employed, and the error in taping a mile using these skills is needed. Since the number of 100-ft lengths in a mile is 52.80,

$$E_{\text{series}} = \pm E\sqrt{n} = \pm 0.02\sqrt{52.80} = \pm 0.15 \text{ ft}$$

As another application, a distance of 1000 ft is to be taped with an error of not more than ± 0.10 ft; and it is desired to determine how accurately each 100-ft length must be measured to insure that the error will not exceed the permissible limit. Since $E_{series} = E\sqrt{n}$, and $n = 10$, the allowable error E in 100 ft is

$$E = \frac{E_{series}}{\sqrt{n}} = \frac{0.10}{\sqrt{10}} = \pm\,0.03 \text{ ft}$$

Now for comparison suppose it is required to tape a length of 10,000 ft with an error of not more than ± 0.10 ft. If 100 ft is again considered the unit length, $n = 100$ and the allowable error E in 100 ft is

$$E = \frac{0.10}{\sqrt{100}} = \pm 0.01 \text{ ft}$$

This analysis shows that a larger number of possibilities provides a greater chance for the errors to cancel out.

2-25. ERROR OF THE MEAN.

In Section 2-18 it was stated that the most probable value of a group of repeating measurements is the arithmetic mean, and the mean itself is subject to error. Nevertheless, in many types of surveys, the error of the mean is commonly used for comparisons.

By applying Eq. (2-9), which is a special form of Eq. (2-7), it is possible to find the error of the sum of a series of measurements where each one has the same error. Since the sum divided by the number of measurements gives the average value, the error of the mean may be found by the relation

$$E_m = \frac{E_{sum}}{n}$$

from which

$$E_m = \frac{E\sqrt{n}}{n} = \frac{E}{\sqrt{n}} \qquad (2\text{-}10)$$

where E is the specified error of a single measurement, E_m some specified error of the mean, and n the number of observations.

The error of the mean at any percent probability can be determined and applied to any of the other criteria which have been developed. The standard error of the mean, $(E_{68})_m$ or σ_m, is

$$(E_{68})_m = \sigma_m = \frac{\sigma}{\sqrt{n}} = \sqrt{\frac{\sum v^2}{n(n-1)}} \qquad (2\text{-}11)$$

The 90% error of the mean is

$$(E_{90})_m = \frac{E_{90}}{\sqrt{n}} = 1.6449\sqrt{\frac{\sum v^2}{n(n-1)}} \qquad (2\text{-}12)$$

These equations show that *the error of the mean varies inversely as the square root of the number of repetitions*. Thus to double the accuracy, that is, to reduce the error by one-half, four times as many measurements must be taken.

In Illustration 2-1, the standard error of the mean might have been the desired quantity. If so,

$$\sigma_m = \frac{\sigma}{\sqrt{n}} = \pm \frac{0.08}{\sqrt{10}} = \pm 0.025 \text{ ft}$$

Also,

$$(E_{90})_m = \pm 0.025(1.6449) = \pm 0.04 \text{ ft}$$

These values show the error limits of 68 and 90% probability for the line's length. It can be said that the exact length of line has a 68% chance of being within ± 0.025 of the mean, and a 90% likelihood of falling not farther than ± 0.04 ft from the mean.

2-26. APPLICATIONS. In the sample problems it has been shown that the equations of probability are applied in two ways:

1. To analyze measurements which have already been made, for comparison with other results or with specification requirements.
2. To establish procedures and specifications in order that the required results will be obtained.

Application of the various probability equations must be tempered with judgment and caution. Remember, a basic assumption made was that an infinite number of errors is being considered. Frequently, in surveying, only a few observations—often from 4 to 10—are taken, If these results are typical and representative, then the answer obtained using probability equations will be reliable; if they are not, the conclusions can be misleading.

2-27. ADJUSTMENTS. In Section 2-9 it was emphasized that the true value of any measured quantity is never known. In some types of problems, however, the sum of several measurements must equal a fixed value; for example, the sum of the interior angles of a polygon has to total $(n-2)(180°)$. In practice, therefore, the measured angles of a polygon are adjusted to make them add up to the required total. Correspondingly, distances—either horizontal or vertical—may be altered slightly to meet certain requirements. The methods employed will be explained in later chapters where the operations are taken up in detail. In making these adjustments, the principles of probability are most important.

For more precise surveys, adjustments are best made on the basis of *least squares*. The principle of least squares, developed from the law of probability, *adjusts the observed values so as to produce a minimum sum of the squares of the errors* (*residuals*).

2-28. WEIGHTS OF MEASUREMENTS. It is evident that some measurements are more accurate than others because of the use of better equipment, improved techniques, and more favorable field conditions. In making adjustments, it is consequently desirable to assign *relative weights* to individual observations. It can be shown that relative weights are inversely proportional to variances, or

$$W_a \propto \frac{1}{\sigma_a^2} \qquad (2\text{-}13)$$

In Eq. (2-13), W_a is the weight of an observation a which has a variance σ_a^2. Thus the higher the precision (the smaller the variance), the larger should be the relative weight of the measured value being adjusted. In some cases variances are unknown originally and a priori weights must be assigned to measured values on the basis of estimates of their relative precisions.

As an example of a weighted adjustment, suppose that four measurements of a distance are recorded as 482.16, 482.17, 482.20, and 482.18, and given weights of 1, 2, 2, and 4, respectively, by the survey-party chief. The weighted mean is found by multiplying each measurement by its weight, adding the products, and dividing the total by the sum of the weights. In this case the weighted mean is

$$\frac{482.16 + 482.17(2) + 482.20(2) + 482.18(4)}{1 + 2 + 2 + 4} = 482.18 \text{ ft}$$

As another example, assume that the measured angles of a certain triangle are: $A = 49°51'15''$, wt. 1; $B = 60°32'08''$, wt. 2; and $C = 69°36'33''$, wt. 3. The angles would be adjusted in inverse proportion to their weights as in the accompanying tabulation. Angle C with the greatest weight (3) gets the smallest correction, $2x$; B receives $3x$; and A, $6x$.

	Angle	Wt.	Correction	Numerical Corr.	Rounded Corr.	Adjusted Angles
A	49°51'15"	1	$6x$	+2.18"	+2.2" (or 2")	49°51'17"
B	60°32'08"	2	$3x$	+1.09"	+1.1" (or 1")	60°32'09"
C	69°36'33"	3	$2x$	+0.73"	+0.7" (or 1")	69°36'34"
Sum	179°59'56"	6	$11x$	+4.00"	+4.0" (or 4")	180°00'00"

$$11x = 4'' \text{ and } x = +0.36''$$

It must be emphasized again that adjustment computations based on the theory of probability are valid only if systematic errors and mistakes have been eliminated by employing proper procedures, equipment, and calculations.

PROBLEMS

A distance *AB* is measured electronically in meters. In problems 2–1 through 2–3 convert the lengths to feet and decimals of a foot.

2–1. 7159.82   **2–2.** 2847.61   **2–3.** 5246.78

For problems 2–4 through 2–6 compute the length in feet corresponding to the distance measured with a Gunter's chain.

2–4. 13 ch 54 lk   **2–5.** 27 ch 12 lk   **2–6.** 38 ch 89 lk

2–7. How many square feet are there in $5^1/_4$ acres ? How many square chains ?

2–8. How many square feet are there in 3 hectares ? How many acres ?

2–9. What is the length in feet and decimals for a distance of 34 ft $7^1/_4$ in. shown on a building blueprint ?

What is the area, in acres, of a rectangular parcel of land measured with a Gunter's chain if the recorded sides are as listed in problems 2–10 through 2–13 ?

2–10. 26 ch 08 lk × 17 ch 45 lk   **2–12.** 26.37 ch × 16.68 ch

2–11. 35 ch 42 lk × 28 ch 06 lk   **2–13.** 16.40 ch × 12 ch 17 lk

Compute the area, in acres, of a triangular lot shown on a village plat, having recorded right-angle sides as listed in problems 2–14 through 2–17.

2–14. 164.14 ft and 56.3 ft   **2–15.** 175.23 ft and 800.0 ft

2–16. 2 ch and 3 ch 21 lk   **2–17.** 4.02 ch and 7.39 ch

In the following problems compute the radian and degree-minute-second equivalents for the angles given in grads.

2–18. 38 grads   **2–19.** 73.5 grads   **2–20.** 174.32 grads

Give the answers for problems 2–21 through 2–24 to the correct number of significant figures.

2–21. Sum of 257.808, 0.007521, 258, and 5.7.

2–22. Sum of 812.21, 0.0176, 2.98, and 0.63.

2–23. Product of 345.1 and 0.451.

2–24. Quotient of 7,283.483 divided by 3.2.

In problems 2–25 through 2–30 express the value in terms of powers of 10 to the indicated number of significant figures.

2–25. 623,000 to six significant figures.

2–26. 21,725 to four significant figures.

2–27. 5,125 to three significant figures.

2–28. Square root of 32,600.

2–29. Square of 6.74.

2–30. Sum of (181.2 + 2.891 + 0.048) divided by 2.74.

In problems 2–31 and 2–32 convert the adjusted angles of a triangle to radians and show the computational check.

2–31. 50°44′06″, 76°23′18″, and 52°52′36″.

2–32. 41°22′50″, 69°16′30″, and 69°20′40″.

2–33. Explain the difference between systematic and random errors.

2–34. List three kinds of random errors and three types of systematic errors that can occur in measuring a line with a steel tape.

2–35. Discuss the difference between precision and accuracy.

2–36. A pair of dice is tossed once. Prepare a table similar to Table 2–1 on probability except that the left-hand column in this case should be labeled "the value of the sum."

A distance XY is measured repeatedly and the results in feet listed in problems 2–37 through 2–41. Calculate the most probable length of the line, the standard error of a single measurement, and the standard error of the mean for each set of results.

2–37. 943.06, 942.91, 942.97, 942.89, 943.01, 942.98, 942.92, 943.04, 942.93, and 943.02.

2–38. Same as problem 2–37 except discard one measurement, 943.06.

2–39. Same as problem 2–37 except discard two measurements, 943.06 and 942.89.

2–40. Same as problem 2–37 except include an additional measurement of 943.00.

2–41. Same as problem 2–37 except include additional measurements of 943.00 and 942.97.

In problems 2–42 through 2–46 determine the limits within which the measured length can be expected to fall 50% of the time, 90% of the time, and the number of values that actually fit within these limits.

2–42. For the data of problem 2–37.

2–43. For the data of problem 2–38.

2–44. For the data of problem 2–39.

2–45. For the data of problem 2–40.

2–46. For the data of problem 2–41.

Two sets of measurements are made with similar equipment, personnel, and field conditions, with the results shown in problems 2–47 and 2–48. Which set is better? Why? Show computations.

2–47. Set A: 274.82 274.80 274.84 274.83 274.81
Set B: 274.85 274.84 274.85 274.85 274.81

2–48. Set A: 423.84 423.87 423.85 423.86 423.88 423.89
Set B: 423.88 423.85 423.86 423.84 423.83 423.88

2–49. Give your interpretation of probable error.

In problems 2–50 through 2–52, calculate the most probable value of the angle, the standard error of a single measurement, and the standard error of the mean for the observations.

2–50. 43°29′10″, 43°28′20″, 43°30′00″, 43°29′00″, 43°28′00″, 43°29′00″.

2–51. Same as problem 2–50 with an additional measurement of 43°29′40″.

2–52. Same as problem 2–50 with additional measurements of 43°29′40″ and 43°29′30″.

Levels are run between points A and B five times with the results listed in problems 2–53 and 2–54. If the elevation of point A is 786.712 ft, and B is higher than A, what is the most probable elevation of B?

2–53. 32.400, 32.406, 32.401, 32.397, and 32.402 ft.

2–54. 63.798, 63.800, 63.801, 63.799, and 63.802 ft.

2–55. A field party is capable of making 100-ft taping measurements with a standard error of ± 0.01 ft. What standard error would be expected if a distance of 1 mile was taped by this party ?

2–56. Same as problem 2–55, except for a standard error of ± 0.02 ft per 100-ft length. What is the 90% error in the mile ?

2–57. A line of differential levels was run and required 16 setups of the instrument. If each backsight and foresight rod reading has a standard error of ± 0.005 ft, what is the standard error in the level line ?

2–58. Same as problem 2–56 except 20 setups were required and each rod reading has a standard error of ± 0.5 mm.

In problems 2–59 and 2–60, a line is measured in three sections with the lengths and standard errors listed in feet. What is the standard error of the total length ?

2–59. 928.28 ± 0.09, 1549.97 ± 0.15, and 523.45 ± 0.06

2–60. 814.91 ± 0.13, 1463.26 ± 0.15, and 985.66 ± 0.14

2–61. For the data of problem 2–59, what are the relative weights of the three sections ?

2–62. A line of differential levels is run from bench marks (defined in section 5–2) BM A to BM B, from BM B to BM C, and then from BM C to BM D. The results obtained, with their standard errors, are, respectively, 37.28 ± 0.09, 76.83 ± 0.11, and 162.40 ± 0.13 ft. What is the standard error in the difference of elevation between BM A and BM D ?

2–63. A distance AB was measured four times as 644.35, 644.33, 644.28, and 644.33. The measurements were given weights of 1, 2, 3, and 2, respectively, by the observer. Calculate the weighted mean for the distance AB. What difference results if later judgment revises the weights to 1, 3, 2, and 2 ?

2–64. Determine the weighted mean for the following angles and weights: 48°21′59″, wt. 1 ; 48°21′55″, wt. 2 ; 48°21′57″, wt. 3 ; and 48°22′02″, wt. 1.

2–65. Same as problem 2–64 except the weights are 2, 1, 2, and 2, respectively.

2–66. Specifications for measuring the angles of an eight-sided figure limit the total angular error to 30″. How accurately must each angle be measured ?

2–67. Same as problem 2–66 except for a 10-sided figure and a total limiting angular error of 1′.

What is the area of a rectangular field, and the error in the area, for the recorded values shown in problems 2–68 and 2–69 ?

2–68. 352.00 ± 0.10 ft by 460.00 ± 0.15 ft.

2–69. 50.41 ± 0.01 m by 231.56 ± 0.03 m.

2–70. A square parcel of land containing 8 acres is to be surveyed for a subdivision. What is the maximum error permissible in the measurement of a side if the area must be correct within ± 100 ft² ?

2–71. In problem 2–66, if the standard error of reading the instrument is ±15″. how many separate readings must be taken at each corner to ensure that (a) the average at the corner will be between the required limits 68% of the time and (b) the mean will fall between the limits 90% of the time ?

Adjust the following angles of a triangle ABC for which the values and respective weights are given in problems 2–72 and 2–73.

2–72. $A = 39°32'46''$, $B = 55°11'51''$, $C = 85°15'16''$; wts. 1, 3, 2, respectively.

2–73. $A = 70°24'18''$, $B = 52°04'36''$, $C = 57°31'10''$; wts. 4, 1, 2, respectively.

2–74. Determine the relative weights and perform a weighted adjustment (to the nearest second) of angles A, B, and C of a plane triangle, given the following observations:

Angle A		Angle B		Angle C	
Observation No.	Value	Observation No.	Value	Observation No.	Value
1	43°10′	1	71°23′	1	65°22′
2	43°11′	2	71°20′	2	65°20′
3	43°11′	3	71°26′	3	65°23′
4	43°10′	4	71°24′	4	65°24′

3
SURVEYING
FIELD NOTES

3-1. GENERAL. Surveying field notes are the only permanent record of work done in the field. If they are incomplete, incorrect, or destroyed, much or all of the time invested in making accurate measurements can be lost. Hence the notekeeper's job is frequently the most important and difficult one in the party. A field book containing information gathered over a period of weeks is worth thousands of dollars, because it costs $300 to $400 per day to maintain a party of three of four men in the field. Therefore it should have the name and address of the owner lettered with India ink on the cover and inside.

Data in field notes are normally used by office personnel to make drawings or computations. Accordingly, it is essential that notes be intelligible to anyone without verbal explanations. The Reinhardt system of slope lettering is generally employed for clarity and speed; it requires a minimum number of simple strokes to form any letter.

Property surveys are subject to court review under some conditions, so the field notes become an important factor in litigation. Also, because they may be used as references in land transactions for generations, it is necessary to index and preserve them properly. The saleable "good will" of a surveyor's business depends largely upon his library of field books. Cash receipts may be kept in an unlocked desk drawer, but field books are stored in a fireproof safe.

Original notes are those taken at the same time measurements are being made. All other sets are copies and must be so marked. Copied notes may not be accepted in court because they are open to question concerning possible mistakes and omissions. The value of a distance or an angle placed in the field book from memory, 10 minutes after the observation, is definitely unreliable.

Students are tempted to scribble notes on scrap sheets of paper for later transference in neater form to the regular field book. This practice defeats the purpose of a surveying course, which is to provide experience in taking notes under job conditions. In a real job situation, a surveyor is not likely to spend his own time at night transcribing scribbled notes. Certainly his employer will not pay him for this evidence of incompetence.

Notes should be lettered with a sharp pencil of at least 3-H hardness so that an indentation is made in the paper. Books so prepared will withstand damp weather in the field (or even a soaking) and still be legible, whereas graphite from a soft pencil leaves an undecipherable smudge under such circumstances.

Erasures of observed data are not permitted in field books. If a number has been recorded incorrectly, a line is run through it without destroying the number's legibility, and the proper value is noted above (see Plate A-3, left page[1]). If an entire page is to be deleted, diagonal lines are drawn through opposite corners and VOID lettered prominently, with the reasons.

3-2. REQUIREMENTS OF GOOD NOTES.   Five points are considered in appraising a set of field notes.[2]

Accuracy. This is the most important quality in all surveying operations.

Integrity. A single omitted measurement or detail can nullify use of the notes for plotting or computing. If the project was far from the office, it is time-consuming and expensive to return for a missing measurement. Notes should be checked carefully for completeness before leaving the survey site, and never "fudged" to improve closures.

Legibility. Notes can be used only if they are legible. A professional-looking set of notes is likely to be professional in quality.

Arrangement. Noteforms appropriate to the particular survey contribute to accuracy, integrity, and legibility.

Clarity. Advance planning and proper field procedures are necessary to ensure clarity of sketches and tabulations, and to make mistakes and omissions more evident. Avoid crowding notes—paper is relatively cheap. Costly mistakes in drafting and computing are the end results of ambiguous notes.

3-3. TYPES OF FIELD BOOKS.   Since field books contain valuable data, take hard wear, and must be permanent in nature, it is poor economy to use

---

[1] See Appendix A for all plates, which are typical field notes.

[2] Some material in this chapter has been abstracted from *Engineers Field Notes*, by Roth and Rice, privately published in 1940 and now out of print. By permission of the authors.

other than the best for practical work. Various kinds of field books are available, but bound and loose-leaf types are the most common.

The bound book, a standard for many years, has a sewed binding, a hard, stiff cover of impregnated canvas, leather, or imitation leather, and contains 80 leaves.

The bound duplicating book permits copies of notes to be made through carbon paper. Alternate pages are perforated for easy removal.

Loose-leaf books have come into wide use because of many advantages which include (a) assurance of a flat working surface, (b) simplicity of filing individual project notes, (c) ready transfer of partial sets of notes between field and office, (d) provision for holding pages of printed tables, diagrams, formulas, and sample forms, (e) the possibility of using different rulings in the same book, (f) a saving in sheets (since none are wasted by filing partially filled books) and (g) lower total cost.

Stapled, sewed, or spiral-bound books are not suitable for practical work. They may be satisfactory for abbreviated surveying courses having only a few field periods because of the limited service required and the low cost.

Special column and page rulings provide for particular needs in leveling, transit work, topographic surveying, and cross sectioning.

New automatic reading and recording systems have been developed in surveying, but the notekeeper's job will become more complicated rather than be eliminated. In one method, numbers are dialed, as on a telephone, and simultaneously recorded on a tape for direct input to digital computers. An electronic display provides a visual check of the data. Sketches cannot be handled automatically, however.

3-4. KINDS OF NOTES. Four types of notes are kept in practice: (1) sketches, (2) tabulations, (3) descriptions, and (4) combinations of these. The most common type is a combination form, but an experienced recorder selects the version best fitted to the job at hand. Appendix A contains typical noteforms illustrating some field problems covered in this text.

For a simple survey, such as measuring the distances between hubs on a series of lines, a sketch showing the lengths is sufficient. In measuring the length of a line forward and backward, a tabulation properly arranged in columns is adequate, as in Plate A-2, Appendix A. The proverb about one picture being worth 10,000 words might well have been written for notekeepers.

The location of a reference point may be difficult to identify without a sketch, but often a few lines of description are enough. Bench marks usually are so described, as in Plate A-3.

In notekeeping this axiom is always pertinent: when in doubt about the need for any information, include it and make a sketch. It is better to have too many data than not enough.

3-5. ARRANGEMENTS OF NOTES. Note styles and arrangement depend upon departmental standards and individual preference. Highway departments, mapping agencies, and other organizations engaged in surveying furnish their field men with sample noteforms, similar to those in Appendix A, to aid in preparing uniform and complete records which can be checked quickly.

It is desirable for students to have an expertly designed set of noteforms covering their first field work as guides, to set high standards and save time. The noteforms shown in Appendix A are a composite of several models. They stress the open style, especially helpful for beginners, in which some lines or spaces are skipped for clarity. Thus angles measured at a point A (Plate A-8) are placed opposite A on the page, but distances measured between hubs A and B on the ground are recorded on the line between A and B in the field book.

Left- and right-hand pages are practically always used in pairs and therefore carry the same number. A complete title should be lettered across the top of the left page and may be extended over the right one. Titles may be abbreviated on succeeding pages for the same survey project. Location and type of work are placed beneath the title. Some surveyors prefer to confine the title on the left page and keep the top of the right one free for date, party, weather, and other items. This design is revised if the entire right page has to be reserved for sketches and bench-mark descriptions. Arrangements shown in Appendix A are eminently satisfactory and demonstrate to students the flexibility of noteforms.

The left page is generally ruled in six columns designed for tabulation only. Column headings are placed between the first two horizontal lines at the page top and follow from left to right in the anticipated order of reading and recording. The upper part of the left or right page must contain four items:

1. *Date, time of day* (AM *or* PM), *starting and finishing time.* These entries are necessary to document the notes and furnish a timetable, as well as to correlate different surveys. Precision, troubles encountered, and other facts may be gleaned from the time required for the survey.
2. *Weather.* Wind velocity, temperature, and diverse weather conditions, such as rain, snow, sunshine, and fog, have a decided effect upon accuracy in surveying operations, A tapeman is unlikely to do the best possible work at a temperature of $-20°F$ or with rain pouring down his neck. Hence weather details are important in reviewing field notes, as well as for applying corrections to tape lengths due to temperature variations and for other purposes.
3. *Party.* The names and initials of members of the party, and their duties, are required for documentation and future reference. Jobs may be shown by symbols, such as ⊼ for instrumentman, ø for rodman, N for notekeeper, and HT for head tapeman. The party chief is frequently the notekeeper.

4. *Instrument type and number.* The type of instrument used and its adjustment affect the accuracy of a survey. Identification of the specific equipment employed aids in isolating errors in some cases.

To permit ready location of desired data, each field book must have a table of contents which is kept current daily. In practice, surveyors cross-index their notes on days when field work is impossible.

3-6. SUGGESTIONS ON RECORDING NOTES. Observing the suggestions listed here will eliminate some common mistakes in recording notes:

1. Use the Reinhardt system of lettering. Reserve uppercase letters for emphasis.
2. Letter the notebook owner's name and address on the cover and first inside page, in India ink.
3. Use a hard pencil, at least 3-H or 4-H, and keep it sharp.
4. Begin a new day's work on a new page. For property surveys having complicated sketches, this rule may be waived.
5. Immediately after a measurement, always record it directly in the field book rather than on a sheet of scrap paper for copying later.
6. Do not erase recorded data. Run a single line through an incorrect value (but retain its legibility), and place the correct value above or below it. Void an entire page by running diagonal lines to the page corners.
7. Carry a straightedge for ruling lines and a small protractor to lay off angles.
8. Run notes down the page, except in route surveys, where they progress upward to conform with sketches made while looking in the forward direction. (See Plate A-13.)
9. Use sketches instead of tabulations when in doubt.
10. Make drawings to general proportions rather than to exact scale or without plan, and recognize that the usual preliminary estimate of space required is too small. Letter parallel with or perpendicular to the appropriate feature, showing clearly to what they apply. Dimension lines, as used in machine graphics, are seldom necessary.
11. Exaggerate details on sketches if clarity is thereby improved, or prepare separate diagrams.
12. Line up descriptions and drawings with corresponding numerical data. For example, the beginning of a bench-mark description should be placed on the same line as its elevation, as in Plate A-3.
13. Avoid crowding. If it is helpful to do so, use several right-hand pages of descriptions and sketches for a single left-hand sheet of tabulation. Similarly, use any number of pages of tabulation for a single drawing.
14. Paper is cheap compared with the value of time that might be wasted in misinterpretation by office personnel of compressed field notes, or in returning to the field for clarification.

15. Use explanatory notes when they are pertinent, always keeping in mind the purpose of the survey and needs of the office force. Put these notes in open spaces to avoid conflict with other parts of the sketch.
16. Employ conventional symbols and signs, for compactness.
17. Have north at the top, or left side, of all sketches if possible. A meridian arrow is vital.
18. Keep tabulated figures inside of and off column rulings, with decimal points and digits in line vertically.
19. Make a mental estimate of all measurements before receiving and recording them in order to eliminate large mistakes.
20. Repeat aloud values given for recording. For example, before putting down a distance of 124.68, call out "one, two, four, point six, eight" for verification by the tapeman who submitted the measurement.
21. Place a zero before the decimal point for numbers less than one, that is, record 0.37 instead of .37.
22. Show the precision of measurements by means of significant figures. For example, record 3.80 instead of 3.8 only if the reading was actually determined to hundredths.
23. Do not superimpose one number over another or on lines of sketches, and do not try to change one figure to another, as a 3 to a 5.
24. Make all possible arithmetic checks on the notes, and record them, before leaving the field.
25. Arrange essential computations made in the field so they can be checked later.
26. Title, index, and cross-reference each new job or continuation of a previous one.
27. Compute all closures and ratios of error while in the field. On large projects where daily assignments are made for several parties, completed work is shown by satisfactory closures.
28. Sign surname and initials in the lower right-hand corner of the right page on all original notes. This places responsibility, just as the signing of a check does. Letter COPY in large size diagonally across the pages of nonoriginal notes, but do not obscure or touch a sketch or any figure in so doing.

PROBLEMS

3–1. Why are sketches in field notes not generally drawn to exact scale?
3–2. When should sketches be made?
3–3. What erasures, if any, are permitted in a field book?
3–4. In general, what information should be included in a good set of field notes?

3–5. Describe two problems that might arise from omission in the field book of the first names and middle initials of a surveying field party.

3–6. List the types of field notes used in each of Plates A–1 to A–13 of Appendix A.

3–7. Using assumed data, prepare a highway-accident field sketch covering a car–truck side collision near the center of a 45° intersection of a main highway and side road.

3–8. Prepare a set of field notes and sketch for measurements of the three angles of a triangle which total 180°00′45″, thus giving a closure of 45″. See Plate A–8.

3–9. Prepare a set of field notes and sketch for the layout of the house in problem 1–15. See Plate A–11.

3–10. Measure the length of each diagonal of a TV screen six times, tabulate the notes, and compare the results with the advertised picture size. Compute the most probable length of the diagonals.

3–11. Measure all sides and projections of the house in which you live, and determine its position on the lot. Draw a sketch giving dimensions.

3–12. Why should a pen not be used in field notekeeping?

3–13. What information should be included in surveying notes for fences, roads, trees, and buildings?

3–14. What similarity exists between the signer of a set of field notes and the signer of a check?

3–15. A resurvey was made of a lot in a 70-year-old subdivision, but the date was omitted by mistake in the field book. What effect might this have on you as the new purchaser of the lot?

3–16. Differentiate between notes that should run down the page and those which generally run up the page.

3–17. A theodolite with digital readout of angles is used in an isolated area. What advantages and disadvantages might result?

3–18. What other information or notes in addition to the four major items listed in Section 3–5 might be helpful on the right-hand page of a field book?

3–19. Why should a zero be placed before a decimal point for values such as 0.76?

3–20. State your idea of a sixth point to be considered in appraising a set of field notes.

3–21. Explain the reasons for item 23 in Section 3–6 when recording notes.

LINEAR MEASUREMENTS

4-1. GENERAL. Linear measurement is the basis of all surveying. Even though angles may be read precisely with elaborate equipment, the length of at least one line must be measured to supplement the angles in locating points.

Standard taping procedure appears so simple that beginners in professional survey parties are traditionally assigned this work. As a result, the importance of correct techniques may be overlooked. Nevertheless, an energetic head tapeman is probably more important than a fast instrumentman in keeping a field party moving.

In plane surveying the distance between two points means the horizontal distance. If the points are at different elevations, the distance is the horizontal length between plumb lines at the points.

Lines may be measured directly by applying a unit of length to them. The unit generally used in plane surveying in the United States is the foot, decimally divided. In architectural and machine work it is the foot divided into inches and fractions of an inch. The meter is usually employed in geodetic surveying. Chains, varas, rods, and other units have been, and still are, utilized in some localities and for special purposes.

4-2. METHODS OF MEASURING HORIZONTAL DISTANCES. In surveying, direct linear measurements are obtained by (a) pacing, (b) odometer readings, (c) tacheometry (stadia), discussed in Chapter 12, (d) subtense bar, (e) taping, and (f) electronic distance measurement (EDM). Of these methods, taping and EDM are most commonly used by surveyors and are described in detail in parts II and III of this chapter. Distances can also be estimated, a technique useful in making field-note sketches and checking measurements for mistakes.

Triangulation is an indirect method for determining horizontal distances (see Chapter 18). In this procedure, lengths of lines are computed trigonometrically from measured base lines and angles. A variation of triangulation is the *Airborne Control* (ABC) system. It utilizes a helicopter with an optical plumb bob (*hoversight*). Electronic distance measurements (and/or angles) are taken to the helicopter as it hovers at a measured height over a ground station.

4-3. PACING.   Distances obtained by pacing are sufficiently accurate for many purposes in surveying, engineering, geology, agriculture, forestry, and military field sketching. Pacing is also used to detect blunders which may occur in taping or stadia readings.

Pacing consists of counting the number of steps or paces in a required distance. The length of an individual's pace must first be determined. This is best done by walking with natural steps back and forth over a measured level course at least 300 ft long, and averaging the number of steps taken. For short distances the length of each pace is needed, but the number of steps taken per 100 ft is desirable for checking long lines. Plate A-1 gives the notes for a field problem on pacing.

It is possible to adjust one's pace to an even 3 ft, but a person of average height finds such a step tiring if maintained very long. The length of an individual's pace shortens when going uphill, lengthens when going downhill, and changes with age. For long distances, a pocket instrument called a *pedometer* can be carried to register the number of paces, or a *passometer* can be attached to the body or leg to count the steps or strides.

Some surveyors prefer to count *strides*. A stride is the distance between the place where one foot is lifted and where it is put down again. A stride equals two paces.

Pacing is one of the most valuable things learned in surveying since it has practical applications for everybody and requires no equipment. Experienced pacers can measure distances of 100 ft or longer with an accuracy of $\frac{1}{50}$ to $\frac{1}{100}$, if the terrain is open and reasonably level.

4-4. ODOMETER READINGS.   An odometer converts the number of revolutions of a wheel of known circumference to distance. Lengths measured by an odometer on a vehicle are suitable for some preliminary surveys in route-location work. They also serve as a rough check on measurements made by other methods. A precision of approximately $\frac{1}{200}$ is reasonable.

Other types of measuring wheels are available and useful for determining short distances, particularly on curved lines.

4-5. TACHEOMETRY.   Tacheometry is a surveying method used to quickly determine the distance, direction, and elevation difference of a point by a single observation from an instrument station. The best example of tacheometry in the United States (where the term is less familiar) is the *stadia* method.

Stadia measurements of horizontal and slope distances are obtained by sighting through a telescope equipped with two or more horizontal cross hairs at a known spacing. The apparent intercepted length between the top and bottom hairs is read on a rod held vertically. The distance from telescope to rod is found by proportional relationships in similar triangles. A precision of $\frac{1}{500}$ is achieved with reasonable care. A detailed explanation of the method is given in Chapter 12.

Rangefinders, which measure distances by the principle of optical focus, have several uses in surveying.

4-6. SUBTENSE BAR.   Several other optical methods of determining distances indirectly have been developed in which the angle subtended by a known distance between endmarks on a horizontal rod or bar (such as a subtense bar) is read on a precise transit or theodolite.

The Invar subtense bar shown in Fig. 4-1 (along with the appropriate

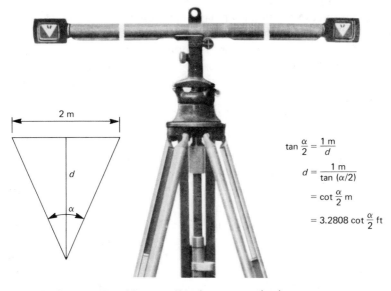

$$\tan \frac{\alpha}{2} = \frac{1 \text{ m}}{d}$$

$$d = \frac{1 \text{ m}}{\tan (\alpha/2)}$$

$$= \cot \frac{\alpha}{2} \text{ m}$$

$$= 3.2808 \cot \frac{\alpha}{2} \text{ ft}$$

Figure 4-1. Subtense bar. (Courtesy Kern Instruments, Inc.)

theory) is set on a tripod and aligned perpendicular to the survey line by means of a sighting device on top of the bar. Fixed targets near the ends of the bar are exactly 2 m apart. The angle between the targets is measured with a theodolite reading to 1″ or less, and the horizontal distance either computed or taken from a table, such as Table B-2. One important advantage of the subtense-bar method is that *the horizontal distance is always obtained directly, even though an inclined sight is taken because α is measured in a horizontal plane.*

For sights of 500 ft or less, and using a 1″ theodolite, the accuracy should be equal to that for an ordinary tape traverse. Accuracy of $\frac{1}{1000}$ to $\frac{1}{5000}$ is attainable by taking several readings of the angle at both ends of the line for averaging.

PART II. TAPING

4-7. INTRODUCTION TO TAPING. Measurement of horizontal distance by taping consists of applying the known length of a graduated tape directly to a line a number of times. Two types of problems arise: (1) measuring a distance between fixed points, such as two stakes in the ground, and (2) laying out a distance with only the starting mark in place.

Taping is performed in six steps: (1) lining in, (2) applying tension, (3) plumbing, (4) marking tape lengths, (5) reading the tape, and (6) recording the distance. Application of these steps in taping on level and sloping ground is detailed in Sections 4-9 and 4-10.

Various types of equipment have been used in the United States to measure lengths. Early surveyors struggled with braced timber panels, wood and metal poles (which resulted in the term *pole* as a unit of measurement), and other devices. The 100-ft steel tape and 50-ft metallic tape are now standard, but other kinds of tapes and chains are important because of their present or past use.

Wires. Before thin flat steel could be produced efficiently, wires were utilized for measuring lengths. They still are practical in special cases, for example, hydrographic surveys.

Gunter's chain. The Gunter's chain was the best measuring device available to surveyors for many years in the United States and is referred to in old field notes and deeds. It was 66 ft long and had 100 links, each link equal to 7.92 in. The links were made of heavy wire, had a loop at each end, and were joined together by three rings (Fig. 4-2). The outside ends of the handles fastened to the end links are the 0 mark and the 66-ft mark. Successive tags, having 1, 2, 3, or 4 teeth, marked every tenth link from each end. The center tag was plain. With 600 or 800 connecting link and ring surfaces subject to frictional wear, hard use elongated the chain, and its length had to be adjusted by means of bolts in the handles.

Figure 4-2. Gunter's chain.

Distances measured with chains were recorded either in chains and links or in chains and decimals of chains; for example, 7 ch 94.5 lk or 7.945 ch. Decimal parts of links were estimated. The 66-ft length of the Gunter's chain was selected because of its relevance to the mile and the relationship of the square chain to an acre. Thus 1 ch = $\frac{1}{80}$ mile, and 10 ch^2 = 10 × 66^2 = 43,560 ft^2 = 1 acre.

Engineer's chain. An engineer's chain had the same construction as a Gunter's chain but was 100 ft long and each of its 100 links had a length of 1 ft.

Chains are seldom if ever used today, although a steel tape graduated like a Gunter's chain is manufactured. Nevertheless, the many chain surveys on record oblige the modern practitioner to understand the limits of accuracy possible with this equipment. The term *chaining* continues to be used interchangeably with taping, even though tapes are employed exclusively.

Surveyor's and engineer's tapes. These tapes are made of steel $\frac{1}{4}$ to $\frac{3}{8}$ in. wide and weigh 2 to 3 lb per 100 ft. They may be wound upon a reel or done up in loops 5 ft long to make a figure 8, then *thrown* into a circle having a diameter of about $9\frac{1}{2}$ in. For heavy-duty taping, *band chains* (also known as *chain tapes*) are available with cross sections $\frac{1}{8}$ to $\frac{5}{16}$ in. by 0.016 to 0.025 in. Lengths of 50, 100, 150, 200, 300, and 500 ft, and 30, 50, or 100 m are standard. The 100-ft tape is most common.

Graduations placed at every foot are marked from 0 to 100. Some tapes have only the last foot at each end subdivided into tenths, or tenths and hundreds, of a foot. Others are graduated in feet, tenths, and hundredths throughout. Still others (*adding tapes*) have an extra graduated foot beyond the zero mark. In all cases, a metal ring or loop at each end allows a handle or leather thong to be attached. The National Bureau of Standards will issue a Report only (*not* a Certificate of Comparison) for (1) tapes having the 0- and 100-ft points at the outer edges of the end loops instead of at line graduations on the band itself; and (2) tapes with graduations on babbitt-metal bosses bonded to the band but not an integral part of it.

Special-purpose tapes. Tapes having suitable cross sections, lengths, composition, and graduation arrangements are manufactured for special purposes, such as base-line measurement, city engineering work, oil riggers' and gaugers' use, and topographic surveys.

Builder's tapes. Builder's tapes have smaller cross sections and are lighter in weight than surveyor's tapes. Since most building plans prepared by engineers and architects carry dimensions in feet and inches, the builder's tape is graduated in those units.

Invar tapes. Invar tapes are made of a special nickel steel (35% nickel and 65% steel) to reduce length variations caused by differences in temperature. The thermal coefficient of expansion and contraction is only about $\frac{1}{30}$ to $\frac{1}{60}$ that of an ordinary steel tape. The metal is soft and somewhat unstable. This weakness of Invar tapes, along with their cost of perhaps ten times that of ordinary tapes, makes them suitable only for precise geodetic work and as a standard for comparison with working tapes.

Lovar tapes. A somewhat newer version, the Lovar tape, has properties and a cost between those for steel and Invar tapes.

Cloth tapes. Cloth (or metallic) tapes are actually made of high-grade linen $\frac{5}{8}$ in. wide with fine copper wires running lengthwise to give additional strength and to prevent excessive elongation. Metallic tapes commonly used are 50, 100, and 200 ft long and come in enclosed reels. Although not suitable for precise work, metallic tapes are convenient and practical for many purposes but should *not* be used around electrical units.

Glass-fiber tapes. Glass-fiber tapes can be employed for the same types of work as metallic tapes, and are safe around electrical equipment.

Accessories. Chaining pins or *taping pins* (surveyor's arrows) are used to mark tape lengths. Most taping pins are made of number 12 steel wire, are sharply pointed at one end, have a round loop at the other end, and are painted with alternate red and white bands. Sets of 11 pins carried on a steel ring are standard.

Hand level. This simple instrument, described in Section 5-17, is used to keep the tape ends at equal elevations when measuring over rough terrain.

Tension handles. Tension handles facilitate application of the exact standard tension. A complete unit consists of a wire handle, a clip to fit the end ring of the tape, and a spring balance reading up to 30 lb in $\frac{1}{2}$-lb calibrations.

Clamp handles. These are used to apply tension by a positive, quick grip using a scissor-type action on any part of a steel tape without damage to the tape or hands.

Pocket thermometer. Thermometers for field use are about 5 in. long, graduated from perhaps $-30°$ to $+120°F$ in $1°$ or $2°$ divisions, and kept in protective metal cases.

Tape-repair kits. A tape-repair kit contains sleeve splices to be placed over the two parts of a broken tape, hammered down, and fastened with eyelets by a combined hand puncher and riveter.

Poles. Range poles (flags or lining rods) are made of wood, steel, or aluminum, and are about 1 in. thick and 6 to 10 ft long. They are round or hexagonal in cross section and marked with alternate red and white bands 1 ft long which can be used for rough measurements. A wooden range pole has a metal shoe at the base. The main utility of range poles is in marking the alignment.

Plumb bobs. Plumb bobs for taping should weigh a minimum of 8 oz and have a fine point. At least 6 ft of fish-line cord free of knots is necessary. Plumb-bob points are now standardized to simplify replacement.

Full equipment for a taping party consists of one 100-ft steel tape, one 50-ft metallic tape, two range poles, 11 chaining pins on a ring, two plumb bobs, one hand level or clinometer, keel (colored lumber crayon), and a field book. Some of this equipment is shown in Fig. 4-3.

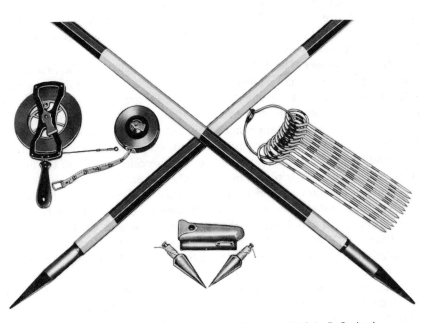

Figure 4-3. Taping equipment for a field party. (Courtesy W. & L. E. Gurley.)

4-8. CARE OF TAPING EQUIPMENT. The following points are pertinent in the care of tapes and range poles:

1. The cross-sectional area of a surveyor's steel tape is $\frac{1}{4} \times \frac{1}{50}$ in. $= 0.005$ in.^{2} At a permissible stress of 20,000 lb/in.^{2}, a pull of $20,000 \times 0.005 = 100$ lb will do no damage. If the tape is kinked, however, a pull of less than 1 lb will break it. Therefore always check to be certain that any loops and kinks are eliminated before tension is applied.
2. If a tape gets wet, it should be wiped first with a dry cloth and then with an oily rag.
3. Tapes should either be kept on a reel or " thrown, " but not handled both ways. Double throwing is not recommended.
4. Each tape should have an individual number or tag to identify it.
5. Broken tapes can be mended by riveting and/or applying a sleeve device, but a mended tape should not be used on important work.
6. Range poles are made with the metal shoe and point in line with the section above. This alignment may be lost if the pole is used improperly.

4-9. TAPING ON LEVEL GROUND. Six steps in the process of taping on level ground will now be described in some detail.

Lining in. The line to be measured should be definitely marked at both ends, and at intermediate points where necessary, to ensure unobstructed sight lines. Range poles are ideal for this purpose. The forward tapeman is lined in by the rear tapeman (or by the transitman, for greater accuracy). Directions are given by vocal or hand signals.

Applying tension. The 100-ft end of a tape is held over the first (rear) point by the rear tapeman while the forward tapeman, holding the zero end, is lined in. For accurate results the tape must be straight and the two ends held at the same elevation. A specified tension, generally 10, 12, or 15 lb, is applied. In order to maintain a steady pull, each tapeman wraps the leather thong at the end of the tape around one hand, keeps his forearms against his body and faces at right angles to the line. In this position he is off the line of sight. Also, he need only tilt his body to hold, decrease, or increase the pull. Sustaining a constant tension with *outstretched* arms is difficult, if not impossible, for a pull of 15 lb or more. Good communication between head and rear tapemen will avoid jerking the tape, save time, and get better results.

Plumbing. Weeds, brush, obstacles, and surface irregularities may make it undesirable to lay the tape on the ground. Instead, the tapeman marks each end point of a measurement by placing the plumb-bob string over the proper tape graduation and securing it with one thumb. The rear tapeman continues to hold a plumb bob over the fixed point while the forward tapeman marks the length. In measuring a distance shorter than a full tape length, the forward tapeman moves the plumb-bob string to a point on the tape over the ground mark.

Marking tape lengths. When the tape has been lined in properly, tension has been applied, and the rear tapeman is over the point, he calls "stick"; the forward tapeman places a pin from his set of 10 (one is in the ground at the rear point) exactly opposite the zero mark of the tape, and calls "stuck." If the point is being plumbed and the ground is soft, the plumb bob is released by raising the thumb. A chaining pin is then carefully set in the hole made by the plumb-bob point. The pin should form a right angle with the tape but approximately a 45° angle with the ground. The point where the pin enters the ground is checked by repeating the measurement.

After checking the measurement, the forward tapeman signals that he is finished, the rear tapeman pulls up the pin beside him, and they move ahead. The forward tapeman drags the tape, paces roughly 100 ft, and stops. Just before the 100-ft end reaches the point which has been set, the rear tapeman calls "tape" to notify the forward tapeman that he has gone 100 ft. The process is repeated until a partial tape length is needed at the end of the line.

When a surveyor is working on pavement, the plumb bob is eased to the surface, and the position of the point is marked by a scratch, a spike, keel, a nail in a bottle cap, or other means.

Reading the tape. There are two common styles of calibrations on surveyor's tapes. *It is necessary to identify the type being used before starting work,* in order to avoid making 1-ft mistakes repeatedly.

The more common type of tape is calibrated from 0 to 100 by full feet in one direction, and has an additional foot beyond the zero end graduated from zero to 1 ft in tenths (and perhaps hundredths) in the other direction, making the complete tape 101 ft long. With a full-foot graduation held by the rear tapeman at the last pin set, as the 87-ft mark in Fig. 4-4(a), the graduations between zero and the end of the tape should straddle the closing point. The head tapeman reads the additional length of 0.68 ft beyond the zero mark. To ensure correct recording, the rear man calls "87." The head man repeats and adds his reading, calling "87.68" for the partial tape length. Since part of a foot has been added, this type of tape is known as an *adding* tape.

The other kind of tape found in practice is calibrated from 0 to 100 by full feet, and the first foot at each end (from 0 to 1 and from 99 to 100) is

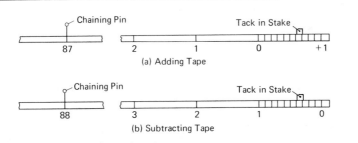

Figure 4-4. Reading partial tape lengths.

graduated in tenths (and perhaps hundredths). Thus the complete tape is 100 ft long. With a full-foot graduation held at the last chaining pin set, the graduated section of the tape between the zero mark and the 1-ft mark should straddle the closing point, as indicated in Fig. 4-4(b), where the 88-ft mark is being held on the last chaining pin and the tack marking the end of the line is opposite 0.32 ft read from the zero end. The partial tape length is then 88.00 − 0.32 = 87.68 ft. The quantity 0.32 ft is said to be *cut off*, and this type of tape is called a *subtracting* or *cut* tape. To ensure subtraction of a foot from the number at the full-foot graduation used, the following field procedure and calls are recommended: Rear tapeman calls "88"; forward tapeman says "0.32" (point three-two); rear tapeman answers "87.68"; forward tapeman replies "check."

Subtraction of the decimal of a foot is avoided if the forward tapeman reads (counts) 0.68 ft backward from the 1-ft graduation. Calls of "88," "0.68," "87.68," and "check" are made in this procedure. The only justification for a subtracting tape, if there is any, appears to be its use in "getting off a plus" (described in Section 4-12) on route surveys, with less chance of an arithmetic error, or to avoid the mistake of using 101 ft for a full tape length.

The same routine should be used throughout all taping by a party and the results tested in every possible way. A single failure to subtract 1 ft in the procedure just described when using a cut tape will destroy the precision of a hundred other measurements. For this reason, the adding tape is more nearly foolproof. The greatest danger arises when changing from one style to the other.

It is customary to have the 100-ft end of the subtracting tape ahead in route surveys, where stationing along the line is continuous. Some surveyors prefer the arrrangement in other work also, when setting intermediate points or measuring partial tape lengths.

Recording the distance. Accurate field work may be canceled by careless recording. After the partial tape length is obtained at the end of a line, the rear tapeman determines the number of full 100-ft tape lengths by counting the pins he has collected from the original set of 11. For distances longer than 1000 ft, a notation is made in the field book when the rear tapeman has 10 pins and one remains in the ground. The forward tapeman starts out again with 10 pins and the process is repeated.

Taping is a skill that can best be taught and learned by field demonstrations and practice.

4-10. HORIZONTAL MEASUREMENTS ON UNEVEN GROUND. In

taping on uneven or sloping ground, it is standard practice to hold the tape horizontal and use a plumb bob at one or perhaps both ends. It is difficult to keep the plumb line steady for heights above the chest. Wind exaggerates this problem and may make accurate work impossible.

Figure 4-5. Breaking tape.

Where a 100-ft length cannot be held horizontal without plumbing from above shoulder level, shorter distances are measured and accumulated to total a full tape length. This procedure, called *breaking tape*, is illustrated in Fig. 4-5.

As an example of this operation, assume that when the 100-ft end of the tape is held at the rear point, the forward tapeman can advance only 30 ft without being forced to plumb from above his chest. A pin is therefore set beneath the 70-ft mark, as in Fig. 4-6. The rear tapeman moves ahead to this pin and holds the 70-ft graduation while another pin is set at, say, the 25-ft mark. Then, with the 25-ft graduation over the second pin, the full 100-ft distance is marked at the zero point.

To avoid kinking the tape, the full length is pulled ahead by the forward tapeman, which does waste some time in the process of walking ahead and then back. But the partial tape lengths are added mechanically to make a full 100 ft by holding the proper graduations. No mental arithmetic is reqired. The rear tapeman returns the pins set at the intermediate points to the forward tapeman, to keep the tally clear on the number of full tape lengths established. In all cases the tape is leveled by eye or hand level, the tapemen keeping in mind the natural tendency to have the downhill end of the tape too low. Practice will develop the knack of holding a tape at right angles to the plumb-bob string.

In an alternate procedure, only the partial length of 30 ft (Fig. 4-6) is pulled ahead, a point marked, another 45 ft advanced, and finally, after adding the partial values (which step is eliminated in the other method), a 25-ft length establishes the full station.

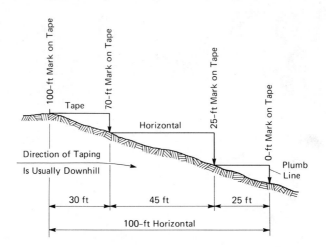

Figure 4-6. Procedure for breaking tape (when tape used is not in a box or on a reel).

Taping downhill is preferable to measuring uphill, since in taping down-hill the rear point is held steady on a fixed object while the other end is plumbed. In taping uphill, the forward point must be set while the other end is wavering somewhat.

4-11. SLOPE MEASUREMENTS.   In measuring the distance between two points on a steep slope, it may be desirable to tape along the slope and determine the angle of inclination α, or the difference in elevation d (see Fig. 4-7), rather than break tape every few feet. Long tapes (200 to 500 ft) are advantageous for measuring along slopes (as well as across rivers and ravines).

In Fig. 4-7, if angle α is determined, the horizontal distance between points A and B can be computed from the relation

$$H = L \cos \alpha \qquad (4\text{-}1)$$

where H is the horizontal distance between the points, L the slope distance between the points, and α the vertical angle from the horizontal, usually obtained with an Abney hand level, clinometer (Fig. 5-18), or transit (Fig. 8-3).

The horizontal projection of the slope distance can also be computed by subtracting a correction, C, from the slope distance. This correction is obtained from the equation

$$C = L(1 - \cos \alpha) = L \text{ versine } \alpha \qquad (4\text{-}2)$$

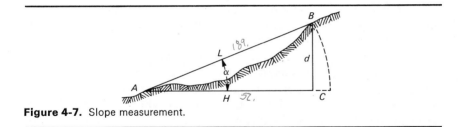

Figure 4-7. Slope measurement.

On base-line work, the difference in elevation, d, between the ends of the tape is found by leveling, and the horizontal projection computed. Thus in Fig. 4-7

$$C = L - H$$

$$d^2 = L^2 - H^2 = (L - H)(L + H) = C(L + H)$$

and
$$C = \frac{d^2}{L + H} \tag{4-3}$$

or
$$C = \frac{d^2}{2L} \quad \text{[approximately]} \tag{4-4}$$

The error in using the approximate formula for a 100-ft length grows with increasing slope but for inclinations up to 10% the answer is correct to the nearest 0.001 ft. More precise results are obtained for slopes steeper than 10% by using the partial series formula

$$C = \frac{d^2}{2L} + \frac{d^4}{8L^3} + \cdots \tag{4-5}$$

4-12. STATIONING. In route surveying, stationing is carried along continuously from a starting point designated as station $0 + 00$. The term *full station* is applied to each 100-ft length, where a stake is normally set. The position of any other point is given by its total distance from the point of beginning. Thus station $7 + 84.9$ is a unique point 784.9 ft from the starting mark, this distance being measured along the survey line. The partial length beyond a *full* station, in this example 84.9 ft, is termed a *plus*.

Taping in stations with a subtracting tape is done most conveniently by carrying the 100-ft end ahead. Since stakes are driven at every change in direction (*angle point*) of a route survey as well as at each full station, it is necessary to follow each plus station with a full one. A special procedure for *determining the plus* at a stake and for *getting off a plus* with the least chance of making an arithmetic error will now be described.

To determine the plus station of an angle point, for example, at station $7 + 84.9$, the 100-ft end of the tape is pulled beyond the angle point and the forward tapeman then walks back and holds a full-foot graduation on the stake (in this case the 85-ft graduation). Meanwhile the rear tapeman reads the number of tenths of a foot from the 1-ft mark (in this illustration 0.9 ft).

To get off the plus and establish the next full station, 8 + 00, the rear tapeman holds the 84-ft graduation at the plus station, and the forward tapeman sets a pin 0.9 ft back from the 100-ft mark. Note that all subtractions are eliminated by holding the foot mark corresponding to the plus at that station, and by reading the decimal part of the plus from the 100-ft graduation. This method, like others to be discussed, exemplifies the advantage of systematizing field procedures to reduce the possibility of mistakes.

4-13. SOURCES OF ERROR IN TAPING.   There are three sources of error in taping:

1. *Instrumental errors.* A tape may be different in length from its nominal length because of a defect in manufacture or repair, or as a result of kinks.
2. *Natural errors.* The horizontal distance between end graduations of a tape varies because of the effects of temperature, wind, and weight of the tape itself.
3. *Personal errors.* Tapemen may be careless in setting pins, reading the tape, and/or manipulating the equipment.

Common types of errors in taping are given under the following nine headings:

1. Incorrect length of tape.
2. Temperature other than the standard 68°F.
3. Pull (tension) not consistent.
4. Sag due to weight and wind.
5. Poor alignment.
6. Tape not horizontal.
7. Improper plumbing.
8. Faulty marking.
9. Incorrect reading or interpolation.

Some of the nine classifications produce systematic errors; others, random errors.

4-14. INCORRECT LENGTH OF TAPE.   Incorrect length of tape always increases, or always decreases, individual measurements and is one of the most important of the errors. It is systematic.

Tape manufacturers do not guarantee steel tapes to be exactly their nominal length, for example, 100.00 ft, or provide a standardization certificate unless requested and paid for as an extra. The true length is obtained by comparing it with a standard tape or distance. The National Bureau of Standards in Gaithersburg, Maryland, will make such a comparison for a nominal fee and certify the exact distance between end graduations under given conditions of temperature, tension, and manner of support.

A 100-ft steel tape usually is standardized for each of two sets of conditions: for example, 68°F, a 10-lb pull, with the tape fully supported throughout; and 68°F, a 12-lb pull with the tape supported at the ends only. Schools and surveying offices normally have at least one standardized tape which is used only to check other tapes subjected to wear.

An error due to incorrect length of a tape occurs each time the tape is laid down. If the true length, known by standardization, is not exactly equal to its nominal value of 100.00 ft recorded for every full length, the correction factor to be applied can be determined from the formula

$$C_l = \frac{l - l'}{l'} \tag{4-6}$$

and the true distance can be found by the expression

$$T = L + \frac{l - l'}{l'} L = L + C_l L \tag{4-6a}$$

where C_l is the correction factor to be applied to the measured (recorded) length to obtain the true length, l the actual tape length, l' nominal tape length, L the measured (recorded) length of line, and T the true length of line.

If a tape is assumed to be 100.00 ft long but when compared with a standardized tape its length is found to be 100.02 ft, then $C_l = (100.02 - 100.00)/100.00 = +0.0002$-ft error/ft of tape used. A line which measured 565.75 ft with this tape has a true length of $565.75 + 565.75(0.0002) = 565.86$ ft. For a tape 99.98 ft long and a measurement of 565.75 ft, the true distance is $565.75 + 565.75(-0.0002) = 565.64$ ft.

An alternate method of making corrections for an incorrect tape length is to compute the figure by which a full tape length is too long or too short; then multiply it by the number of tape lengths in the line. Thus in the example given, the tape is 0.02 ft too long and the total correction $= 5.6575 \times 0.02 = 0.11$ ft. This value is then added to the measured length of 565.75 to get 565.86 ft.

From a practical standpoint, the effect of any error is to make the tape length incorrect. Note that the true (actual) distance equals the measured distance plus a correction, and the proper algebraic sign for Eq. 4-6a is "built in." This is also true for the corrections discussed in succeeding sections. However, students should still try to reason whether a certain condition "makes" a tape too long or too short, and apply the correction accordingly.

4-15. TEMPERATURE. Steel tapes are standardized for 68°F in the United States. A temperature greater or less than this value causes a change in length which must be considered.

The coefficient of thermal expansion and contraction of steel used in ordinary tapes is approximately 0.0000065 per unit length per degree Fahrenheit. For any tape.

$$C_t = k(T_1 - T)L \tag{4-7}$$

where C_t is the correction in length of line due to nonstandard temperature, k the coefficient of thermal expansion and contraction of the tape, T_1 the temperature of the tape at time of measurement, T the temperature of the tape when it has standard length, and L the measured (recorded) length of line.

The error due to temperature changes may be eliminated in either of two ways:

1. The correction to the measured length of a line may be calculated by Eq. (4-7). For example, assume the recorded length of a line measured at 30.5°F with a steel tape 100.00 ft long at 68°F is 872.54 ft. The change in recorded length of the line due to temperature is

$$0.0000065(30.5 - 68)872.54 = -0.21 \text{ ft}$$

The correct length of the line is

$$872.54 - 0.21 = 872.33 \text{ ft}$$

2. An Invar tape whose coefficient of thermal expansion and contraction is 0.0000001 or 0.0000002, or a Lovar tape with a coefficient of perhaps 0.0000022, can be used. The temperature effect on the length of an Invar tape is negligible for most practical work.

Errors due to temperature changes are systematic and have the same sign if the temperature is always above 68°F, or always below that standard. When the temperature is above 68°F during part of the time occupied in measuring a long line, and below 68°F for the remainder of the time, the errors tend to partially balance each other.

Temperature effects are difficult to assess in taping. The air temperature read from a thermometer may be quite different from that of the tape to which it is attached. Sunshine, shade, wind, evaporation from a wet tape, and other conditions make the tape temperature uncertain. Field experiments prove that temperatures on the ground or in the grass may be 10° to 25° higher or lower than those at shoulder height because of a 6-in. "layer of weather" (microclimate) on top of the ground. Since a temperature difference of 15°F produces a change of 0.01 ft per tape length, the importance of large variations is obvious.

Shop measurements made with steel scales and other devices likewise are subject to temperature effects. The precision required in fabricating a large airplane or ship can be lost by this one cause alone.

4-16. PULL. When a steel tape is pulled with a tension greater than the standard figure, it elongates in an elastic manner. The modulus of elasticity of a material is the ratio of unit stress to unit elongation, or

$$E = \frac{\text{unit stress}}{\text{elongation per unit length}} = \frac{P/A}{e/L}$$

Also, the correction for pull is

$$C_p = e = (P_1 - P)\frac{L}{AE} \tag{4-8}$$

where both C_p and e are the total elongation in one tape length due to increase in pull, in feet; P_1 the pull applied to the tape, in pounds; P the standard pull for the tape in pounds; L the length of tape, in feet; A the cross-sectional area of the tape, in square inches; and E the modulus of elasticity of steel, in lb/in.^{2}

The average value of E is 29,000,000 lb/in.^{2} for the kind of steel used in tapes.

Errors due to incorrect pull may be either systematic or random. The pull applied by even an experienced tapeman is sometimes greater or less than the desired value. An inexperienced person, particularly one who has not used a spring balance on a tape, is likely to apply less than the standard tension consistently.

Errors resulting from incorrect tension are eliminated by three methods:

1. A spring balance can be used to measure and maintain the standard pull.
2. The elongation caused by pull can be calculated. Assume that a steel tape is 100.000 ft long under a pull of 12.0 lb, when supported throughout, and has a cross-sectional area of 0.005 in.^{2}. The increase in length of the tape for a pull of 20.0 lb is

$$\frac{(20 - 12)100}{29,000,000 \times 0.005} = 0.0055 \text{ ft or } 0.006 \text{ ft}$$

A line measuring 872.54 ft with this tape and tension requires a correction of $8.7254 \times 0.0055 = 0.048$ ft; hence the adjusted length is 872.59 ft.

3. Sag is decreased by greater tension; therefore, these factors can be regulated to offset each other. Either of the following formulas can be solved by trial to obtain a balanced value:

$$P_1 = \frac{0.2W\sqrt{AE}}{\sqrt{P_1 - P}} \tag{4-9a}$$

or

$$P_1^2 = \frac{K}{P_1 - P} \tag{4-9b}$$

where P_1 is the total pull on the tape, in pounds; P the pull for the stan-dardized tape, in pounds (supported throughout and giving $L = 100.000$);

W the weight of the tape, in pounds; A the cross-sectional area of the tape, in square inches; E the modulus of elasticity of steel, in pounds per square inch; and $K = 0.04W^2AE$, in pounds.

The cross-sectional area of a steel tape can be obtained from the manufacturer or by measuring its width and thickness with calipers (1 lb of steel occupies 3.526 in.^{3}), or by dividing total weight of the tape by the unit weight of steel (490 lb/ft^3).

The pull required to balance sag for a tape having a cross-sectional area of 0.0050 in.^{2} and a weight of 1.7 lb is found by trial to be 30.3 lb. Thus

$$30.3 = \frac{0.2(1.7)\sqrt{0.0050 \times 29,000,000}}{\sqrt{30.3 - 12.0}}$$

The pull required to make the distance between end graduations exactly 100.00 ft under given conditions of temperature and end support is called the *normal tension*. Normal tension is not commonly used, because it may be too large for convenient application and it changes with temperature variations.

4-17. SAG.   A steel tape not supported along its entire length sags in the form of a catenary, a good example being the cable of a suspension bridge. Sag shortens the horizontal (chord) distance between end graduations, since the tape length remains the same (Fig. 4-8). Sag can be diminished (by greater tension) but not eliminated, unless the tape is supported throughout.

The actual sag of a tape (for example, 6 in. below the horizontal) is not important. The reduced chord distance between the end graduations is the critical factor.

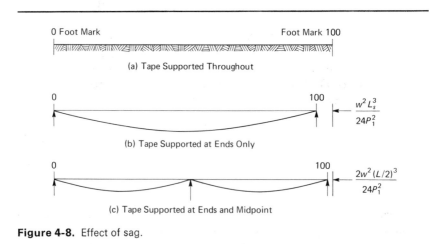

(a) Tape Supported Throughout

(b) Tape Supported at Ends Only

(c) Tape Supported at Ends and Midpoint

Figure 4-8. Effect of sag.

For a small deflection v at the center of the length of a tape, the equation of a parabola can be used to investigate the sag effect. If C_s is the correction for sag (difference between length of curve and straight line from one support to the next), in feet; L_s is the unsupported length of the tape, in feet; d the chord distance between supports, in feet; w the weight of the tape per foot of length, in pounds; both W and wL_s the total weight of tape between supports, in pounds; and P_1 the pull on the tape, in pounds, then

$$L_s - d = \frac{8v^2}{3d}$$

Also, by mechanics,

$$P_1 v = \frac{wd^2}{8}$$

Combining these two relations, and assuming that $L_s = d$ in order to simplify the results, the following equation is obtained:

$$C_s = -\frac{L_s}{24}\left(\frac{W}{P_1}\right)^2 = -\frac{W^2 L_s}{24 P_1^2} = -\frac{w^2 L_s^3}{24 P_1^2} \tag{4-10}$$

Theoretically a term $\cos^2 \alpha$ (where α is the vertical angle) should be included on the right side of Eq. (4-10). Practically, however, it has little significance except on steep slopes and long tape lengths.

The correction C_s is added algebraically to L_s to obtain d, and its sign must always be negative. Therefore, errors due to sag alone are systematic. However, the error due to sag depends on the tension applied to the tape, and the error due to pull and sag combined may be either systematic or random.

Three methods can be used to eliminate errors caused by sag:

1. Support the tape at short intervals or throughout.
2. Increase the pull to make the tape stretch an amount equal to the sag correction required.
3. Calculate the sag correction for each measurement and apply it to the recorded length.

As an example of method 3, assume that a steel tape 100.000 ft long weighs 1.50 lb and is supported at its ends only, as in Fig. 4-8(b). If a 12.0-lb pull is applied, the correction for sag is $-100(1.50)^2/24(12.0)^2 = -0.065$ ft. The correction for sag is proportional to the cube of the unsupported length, since $W^2 = w^2 L_s^2$ and w and P_1 are constants in a given case. If the 100-ft tape is supported at its center, as well as at its ends [see Fig. 4-8(c)], there are two unsupported lengths of 50 ft and the correction for sag in each such length would be $-0.065/2^3 = -0.008$ ft. The total correction for the tape length of 100 ft would then be $-0.008 \times 2 = -0.016$ ft.

On slopes where measurements less than 100 ft are used in breaking tape, it may be desirable to vary the pull or compute special sag corrections.

4-18. ALIGNMENT.   If one end of a tape is off line, or if the tape is snagged on an obstruction, a systematic error is introduced. The correction for offset from alignment, C_a, can be calculated by Eq. (4-4) with both d and L in the horizontal plane; that is,

$$C_a = -\frac{d^2}{2L} \qquad (4\text{-}11)$$

where d is the distance the tape is off line, and L the length of tape involved.

When a pin marking the end of a 100-ft length is set 1.4 ft off line, the error in that measurement is $1.4^2/200 = -0.01$ ft. A similar error enters the next tape length when the succeeding pin is put correctly on line.

If the center of a 100-ft tape catches on brush and is 1.0 ft off line, the error produced in the two 50-ft lengths is

$$-\frac{2 \times 1.0^2}{2 \times 50} = -0.02 \text{ ft}$$

Errors resulting from poor alignment are but systematic in effect and always make the recorded lentgh longer than the true distance. They may be reduced (but never eliminated) by care in setting pins, lining in properly, and keeping the tape straight. Snapping the tape while applying tension will straighten it. A moderate amount of field practice enables a rear tapeman to keep the forward tapeman (who sights along marks on the back line) within much less than a foot of the correct course.

4-19. TAPE NOT HORIZONTAL.   The error caused by a tape being inclined in the vertical plane is the same as that resulting from the tape being off line in the horizontal plane. Its value can also be determined by Eq. (4-4) to get the grade correction C_g; that is,

$$C_g = -\frac{h^2}{2L} \qquad (4\text{-}12)$$

where h is the difference in elevation between the tape ends and L is the length of the tape.

Errors due to the tape not being horizontal are systematic and always make the recorded length longer than the true length. They are reduced by using a hand level to check elevations of the tape ends, or by running differential levels over the taping points. The errors cannot be completely eliminated since the tape is certain to be out of level on some measurements despite the best efforts of a tapeman.

4-20. PLUMBING.   Practice and steady nerves are necessary to hold a plumb bob still for a period long enough to mark a point or permit an instrument sight. The plumb bob moves around, even in calm weather. On very light slopes, and on smooth surfaces such as pavements, inexperienced tapemen obtain better results by laying the tape on the ground instead of plumbing. Experienced tapemen plumb most measurements.

Errors due to improper plumbing are random, since they may make distances either too long or too short. The errors would be systematic, however, when taping directly against or in the direction of a strong wind.

Touching the plumb bob on the ground, or steadying it with one foot, decreases its swing. Practice in plumbing will reduce errors.

4-21. INCORRECT MARKING. Chaining pins should be set perpendicular to the taped line but inclined 45° to the ground. This position permits plumbing to the point where the pin enters the ground without interference from the loop.

Brush, stones, and roots deflect a chaining pin and may increase the effect of incorrect marking. Errors from these sources tend to be random and are kept small by carefully locating a point and then checking it.

4-22. INTERPOLATION. The process of reading to hundredths on tapes graduated only to tenths is called interpolation. This process is readily learned and can be applied in many branches of engineering.

Errors due to interpolation are random over the length of a line. They can be reduced by care in reading, by using a small scale to determine the last figure, and by correcting any disposition toward particular values. Tabulating the number of times each digit from 0 through 9 is interpolated in work covering a period of several days, and plotting a polar graph of the results, will expose any predilection for a few numerals.

4-23. SUMMARY OF EFFECTS OF TAPING ERRORS. An error of 0.01 ft is significant in many surveying measurements. Table 4-1 lists the nine types of errors; classifies them as instrumental (I), natural (N), or personal (P), and systematic (S) or random (R); and gives the departure from normal that produces an error of 0.01 ft in a 100-ft length. The summary verifies practical experience that recorded lengths of lines are more often too long than too short.

The accepted method of reducing errors on precise work is to make several measurements of the same line with various tapes, at different times of day, and in opposite directions. An accuracy of $\frac{1}{3000}$ to $\frac{1}{10,000}$ can be obtained by careful attention to details.

TABLE 4-1. TYPES OF ERRORS

Type and Class of Error	Systematic (S) or Random (R)	Departure from Normal to Produce 0.01-ft Error for a 100-ft Tape
Tape length I	S	0.01 ft
Temperature ...N	S or R	15°F
Pull...........P	S or R	15 lb
Sag ....N, P	S	7⅜ in. at center for 100-ft tape standardized by support throughout
Alignment ......P	S	1.4 ft at one end of 100-ft tape or 8½ in. at midpoint
Tape not level...P	S	1.4 ft
Plumbing.......P	R	0.01 ft
Marking........P	R	0.01 ft
Interpolation....P	R	0.01 ft

4-24. MISTAKES OR BLUNDERS. Careless manipulation of equipment results in large mistakes or blunders, causing serious problems. Examples are:

1. Reading the tape incorrectly.
2. Miscounting the number of full tape lengths.
3. Using the endmark as zero on an adding tape.
4. Transposing figures, or recording a distance improperly.

Mistakes are not compensating in nature. They are reduced or eliminated by standard field procedures and by measuring lines in both directions.

4-25. TAPE PROBLEMS. All tape problems develop from the fact that a nominal 100-ft tape is longer or shorter than 100.00 ft because of manufacture, temperature changes, tension applied, or for some other reason. There are only four versions of the problem: a line can be *measured* between two fixed points, or a distance *laid off* from one fixed point, with a tape which is either too long or too short. The solution of a particular problem is always simplified and verified by drawing a sketch.

Assume that the fixed distance *AB* in Fig. 4-9 is measured with a tape that is later found to be 100.03 ft long. Then (the conditions in the figure are greatly exaggerated) the first tape length would extend to point 1; the next, to point 2; and the third, to point 3. Since the distance remaining from 3 to *B* is less than the correct distance from the 300-ft mark to *B*, the *recorded* length *AB* is too small and must be increased by a correction. If the tape had been too short, the *recorded* distance would be too large, and the correction must be subtracted.

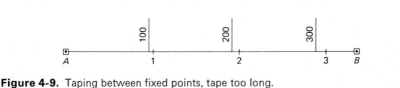

Figure 4-9. Taping between fixed points, tape too long.

In laying out a given distance from one fixed point, the reverse is true. The correction must be subtracted from the desired length for tapes longer than the nominal value and added for tapes shorter than the assumed length.

4-26. SOLUTION OF A TAPING PROBLEM. The reduction of a typical base-line measurement will illustrate the method of making tape corrections. Data taken in the field are shown in the first four columns of Table 4-2. The tape ends were supported on *chaining bucks* (tripods), and 15-lb tension (pull) applied.

Properties of the tape are as follows:

Tape NBS 5269 (the number is the NBS record designation)
Standardization by the National Bureau of Standards when supported on a horizontal flat surface:

Tension, 15 lb   Interval 0 mark to 100 mark, 100.008 ft

Standardization when supported at ends only:

Tension, 15 lb   Interval 0 mark to 100 mark, 99.963 ft

TABLE 4-2. BASE-LINE TAPING ON BUCKS

Section	Measured (Recorded) Distance (ft)	Temperature (°F)	Difference in Elevation (ft)	Inclination Correction (ft)
A–1	100.000	58	1.26	0.0079
1–2	100.000	58	0.98	0.0048
2–3	100.000	59	0.60	0.0018
3–4	100.348	59	0.81	0.0033
4–5	100.000	59	1.22	0.0074
5–6	100.000	60	2.06	0.0212
6–7	100.000	60	2.54	0.0323
7–8	100.000	60	2.68	0.0359
8–B	70.216	61	1.87	0.0249
Sum or average	870.564	59.3		0.1395

Four corrections will be applied: (1) inclination (slope) correction, (2) temperature correction, (3) standard-length correction, and (4) sag corrections.

In geodetic work, a fifth correction is made to reduce the measurement to sea level. The formula used is $C_r = -Lh/R_e$, where C_r is the correction to be subtracted (unless the line is below sea level) from the measured length L at an average elevation h, and R_e is the radius of the earth, or approximately 20,906,000 ft. Reduction to mean sea level makes all lengths throughout the country comparable, regardless of the elevations at which they are measured.

Inclination correction. Individual corrections for each tape measurement shown in the last column of Table 4-2 were computed by Eq. (4-12), which is $C_g = h^2/2L$. Their total is -0.140 ft.

Temperature correction. Using the average temperature and substituting in Eq. (4-7), the total correction is

$$C_t = (59.3 - 68) \times 0.0000065 \times 870.424 = -0.049 \text{ ft}$$

Standard-length corrections. The standard distance between the 0- and 100-ft marks (tape supported throughout) differs from the nominal length by $100.008 - 100.000 = +0.008$ ft. For 8.706 tape lengths the correction is equal to $8.706 \times +0.008 = +0.070$ ft.

Sag correction. The sag correction from standardization data (tape supported at the ends only) is equal to $99.963 - 100.008 = -0.045$ ft. For eight full tape lengths it is $8 \times -0.045 = -0.360$ ft.

By Eq. (4-10), the correction C_s for sag is proportional to L_s^3 when the weight per foot of tape and tension are constant as in this example. The sag correction for approximately a 70-ft span then is $(70/100)^3 \times -0.045 = -0.015$ ft.

True length of the base line is $870.564 - 0.140 + 0.070 - 0.360 - 0.015 = 870.564 - 0.494 = 870.070$ ft.

Field data and corrections for this base-line computation have been carried out consistently. Ordinary taping precision does not justify working in thousandths of a foot, but the procedure is the same.

It is immaterial whether the inclination correction is made before or after the temperature adjustment. The temperature correction for the partial tape length should be computed separately if the temperature deviates considerably from the average.

4-27. LAYING OUT A RIGHT ANGLE WITH A TAPE. Many problems arising in the field, such as laying out an angle, can be solved by taping. For example, a right angle is laid out readily by the 3–4–5 method. In Fig. 4-10(a), to erect a perpendicular to AD at A, measure 30 ft along AD and set point B. Then with the zero graduation of the tape at B and the 100-ft mark at A, form a loop in the tape by bringing the 50- and 60-ft graduations together and pull each part of the tape taut to locate C. One person can make the layout alone by tying the tape thongs to stakes beyond A and B.

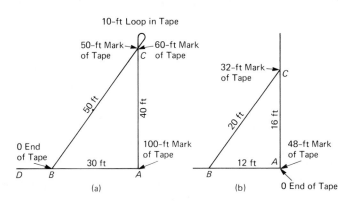

Figure 4-10. Laying out right angle with tape.

If a 50-ft metallic tape is used, a possible procedure is indicated in Fig. 4-10(b). The zero mark is held at A, the 12-ft mark at B, the 32-ft mark at C, and the 48-ft mark at A. Any other distances in the proportions of 3, 4, and 5 can be used.

4-28. MEASURING AN ANGLE WITH A TAPE BY THE CHORD METHOD. If all three sides of a triangle are known, the angles can be computed. To find angle A, Fig. 4-11, measure any definite lengths along AM and AN, such as AB and AC. Also measure BC. Then

$$\sin \frac{1}{2} A = \sqrt{\frac{(s-b)(s-c)}{bc}} \tag{4-13}$$

where a, b, and c are the sides of triangle ABC, and $s = \frac{1}{2}(a + b + c)$.

For $b = 30.0$ ft, $c = 25.0$ ft, and $a = 12.5$ ft, angle A is calculated equal to 24°09′.

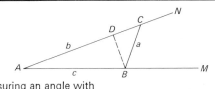

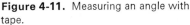

Figure 4-11. Measuring an angle with tape.

An isosceles triangle may be formed by making AB equal to AC. Then

$$\sin \frac{1}{2} A = \frac{a}{2c} \tag{4-14}$$

Selecting a value of 50 ft for AB and AC simplifies the arithmetic. Thus if $AB = AC = 50.0$ ft, and BC measures 20.90 ft, then $\sin \frac{1}{2}A = 0.2090$ and angle $A = 24°08'$.

4-29. MEASURING AN ANGLE WITH A TAPE BY THE TANGENT METHOD. If AD and a perpendicular BD are measured (Fig. 4-11), $\tan A = BD/AD$. By making AD equal to 50 or 100 ft, the tangent is easily computed. To illustrate, if $AD = 100.00$ ft and BD measures 44.80 ft, then $\tan A = 0.4480$ and angle $A = 24°08'$.

4-30. LAYING OFF ANGLES.   An angle can be laid off by reversing the tangent method just described. Along the initial side of the angle, a unit distance of 10, 20, 50, or 100 ft is laid off, as AB in Fig. 4-12. A perpendicular BC is erected, and its length is made equal to 100 times the natural tangent of the desired angle A. Points A and C are connected to give the required angle at A. This accurate method is used by draftsmen as well as surveyors in the field.

4-31. TAPE SURVEY OF A FIELD.   A field may be completely surveyed by taping. In fact, this was the only method available before instruments for measuring angles were built. Now EDM equipment makes the method useful again.

The procedure consists of dividing the area into a series of triangles and measuring the sides of each one. For small areas, one corner of the field is selected as the apex, and the distances to all other corners and the perimeter are measured. In Fig. 4-13, if corner G is chosen as the reference point, distances GA, AB, BC, CD, DE, EF, and FG along the perimeter, and diagonal lengths GB, GC, GD, and GE locate all corners of the field.

For larger areas it is better to establish a central point, such as P in

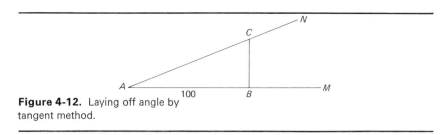

Figure 4-12. Laying off angle by tangent method.

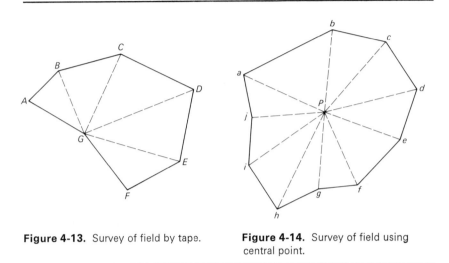

Figure 4-13. Survey of field by tape.

Figure 4-14. Survey of field using central point.

Fig. 4-14, and measure the perimeter and all lines radiating from P to the corners. The field can be plotted and the area determined from these data. The central-point method may appear to require more work, but the short lengths of the interior distances compensate for their greater number. Also, all corners are more likely to be visible from a selected point within the field.

PART III.   ELECTRONIC DISTANCE MEASUREMENT

4-32. INTRODUCTION.   A major advance in surveying in recent years has been the development of electronic distance measuring (EDM) instruments to determine lengths based upon the time it takes electromagnetic energy to travel from one end of a line to the other and return.

The first EDM instrument was introduced in 1948 by the Swedish physicist Erik Bergstrand. His device, called the *Geodimeter* (an acronym for *Geo*detic *Di*stance *Meter*), resulted from attempts to improve methods for measuring the velocity of light. The instrument transmitted visible light and was capable of accurately measuring distances up to about 40 km at night. In 1957 a second EDM apparatus, the *Tellurometer*, designed by Dr. T. L. Wadley and introduced in South Africa, transmitted invisible microwaves and was capable of measuring distances up to 80 km or more, day or night.

The potential value of these early EDM models to the surveying profession was immediately recognized. However, the first instruments were expensive and not very portable for field operations. Furthermore, measuring procedures were lengthy and mathematical reductions to obtain distances from observed values difficult and time-consuming. In addition, range of operation of the first geodimeter was severely limited in daytime use. Continued research and development have overcome all these deficiencies.

The chief advantages of electronic surveying are the speed and accuracy with which distances can be measured. If a line of sight is available, long or short lengths can be measured over bodies of water or terrain that are inaccessible for taping. With modern EDM equipment, distances are automatically displayed in digital form in feet or meters, and some give results internally reduced to the horizontal. Their many significant advantages have revolutionized surveying procedures and gained worldwide acceptance. The long-distance measurements possible with EDM equipment make use of walkie-talkies for communication almost an absolute necessity in modern practice.

4-33. CLASSIFICATION OF EDM INSTRUMENTS. The most convenient classification systems for EDM instruments are by wavelength of transmitted electromagnetic energy or by operational range. In the former, the following three general categories exist:

1. *Electro-optical* instruments which transmit modulated light, either visible or infrared, of wavelengths near 0.9 μm, which are beyond the visible portion of the spectrum.
2. *Microwave* equipment which transmits microwaves with frequencies in the range of 3 to 35 GHz.
3. *Long radio-wave* instruments to transmit energy having very long wavelengths, often more than a kilometer.

Classification of EDM instruments by operational range is rather subjective, but in general three divisions fit into this system: *short, medium,* and *long* range. The short-range group includes those devices whose maximum measuring capability does not exceed about 5 km. Most equipment in this division is the electro-optical type—small, portable, easy to operate, suitable for a wide variety of field surveying work, and used by many practitioners.

Instruments in the medium group are those having a range extending to about 100 km, and either the electro-optical or microwave type. Although frequently used in precise geodetic work, they are also suitable for land and engineering surveys. Long-range devices can measure lines of 100 km or more. Most operate by transmitting long radio waves, but some employ microwaves. They are used primarily in oceanographic and hydrographic surveying and in navigation.

4-34. PRINCIPLES OF EDM INSTRUMENT OPERATION. In general, EDM equipment measures distances by comparing a line of unknown length to the known wavelength of modulated electromagnetic energy. This is similar to relating a needed distance to the calibrated length of a steel tape.

Electromagnetic energy propagates through the atmosphere in accordance with the following equation:

$$V = f\lambda \qquad (4\text{-}15)$$

where V is the velocity of electromagnetic energy in meters per second,[1] f the modulating frequency of the energy in hertz,[2] and λ the wavelength in meters.

With EDM instruments, frequency can be precisely controlled but velocity varies with atmospheric temperature, pressure, and humidity. Thus wavelength and frequency must vary in conformance with Eq. (4-15). For accurate electronic distance measurement, therefore, the atmosphere must be sampled and corrections made accordingly.

The generalized procedure of measuring distance electronically is depicted in Fig. 4-15. An EDM device, centered by means of a plumb bob or optical plummet over station A, transmits a *carrier signal* of electromagnetic energy upon which a reference frequency has been superimposed or *modulated*. The signal is returned from station B to the receiver, so its travel path is double the slope distance AB. In Fig. 4-15, the modulated electromagnetic energy is represented by a series of sine waves having wavelength λ. Any position along a given wave can be specified by its *phase angle*, which is 0° at its beginning, 180° at the midpoint, and 360° at its end.

EDM devices used in surveying operate by measuring *phase shift*. In this procedure, the returned energy undergoes a complete 360° phase change

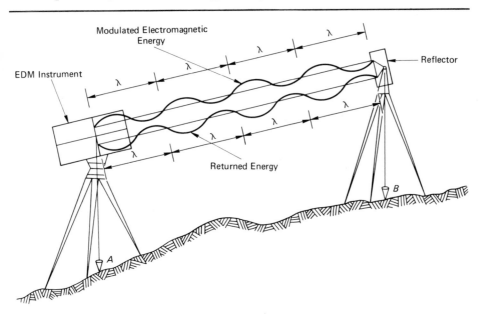

Figure 4-15. Generalized EDM measurement procedure.

[1] The velocity of electromagnetic energy in a vacuum is 299,792.5 km/sec. Its speed is slowed somewhat in the atmosphere according to the equation $V = c/n$, where c is the velocity in a vacuum and n the atmospheric *index of refraction*, which varies but is approximately equal to 1.0003.

[2] The *hertz* (Hz) is a unit of frequency equal to 1 cycle/sec.

TABLE 4-3. ELECTRO-OPTICAL EDM INSTRUMENTS

Instrument	Manufacturer	Radiation Source	Range (m)	Weight (kg)
Geodimeter 76	AGA, Sweden	Laser	3000	8
Geodimeter 12[a]	AGA, Sweden	Infrared	1600	3
Geodimeter 710[b,c]	AGA, Sweden	Laser	5000	14
Geodimeter 6BL	AGA, Sweden	Laser	25000	15
Geodimeter 8	AGA, Sweden	Laser	60000	23
DM 2000	Kern, Switzerland	Infrared	2500	11
DM 500[a]	Kern, Switzerland	Infrared	500	2
Mekometer ME 3000	Kern, Switzerland	Xenon lamp	3000	15
DI 10[a]	Wild, Switzerland	Infrared	2000	18
DI 3[a,c]	Wild, Switzerland	Infrared	900	7
SM 11[b,c]	Zeiss, West Germany	Infrared	2000	20
Reg Elta 14[b,c,d]	Zeiss, West Germany	Infrared	2000	20
3800	Hewlett-Packard, USA	Infrared	3000	8
3805	Hewlett-Packard, USA	Infrared	1600	8
3810[b,c]	Hewlett-Packard, USA	Infrared	1600	12
Micro-ranger[a]	Keuffel & Esser, USA	Infrared	1600	6
Ranger IV	Keuffel & Esser, USA	Laser	12800	16
Rangemaster	Keuffel & Esser, USA	Laser	60000	30
DM 60 Cubitape	Cubic Corp., USA	Infrared	2000	7
Beetle 500[a]	Precision International, USA	Infrared	500	3
MA 100	Tellurometer (Plessey) Corp., USA	Infrared	2000	14
CD 6[a]	Tellurometer (Plessey) Corp., USA	Infrared	2000	4

[a] EDM unit mounts on standard theodolite.
[b] Unit includes built-in horizontal- and vertical-angle measuring devices.
[c] Unit includes built-in computer for automatic reduction of horizontal distances and differences in elevation.
[d] Unit has punched paper-tape recording device.

for each even multiple of exactly one-half the wavelength separating the line's endpoints. If, therefore, the distance is precisely equal to a full multiple of the half-wavelength, the indicated phase change will be zero. In Fig. 4-15, for example, stations *A* and *B* are exactly eight half-wavelengths apart; hence the phase change is zero. When the line is not exactly an even multiple of the half-wavelength (the usual case), the fractional part is shown by the instrument as a nonzero phase angle or phase change. If the precise length of a wave is known, the fractional part can be converted to distance.

EDM instruments directly resolve the fractional wavelength but do not count the full cycles the returned energy has undergone in traveling its double path. This ambiguity is resolved, however, by transmitting energy of lower frequency and longer wavelength.

4-35. ELECTRO-OPTICAL INSTRUMENTS. Electro-optical EDM instruments transmit either visible light or invisible infrared light as their carrier signals. The earlier models used tungsten or mercury lamps for the light source. Their short operating range, especially during the day, was due primarily to excessive atmospheric scatter of this incoherent light. Coherent light produced by gas lasers has overcome these problems and greatly increased daytime range. The Geodimeter Model 8, for example, has a range of up to 60 km.

In recent years a new class of short-range electro-optical EDM devices using a carrier of infrared light has been introduced. Their range is restricted to a few kilometers by power limitations of the gallium arsenide (GaAs) diode which produces the infrared light, but for much routine surveying, this is adequate. Perhaps the greatest advantage of infrared as a carrier is that it can be directly modulated in intensity, thus considerably simplifying equipment using this source of radiation.

Specific operating principles of different electro-optical instruments vary, which makes it impractical to analyze all of them here in detail. Therefore only one representative device, the Hewlett–Packard Model 3800 shown in Fig. 4-16, will be described. To retain simplicity, discussion will be highly generalized without resort to description of specific electronic components. Table 4-3 gives names and limited data on many electro-optical instruments in service in the United States today. For detailed specifications and operational characteristics of each model, readers are directed to the manufacturer's literature.

Figure 4-17 is a generalized representation of the operating characteristics of a Hewlett-Packard 3800. The transmitter uses a GaAs diode which emits *amplitude-modulated* (AM) infrared light. Frequency of modulation is precisely controlled by a crystal oscillator. The modulation process may be thought of as similar to passing light through a stove pipe in which a damper plate is spinning at a precisely controlled rate or frequency. When the damper is closed, no light passes. As it begins to open, light intensity increases to a

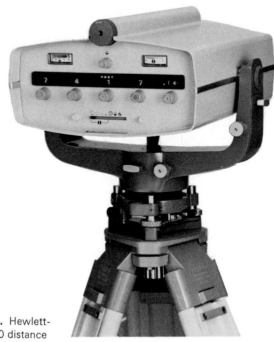

Figure 4-16. Hewlett-Packard 3800 distance meter. (Courtesy Hewlett-Packard.)

maximum at a phase angle of 90° with the plate completely open. Intensity reduces to zero again with the damper closed at a phase angle of 180°, and so on. This intensity variation or amplitude modulation is properly represented by sine waves.

Local atmospheric ground pressure and temperature are determined by an operator at the time of measurement, and an environmental correction factor based upon them taken from a chart. A correction factor is dialed into the transmitter to vary the frequency slightly so that the exact wavelength is maintained despite atmospheric variations, thereby eliminating the need to mathematically adjust the measured distance later. Note that humidity has a negligible effect on propagation of infrared light and hence is not determined.

A chopper-splitter divides the light emitted from the diode into two separate beams, an *external* measurement beam and an *internal* reference beam. The external one is directed toward a retro-reflector which has been centered over a point at the other end of the line and returns any signal parallel to the direction from which it came (Fig. 4-18). The external beam, which has been carefully aimed at the retro-reflector, is returned to the receiver. The

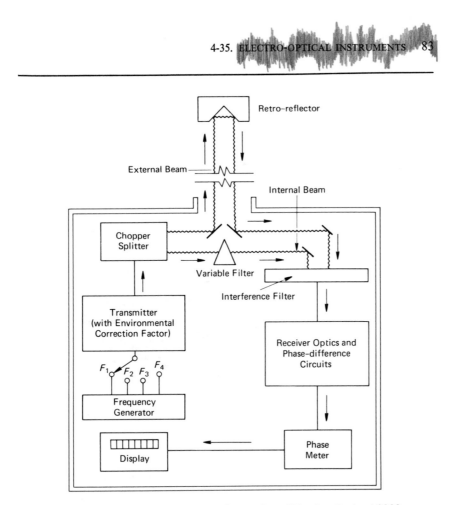

Figure 4-17. Generalized block diagram of operation of Hewlett-Packard 3800.

internal beam passes through a variable density filter and is reduced in intensity to a level equal to that of the returned external signal, enabling a more accurate measurement to be made. Both internal and external signals go through an interference filter which eliminates all unwanted energy such as sunlight. The internal and external beams then pass through components which convert them into electrical energy while preserving the phase-shift relationship resulting from their different travel path lengths. A phase meter converts this phase difference into direct current having a magnitude proportional to the differential phase. This current is connected to a null meter which can be manually adjusted to null the current. The fractional wavelength is mechanically resolved to distance during the nulling process and displayed on instrument dials.

To resolve the ambiguity of the unknown number of full cycles a wave has undergone, the Hewlett-Packard 3800 transmits four different modulation frequencies, F_1, F_2, F_3, and F_4, as indicated on the block

Figure 4-18. Triple retro-
reflector. (Courtesy Hewlett-
Packard.)

diagram of Fig. 4-17. A Model 3800 instrument measuring in feet uses modulation frequencies of 24.5 MHz, 2.45 MHz, 245 kHz, and 24.5 kHz, respectively. Wavelengths associated with these frequencies are 10, 100, 1000, and
10,000 ft long, respectively.[3]

The unit illustrated in Fig. 4-16 shows the digital display obtained
from measuring a line 7417.14 ft long. The three rightmost digits, 7.14, were
obtained first by nulling the phase meter while transmitting frequency F_1.
Distance 7.14 is equivalent to a phase shift of $(7.14/10) \times 360°$, or 257°.
Frequency F_2 is then sent and nulled, yielding a fraction of 100 ft for the
second digit to the left of the decimal, or number 1. Frequencies F_3 and F_4
are dialed in turn to get the digits 4 and 7, respectively. Observe that an
accurate measurement result is secured by very carefully nulling the 10-ft
wavelength; the longer ones only resolve the unknown number of shorter
wavelengths.

---

[3] The true modulation wavelength is 40 ft, but doubler circuitry multiplies the modulation frequency by 2. Furthermore, the wave travels double the distance being measured. A
360° phase change for the 24.5 MHz therefore has an "effective" wavelength of 10 ft.
The wavelength of 40 ft is calculated as follows:

$$\lambda = \frac{299{,}792 \cdot 5 \text{ km/sec} \times 1000 \text{ m/km}}{24{,}500{,}000 \text{ cy/sec (Hz)} \times 0.3048 \text{ m/ft}} = 40 \text{ ft/cy}$$

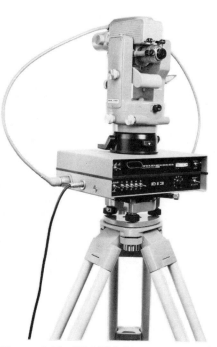

Figure 4-19. Kern DM 500 mounted on DKM2 theodolite. (Courtesy Kern Instruments, Inc.)

Figure 4-20. Wild DI 3 Distomat mounted above a Wild T-16. (Courtesy Wild Heerbrugg Instruments, Inc.)

Figures 4-19 through 4-21 illustrate additional electro-optical EDM instruments. Their operating principles are basically the same as those described for the Hewlett-Packard 3800.

A Kern DM 500, Fig. 4-19, shown mounted on a DKM2 theodolite, transmits infrared energy with a maximum range of 500 m. Horizontal and vertical angles, and slope distances, can be read from a single setup.

The Cubitape DM 60 also transmits infrared energy and has a maximum range of about 2 km. It features automatic nulling and beam interuption circuitry that makes measurements possible in pedestrian and vehicular traffic.

Set on a Wild T-16, the DI 3 Distomat pictured in Fig. 4-20 likewise uses infrared energy, has a range up to 900 m, is capable of measuring horizontal and vertical angles plus slope distances with a single setup, and contains a built-in computer to reduce slope distance and vertical angle to horizontal length and difference in elevation.

The DI 10 Distomat has a range of 1000 to 2000 m, depending on the number of prisms used and atmospheric conditions.

The Ranger IV determines lengths in feet or meters, has a maximum range of over 12 km, and has a built-in computer which automatically corrects for atmospheric variations.

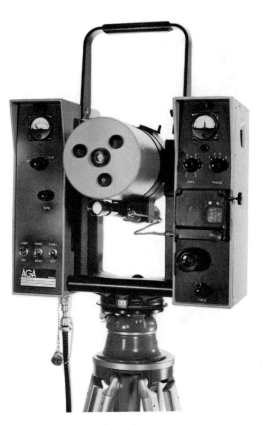

Figure 4-21. Geodimeter
Model 6BL. (Courtesy AGA
Corporation.)

Figure 4-21 shows the Geodimeter Model 6BL, which transmits laser light and has a range of up to 25 km. This instrument and its predecessors have been used extensively in geodetic and control surveys.

4-36. MICROWAVE INSTRUMENTS.   The measurement signal employed by microwave devices consists of frequency modulation (FM) superimposed on the carrier wave. Like electro-optical instruments, microwave equipment operates on the phase-shift principle and uses varying frequencies to resolve ambiguities in the unknown number of full wavelengths in a distance. The range of microwave devices is comparatively long, and they can operate in darkness, fog, or light rain. Measurements made in such adverse weather conditions are somewhat limited in range, however.

A complete microwave EDM system consists of two portable identical units. Each includes all components necessary to make measurements: transmitter, receiver, antenna, circuitry, and built-in communication arrangement. Units are centered by plumb bobs or optical plummets over the terminal points of a course, one instrument functioning in the "master" mode, the other in the "remote" mode. Either may be operated as master or remote by simply changing a switch position.

Measurement with microwave devices requires an operator at each end of the line to take a set of readings while using his instrument in the master mode. Since both units contain temperature-stabilized wavelength calibration, this procedure gives two independent measurements of the distance and a valuable check. The operators, who may not be in sight of each other, coordinate their work procedures by communicating on the built-in radio telephone.

The Tellurometer CA 1000 is a microwave instrument which evolved from the original MRA 1 first marketed in 1958. It weighs only 4 lb and has a range of up to 30 km.

Tellurometer MRA 5 (Fig. 4-22) has an antenna mountable on the instrument or separated from it by as much as 25 mm. Its range is about 50 km.

4-37. LONG-RADIO-WAVE INSTRUMENTS. Equipment using long radio waves is capable of measuring distances from approximately 100 to

Figure 4-22.
Tellurometer
MRA 5. (Courtesy
Tellurometer USA.)

8000 km. It is utilized primarily in marine navigation, to provide position control for airborne photographs and magnetometer surveys, for oceanographic and hydrographic work, and in special surveys for harbor dredging, cable laying, and placing oil-drilling platforms and buildings (almost 1000 of them are now located off U.S. shores, some as far as 150 miles). Table 4-4 lists applications and ranges of some long-radio-wave instruments presently being operated.

TABLE 4-4. INSTRUMENTS USING LONG RADIO WAVES

Instrument	Application	Range (km)
Autotape	Precision hydrographic surveys	100
Decca	Medium-range navigation and surveying	500
Hi-Fix	Medium-range hydrographic surveying	200
Lambda	Long-range surveying	750
Loran-C	Extra-long-range navigation	2000
Omega	Worldwide navigation	8000
Raydist	Medium-range hydrographic surveys	200

In general, long-radio-wave devices employ one of two basic measurement techniques, the *hyperbolic* method or the *two-range* mode. In the former, two instruments transmit signals of the same frequency from the ends of a base line. A roving receiver at stations of unknown positions compares phase differences of the incoming signals. The loci of points having equal phase differences create a family of hyperbolas with foci at the base stations. Transmission to the roving station from a second base line provides another series of hyperbolas, and their intersections become points of known locations.

In the two-range mode, two signals of different frequencies transmitted from the roving station are received and retransmitted at the base station. Phase angles of the returned signals are compared at the roving and base points to establish a series of intersecting concentric circles centered at the base location to fix points of known position. With either system, accuracy diminishes as the intersection angles between hyperbolas or circles decrease.

4-38. ERRORS IN ELECTRONIC DISTANCE MEASUREMENT.
Sources of error in EDM work may be personal, instrumental, or natural. Personal errors include misreading, improperly setting over the stations, failing to exactly center the null meter, and incorrectly measuring meteorological factors and instrument heights.

If EDM equipment is carefully adjusted and precisely calibrated, instrumental errors should be extremely small. Manufacturers specify accuracies of their products in two parts, a constant error and a value proportional to the distance measured. Listed errors vary for different instruments, but the constant portion is usually ± 0.02 to ± 0.05 ft, while the proportion part ranges from 2 to 10 parts per million (ppm). The constant error is most significant for short distances; for example, for an instrument having a constant error of ± 0.05 ft, a measurement of 200 ft is only good to $0.05/200 = \frac{1}{4000}$, or 250 ppm. For very long distances the constant error becomes negligible, but the proportional part is important.

EDM equipment should be checked against a first-order base line at regular time intervals to assure its accuracy and reliability. By comparing the base-line length and distance obtained electronically, an *instrument constant* is ascertained. A correction for this systematic error can then be applied to all subsequent measurements. The constant thus determined combines the amount by which the " electrical center" of the instrument is offset forward or back of the plummet, and for electro-optical equipment, the *reflector constant* (any offset of the " optical center" of the reflector).

Reflection of microwaves from a ground or water surface can set up a condition designated as *ground swing* which affects the accuracy of readings taken with microwave instruments. Experienced observers are able to detect this condition by examining readings obtained from waves transmitted over a range of carrier frequencies. Ground swing occurs in a cyclic manner and can be eliminated by getting a set of readings using perhaps a dozen or so different carrier frequencies, each altered from the previous one by a constant increment. The final answer may be found by graphing the readings versus carrier frequencies, connecting the plotted points with a best-fit sine wave, and then selecting the zero axis. Satisfactory results are generally secured however, by just averaging the values.

Natural errors in EDM operations stem primarily from atmospheric variations in temperature, pressure, and humidity which affect the index of refraction and modify the wavelength of electromagnetic energy. These three variables are measured and considered in accurate microwave distance determination, but humidity can be neglected when using electro-optical instruments.

Some EDM's handle atmospheric variables directly during the measuring process, as described for the Hewlett-Packard 3800. For others, corrections must be made mathematically later. Equipment manufacturers provide tables and charts which give the necessary correction factors and explain the reduction process.

The magnitude of error in electronic distance measurement due to atmospheric temperature and pressure effects is indicated in Fig. 4-23. Note that a $10°C$ change and a pressure difference of 25 mm of mercury each produce a distance error of about 10 ppm. Humidity is determined with a psychrometer which gives wet and dry bulb temperatures. An error of $1.5°C$ in difference of the two bulbs is equivalent to approximately 10 ppm in distances established using microwave instruments.

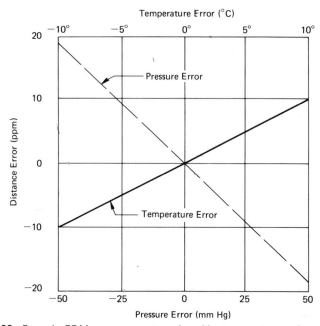

Figure 4-23. Errors in EDM measurement produced by temperature and pressure errors (based on atmospheric temperature and pressure of 15°C and 760 mm of mercury).

4-39. COMPUTING HORIZONTAL DISTANCES FROM SLOPE DISTANCES. All EDM equipment measures slope distance between stations (reduced to the horizontal in plane surveying by means of the equations given in Section 4-11). A slope length should, of course, first be corrected for instrumental and atmospheric conditions.

During field operations, heights h_e of the EDM and h_r of the reflector above their stations are measured and recorded (see Fig. 4-24). These values are then used in the reduction to horizontal.

If elevations of stations A and B in Fig. 4-24 are known, either Eq. (4-4) or (4-5) will reduce the slope distance to horizontal with the value of d (the difference in elevation between the EDM instrument and reflector) computed as follows:

$$d = (\text{Elev}_A + h_e) - (\text{Elev}_B + h_r) \tag{4-16}$$

Example 4-1. A slope distance of 165.360 m (corrected for meteorological conditions) was measured from A to B, whose elevations were 447.401 and 445.389 m above datum, respectively. Find the horizontal length of line AB if heights of the EDM and reflector were 1.417 and 1.615 m above their respective stations.

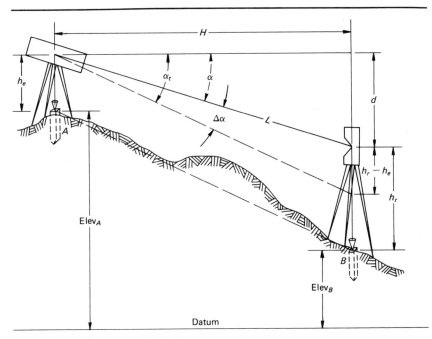

Figure 4-24. Reduction of EDM slope distance to horizontal.

$$H_T - H_R - H_E + H_I \quad cos$$
$$\overline{\qquad S \; SIN \; 1'' \qquad}$$

SOLUTION: By Eq. (4-16):

$$d = (447.401 + 1.417) - (445.389 + 1.615) = 1.813 \text{ m}$$

By Eq. (4-4):

ONLY
GOOD TO
10%

$$C = \frac{(1.813)^2}{2 \times 165.360} = 0.010 \text{ m}$$

$$C = \frac{h^2}{2S}$$

$$H = L - C = 165.360 - 0.010 = 165.350 \text{ m}$$

If a theodolite was used to measure the true vertical angle α_t between stations A and B shown in Fig. 4-24, then Eq. (4-1) is applicable. In this case however, angle α is found by subtracting $\Delta\alpha$ from α_t. The value of $\Delta\alpha$ in seconds can be calculated by

$$\Delta\alpha'' = \frac{(h_r - h_e) \cos \alpha_t}{L \sin 1''} \tag{4-17}$$

with an accuracy of 1 part in 10,000 for lines up to about 5 miles in length. For longer distances, geodetic equations beyond the scope of this text provide comparable accuracy.

PROBLEMS

4–1. List six methods of measuring distances. Give an advantage and a disadvantage of each.

4–2. Illustrate, by means of assumed values of measurements from A to B and from B to A, reasonable values of precision for (a) pacing, (b) stadia, (c) subtense bar, (d) taping, and (e) electronic distance measurement. Use distances of approximately 1000 ft.

4–3. A student counted 205, 208, 206, 208, 206, and 207 paces in walking along a 600-ft course on level ground. He then took 165, 164, 162, and 166 paces in walking an unknown distance AB. What is the length of AB ?

The readings in problems 4–4 through 4–7 were taken on a 2-m subtense bar with a 1″ theodolite. Compute the horizontal distance from theodolite to subtense bar and check by means of Table B–1.

4–4. 0°31′14″   0°31′16″   0°31′15″   0°31′15″
4–5. 0°33′35″   0°33′34″   0°33′35″   0°33′34″
4–6. 0°32′46″   0°32′45″   0°32′47″   0°32′46″
4–7. 0°30′52″   0°30′53″   0°30′52″   0°30′53″

In problems 4–8 through 4–10 compute the horizontal distance for the recorded slope distance AB.

4–8. $AB = 324.18$ ft, slope angle $= 3°50'$.
4–9. $AB = 285.69$ m, difference in elevation A to $B = 11.2$ m.
4–10. $AB = 561.45$ ft, grade $= 4.00\%$.

4–11. Compute the slope corrections for a 100-ft tape length, using the appropriate approximate formula, and an exact method, for differences in elevation of 5, 10, 15, 20, and 25 ft. Carry out the computations far enough to show differences in results, and tabulate your answers.

A 100-ft steel tape, NBS 420, cross-sectional area 0.0030 in.², weight 1 lb, and standardized at 68 °F, is 100.017 ft between endmarks when supported throughout under 12-lb pull, and 100.001 ft when supported at the ends only with a 15-lb pull. What is the true length of a recorded distance AB for the conditions given in problems 4–12 through 4–15? (Assume all full tape lengths except the last.)

	Recorded Dist. AB	Av. Temp.	Means of Support	Tension
4–12.	324.18 ft	68 °F	Throughout	12 lb
4–13.	673.20 ft	68 °F	Ends only	15 lb
4–14.	462.64 ft	60 °F	Throughout	12 lb
4–15.	781.29 ft	88 °F	Ends only	15 lb

For the NBS 420 tape of problems 4–12 through 4–15, determine the true length of the recorded distance BC for the conditions shown in problems 4–16 through 4–19. (Assume all full tape lengths except the last.)

	Recorded Dist. BC	Av. Temp.	Means of Support	Tension	Elev. Diff. per 100 ft
4–16.	423.18 ft	43 °F	Throughout	17 lb	2.7 ft
4–17.	752.97 ft	87 °F	Ends only	20 lb	4.1 ft
4–18.	100.00 ft	102 °F	Throughout	22 lb	3.1 ft
4–19.	623.56 ft	38 °F	Ends only	18 lb	1.9 ft

In problems 4–20 through 4–25 determine the length CD to be laid out using a 100-ft steel tape, NBS 422, cross-sectional area 0.0060 in.², weight 2.0 lb, and standardized at 68°F to be 100.008 ft between end marks when supported throughout with a 12-lb pull, and 99.945 ft if supported at the ends only under 16-lb tension.

	Required Dist. CD	Av. Temp.	Means of Support	Tension	Elev. Diff. per 100 ft
4–20.	87.00 ft	68°F	Throughout	12 lb	0
4–21.	78.86 ft	79°F	Ends only	16 lb	0
4–22.	148.62 ft	85°F	Throughout	14 lb	4.2 ft
4–23.	87.00 ft	38°F	Ends only	20 lb	3.4 ft
4–24.	262.85 ft	108°F	Ends only	18 lb	2.5% grade
4–25.	530.00 ft	32°F	Throughout	12 lb	2° slope

4–26. Plot a graph of the corrections to be applied for a 100-ft tape not horizontal on the ordinate, versus difference in elevation between the ends of the tape on the abscissa.

4–27. What difference in temperature from standard, if neglected in the use of a steel tape, will cause an error of 1 part in 3000? One part in 5000? One part in 10,000?

4–28. When measuring a distance DE, the first taping pin was placed 1 ft to the right of line DE and the second pin was set 1 ft to the left of line DE. The recorded distance was 231.32 ft. Calculate the corrected distance.

4–29. In taping from A to B, a tree on line necessitated setting an intermediate point C offset 6 ft to the side of line AB. Line AC was then measured as 400.37 ft along a uniform 3% slope. Line BC on horizontal ground was measured as 210.65 ft. Find the length of AB.

4–30. The chaining pins for a line measured with a 100-ft steel (adding) tape which has an extra graduated foot are set by mistake at the 101-ft mark, and the length is recorded as exactly 600 ft. What is the correct distance?

4–31. The distance between two fixed points on a construction site was measured at a temperature of 109°F with a 100-ft steel tape which had been standardized at 68°F, and was recorded as 2805.60 ft. Compute the distance corrected for temperature. What distance would have been recorded if the temperature at the time of measurement had been 25°F? Determine the accuracies obtained if the measurements at 109°F and 25°F are not corrected for temperature.

4–32. A distance of 872.34 ft is recorded for the measurement of a line with a 100-ft steel tape supported at the ends only and under a 15-lb tension. The tape weighs 1.5 lb, and is 100.00 ft long when supported throughout under 15-lb tension. Compute (a) the correction for sag for a full tape length, (b) the correction for sag for the partial tape length, and (c) the total distance after correction for sag.

4–33. A tape 3/8 × 0.025 in. is 100.06 ft long when supported throughout at a tension of 15 lb. What is the length between end graduations if the same tension is applied but the tape is supported at the ends and the midpoint? If it is supported at the ends and the quarter points?

4–34. What is the normal tension for a 100-ft steel tape having a cross-sectional area of 0.0045 in.² when supported only at the ends at 68°F, if the tape is

99.994 ft long at the same temperature when similarly supported but subjected to a 16-lb pull?

4–35. Same as problem 4–34, except for a tape of cross section 0.0055 in.^{2} and 100.05 ft at 68°F for a 15-lb pull.

4–36. In measuring a length in one direction with a 100-ft steel tape on a day when the temperature is about 75°F, and without a thermometer, hand level, spring balance, or instrument for alignment, what maximum error might you expect in 500 ft? 1000 ft? 2000 ft?

In problems 4–37 through 4–40 what error results from the condition noted?

4–37. One end of a 40-ft length of tape is off line by 1.0 ft.

4–38. One end of a 70-ft length of tape is too high by 2.2 ft.

4–39. One end of a 100-ft tape is off line by 1.2 ft and too low by 1.8 ft.

4–40. One end of a 100-ft tape is off line by 2.0 ft and too high by 1.4 ft.

4–41. To determine the angle AOB between two intersecting fences without setting up a transit, convenient distances $OA=100.00$ ft and $OB=85.00$ ft are measured from the intersection along the fence lines. If the distance AB is 57.80 ft, what is the intersection angle?

4–42. Similar to problem 4–41, except that $OA=OB=100.00$ ft and $AB=43.79$ ft.

4–43. In a seven-sided figure similar to Figure 4–13, the following lengths were obtained in measuring the sides: $AB=398.3$ ft, $BC=688.7$ ft, $CD=319.1$ ft, $DE=403.6$ ft, $EF=414.2$ ft, $FG=651.8$ ft, $GA=667.6$ ft, $GB=368.9$ ft, $GC=351.6$ ft, $GD=422.8$ ft, and $GE=384.5$ ft. Compute the angles at each corner.

4–44. Compute the total area enclosed in the figure of problem 4–43.

4–45. A base line taped on chaining bucks has a recorded length of 1560.243 ft. The average temperature was 86.3°F, and the total inclination correction for the line is −0.417 ft. Standardization data for the tape used· (in practice several tapes should be employed for checking purposes) are as follows: supported throughout and tension 16 lb, 0 to 100 mark= 100.015 ft; supported at ends only and tension of 16 lb, 0 to 100 mark= 99.970 ft. Compute the sea-level length of the base line, making all five corrections. The average elevation of the line is 4850 ft above MSL. (Mean sea level, MSL, is discussed in Section 5–2.)

4–46. Determine the most probable length of a line AB, the standard error, and the 90% error of a single measurement for the following series of measurements made under the same conditions: 521.32, 521.38, 521.35, 521.37, 521.36, and 521.38 ft.

4–47. Similar to problem 4–46, except that the recorded distances are 383.74, 383.73, 383.77, 383.71, 383.75, and 383.74 ft.

4–48. The standard error of taping a 600-ft distance is ±0.10 ft. Using the same procedures, what should it be for a 1500-ft distance?

4–49. A property line is to be measured with an accuracy of $^1/_{5000}$ using a 100-ft steel tape. If the standard error of a single tape measurement is ±0.015 ft, describe a suitable field procedure for this work.

4–50. An irregular field is measured with a 100-ft. steel tape that is 100.08 ft long, and the area is erroneously found to be 34.627 acres. What is the true area?

4–51. In taping a 1000-ft-long line on a property survey with a 100-ft standard-ized steel tape $^1/_4 \times 0.025$ in., which of the following errors is most serious? (a) A constant temperature difference of $+5°F$ from standard, (b) an alignment error of 0.2 ft on each tape length, (c) tape out of level 0.2 ft on each length, (d) a tension variation of 4 lb from standard on each tape length.

4–52. If the one-fifth point (20-ft mark) of a 100-ft tape is snagged 1.5 ft off line, but the tape is pulled tight, what error in the full-tape length will result?

4–53. A line 5 miles long to be laid off must have an error less than 10 ft. Would standard taping procedures be satisfactory for this measurement? Discuss the reasons for your decision.

4–54. State some of the advantages of electronic distance measurement.

4–55. Analyze the differences between electro-optical and microwave EDM instruments.

4–56. Explain briefly how a distance can be measured by the method of phase comparison.

4–57. If electromagnetic energy travels 186,000 miles/sec under given con-ditions, what unit of distance corresponds to each millimicro-second of time?

4–58. The speed of electromagnetic energy through the atmosphere at standard barometric pressure of 29.92 in. Hg is accepted as 299,792.5 km/sec for measurements with an EDM instrument. What time lag in the equipment will produce an error of 100 ft in the distance to a target 40 miles away?

4–59. Discuss what is meant by "ground swing." How is it eliminated?

4–60. How are variations in the propagation of electromagnetic energy due to atmospheric conditions accounted for in measuring distances with the Hewlett-Packard 3800?

4–61. List the modulation frequencies of the electromagnetic energy trans-mitted by the Hewlett-Packard 3800. Explain why four different frequencies are transmitted.

4–62. Which causes a greater error in a line measured with an EDM? (a) A disregarded $10°C$ temperature variation from standard or (b) a neglected atmospheric pressure difference from standard of 10 mm of mercury.

4–63. What will be the error in the electronic measurement of a line of 10-miles length if the temperature at the time of observing is recorded $10°C$ too low?

4–64. In EDM work, what neglected temperature difference from standard causes an error of 1 part in 100,000? 1 part in 50,000?

4–65. In Figure 4–23, h_e, h_r, $Elev_A$, $Elev_B$, and the measured slope length were 5.25, 4.70, 753.55, 925.05, and 1376.28 ft, respectively. Calcu-late the horizontal length between A and B. What is the length reduced to MSL?

4–66. Similar to problem 4–65, except that the values are respectively 1.362, 1.703, 1267.42, 948.71, and 1438.281 m.

4–67. Calculate the horizontal length of line AB for the data of problem 4–65, except that instead of having $Elev_A$ and $Elev_B$, the vertical angle from A to B was $-12°17'18''$.

LEVELING

PART I. INTRODUCTION

5-1. GENERAL. Leveling, the general term applied to any of the various processes by which elevations of points or differences in elevation are determined, is a vital operation for deriving necessary data for mapping, engineering design, and construction. Leveling results are used to (a) design highways, railroads, and canals having grade lines which best conform to existing topography; (b) lay out construction projects according to planned elevations; (c) calculate volumes of earthwork; (d) investigate drainage characteristics of an area; and (e) develop maps showing the general configuration of the ground.

5-2. DEFINITIONS. The basic terms in leveling defined below are illustrated in Fig. 5-1.

Vertical line. A line to the center of the earth from any point. It is commonly considered to coincide with a plumb line.

Level surface. A curved surface which at every point is perpendicular to the plumb line (the direction in which gravity acts). Level surfaces are approximately spheroidal in shape. A body of still water is the best example. In the survey of a limited area, a level surface is sometimes treated as a plane surface.

Level line. A line in a level surface, therefore a curved line.

Horizontal plane. A plane perpendicular to the plumb line.

Horizontal line. A straight line perpendicular to the vertical.

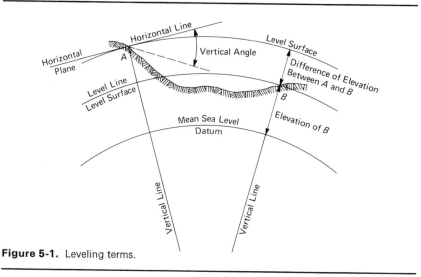

Figure 5-1. Leveling terms.

Datum. Any level surface to which elevations are referred (for example, mean sea level). Also called datum plane, although not actually a plane.

Mean sea level (MSL). The average height of the surface of the sea for all stages of the tide over a 19-year period. It was arrived at from readings, usually taken at hourly intervals, at 26 stations along the Atlantic and Pacific Oceans and the Gulf of Mexico. The elevation of the sea differs from station to station depending upon local influences of the tide; for example, at two points ½ mile apart on opposite sides of an island in the Florida Keys, it varies by 0.3 ft. Therefore, to provide a common reference for elevations throughout North America, it was necessary to adopt a mean sea level.

National Geodetic Vertical Datum (NGVD). The nationwide reference surface for elevations throughout the United States made available to local surveyors by the National Geodetic Survey with the establishment of thousands of bench marks throughout the continent.[1] It was obtained through a least-squares adjustment in 1929 of all first-order leveling in the United States and Canada. The adjustment included the 26 tide stations, and thus referenced the NGVD to MSL.

Convergence of level surfaces. A phenomenon due to flattening of the earth in the polar direction so that level surfaces are not parallel. This condition requires an *orthometric correction* for long north-south level circuits in precise work. (It amounts to more than a meter from San Diego to Seattle.)

---

[1] Locations and elevations of bench marks can be obtained by writing to the Director, National Geodetic Survey, National Oceanic and Atmospheric Administration, Rockville, Md. 20852.

Elevation. The vertical distance from a datum, usually the NGVD, to a point or object. If the elevation of point *A* is 802.46 ft, the point is 802.46 ft above some datum.

Bench mark (BM). A relatively permanent object, natural or artificial, bearing a marked point whose elevation above or below an adopted datum is known or assumed. Common examples are metal disks set in concrete, large rocks, nonmovable parts of fire hydrants, and curbs.

Leveling. The process of finding elevations of points or the difference in elevation of points.

Vertical control. A series of bench marks or other points of known elevation established throughout a project; also termed *basic control* or *level control.* The basic vertical control for topographic mapping of the United States was derived from first- and second-order leveling. Less precise third-order leveling is satisfactory for filling gaps between second-order bench marks as well as for many other projects. (See Chapter 18.)

5-3. CURVATURE AND REFRACTION.

From the definitions of a level surface and a horizontal line, it is evident that the latter departs from a level surface because of *curvature* of the earth. In Fig. 5-2 the deviation *DB* from a horizontal line through point *A* is expressed approximately by the formulas

$$C_f = 0.667M^2 = 0.0239\,F^2 \qquad\qquad (5\text{-}1a)$$

or

$$C_m = 0.0785\,K^2 \qquad\qquad (5\text{-}1b)$$

where the departure of a level surface from a horizontal line is C_f in feet or C_m in meters, *M* is the distance in miles, *F* is the distance in thousands of feet, and *K* is the distance in kilometers.

Since points *A* and *B* are on a level line, they have the same elevation. If the line of sight were horizontal, curvature of the earth would cause a rod held on *B* to be read too high by an amount *BD*.

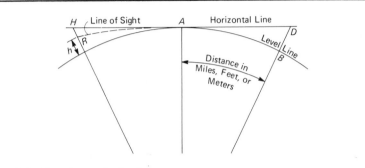

Figure 5-2. Curvature and refraction.

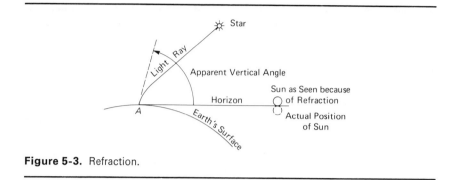

Figure 5-3. Refraction.

Light rays passing through the earth's atmosphere are bent or refracted toward the earth's surface as shown in Fig. 5-3. Thus a theoretically horizontal line of sight, as AH in Fig. 5-2, is bent to the curved form AR. The result is that an object at R appears to be at H, and the reading on a rod held at R is diminished by the distance RH.

The effect of *refraction* in making objects appear higher than they really are (and thus rod readings too small) can be remembered by considering what happens when the sun is on the horizon, as in Fig. 5-3. At the moment the sun has just passed below the horizon, it is seen just above the horizon. The sun's diameter of approximately $32'$ is roughly equal to the average refraction on a horizontal sight.

The angular displacement resulting from refraction is variable. It depends upon atmospheric conditions and the angle the line of sight makes with the vertical. For a horizontal sight, refraction R_f in feet or R_m in meters, is expressed approximately by the formulas

$$R_f = 0.093M^2 = 0.0033F^2 \qquad (5\text{-}2a)$$

or

$$R_m = 0.011K^2 \qquad (5\text{-}2b)$$

This is closely one-seventh of the effect of curvature of the earth, but in the opposite direction.

The combined effect of curvature and refraction, h_f in feet or h_m in meters, is approximately

$$h_f = 0.574M^2 = 0.0206F^2 \qquad (5\text{-}3a)$$

or

$$h_m = 0.0675K^2 \qquad (5\text{-}3b)$$

For sights of 100, 200, and 300 ft, h_f equals 0.00021 ft, 0.00082 ft, and 0.0019 ft, respectively. It will be explained in Section 5-22 that although the combined effects of curvature and refraction produce rod readings that are too large, proper field procedures can completely eliminate the error due to these causes.

5-4. METHODS OF DETERMINING DIFFERENCES IN ELEVATION.

Differences in elevation are determined directly by taping, differential leveling or barometric leveling, and indirectly by trigonometric leveling.

TAPING METHOD

Application of a tape to the vertical line between two points is sometimes possible. This method is used in determining depths of mine shafts and in the layout and construction of multistory buildings. When a water or sewer pipe is being laid, a graduated rod or pole may replace the tape.

DIFFERENTIAL LEVELING

In this procedure, a horizontal plane of sight is established by means of a level vial or automatic compensator. A telescope with magnification enables vertical distances to be read on graduated rods. This is the most commonly used leveling method.

Differential leveling, in its most basic form, is illustrated in Fig. 5-4. An instrument is set up approximately halfway between BM Rock and point X. Assume that the elevation of BM Rock is known to be 820.00 ft. After leveling the instrument, a plus sight taken on a rod held on the BM gives a reading of 8.42 ft. A *plus sight* (+S), also termed *backsight* (BS), is the reading on a rod held on a point of known or assumed elevation. This reading is used to compute the *height of instrument* (HI), defined as the vertical distance from datum to the line of sight of the instrument. The direction of the sight—whether forward, backward, or sideways—is not important. The term *plus sight* is preferable to *backsight*, but both are used. Adding the plus sight 8.42 ft to the elevation of BM Rock, 820.00, gives the HI as 828.42 ft.

Turning the telescope to bring into view the rod held on point X, a *minus sight* (−S), also called *foresight* (FS), of 1.20 ft is obtained. A minus sight is defined as the reading on a rod held at a point whose elevation is to be determined. The term *minus sight* is preferable to *foresight*.

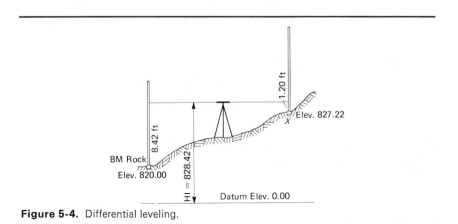

Figure 5-4. Differential leveling.

Subtracting the minus sight 1.20 ft from the HI, 828.42, gives the elevation of point X as 827.22 ft.

All leveling theory and applications can thus be expressed by two equations which are repeated over and over:

$$Elev + BS = HI \qquad (5\text{-}4)$$

$$HI - FS = Elev \qquad (5\text{-}5)$$

Instruments and procedures for differential leveling are described in greater detail in parts II and III of this chapter.

BAROMETRIC LEVELING

The barometer, an instrument which measures air pressure, can be used to find relative elevations of points on the surface of the earth. Figure 5-5 shows a modern surveying *altimeter*. Calibration of the scale on different models is in multiples of 2 to 10 ft.

Air pressures are affected by circumstances other than difference in elevation—for example, sudden changes in temperature and changing weather conditions due to storms. Also, there is during each day a normal variation in barometric pressure amounting to perhaps 100 ft difference in elevation; this variation is known as the *diurnal range*.

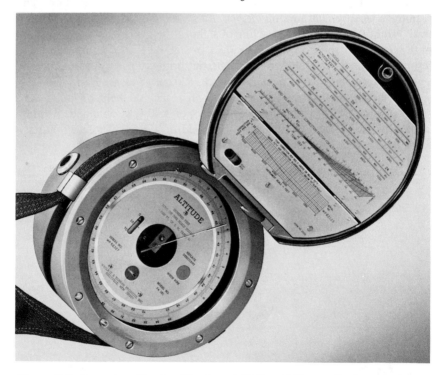

Figure 5-5. Surveying altimeter. (Courtesy of Wallace & Tiernan Products, Inc.)

In barometric leveling, one or more control barometers remain on a bench mark (base) while the *roving* instrument is taken to points whose elevations are desired. Readings are made on the bases at stated intervals of time, perhaps every 10 min, and the elevations recorded along with the temperature and time. Readings of the roving barometer are taken at critical points and adjusted later in accordance with changes observed at the control points. Methods of making field surveys by barometer have been developed in which one, two, or three bases may be used. Other methods employ leapfrog or semileapfrog techniques.

The barometric method is particularly suited for work in rough country where extensive areas must be covered but a high order of accuracy is not required.

TRIGONOMETRIC LEVELING

The difference in elevation between two points can be determined by measuring (a) the inclined distance between them and (b) the vertical angle to one point from a horizontal plane through the other. Thus in Fig. 5-6 if the slope distance AB or DC and the vertical angle EDC are measured, then the difference in elevation between A and B is $EC = DC \sin EDC$.

Trigonometric leveling is commonly used in topographical work and over very rugged terrain. For long sights, errors due to earth curvature and refraction are significant but can be eliminated by applying a correction using either Eq. 5-3a or 5-3b, or by taking the average of vertical angles observed from both ends of every line.

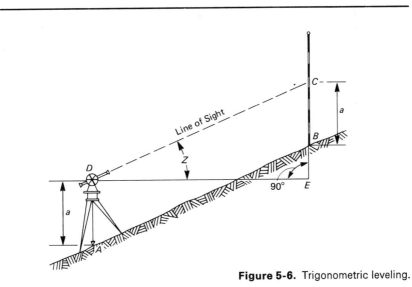

Figure 5-6. Trigonometric leveling.

PART II. INSTRUMENTS FOR DIFFERENTIAL LEVELING

5-5. TYPES OF INSTRUMENTS FOR DIFFERENTIAL LEVELING.
The types of instruments used for differential leveling are the *dumpy* and
wye levels shown in Figs. 5-9 and 5-11 respectively; the *tilting dumpy* level,
Figs. 5-12 and 5-13; and the *automatic* level, Figs. 5-14 and 5-15. For first-
order control surveys, *precise geodetic* levels, described in Chapter 18, are
available. For less accurate work, the *hand* level, Fig. 5-17, is often used.

Although each differs somewhat in design, every leveling instrument has
a telescope and a means for orienting its line of sight in a horizontal plane.
Except for automatic levels, this orientation is accomplished by means of
level vials.

5-6. LEVEL VIALS.   A level vial is a glass tube, sealed at both ends, containing a sensitive liquid and small air bubble. The liquid must be non-
freezing, quick-acting, and relatively stable in length for normal temperature
variations. Purified synthetic alcohol has generally replaced the mixture of
alcohol and ether formerly used. Uniformly spaced graduations are etched on
the exterior surface of the tube to show the exact position of the bubble.
On vials now made, the divisions are generally 2 mm long, but 0.01-ft and
0.1-in. spacing have also been used.

The *axis* of a level vial is the imaginary longitudinal line tangent to the
upper inside surface at the midpoint. When the bubble is in the center of its
run, the axis should be a horizontal line, as in Fig. 5-7.

Sensitivity of a level vial is determined by the radius of curvature established in grinding. The larger the radius, the more sensitive the bubble. A
highly sensitive bubble is necessary for precise work but may be a handicap
in rough surveys because of the longer time required to center it.

A properly designed instrument has a level vial sensitivity correlated

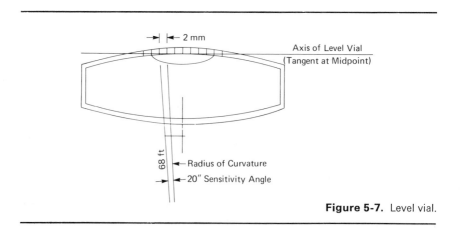

Figure 5-7. Level vial.

Figure 5-8. Coincident type of level bubble. Correctly set in left view; twice the deviation of the bubble shown in right view. (Courtesy of Kern Instruments, Inc.)

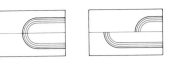

with the resolving power, or resolution, of the telescope. A slight movement of the bubble should be accompanied by a minute change in the observed rod reading at a distance of perhaps 200 ft. Sensitivity of a level vial is expressed in two ways: by (a) the angle, in seconds, subtended by one division on the scale and (b) the radius of curvature of the tube.

If one division subtends an angle of 20″ at the center, it is called a 20″ bubble. Because of the variable lengths of divisions that have been used, this is not always a fair comparison. A 20″ bubble on a vial having 2-mm divisions has a radius of 68 ft. The sensitivity of level vials on wye and dumpy levels ranges from about 20 to 90″, the usual value being approximately 20″ for 2-mm divisions.

Figure 5-8 illustrates the *coincident* type of level bubble used on precise equipment. The bubble is centered by bringing the two ends together to form a smooth curve. A prism splits the bubble and makes the two ends visible simultaneously.

A noncoincident type of bubble can be centered with an accuracy of about $\frac{1}{10}$ of its sensitivity. A coincident bubble, because of the opposite motions of the two ends and the magnification provided in an optical-reading instrument, can be centered with an accuracy of perhaps $\frac{1}{40}$ of its sensitivity. Thus the precision possible in centering, as well as the sensitivity of the bubble, must be considered in estimating the results to be obtained.

5-7. TELESCOPES. The telescope on a dumpy level, Fig. 5-9, is a metal tube containing four main parts: objective lens, negative lens, reticle, and eyepiece.

Objective lens. This compound lens is securely mounted in the object end of the main tube with its optical axis reasonably concentric with the tube axis. Some light striking a lens is lost (approximately 4 to 5%) by reflection and absorption, even though the rays are perpendicular to its surface. For a compound lens system the reduction of light is multiplied and may become critical. Loss by reflection is practically eliminated by means of a thin (¼ wavelength of light) uniform coating evaporated onto the lens surfaces to be in contact with air. The coating material has an index of refraction less than that of glass. Loss of light by absorption usually is not serious unless the lenses are very thick.

Negative lens. The negative lens is mounted in a sliding tube so that its optical axis coincides with that of the objective lens. Its purpose is to bring

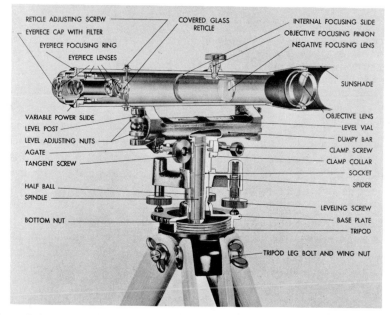

Figure 5-9. Dumpy level.

rays of light entering through the objective lens to focus at the plane of the reticle. It is important that the bearings of the slide and receive tubes be so fitted that there will be no deviation of either lens axis—objective or negative —during the focusing process from maximum to minimum distances. If an object infinitely far away is sighted (for example, a star), the distance from a lens to the image it forms is called its focal length, f. Practically, a sight distance of a few thousand feet reproduces this condition.

Reticle. A reticle is a pair of lines mounted near the eyepiece end of the main tube and located at the point of principal focus of the objective optical system. The point of intersection of these lines, together with the optical center of the objective system, forms the directing axis of the telescope commonly called the line of collimation or *line of sight*. The reticle is mounted by two pairs of opposing capstan screws placed at right angles to each other so that the directing line of sight (line of collimation) can be adjusted at right angles to the trunnion axis of the telescope.

Cross hairs may be spider web, or filaments of platinum or glass stretched across an annular ring (doughnut). In many newer instruments, a thin glass plate with lines ruled, etched, and filaments of dark metal deposited in them, serves as the reticle. Additional lines parallel to and equidistant from the cross lines are added when desired. If a glass reticle is used, the extra lines are shortened to avoid confusing them with the primary ones. The reticle is mounted to place the lines in a horizontal-vertical position.

Eyepiece. The eyepiece is a microscope with magnification of about 35 diameters (diam) for viewing the image focused by the objective lens system at the plane of the reticle. It may consist of two lenses (giving an inverted image to the eye), or four lenses (producing an erected image). The former gives a slightly better optical acuity but may temporarily confuse beginners. Eyepieces are furnished with a focusing movement to accommodate the difference in vision of individual observers.

The focusing process is the most important function to be performed in using a telescope. Today's telescopes generally require internal focusing (an interior auxiliary lens moves on a rack), although some older ones in service are external-focusing [the objective lens moves in accordance with Eq. (5.6)]. Dust and wear affect the slide and may disturb the optical axis of the external type. An internal-focusing telescope is more dust- resistant.

The fundamental principle of lenses is given by the formula

$$\frac{1}{f_1} + \frac{1}{f_2} = \frac{1}{f} \tag{5-6}$$

where f_1 is the distance from lens to image at the plane of the reticle, f_2 is the distance from lens to object (see Fig. 12-1), and f is the focal length of the lens.

The focal length is a constant for any particular set of lenses. Therefore, as the distance f_1 changes, f_2 must also change.

Since the reticle remains fixed in the telescope tube, the distance between it and the eyepiece must be adjusted to suit the eye of an individual observer. This is done by bringing the cross hairs to a clear focus, that is, making them appear as black as possible when sighting at the sky or a distant, light-colored object. Once this has been accomplished, the adjustment need not be changed for the same observer, regardless of the length of sight, unless his eyes tire from long observation or from high magnification of the telescope.

After the eyepiece has been adjusted, objects are brought to sharp focus at the plane of the cross hairs by moving the objective lens. If the cross hairs appear to travel over the object sighted when the eye is shifted slightly in any direction, *parallax* exists. Either the objective lens, the eyepiece, or both, must be adjusted to eliminate this effect if accurate work is to be done.

The " visible " rule *near-far, far-near* may be helpful to beginners using an old external focusing telescope. If the object is near the observer, the objective lens is run far out. When the object is far away, the objective lens is brought nearer to the observer's eye.

The level vial is attached to the telescope tube in such a manner that (when in adjustment) the axis of the level vial is exactly parallel to the line of sight through the center of the telescope. Centering the level bubble therefore makes the line of sight horizontal.

5-8. OPTICS.[1]   A brief discussion of the optics of surveying instruments is desirable before leaving the subject of telescopes.

[1] This section on optics includes some material from *Optical Alignment Equipment*, published by Keuffel & Esser Company and reprinted here by permission.

The purpose of a telescope is to create for the observer a picture that shows the position of the cross hairs on the target with the greatest possible clarity and precision. This end is attained by skillful design and perfection in manufacture to secure the combination of optical qualities best suited to a particular application. Optical factors include resolving power, magnification, definition, eye distance, size of pupil, and field of view.

Specifications alone can seldom indicate the true qualities of one telescope as compared with those of another. The most important test for a telescope, and in fact the only true test, is a simultaneous comparison with another one, under the same conditions.

Some important optical terms will be explained.

RESOLVING POWER

The ability of a lens to show detail is termed *resolving power*. It is measured by the smallest angular distance, expressed in seconds of arc, between two points just far enough apart to be distinguished as separate objects, rather than as a single blurred one.

The maximum resolving power that theoretically can be attained with a telescope when the optical parts are perfectly designed, and exactly placed, depends entirely on the diameter of that part of the objective lens actually used (the effective aperture). The resolving power of an objective lens is independent of magnification. It can be computed by the formula

$$R = \frac{5.5''}{D} \tag{5-7}$$

where R is the angle that can be resolved, in seconds, and D the diameter of the lens aperture in inches. For example, if the objective lens of a certain telescope has an aperture 1.18 in. in diameter, its resolving power is 4.6".

The accepted theoretical standard for the resolving power of a human eye is 60", although a value between 80" and 90" would probably be more practical. Hence the resolving power of the objective lens has to be brought at least to this limit by magnification. If the angular distance resolved by the telescope is 4.6", this resolving power must be magnified 13 times to obtain 60". Since the eyesight of different observers varies, more magnification is always used.

MAGNIFICATION

The value of magnification (power) is the ratio of the apparent size of an object viewed through a telescope to its size as seen by the unaided eye from the same distance. Magnification varies slightly when the focus of the telescope is changed. Therefore it is affected somewhat by the distance to the object.

Although telescopic magnification must be greater than $60/R$, there is a limiting point beyond which it is impossible to increase magnification without sacrificing definition. This point is reached when the magnification becomes greater than two or three times $60/R$. For larger values the quality of the image seen is impaired, and the accuracy with which the line of sight can be made to coincide with a target is reduced.

Certain disadvantages result from the use of too high a magnification, even when the objective lens is large enough to give the necessary resolution. With high magnification the field of view is reduced, and any heat waves, turbulence, or vibration cause the image of an object to move over the cross hairs too fast for accurate observation. The magnifying power of telescopes on modern levels ranges from 26 to 41 diam, and averages perhaps 32 diam.

DEFINITION

Definition is a term used to define the overall results produced by a telescope. Better definition permits objects to be seen more clearly through the telescope. It depends upon a number of optical features and is the quality that gives the greatest pointing accuracy.

Since definition is a relative term, it can be determined best by comparing the appearance of the same object when viewed through the telescope to be tested and when viewed through a telescope with which the observer is familiar.

POINTING ACCURACY

The exactness with which the line of sight can be directed toward a target, or a rod aligned, is called *pointing accuracy*. It depends upon magnification, definition, arrangement of the cross hairs, and design of the target or scale sighted. The general relationship between magnification and pointing accuracy for telescopes having the same definition is shown in Fig. 5-10.

5-9. LEVEL BAR AND SUPPORTS FOR WYE AND DUMPY LEVELS. The telescope of wye and dumpy levels rests upon vertical supports at each end of a horizontal member called the level bar. The level bar in turn is centered on an accurately machined vertical spindle that sits in a conical socket of the leveling head. The spindle ensures that the level bar will revolve in a horizontal plane when the instrument is properly adjusted.

5-10. LEVELING HEAD.   For wye and dumpy levels, the conical socket into which the vertical axis of the level bar fits is carried by four large thumb-screws called leveling screws. These rest upon a plate that is screwed on top of the tripod. The four leveling screws are in two pairs at right angles to each other. The telescope is placed alternately over each pair of opposite screws, which are turned until the bubble remains in the center of the vial for a complete revolution. The line of sight will then generate a horizontal plane.

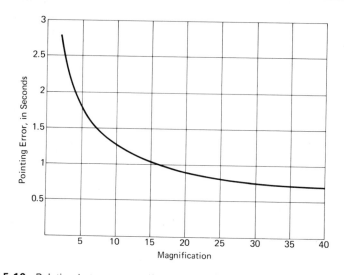

Figure 5-10. Relation between magnification and pointing error. (Courtesy of Keuffel & Esser Company.)

Most modern instruments have three rather than four leveling screws. The three-screw arrangement is faster and not subject to rocking that takes place in the four-screw type when two opposite screws are turned up or down slightly more than the other two. The disadvantage of the three-screw type is that slight differences in elevation of the line of sight result if all three screws are turned up or all three turned down. Manipulation of the four-screw head does not change the telescope elevation. Also, after the threads become worn on a three-screw leveling head, there is some loss of rigidity and the screw must be replaced. Tightening one screw of each pair in the four-screw arrangement results in a clamping action and produces a stable setup.

5-11. WYE LEVEL. The wye level, Fig. 5-11, has a telescope tube *A* resting in supports *B*, called *wyes* because of their shape. Curved clips *C*, hinged at one end and pinned at the other, fasten the telescope in place. If the clips are raised, the telescope can be rotated in the wyes, or removed and turned end for end as part of the adjustment procedure. The sunshade *X* should always be used when observing, even in cloudy weather. A cap covers the objective lens when the instrument is not being used.

A level tube *D* is attached to the telescope but can be adjusted in the horizontal and vertical planes by capstan-headed screws *Z*. The wyes are supported by *level bar E* which can be individually raised or lowered vertically using the capstan nuts *F*.

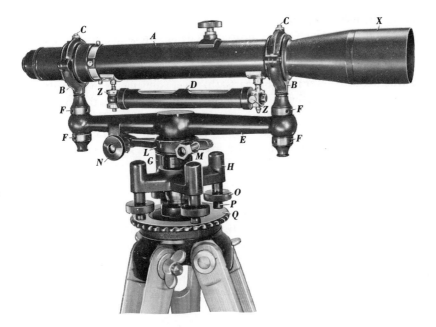

Figure 5-11. Wye level. (Courtesy of W. & L. E. Gurley.)

The *spindle* (visible in Fig. 5-9) is constructed at right angles to the level bar and rotates in a socket G (Fig. 5-11) in the leveling head H. A collar L turning on the socket can be secured by *clamp screw M* to hold the telescope in any vertical plane. *Tangent screw N*, also called the *slow-motion screw*, rotates the telescope through a small angle for precise settings but operates only when the clamp screw is tightened.

Four *leveling screws O*, resting in cups P upon the bed or *foot plate Q*, control the leveling head. A ball-and-socket joint at the lower end of the spindle provides a flexible connection to the bed plate and a means of rotation as the leveling screws are raised or lowered. Threads on the inside of the bed plate fasten the head of the instrument to the tripod.

The wye level is simpler to adjust than the dumpy level because the telescope can be lifted from the wyes and turned end for end. This feature permits one man to make all adjustments by himself. Although more adjustments are required for the wye level, they are thus easier to make. The advantage is lost if the collars on the telescope, or the bearings of the wyes upon which they rest, become worn. The instrument then must be adjusted in the same way as the dumpy level.

5-12. DUMPY LEVEL. In the dumpy level, Fig. 5-9, the telescope is rigidly attached to, and parallel with, the level bar. The level vial, set in the level bar and thereby protected somewhat, always remains in the same vertical plane as the telescope, but screws at each end permit vertical adjustment or replacement of the vial. Other construction details are similar to those of the wye level.

The advantages of the dumpy level over the wye level are (a) simpler construction with fewer movable parts, (b) fewer adjustments to be made, and (c) probably longer life for the adjustments. A disadvantage is that one of the adjustments requires a second man (rodman) and is more time-consuming. This difficulty can be eliminated if two points of known elevation are established several hundred feet apart and fixed targets set up on them. (Adjustments of levels are described in detail in Appendix A.)

5-13. TILTING DUMPY LEVEL. Tilting dumpy levels, always used on the most precise work, are also widely employed for general use. A bull's-eye (circular) spirit level is available for quick approximate leveling by means of the leveling screws. Exact level is obtained by tilting or rotating the telescope slightly in a vertical plane about a fulcrum at the vertical axis of the instrument without changing the height of instrument. A micrometer screw under the eyepiece controls this movement.

The tilting feature saves time and increases accuracy, since only one screw need be manipulated to keep the line of sight horizontal as the telescope is turned about a vertical axis. The telescope bubble is viewed through a system of prisms from the observer's normal position behind the eyepiece. A prism arrangement splits the bubble image into two parts. Centering the bubble is accomplished by making the images of the two ends coincide.

The tilting dumpy level shown in Fig. 5-12 has a four-screw leveling head, $30\times$ magnification, resolving power of 4″, minimum focusing distance of 6 ft, glass reticle, and sensitivity of the level vial equal to 20″/2 mm.

Figure 5-12. Tilting dumpy level. (Courtesy of Keuffel & Esser Company.)

Figure 5-13. GK23 tilting dumpy level. (Courtesy of Kern Instruments, Inc.)

The instrument shown in Fig. 5-13 is a tilting dumpy level with three-screw (or three-cam) leveling head. It is characterized by its short telescope, streamlined construction, small size, and light weight. The instrument has a telescope level vial with sensitivity of 18″/2 mm and a centering precision of ±4″, telescope magnification of 30×, and weight of only 3.3 lb. A 2.44-in. horizontal glass circle, which can be read with its microscope by estimation to 1′, is incorporated.

5-14. AUTOMATIC LEVELS. Automatic levels of the type shown in Figs. 5-14 and 5-15 incorporate a self-leveling feature. If the instrument is leveled roughly using a bull's-eye bubble, a *compensator* automatically levels the line of sight and keeps it precisely level. The principles of operation of the compensator are shown schematically in Fig. 5-16. Because of the ease and rapidity with which they can be operated, automatic levels have become very popular for general use.

5-15. TRIPODS. Several types of tripods are available. The legs may be fixed or adjustable in length, and solid or split. All types are shod with metallic conical points and hinged at the top where they connect to a metal head. An adjustable-leg tripod is advantageous for setups in rough terrain or in a shop, but the type with a fixed-length leg may be slightly more rigid. The split-leg model is lighter than the solid type but less rugged. A wide-framed tripod, first

Figure 5-14. Zeiss automatic or self-leveling level. (Courtesy of Keuffel & Esser Company.)

used on European instruments, is now available from American manufacturers. A sturdy tripod in good condition is necessary to obtain the best results from a fine instrument. An 8-ft extension-leg tripod is available and very useful when high setups are necessary to sight above cornfields, brush, and low obstructions.

In the past, many different thread types were used on tripods. The standard now adopted by all American manufacturers is eight threads per inch on a $3\frac{1}{2}$-in.-diameter cap.

5-16. HAND LEVEL. The hand level, Fig. 5-17, is a hand-held instrument used on low-precision work and for checking purposes. It consists of a brass

Figure 5-15. Wild NAK2 automatic level. (Courtesy Wild Heerbrugg Instruments, Inc.)

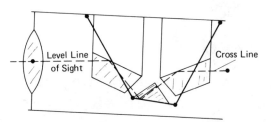

When telescope tilts up, compensator swings backward.

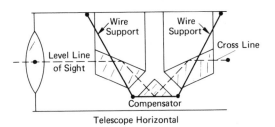

Telescope Horizontal

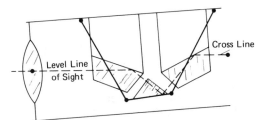

When telescope tilts down, compensator swings forward.

Figure 5-16. Compensator of self-leveling level. (Courtesy of Keuffel & Esser Company.)

tube 5 or 6 in. long having a plain glass objective and a peep-sight eyepiece. A small level vial mounted above a slot in the tube is viewed through the eyepiece by means of a prism or a 45°-angle mirror. A horizontal hair extends across the tube.

The prism or mirror occupies only one-half the inside of the tube, the other part being open to provide a clear sight through the objective. Thus the

Figure 5-17. Hand level. (Courtesy of Keuffel & Esser Company.)

Figure 5-18. Abney hand level and clinometer. (Courtesy of Keuffel & Esser Company.)

rod being sighted and the reflected image of the bubble are visible beside each other, with the cross hair superimposed.

The instrument is held in one hand and leveled by raising or lowering the objective end until the cross hair bisects the bubble. The tube can be steadied by making a tripod with a thumb on a cheekbone, the first finger on the forehead, and the eyepiece against the brow. Holding the level against a staff, or better still, resting it in a Y-shaped stick, increases the accuracy.

Stadia hairs reading 1:10 may be included (see Chapter 12). Magnification of 1½ diam is usually provided for observing the bubble and the cross hair, but the rod is seen through plain glass. The length of sight possible is limited, therefore, to the distance at which a rod can be read with natural vision.

The Abney hand level and clinometer, shown in Fig. 5-18, has limited application in measuring vertical angles and slopes, and for direct leveling. It includes an arc graduated in degrees up to 90°, a vernier (Section 5-19) reading to 10′, and several scales for slopes ranging from a ratio of 1 to 1 to a ratio of 1 to 10.

5-17. LEVEL RODS.   Level rods are made of wood, fiberglass, or metal and have graduations in feet and decimals or in meters and decimals.

Two main classes of level rods are:

1. Self-reading rods, which can be read by the levelman as he sights through the telescope and notes the apparent intersection of the horizontal cross hair with the rod. This is the most common type.
2. Target rods, which contain a movable target that is set by the rodman at the position indicated by signals from the levelman.

A wide choice of patterns, colors, and graduations on single-piece, two-section, and three-section leveling rods is available. The various types, usually named for cities or states, include the Philadelphia, New York, Boston, Troy, Chicago, San Francisco, and Florida rods.

Rods for general leveling, and for special purposes such as slope staking, can be made by fastening a flexible ribbon of treated fabric to a wooden strip. Such strips, divided in diverse ways, can be purchased from manufacturers. Use of the direct-reading Lenker level rod, Fig. 5-19(d), is discussed in Chapter 21.

A self-reading rod consisting of a wooden frame and an invar strip (graduated in decimals of meters) to eliminate the effects of humidity and temperature changes is used on precise work. The invar strip, attached at the ends only, is free to slide in grooves on each side of the wooden frame.

The Philadelphia rod is a combination self-reading and target rod, and is the most common type in university surveying instrument rooms. The 7 × 13-ft model will be described in detail. Other lengths are also made, the 6.5 × 12-ft rod being popular.

The Chicago rod is the kind most used on construction surveys, and the San Francisco rod is generally employed on control, land, and other surveys.

5-18. PHILADELPHIA ROD.   The Philadelphia rod shown in Fig. 5-19(a) and (b) consists of two sliding sections graduated in hundredths of a foot and joined by brass sleeves a and b. The rear section can be locked in position by a clamp screw c to provide any length from a *short rod* for readings of 7 ft or less, to a *long rod* (*high rod*) for readings up to 13 ft. When the high rod is needed, it must be fully extended. Graduations on the front faces of the two sections read continuously from zero at the base to 13 ft at the top for the high-rod setting.

Rod graduations are accurately painted alternate black and white spaces 0.01 ft wide. The 0.1- and 0.05-ft marks are emphasized by spurs extending the black painting. Tenths are designated by black figures, foot marks by red numbers, all straddling the proper graduation. A Philadelphia rod can be read accurately with a level at distances up to 250 ft.

On long sights, or when readings to the nearest 0.001 ft are desired, a target d may be used. Circular, oval, and angular targets are made. All are approximately 5 in. high and painted red and white in alternate quadrants. A clamp e and vernier scale f are part of the target. For readings of less than 7 ft, the target is set at the proper elevation in accordance with directions given by the instrumentman. When the rod is extended, the target is clamped at 7.000 ft and the rear section raised to bring the target to the correct height. Divisions on the back of the rod are marked from 7 to 13 ft in a downward direction. As the rod is extended, a fixed vernier scale g attached to sleeve b enables the rodman to read the target height.

Level rods are made of carefully selected, kiln-dried, well-seasoned hardwood, and graduated in accordance with rigid specifications. They *should not* be used as seats or for pole vaulting, nor should they be left leaning against a tree or building, or laid on any surface with the graduated face down. Hands must be kept off the painted markings, particularly in the 3-

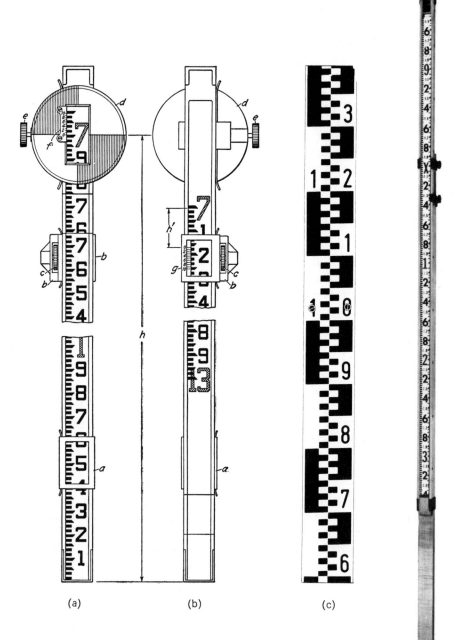

(a) (b) (c)

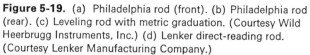

Figure 5-19. (a) Philadelphia rod (front). (b) Philadelphia rod (rear). (c) Leveling rod with metric graduation. (Courtesy Wild Heerbrugg Instruments, Inc.) (d) Lenker direct-reading rod. (Courtesy Lenker Manufacturing Company.)

(d)

to 5-ft section, where a worn face will make the rod unfit for use. Letting the rod down " on the run" batters both sections and may change the vernier reading to less than 7.000 ft, for example to 6.998 ft. If this happens, the target must be set to the same reading, as 6.998 ft, for high rods.

5-19. VERNIERS.   A vernier is a short auxiliary scale set parallel with and beside a primary scale. It is used to obtain fractional parts of the smallest divisions of the main scale without interpolation. Figure 5-20 shows the simple type of direct vernier used on leveling rods. Somewhat more complicated verniers used on transits are described and shown in Sections 8-7 through 8-9.

As illustrated in Fig. 5-20(a), the vernier has n divisions in a space covered by $n - 1$ of the smallest divisions on the scale. Then

$$(n - 1)d = nv \tag{5-8}$$

where d is the length of a scale division and v the length of a vernier division.

This is the fundamental basis for all vernier construction. For most level-rod verniers, $n = 10$, $d = 0.01$ ft, and $v = 0.09/10 = 0.009$ ft.

In Fig. 5-20(a) the reading is 0.300. If the vernier is moved so that its first graduation from zero coincides with the first graduation of the scale beyond 0.300, as in Fig. 5-20(b), the vernier index has moved a distance equal to

$$d - v = 0.010 - 0.009 = 0.001 \text{ ft}$$

The reading is therefore 0.301 ft.

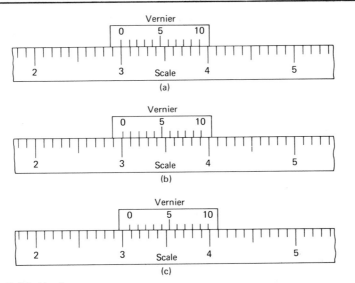

Figure 5-20. Vernier.

If the vernier is moved so that the second graduation on the vernier is coincident with the graduation representing 0.32 on the scale, the movement from the position in Fig. 5-20(a) has been $2(d - v) = 0.002$ ft. Thus the fractional part of a scale division from the preceding scale graduation to the vernier index is read by determining the number of the vernier line which is coincident with *any* scale graduation. The reading for the decimal part of a foot in Fig. 5-20(c) is 0.308 ft.

From Eq. (5-8),

$$nv = (n - 1)d$$

or

$$nv = nd - d$$

and

$$d - v = \frac{d}{n} \tag{5-9}$$

When a vernier is used, $d - v$ is the smallest reading obtainable without interpolating. It is termed the *least count* of the vernier, and given by the expression d/n, or in words,

$$\text{least count} = \frac{\text{value of the smallest division on the scale}}{\text{number of divisions on the vernier}}$$

An observer cannot be certain he is reading a scale and vernier correctly until he has determined the least count.

In selecting the vernier line which is coincident with a scale division, an observer must assume a position directly behind the lines, or over them, to avoid parallax. The second graduation on each side of the apparently coincident lines should be checked to see that a symmetrical pattern is formed about them. In Fig. 5-20(c), vernier graduations 6 and 10 fall inside (toward division 8) the scale lines by equal distances; therefore, 8 is the correct reading.

PART III. FIELD PROCEDURES AND COMPUTATIONS FOR DIFFERENTIAL LEVELING

5-20. CARRYING AND SETTING UP THE LEVEL.   The safest way to carry a leveling instrument in a car is to keep it in its box. The box closes properly only when the instrument is set perfectly in the padded supports.

A level should be removed from its box by lifting on the level bar or base, *not* by grasping the telescope. The head must be screwed snugly on the tripod. If the head is too loose, the instrument is unstable; if too tight, it may "freeze" on the tripod. A grain of sand, roughness in the threads, or a change in temperature makes the head stick. Spreading the tripod legs until the head of the instrument almost touches the ground often helps to release the head in case it freezes.

The legs of a tripod must be tightened correctly. If each leg falls slowly of its own weight after being placed in a horizontal position, it is properly adjusted. Clamping them too tightly strains the plate and screws. If the legs are loose, the setup is wobbly.

It is generally unnecessary to set the level up over any particular point. It is inexcusable, therefore, to have the base plate badly out of level before using the leveling screws. Moving one leg radially, or circumferentially, will level the instrument. On side-hill setups, placing one leg on the uphill side and two on the downhill slope eases the problem. On very steep slopes some instrumentmen prefer two legs uphill and one down for a stable setup. The most convenient height of setup is one which enables the observer to sight through the telescope without stooping or stretching.

In leveling the four-screw head, the telescope is rotated until it is over two opposite screws. The bubble is approximately centered by using the thumb and first finger of each hand to adjust the opposite screws. The procedure is repeated with the telescope over the other two leveling screws. Time is wasted by centering the bubble exactly on the first try, since it will be thrown off during the cross-leveling. Working with each pair of screws about three times should complete the job.

The leveling screws are turned in opposite directions at the same speed by both hands, unless the intention is to tighten or loosen the leveling head. A simple rule is that the bubble follows the left thumb. This is illustrated in Fig. 5-21.

If one hand turns faster than the other, the screws loosen and the head rocks on two screws, or the screws bind. Final precise adjustment may be made with one hand only. Leveling screws should be snug, not wrench-tight, to save time and avoid damage to the threads and base plate. A good in-

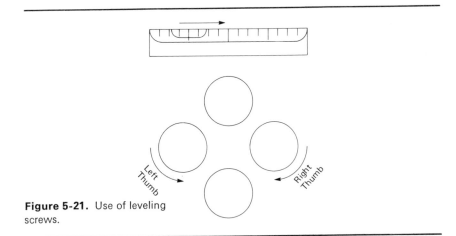

Figure 5-21. Use of leveling screws.

strumentman senses the proper setting of the leveling screws to permit ready movement without jamming the threads. The instrument should be leveled on the base plate before it is returned to the box.

For automatic and tilting levels having a three-screw head and bull's-eye bubble, the telescope is aligned over one screw and thus made perpendicular to the line through the other two. The bull's-eye bubble is centered by alternately turning one screw and then the other two, and the telescope need not be rotated during the process.

Inexperienced instrumentmen working on a steep hillside are likely to find after completing the leveling process that the telescope is too low for uphill sights. To avoid this, set the instrument without attempting to level it but have the bubble somewhat back of center. Sight the rod, and if it is visible for this condition, it obviously will also be visible when the instrument is leveled. As an alternative, a hand level may be used to check for proper height of setup before starting to carefully level the instrument.

5-21. DUTIES OF A RODMAN.   The duties of a rodman are relatively simple. Like a tapeman, however, he can nullify the best efforts of the observer if he fails to follow a few simple rules.

The level rod must be plumb to give a correct reading. In Fig. 5-22, point A is below the line of sight by a distance equal to AB. If the rod is tilted to position AD, an erroneous reading AE is obtained. It can be seen that the smallest reading possible, AB, is the correct one and secured only when the rod is plumb.

Waving the rod is a procedure used to ensure that the rod is plumb when a reading is taken. The method consists of slowly tilting the top of the rod, first toward the instrument, then away from it. The instrumentman observes the readings alternately increasing and decreasing, and selects the minimum value, which is the correct one. Beginners tend to swing the rod too fast and through too long an arc, and small errors can be introduced depending upon the kind of mark used (see problem 5-48).

On still days the rod can be plumbed by letting it balance of its own weight while lightly supported by the finger tips. The instrumentman makes certain the rod is plumbed in the lateral direction by checking its coincidence

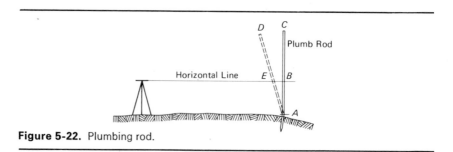

Figure 5-22. Plumbing rod.

Figure 5-23. Rod level. (Courtesy of Keuffel & Esser Company.)

with the vertical cross hair and signaling for any adjustments necessary. The rodman can save time by squinting along the side of the rod to line it up with a telephone pole, a tree, or the side of a building. Plumbing on the line toward the instrument is more difficult, but holding the rod against the toes, stomach, and nose will bring it close to the plumb position.

A rod level of the type shown in Fig. 5-23 ensures fast and correct rod plumbing. Its L shape is designed to fit the rear and side faces of the rod while the bull's-eye bubble is centered to plumb the rod *in both directions.* The simplicity and reasonable cost of a rod level should encourage greater use of this accessory.

Equation (4-4) of Section 4-11 can be applied to determine approximately the error in reading caused by the rod not being plumb. For example, if $AB = 10$ ft and $EB = 6$ in. in Fig. 5-22, the error is

$$C = \frac{d^2}{2L} = \frac{0.5^2}{2 \times 10} = 0.012 \text{ ft}$$

Errors of this magnitude are serious, whether results are being carried to hundredths or thousandths, and make careful plumbing necessary for high-rod readings.

5-22. DIFFERENTIAL LEVELING. Figure 5-24 illustrates the procedure followed in differential leveling. Note that several instrument setups were required to complete this run. Field notes for the work are shown in Plate A-3.

The positions on which a rod is held to carry the line from one setup to the next are called *turning points* (TP's). A turning point is defined as a solid point on which both a plus and minus sight are taken on a line of levels. Horizontal distances for the plus and minus sights should be made approximately equal by pacing, stadia measurements, counting lengths of rails if working along a track, or by some other easy method. In doing this, the combined effects of earth curvature and refraction are eliminated, as shown in Fig. 5-25, where e_1 and e_2 are the combined curvature and refraction errors for the plus sight and minus sight, respectively. Because D_1 and D_2 are equal, e_1 and e_2 are also equal. In calculations the former is added, the latter subtracted, thus canceling each other.

On slopes it may be somewhat difficult to balance the lengths of plus and minus sights, but it can usually be accomplished by following a zigzag path.

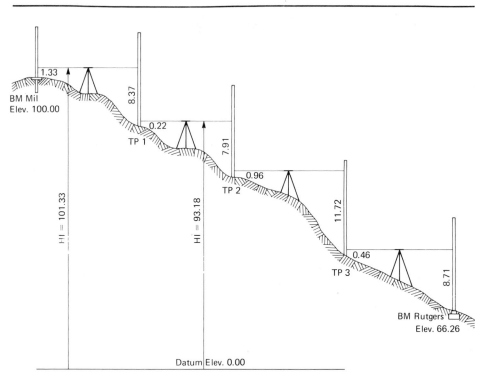

Figure 5-24. Differential leveling.

Bench marks are described the first time used, and thereafter are referred to by noting the page number on which detailed. A description should give the general location first and include enough particulars to enable a person unfamiliar with the area to find the mark readily. Bench marks are usually named for some prominent object which is nearby to aid in describing

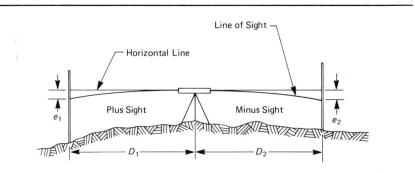
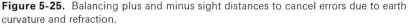

Figure 5-25. Balancing plus and minus sight distances to cancel errors due to earth curvature and refraction.

their location, one word being preferable. Examples are BM River, BM Tower, BM Corner, and BM Bridge. On extensive surveys, bench marks are given numbers. These have the advantage of identifying relative positions along a line, but the numbers are more subject to mistakes in recording. Turning points are numbered consecutively along a line of levels but need not be described since they are merely a means to an end and will seldom have to be relocated.

Before a party leaves the field, all possible note checks must be made to detect any mistakes in arithmetic and to verify achievement of acceptable closure. The algebraic sum of the plus and minus sights applied to the first elevation should give the last elevation. This computation checks the values of all HI's and TP's unless compensating errors have been made. When carried out for each left-hand page of tabulations, it is termed the "page check."

Important work is checked by leveling forward and backward between endpoints. The difference between the *rod sum* (algebraic total of plus and minus sights) on the run out and the rod sum on the run back is called the *loop closure*. Specifications, or the purpose of the survey, fix the permissible loop closure (see Section 5-31). If the permissible closure is exceeded, one or more additional runs must be made. Note that a new instrument setup must be made before starting the return run to obtain a complete check. Otherwise an error in reading the final minus sight will be accepted for the first plus sight on the run back.

The difference in elevation between the endpoints is considered to be the average of the rod sums on the runs out and back. Where a number of interlocking "loops" are used in a network of levels, an approximate "loop adjustment" method (see Section 5-33) or a least-squares adjustment can be employed to distribute the closure. True elevations can be obtained by starting from a bench mark whose elevation above mean sea level is known. If this is not possible, an assumed elevation may be used, and later all values can be converted to true elevations by application of a constant, as in Plate A-3.

A lake or pond not disturbed by wind, inflow, or outflow, and even a very slow-moving stream, can serve as a huge bench mark.

Double-rodded lines of levels are sometimes used on important work. Plus and minus sights are taken on two rods from each setup of the instrument and carried in separate noteform columns. Special precautions are required to prevent errors in recording.

Flying levels may be run at the end of the work day to check the results of an extended line run in one direction only. Longer sights and fewer setups are used, the purpose being to detect any large mistakes.

Three-wire leveling, formerly used mainly in precise work, now is employed on projects requiring only ordinary precision. Readings of the upper, middle, and lower cross hairs are averaged to obtain a better value. A check on the work is obtained by noting the difference between the middle and upper hairs, and between the middle and lower hairs. If these fail to agree within one or two of the smallest units being read, the readings are repeated. The intercept between the upper and lower hairs gives the sight distance for checking the lengths of plus and minus sights. The procedure is described in more detail in Section 18-15.

5-23. RECIPROCAL LEVELING. Topographic features such as rivers, lakes, and canyons make it difficult or impossible to keep plus and minus sights short and equal. Reciprocal leveling is employed at such locations.

As shown in Fig. 5-26, the level is set up on one side of a stream at X, and rod readings taken on points A and B. Since sight XB is very long, several readings are secured for averaging. This is done by reading, turning the leveling screws to throw the instrument out of level, then releveling and reading again. The process is repeated two, three, four, or more times. The instrument is now moved to Y and the same procedure followed.

The differences in elevation between A and B determined with the instrument at X and Y may not agree because of curvature and refraction, and personal and instrumental errors. The average of the two differences in elevation is accepted as the correct value, if their precision is satisfactory. This procedure, which is a method of reversion, is used in making adjustments of levels and transits. Plate A-4 is a sample set of field notes for reciprocal leveling.

5-24. PROFILE LEVELING. On route surveys for highways and pipelines, elevations are required at every 100-ft station, at angle points (points marking changes in direction), at breaks in the slope of the ground surface, and at critical points such as roads, bridges, and culverts. These elevations when plotted show a *profile*—a vertical section of the surface of the ground

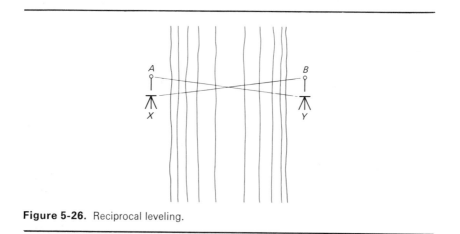

Figure 5-26. Reciprocal leveling.

along any fixed line. For most engineering projects the profile is taken along the center line, which is staked out in 100-ft stations or, if necessary, in 50- or 25-ft stations.

Profile leveling, a special form of differential leveling, also requires the establishment of turning points on which both plus and minus sights are taken. In addition, any number of *intermediate sights* (minus sights) may be obtained on points along the line from each setup of the instrument, as shown in Fig. 5-27. Plate A-5 is a sample set of level notes covering the profile shown in Fig. 5-27.

As shown in the notes, a plus sight is taken upon a bench mark, and intermediate sights read on the stations, at breaks in the ground surface, and at critical points, until the limit of accurate sighting distance is reached. A turning point is then selected, the instrument moved ahead, and the process repeated. The level itself is usually set up *off* the center line so that sights of more uniform length can be procured. Bench marks out of the way of future construction are established along the route on a long line.

It is evident that when the "page check" is made on arithmetic computations, only the minus sights taken on turning points can be used. For this reason, and to isolate the points to be plotted, a separate column is preferred for the intermediate sights.

Readings on paved surfaces, such as concrete roadways, curbs, and sidewalks, can be taken to 0.01 ft. Readings on the ground closer than 0.1 ft are not practical.

An elevation meter used in highway surveys is a mechanical or electromechanical device on wheels that measures slope and distance, and automatically and continuously integrates and records their product into difference in elevation. A fourth-order accuracy profile can be secured at speeds of 25 miles/hr.

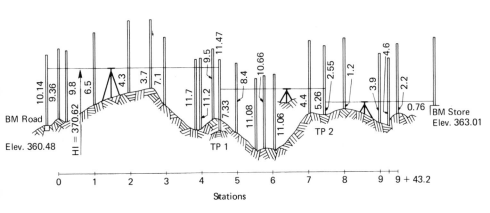

Figure 5-27. Profile leveling.

5-25. AIRBORNE PROFILE RECORDER. Development of an airborne profile recorder was begun in the early 1940s to get a profile of the terrain beneath the path of an aircraft carrying radar equipment. The ground profile, with respect to an isobaric reference surface, was obtained by measuring the elapsed time required for radar signals to travel from the aircraft to the ground, be reflected, and return to the aircraft. By the late 1950s, equipment was capable of vertical accuracies of 10 ft in flat terrain and 20 ft over mountainous areas.

Accuracy of airborne profile recording systems has now been improved through the use of laser energy. The system operates similarly to electronic distance measuring devices in that the frequency of the laser energy is varied, the output signal is modulated onto a carrier wave, and distance is determined by utilizing the phase-shift principle.

Flying heights are normally kept low during laser profiling to get better accuracy. Altitudes of the aircraft above the terrain are usually recorded in digital form. The accuracy of laser airborne profile recorders is quite phenomenal, tests showing elevations to be correct to within 1 ft at flying heights of 1000 ft. Resolution of the system actually approximates 0.1 ft (a precision of $\frac{1}{10,000}$) but the accuracy of the isobaric reference datum limits the terrain profile correctness to the higher figure.

5-26. DRAWING AND USE OF THE PROFILE. Profiles are plotted on a special paper called *Plate A profile paper* which is ruled as shown in Fig. 5-28. Vertical lines are spaced $\frac{1}{4}$ in. apart, with every tenth line heavier. Horizontal lines are $\frac{1}{20}$ in. apart, each fifth line thicker and every fiftieth line still heavier.

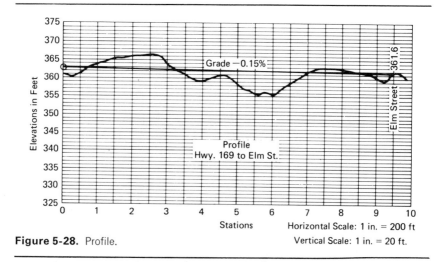

Figure 5-28. Profile.

Horizontal Scale: 1 in. = 200 ft
Vertical Scale: 1 in. = 20 ft

The vertical scale of a profile is generally exaggerated with respect to the horizontal scale in order to make differences of elevation more pronounced. A ratio of 10 to 1 is frequently used. Thus for a horizontal scale of 1 in. = 100 ft, the vertical scale would be 1 in. = 10 ft. The heaviest lines of Plate A paper make blocks 2½ × 2½ in. and are best suited to a scale of 1 in. = 40 ft (or 400 ft) horizontally, and 1 in. = 4 ft (or 40 ft) vertically. The scale actually used should be plainly marked.

Curves, or in some cases straight lines, are drawn to connect the plotted elevations.

The plotted profile is used for many purposes, such as (a) determination of the depth of cut and fill on a proposed highway or airport, (b) study of grade-crossing problems, (c) investigation and selection of the most economical grade, location, and depth for sewers, pipelines, tunnels, irrigation ditches, and other projects.

Rate of grade (or *gradient*, or *per cent grade*) is the rise or fall in feet per 100 ft. Thus a grade of 2.5% means a 2.5-ft difference in elevation per 100 ft horizontally. Ascending grades are plus, descending grades minus. A grade line selected to give somewhat equal cuts and fills is shown in Fig. 5-28. The process of staking out grades is described in Chapter 21.

The term "grade" is also employed to denote the elevation of the finished surface of an engineering project.

5-27. BORROW-PIT, CHECKERBOARD, OR CROSS-SECTION LEVELING.
The amount of earth, gravel, rock, or other material excavated or filled on a construction project may be determined by borrow-pit leveling. The quantities computed form the basis for payment to the contractor or materials supplier. The number of cubic yards of coal or other loose materials in stockpiles can be found in the same way.

As an example, assume the area shown in Fig. 5-29 is to be graded to an

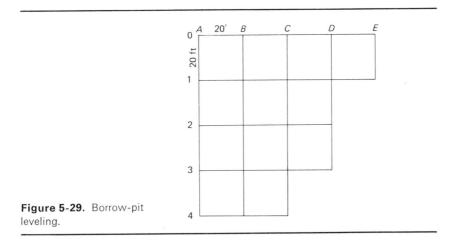

Figure 5-29. Borrow-pit leveling.

elevation of 358.0 for a building site. Notes for the field work are shown in Plate A-6.

The area to be covered is staked in squares of 10, 20, 50, 100, or more feet, the choice depending upon project size and accuracy desired. A transit and/or tape may be used for the layout. A bench mark of known or assumed elevation is established outside the area in a place not likely to be disturbed.

The level is set up at any convenient location, a plus sight taken on the bench mark, and minus sights read on the corners of the squares. If the terrain is not too rough, it may be possible to select a point near the center of the area and take sights on all corners from the same setup, as in this example.

Corners of the squares are designated by letters and numbers, such as A-1, C-4, and D-2. Since the site is to be graded to an elevation of 358.0, the amount of cut or fill at each corner can be obtained by subtracting 358.0 from its elevation. For each square, then, the average height of the four corners of the prism of cut or fill is determined and multiplied by the base area, 20×20 ft $= 400$ ft^2, to get the volume. The total volume is found by adding the individual values for each block and dividing by 27 to obtain a result in cubic yards.

As a simplification, the cut at each corner multiplied by the number of times it enters the volume computation can be shown in a separate column, a total secured, and divided by 4. The result multiplied by the base area of one block gives the volume. This procedure is shown in the sample noteform.

5-28. USE OF THE HAND LEVEL.   A hand level can be used for some types of work, such as differential leveling, when a high order of precision is not required. The instrumentman takes a plus and a minus sight while standing in one position, then moves ahead to repeat the process.

5-29. SIZE OF FIELD PARTY.   Ordinary differential leveling can be done efficiently by a two-man party. The instrumentman keeps notes if a self-reading rod is used; the rodman records if a target rod is employed. On precise leveling, an observer, an umbrellaman, a notekeeper, and two rodmen are required.

A self-reading rod is frequently used on borrow-pit and profile leveling; hence a party of two men is sufficient. Using a third man to keep notes relieves the observer of this task, however, and permits the party to move faster.

5-30. SIGNALS.   The distance between personnel, and noise from traffic or other sources, make it necessary to communicate by hand signals on many surveys if walkie-talkies are not available. Some typical gestures used in leveling are listed in the following paragraphs of this section. Special signals to fit unusual requirements may be invented for a particular job. They should simulate as closely as possible the action to be taken. The instrumentman must remember that he has the advantage of telescopic magnification and give clear signals which cannot be misunderstood by a rodman using only natural vision. Equipping the rodman with a small telescope is helpful.

Plumb rod. If the rod is to the right of a plumb position, the instrumentman extends his right arm full length upward and inclined to the vertical. This position is maintained until the rod is plumb.

Establish a TP. Either the instrumentman or the rodman may give this signal by holding one arm straight up and moving it in a horizontal circle.

High rod. Instrumentman extends both arms horizontally and sideways, palms up, and brings them together over his head.

Raise for red. Instrumentman holds one arm straight forward, palm up, and raises the arm slowly to a position about 45° above the horizontal. (On very close sights, the red foot-mark numbers may not be in the telescope's field of view.)

Raise target. Instrumentman raises an extended arm above his shoulder, holding it high if considerable movement is required. The arm is moved toward the horizontal position as the target approaches the desired setting.

Lower target. Same as "raise target," but the extended arm is held below the shoulder and moved up.

Clamp target. Instrumentman waves one hand in a vertical circle with his arm in a horizontal position.

TP or BM. Rodman holds the rod horizontally above his head, then places it on the TP or BM. Used in profile leveling to differentiate between intermediate sights and TP's or BM's for the benefit of the instrumentman and notekeeper.

All right. Arms are extended sideways, palms forward, and waved up and down several times. Used by any member of the party in all types of surveying.

Signals for numbers. One of the systems used is shown in Fig. 5-30.

5-31. PRECISION. Precision in leveling, as in taping, is determined by repeating the measurement or tying in to control points. The elevation of a bench mark may be obtained by leveling over two different routes, or by a closed circuit of levels returning to the point of beginning. If an accurately established bench mark is available at or near the end of the line run, a check can be made upon it.

Closures are compared with permissible values on the basis of either the number of setups or the distance covered. The type of formula generally used to compute the allowable closure is

$$C = m\sqrt{K} \qquad (5\text{-}10)$$

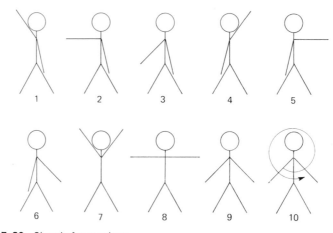

Figure 5-30. Signals for numbers.

where C is the allowable closure, in millimeters; m a constant, in milli-meters; and K the distance leveled, in kilometers.

The National Geodetic Survey specifies constants of 3, 4, 6, 8, and 12 mm for its five classes of leveling now designated respectively, as (1) first order —class I, (2) first order—class II, (3) second order—class I, (4) second order—class II, and (5) third order (see Table 18-2). As an example, if differential levels are run from an established BM A to a new BM B $\frac{3}{4}$ km away, and back, with elevation differences of 3.0556 m and 3.0620 m respec-tively, the closure is 0.0064 m. Then $m = C/\sqrt{K} = 6.4/\sqrt{\frac{3}{4} + \frac{3}{4}} = 5.2$ mm, and the leveling meets second order—class I accuracy.

If sights of 300 ft are taken, thereby spacing instrument setups at 600 ft, approximately $5\frac{1}{2}$ setups/km would be used. For third-order work, the allow-able error of closure would then be

$$E_c = 28\sqrt{N} \qquad (5\text{-}11)$$

where E_c is the allowable closure in millimeters, and N is the number of times the instrument is set up. Other values of m may be specified to meet the precision required and average length of sight. On first-order leveling the length of sight is varied during the day to conform to atmospheric conditions, with a maximum of 75 m.

5-32. ADJUSTMENT OF SIMPLE LEVEL CIRCUITS. Since permis-sible closures for level circuits are based upon lengths of lines or numbers of setups, it is logical to adjust elevations on these bases. Elevation dif-ferences and lengths of lines are shown for a circuit in Fig. 5-31. Adjustment of this circuit will be demonstrated on the basis of the lengths of lines. The

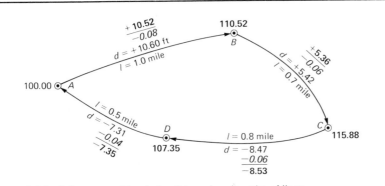

Figure 5-31. Adjustment of level circuit based on lengths of lines.

closure found by algebraic summation of the elevation differences is $+0.24$ ft. Adding the lengths of the lines yields a total circuit length of 3.0 miles. Elevation adjustments are then (0.24 ft/3.0) times the corresponding lengths, giving -0.08, -0.06, -0.06, and -0.04 ft as shown in italics. The adjusted elevation differences are used for finding final elevations (shown in boldface type) of the bench marks, based upon elevation of BM $A = 100.00$.

Level circuits with different lengths and routes are sometimes run from scattered reference points to obtain the elevation of a given bench mark. The most probable value of the bench-mark elevation can then be computed from the weighted mean of the observations, the weights varying inversely with the lengths of lines.

5-33. ADJUSTMENT OF INTERLOCKING LOOPS. Adjustment of an interlocking network of level circuits is best accomplished by the least-squares method or one of several approximate methods available. An interlocking two-loop level circuit and the corresponding field notes are shown in Fig. 5-32. Adjustment by an approximate "loop circuit" method on the basis of the number of instrument setups will be described.

In Fig. 5-32, the instrument setup number is given in parentheses. In the field notes, a second determination of the elevation of points (loop closures) is marked with an asterisk. The outer circuit, or loop 2, is adjusted first. From the notes it is seen that the elevation of BM B was first computed as 100.62 and after running levels around loop 2 and returning, the elevation of BM B^* was found to be 100.70, giving a closure error of $+0.08$ ft for loop 2. This error of closure is distributed based on the number of instrument setups in the loop, as $-0.08/4 = -0.02$ ft per setup. Corrections of -0.02 ft per setup result in values of -0.02, -0.04, -0.06, and -0.08 ft, respectively, for TP 2, BM C, TP 3, and BM B^*. When applied to loop 2, the initial corrected elevations for these points are shown directly above the crossed-out original unadjusted elevations in the notes.

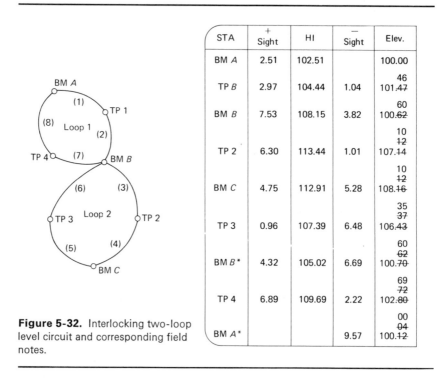

STA	+ Sight	HI	− Sight	Elev.
BM A	2.51	102.51		100.00
TP B	2.97	104.44	1.04	46 101.~~47~~
BM B	7.53	108.15	3.82	60 100.~~62~~
TP 2	6.30	113.44	1.01	10 ~~12~~ 107.~~14~~
BM C	4.75	112.91	5.28	10 ~~12~~ 108.~~16~~
TP 3	0.96	107.39	6.48	35 ~~37~~ 106.~~43~~
BM B*	4.32	105.02	6.69	60 ~~62~~ 100.~~70~~
TP 4	6.89	109.69	2.22	69 ~~72~~ 102.~~80~~
BM A*			9.57	00 ~~04~~ 100.~~12~~

Figure 5-32. Interlocking two-loop level circuit and corresponding field notes.

Since the elevation of BM B^* has been corrected by −0.08 ft to 100.62, and setups 7 and 8 depend upon BM B^* as a reference base, the elevations of TP 4 and BM A^* which follow must also be corrected by −0.08 ft. As a result of the adjustment of loop 2, the adjusted elevation of BM A^* is 100.12 − 0.08 = 100.04. The final elevation of BM A^* must be 100.00, therefore a +0.04-ft error of closure exists in loop 1 which is also distributed on the basis of the number of instrument setups in loop 1, as −0.04/4 = −0.01 ft per setup. TP 1 and BM B are corrected by −0.01 and −0.02 ft respectively. Instrument setups 3 through 6 depend upon BM B as a reference elevation, and since BM B has just been corrected by −0.02 ft, the elevations of TP 2, BM C, TP 3, and BM B^* are also adjusted by −0.02 ft. Finally, continuing around loop 1, corrections of −0.03 and −0.04 ft are applied to TP 4 and BM A^*, respectively. This completes the "loop circuit" adjustment and the final elevations for all points are shown above the crossed-out original and initial corrected elevations.

5-34. SOURCES OF ERROR IN LEVELING. All leveling measurements are subject to three sources of error: (1) instrumental, (2) natural, and (3) personal.

INSTRUMENTAL ERRORS

Instrument not in adjustment. The most important adjustment of the level makes the line of sight parallel to the axis of the level vial so that a horizontal plane, rather than a conical surface, is generated as the telescope is revolved. Serious errors in rod readings result if the instrument is not so adjusted, unless the horizontal lengths of plus and minus sights are kept equal to utilize the principle of reversion (see Appendix A). The error is likely to be systematic, particularly in going up or down a steep hill where all plus sights are longer or shorter than all minus sights, unless care is taken to run a zigzag line.

Rod not correct length. Inaccurate divisions on a rod cause errors similar to those resulting from incorrect markings on a tape. Uniform wearing of the shoe at the bottom of the rod makes HI values incorrect, but the effect is canceled when included in both plus and minus sights. Rod graduations should be checked by comparing them with those on a standardized tape.

Tripod legs loose. Tripod leg bolts which are too loose or too tight allow movement or strain which affect the instrument head. Loose metal tripod shoes cause unstable setups.

NATURAL ERRORS

Curvature of the earth. As noted in Section 5-3, a level surface deflects from a horizontal plane at the rate of $0.667M^2$, or about 8 in. in 1 mile. The effect of curvature of the earth is to increase the rod reading. Equalizing lengths of plus and minus sights cancels the errors due to this cause.

Refraction. Light rays coming from an object to the telescope are bent, making the line of sight a curve concave to the surface of the earth and thereby decreasing the rod reading. Balancing the lengths of plus and minus sights usually eliminates the errors due to refraction. Large and sudden changes in atmospheric refraction may be important in precise work, however. Errors due to refraction tend to be random over a long period of time but could be systematic on one day's run.

Temperature variations. Heat causes leveling rods to expand, but the effect is not important in ordinary leveling.

If a level vial is heated, the liquid expands and the bubble shortens. This does not produce an error (although it may be inconvenient), unless one end of the tube is warmed more than the other and the bubble therefore moves toward the heated end. Other parts of the instrument warp because of uneven heating, and this distortion affects the adjustments. Shading the level by means of a cover when carrying it, and by an umbrella when it is set up, will reduce or eliminate heat effects. These precautions are followed in precise leveling.

Air boiling or heat waves, near the ground surface or adjacent to heated objects, make the rod appear to wave, and prevent accurate sighting. Raising the line of sight by high-tripod setups, avoiding sights which pass close to heat sources (such as buildings and stacks), and using the lower magnification of a variable-power eyepiece reduce the effect.

Wind. Strong wind causes the instrument to vibrate and makes the rod unsteady. Precise leveling is not attempted on windy days.

Settlement of the instrument. Settlement of the instrument after the plus sight has been taken makes the minus sight too small and therefore the recorded elevation of the next point too large. The error is cumulative in a series of setups on soft material. Unusual care is required in setting up the level on spongy ground, blacktop, or ice, and readings must be taken in quick order, perhaps using two rods, and without walking around the instrument. Alternating the order of taking plus and minus sights helps somewhat.

Settlement of the rod. This condition causes an error similar to that resulting from settlement of the instrument. It can be avoided by selecting firm, solid turning points or, if none are available, using a steel *turning pin.*

PERSONAL ERRORS

Bubble not centered. Errors due to the bubble not being exactly centered at the time of sighting are the most important of any, particularly on long sights. If the bubble goes off between the plus and minus sights, *it must be recentered before the minus sight is taken.* Experienced levelmen develop the habit of checking the bubble before and after each sight, a procedure simplified by having a mirror-prism arrangement permitting simultaneous view of level vial and rod.

Parallax. Parallax caused by improper focusing of the objective and/or eyepiece lens results in incorrect rod readings. Careful focusing eliminates this condition.

Faulty rod readings. Incorrect rod readings result from parallax, poor weather conditions, long sights, improper target setting and rodding, and other causes, including mistakes such as those due to careless interpolation and transposition of figures. Short sights selected to fit weather and instrument conditions reduce the number of reading errors. If a target is used, the rodman should read the rod for the plus sight and have the instrumentman check it independently as the rodman passes on the way to the next TP. The observer stops to read the minus-sight setting as he moves ahead for the next setup.

Cross hair not exactly horizontal. Reading the rod near the center of the horizontal cross hair will eliminate or minimize this potential error.

Rod handling. Serious errors caused by improper rod handling (plumbing) are eliminated by using a rod level that is in adjustment. Banging the rod on a TP for the second (plus) sight may change the elevation of the point.

Target setting. The target may not be clamped at the exact place signaled by the instrumentman because of slippage. A check sight should always be taken after the target is clamped.

5-35. MISTAKES. A few common mistakes in leveling are listed here for study.

Use of long rod. If the vernier reading on the back of a damaged rod is not exactly 6.500 or 7.000 for the short rod, the target must be set to read the same value before extending the rod.

Holding the rod in different places for the plus and minus sights on a TP. The rodman can avoid such mistakes by using a well-defined point or by outlining the base of the rod with keel.

Reading a foot too high. This error occurs because the incorrect foot-mark is in sight near the cross line. For example, the observer may read 5.98 instead of 4.98. Noting the foot-marks above and below the vernier zero or cross line will usually prevent this mistake.

Waving the ordinary flat-bottom rod while holding it on a flat surface. This action produces an error because the rotation is about the rod edges instead of the center or the front face. Plumbing by using a rod level or other means is preferable to waving.

Recording notes. Mistakes in recording, such as transposition of figures, entering values in the wrong column, and arithmetic mistakes, can be minimized by having the notekeeper mentally estimate the reading, repeating the value called out by the observer, and making the standard field-book checks on rod sums and elevations.

Touching tripod during reading process. Beginners may center the bubble, put one hand on the tripod while reading the rod, and remove the hand while checking the bubble which has returned to center but was off during the sighting.

5-36. REDUCTION OF ERRORS AND ELIMINATION OF MISTAKES. Errors in leveling are reduced (but never eliminated) by careful adjustment and manipulation of both instrument and rod (see Appendix A for procedures), and establishing standard field methods and routines. The following procedures eliminate most large errors or quickly disclose mistakes: (a) checking the bubble before and after each reading; (b) using a rod level; (c) keeping the horizontal lengths of plus and minus sights equal; (d) running lines forward and backward; and (e) making the usual field-book arithmetic checks.

PROBLEMS

5–1. Compute and tabulate the combined effect of curvature and refraction on level sights of 100-, 200-, 300-, 400-, 500-, and 1000-ft length.

5–2. Similar to problem 5–1, except for sights of 50, 100, 150, 200, 250, and 300 m.

5–3. On a large lake without waves, how far from shore will a boat with a 25-ft mast disappear from view of a person lying on the beach at the water's edge?

5–4. Similar to problem 5–3, except the person is standing at the water's edge and his height of eye is 5.3 ft.

What error in elevation results from the combined effects of curvature and refraction on a downhill line of differential levels having the successive backsight and foresight distances listed in problems 5–5 through 5–7?

5–5. 125, 250 ; 190, 280 ; 150, 250 ; 260, 140 ft.

5–6. 80, 45 ; 100, 70 ; 28, 65 ; 35, 90 m.

5–7. 160, 180 ; 150, 200 ; 240, 180 ; 90, 175 ft.

5–8. A reading of 4.68 ft is taken on a rod 200 ft from a level with the bubble centered. The bubble is then moved 4 divisions off center, and a rod reading of 4.84 is obtained. For vial divisions of 0.1 in., what is (a) the radius of curvature of the vial in feet and (b) the angle in seconds subtended at the center by one vial division?

5–9. Similar to problem 5–8, except that each vial division is 2 mm.

5–10. Similar to problem 5–8, except that each vial division is 0.01 ft.

5–11. The bubble in a level vial on a dumpy level is drawn off 2 divisions by heating of the forward (objective-lens) end of the tube. After re-leveling, a plus sight of 8.16 ft is obtained on a shot of 200 ft. Sensitivity of the vial is 20″/2-mm division. Compute the correct rod reading.

5–12. It is required to obtain the elevation of the top of a smokestack. Since direct measurement is not feasible, the following field data were obtained: a line AB, 473.2 ft long, was staked out and horizontal angles to the smokestack $A = 48°16'$ and $B = 37°54'$ measured. At point B a backsight of 4.83 ft was taken on a bench mark of elevation 855.07 ft, and the vertical angle to the top of the smokestack found to be 44°25′. Calculate the elevation of the top of the smokestack.

5–13. Similar to problem 5–12, except that line AB equaled 628.76 ft, the horizontal angles were $A = 32°59'$ and $B = 52°44'$, a backsight on the bench mark whose elevation was 743.56 ft equaled 5.37 ft, and the vertical angle was 39°18′.

What is the sensitivity of a level vial for the conditions of problems 5–14 through 5–16?

5–14. Radius of curvature of 120 ft and 0.01-ft graduations.

5–15. Radius of curvature of 80 ft and 2-mm graduations.

5–16. Radius of curvature of 20 ft and 0.1-in. graduations.

5–17. What relationship should exist between the sensitivity of the level vial and the resolution-magnification of the telescope on a dumpy level?

5–18. A levelman fails to check the bubble and it is off two divisions on a sight of 250 ft. What error results for a 30″ bubble?

5–19. Similar to problem 5–18, except that the bubble is three divisions off on a sight of 80 m and the bubble has a sensitivity of 20″.

5–20. An instrumentman using an unfamiliar dumpy level has been told that it has a 20″ vial, but he does not know whether the divisions on the tube are 2 mm, 0.1 in., or 0.01 ft. What error in reading would result for each type if the bubble is off $1\frac{1}{2}$ divisions on a 225-ft sight?

5–21. Describe two ways of determining the approximate magnifying power of a telescope.

5–22. List in tabular form, for comparison, the advantages and disadvantages of a tilting level versus an automatic level.

5–23. A slope distance of 160 ft and a slope of 15% are read with an Abney level. Compute the horizontal distance and the difference in elevation.

Sketch scales and verniers to fit the requirements given in problems 5–24 and 5–25.

5–24. Scale, $1/2$–in. divisions; required reading to $1/32$ in. Scale, $1°$ graduations; required reading to 5 min.

5–25. Vernier has 12 divisions; required reading to 3″. Scale, 4′ spaces; least count if vernier has 48 divisions.

5–26. Compute the distance a rod extended for a 12-ft reading must be out of plumb to introduce an error of 0.005 ft.

5–27. Similar to problem 5–26, except for a 3-m rod reading and an error of 1 mm.

5–28. What error results on a 200-ft sight with a level if the rod reading is 10.00, but the top of the 12-ft rod being used is 6 in. out of plumb?

5–29. Prepare a set of level notes for the data listed. The elevation of BM 5 is 850.77 ft. What order of leveling does this work represent if the distance from BM 5 back to BM 5 along the circuit is 1600 ft?

Point	+S(BS)	−S(FS)
BM 5	10.26	
TP 1	5.82	7.84
BM 6		5.13
BM 6	5.08	
TP 2	3.71	9.89
TP 3	6.82	6.03
BM 5		2.76

5–30. Prepare a set of level notes for the data listed. Show the arithmetic check. The elevation of BM 1 is 120.64 ft. Note that readings with an asterisk are side shots on critical points.

Point	+S(BS)	−S(FS)
BM 1	4.27	
TP 1	0.38	9.43
A		*6.21
TP 2	2.44	12.10
TP 3	7.62	7.78
B		*4.41
TP 4	9.06	11.32
BM 2		7.80

5–31. Similar to problem 5–29, except assume that BM 5 is on the underside of a roof and above the HI and that the readings on it are therefore obtained by holding the rod upside down on the BM.

5–32. Similar to problem 5–30, but assume that BM 1 is a mark on a building column above the line of sight and therefore the +S reading is −4.27.

5–33. A differential leveling loop started and closed on BM Hydrant, elevation 561.48 ft. The loop was run over fairly uniform terrain, and the BS and FS distances kept approximately equal. Readings were taken in the following order: 2.84, 9.66; 2.55, 11.93; 5.71, 6.85; 10.84, 3.89; 12.87, 2.43. Prepare a set of level notes on ruled paper and make the usual arithmetic check.

5-34. Prepare a set of differential leveling notes for a double rodded line for the data given. Show the standard page check, and determine the final elevation of BM 76. The elevation of BM 75 is 4571.483 ft. Rod readings (H for high line and L for low line) are as follows: BS on BM 75 8.287, FS on TP 1H 7.675, FS on TP 1L 7.925; BS on TP 1H 3.620, BS on TP 1L 3.889, FS on TP 2H 8.106, FS on TP 2L 8.821; BS on TP 2H 3.724, BS on TP 2L 4.442, FS on TP 3H 10.230, FS on TP 3L 10.856; BS on TP 3H 3.675, BS on TP 3L 4.289, FS on BM 76 8.976.

5-35. For a peg adjustment (described in Sec. A–4, Appendix A) a level is set midway between points A and B and rod readings of 7.82 and 5.16 ft taken on A and B, respectively. The instrument is then moved to within a few feet of A, and readings of 6.95 ft on A and 4.21 ft on B are recorded. Determine the true difference in elevation between A and B. With the instrument still near A, what rod reading is required on B to put the instrument in adjustment?

5-36. A level set up near point A reads 1.417 m on A and 1.884 m on point B. The instrument is then moved near point B, where readings of 1.823 m on B and 1.375 m on A are obtained. Determine the true difference in elevation between points A and B. For the same setup near B, what should be the rod reading on A to put the instrument in adjustment?

5-37. The line of sight of a dumpy level is found by the peg adjustment test (similar to problems 5–35 and 5–36 and described in Appendix A) to be inclined downward 0.008 ft/100 ft of distance. Calculate the allowable difference between the BS and FS distances at each setup (neglecting curvature and refraction) if successive elevations are to be correct within 0.002 ft.

5-38. Prepare a set of profile leveling notes for the data given and show the standard arithmetic check. The elevation of BM X is 86.75. Rod readings are as follows: BS on BM X 2.54, FS on TP 1 11.69; BS on TP 1 2.41, IFS on 1+00 6.4, IFS on 2+00 8.2, IFS on 3+00 7.6, FS on TP 2 10.68; BS on TP 2 3.67, IFS on 3+40 1.1, IFS on 4+00 3.4, IFS on 5+00 5.8, FS on TP 3 9.89; BS on TP 3 4.94, FS on BM Y 8.21.

5-39. Prepare a set of profile leveling notes for the data given and show the arithmetic check. The elevation of BM A is 912.635. Rod readings are: BS on BM A 5.193, IFS on 0+00 1.8, IFS on 1+00 7.2, IFS on 2+00 10.9, IFS on 3+00 9.7, FS on TP 1 7.286; BS on TP 1 4.656, IFS on 3+60 6.9, IFS on 4+00 3.8, IFS on 4+50 2.86, IFS on 5+00 1.5, IFS on 5+65 1.12, FS on BM B 6.525.

5-40. Reciprocal leveling across a river gives the following readings in feet from the first setup near A: on A, 4.367; on B, 7.925, 7.924, 7.926. For the setup near B the readings are: on B, 9.471; on A, 5.909, 5.908, 5.910. If the elevation of B is 459.323 ft, compute the elevation of A. What is the error of closure?

5-41. Reciprocal leveling across a canyon between BM's A and B gives the results shown. The correct elevation of A is 567.89 ft. Determine the elevation of B.

Instrument at A: +S=3.72; −S=6.89, 6.90, 6.89 ft.
Instrument at B: +S=7.31; −S=4.13, 4.13, 4.12 ft.

*5-42. A rectangular lot 150 ft N–S by 200 ft E–W is to be graded to an elevation of 325.0 ft. After division into 50-ft squares, rod readings are taken at the corners successively from east to west along E–W lines with an HI of 338.9 ft. The readings in feet are as follows: 8.1, 7.5, 6.3, 5.3, 3.6; 7.2, 5.7, 4.4, 3.8, 3.7; 6.5, 4.1, 2.8, 1.9, 2.4; 5.4, 4.3, 1.5, 2.7, 0.8. Compute the volume of material (in cubic yards) to be excavated.

*5-43. Similar to problem 5–42, but assume that the HI is 324.2 and the area is to be filled to an elevation of 325.0 ft.

5-44. Leveling between BM's A, B, C, D, and A gives differences of elevation in feet of -26.740, $+43.563$, $+49.324$, and -66.133, and distances in miles of 0.5, 0.6, 0.5, and 0.7, respectively. If the elevation of A is 764.325 ft, calculate the adjusted elevations of BM's B, C, and D. What order of leveling does this represent?

5-45. Similar to problem 5–44, except the adjusted elevation of A is 527.410 m, the differences in elevation are $+16.273$, -7.483, $+13.827$, and -22.633 m, respectively, and the courses are 0.8, 0.6, 1.2, and 1.4 km long, respectively.

5-46. Differential leveling from BM's A to X, B to X, and C to X gives results in feet of -19.14, 21.29, and 37.31, respectively. The distances in feet are: $AX=4000$, $BX=3000$, and $CX=2000$. Accepted elevations of the BM's in feet are: $A=681.97$, $B=641.58$, and $C=625.47$. Compute the adjusted elevation of BM X.

5-47. A precise level is used on a tower to sight across a 25-mile lake to a target on a tower of equal height. If the line of sight must be kept 10 ft above the water surface, calculate the required height of the towers above the shoreline.

5-48. A level rod $1^1/_2$ in. square is held on the flat top of a granite step for a turning point. The line of sight of the level is just above the rod base. Instead of plumbing with a rod level, the rodman waves the rod to let the instrumentman get the smallest reading; hence the rod tips alternately on the front and rear edges of the base plate. If a minimum reading of 0.16 ft is obtained while the rod is tipped on the rear edge, determine the true height of the instrument above the turning point.

5-49. Readings on a line of differential levels are being taken to the nearest 0.01 ft. What is the maximum length of sight for which curvature of the earth and refraction can be neglected?

5-50. Similar to problem 5–49, except that readings are being taken to the nearest millimeter.

5-51. What two factors determine the size of squares used in borrow-pit surveys?

5-52. Explain the principle of operation of the compensator of an automatic level.

5-53. Develop an expression similar to Eq. (5–11) but for second-order—class-II leveling if average sight lengths are 100 m.

5-54. A line of levels was run between BM 5 and BM 6. Later it was noticed that the level rod used had a repaired base plate attached to the bottom which made the rod too long. Is the elevation of BM 6 correct? Explain.

* The asterisks indicate problems whose solutions are used again in problems for Chapter 11.

5–55. Explain why surveyors and engineers can often ignore the error due to curvature and refraction in level work.

5–56. What errors in leveling are eliminated by keeping the lengths of plus and minus sights equal?

5–57. Why should a long base be used in determining the height of an inaccessible point by trigonometric leveling?

5–58. Explain how errors due to lack of adjustment of the instrument can be practically eliminated in running a line of differential levels.

5–59. List the considerations that govern a rodman in selecting turning points and bench marks.

5–60. How can errors due to settlement of the instrument and rod be reduced?

5–61. List 10 common errors in leveling, indicate whether they are systematic or random, and state how each can be reduced or eliminated.

5–62. From your study of the theory of errors, taping, and leveling, explain why it is usually easier to do good leveling than good taping.

5–63. What is the order of leveling of a 10-mile loop with a closure of 0.09 ft?

Compute the permissible error of closure for the lines of levels given in problems 5–64 through 5–66.

5–64. A line of third-order levels, 15 miles long.

5–65. A line of second-order—class-I levels, 25 km long.

5–66. A first-order—class-I level circuit of 50 km.

5–67. A level party began at BM A (Elev. 875.18) and ran to BM B (Elev. 987.50) but got an elevation of 987.43. Using elevation 987.43 for BM B as the starting value, return levels to BM A found its elevation to be 875.18. Rerunning the entire level circuit from BM A to BM B and back to BM A in the same manner produced identical results. What is the most probable explanation for this situation, assuming BS and FS distances were balanced, and that 875.18 and 987.50 are correct elevations for BM A and BM B respectively?

5–68. Prepare a set of leveling notes for a two-loop level circuit for the data given. Adjust according to the method discussed in Section 5–33. The elevation of BM A is 866.14 ft. Rod readings are: BS on BM A 3.76, FS on TP 1 4.00; BS on TP 1 8.13, FS on TP Rock 2.96; BS on TP Rock 9.69, FS on BM B 4.90; BS on BM B 0.64, FS on TP 2 2.21; BS on TP 2 7.85, FS on TP 3 5.11; BS on TP 3 10.07, FS on BM B 11.30; BS on BM B 4.61, FS on TP 4 11.93; BS on TP 4 5.88, FS on TP 5 4.70; BS on TP 5 2.51, FS on BM A 6.05.

5–69. A line of levels was run from BM X to BM Y with rod readings taken to the nearest 0.01 ft so that an individual reading could have an error of ±0.005 ft. There were 18 setups (36 rod readings) during the run. Considering reading error only, what total error can be expected in the elevation of BM Y?

5–70. Similar to problem 5–69, except rod readings were taken to the nearest millimeter, and there were 28 setups.

6
ANGLES,
BEARINGS,
AND AZIMUTHS

6-1. GENERAL. The location of points and orientation of lines frequently depends upon measurement of angles and directions. In surveying, directions are given by bearings and azimuths.

As described in Section 2-2, angles measured in surveying are classified either as *horizontal* or *vertical*, depending upon the plane in which they are measured. Horizontal angles are the basic measurements needed for determining bearings and azimuths. The use of vertical angles is explained elsewhere in this text.

Angles are measured *directly* in the field using a device such as a compass, transit, theodolite, or sextant, or they can be constructed without measurement on a plane table sheet (see Chapter 15). The compass, transit, and theodolite are discussed in succeeding chapters.

An angle can also be measured *indirectly* by the tape method described in Sections 4-28 and 4-29, and its value computed from the relation of known quantities in a triangle or other simple geometric figure.

There are three basic requirements in determining an angle. As shown in Fig. 6-1, they are the (1) *reference or starting line*, (2) *direction of turning*, and (3) *angular distance* (value of the angle). Methods of computing bearings and azimuths described in this chapter are based on those three elements.

6-2. UNITS OF ANGLE MEASUREMENT. A purely arbitrary unit defines the value of an angle. The *sexagesimal* system used in the United States is based on degrees, minutes, and seconds, with the last further divided decimally. In Europe the *grad* is the standard unit (see Section 2-3). Radians

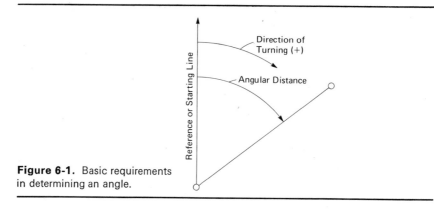

Figure 6-1. Basic requirements in determining an angle.

may be used in computations, in fact are employed extensively in high-speed electronic computers.

6-3. KINDS OF HORIZONTAL ANGLES. The kinds of horizontal angles most commonly measured in surveying are (1) *interior angles*, (2) *angles to the right*, and (3) *deflection angles*. Because they differ considerably, the kinds used must be clearly indicated in the field notes.

Interior angles, shown in Fig. 6-2, are on the inside of a closed polygon. *Exterior angles*, located outside of a closed polygon, are explements of interior angles. There is rarely an advantage to be gained by measuring them, except that they may be used as a check since the sum of the interior and exterior angles at any station must equal 360°.

As illustrated in Figs. 6-2(a) and (b), interior angles can be turned

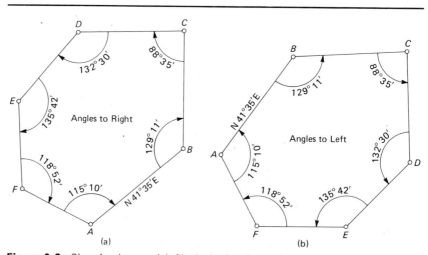

Figure 6-2. Closed polygons. (a) Clockwise interior angles, also angles to the right. (b) Counterclockwise interior angles, also angles to the left.

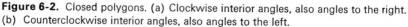

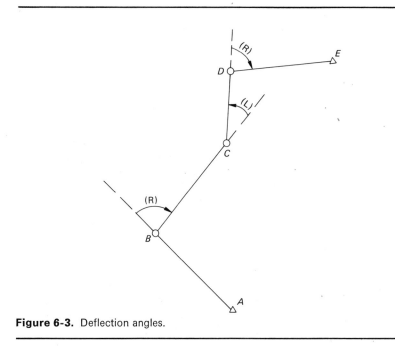

Figure 6-3. Deflection angles.

clockwise (right) or counterclockwise (left). By definition, *angles to the right* are measured clockwise from the rear station to the forward station. Thus the interior angles of Fig. 6-2(a) are also angles to the right. *Angles to the left,* turned counterclockwise from the rear to forward station, are illustrated in Fig. 6-2(b). Note that the polygons of Figs. 6-2(a) and (b) are "right" and "left," that is, similar in shape but turned over like the right and left hands. Obviously, confusing the direction of turning produces mistakes, and therefore it is recommended that uniform field procedures be adopted, such as always measuring angles clockwise.

Deflection angles, Fig. 6-3, are measured either right (clockwise) or left (counterclockwise) from the extension of the back line to the forward station. Deflection angles are always less than 180°, and the direction of turning must be specified in the field notes. Thus the angle at *B* in Fig. 6-3 is right (R), and that at *C* is left (L).

6-4. DIRECTION OF A LINE. The direction of a line is its horizontal angle from an established line of reference, called a *reference meridian.* The reference line generally adopted is either the *true* (geographic) *meridian,* or the *magnetic meridian.* If neither of these can be secured readily, an *assumed meridian* may be selected and its relation to the true or magnetic line ascertained later.

The true meridian for any point on the earth's surface is the great circle, projected on the earth, which passes through the point and the north and south *geographic poles*.

Direction of a magnetic meridian is defined by a freely suspended magnetic needle which is influenced by the earth's magnetic field only. A *magnetic pole* is the center of convergence of magnetic meridians.

An assumed meridian can be established by simply assigning an arbitrary direction, for example, taking a certain line to be true north. Directions of all other lines are then found in relation to it. The disadvantage of using an assumed meridian is the difficulty, or perhaps impossibility, of reestablishing it if the original points are lost.

Surveys based upon a state or other plane coordinate system employ a *grid meridian* reference. Grid north is the direction of true north for a selected central meridian, and held parallel to it over the entire area covered by the plane coordinate system (see Chapter 17).

6-5. BEARINGS.   Bearings represent one system of designating directions of lines. The bearing of a line is the *acute* horizontal angle between a reference meridian and the line. The angle is measured from either the north or south, toward the east or west, to give a reading less than 90°. The proper quadrant is shown by a letter N or S preceding the angle, and E or W following it. An example is N 80° E.

In Fig. 6-4, all bearings in quadrant *NOE* are measured clockwise from the meridian. Thus bearing of line *OA* is N 70° E. All bearings in quadrant *SOE* are counterclockwise from the meridian, so *OB* is S 35° E. Similarly, the bearing of *OC* is S 55° W, and that of *OD* N 30° W.

True bearings are measured from the local geographic meridian; *mag-*

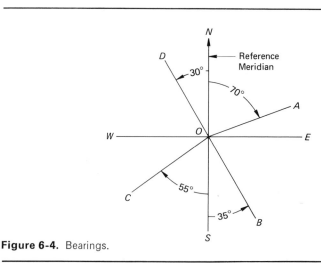

Figure 6-4. Bearings.

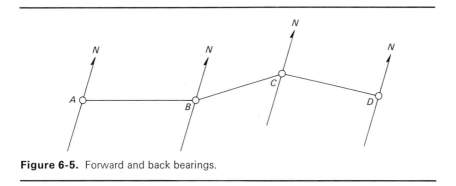

Figure 6-5. Forward and back bearings.

netic bearings from the local magnetic meridian; *assumed bearings* from any adopted meridian; and *grid bearings* from the appropriate grid meridian. Magnetic bearings can be obtained in the field by observing a magnetic needle in a compass box, and used along with measured angles to get *computed bearings.*

In Fig. 6-5 assume that a compass is set up successively at points *A*, *B*, *C*, and *D*, and bearings read on lines *AB*, *BA*, *BC*, *CB*, *CD*, and *DC*. Bearings *AB*, *BC*, and *CD* are called *forward bearings*, and those of *BA*, *CB*, and *DC* *back bearings.* Forward bearings have the same numerical value as back bearings but opposite letters. If bearing *AB* is N 72° E, bearing *BA* is S 72° W.

6-6. AZIMUTHS. Azimuths are angles measured clockwise from any reference meridian. In plane surveying, azimuths are generally measured from north, but astronomers and the National Geodetic Survey use south as the reference point. South is also used in connection with the grid azimuth of the state plane coordinate system.

As shown in Fig. 6-6, azimuths range from 0° to 360° and do not require letters to identify the quadrant. Thus the azimuth of *OA* is 70°; of *OB*, 145°; of *OC*, 235°; and of *OD*, 330°. It is necessary to state in the field notes, at the beginning of the work, whether azimuths are measured from north or south.

Azimuths may be *true*, *magnetic*, *grid*, or *assumed*, depending upon the meridian used. They may also be *forward*, or *back* azimuths. Forward azimuths are converted to back azimuths, and vice versa, by adding or subtracting 180°. For example, if the azimuth of *OA* is 70°, the azimuth of *AO* is 250°. If the azimuth of *OC* is 235°, the azimuth of *CO* is 235° − 180° = 55°.

Azimuths can be read on the graduated circle of a transit or repeating theodolite after the instrument has been oriented properly. This can be done by sighting along a line with its known azimuth on the plates and then turning to the desired course. Azimuths (*directions*) are used advantageously in some data adjustment computations.

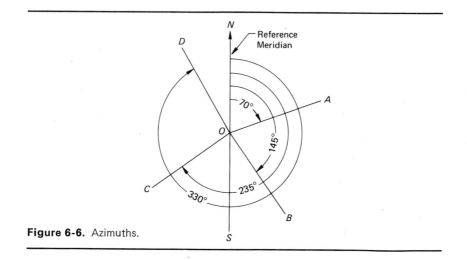

Figure 6-6. Azimuths.

6-7. COMPARISON OF BEARINGS AND AZIMUTHS. Because bearings and azimuths are encountered in so many surveying operations, a comparative summary of their properties given in Table 6-1 may be helpful. Bearings are readily computed from azimuths by noting the quadrant in which the aximuth falls, and then converting as shown in the table.

TABLE 6-1. COMPARISON OF BEARINGS AND AZIMUTHS

Bearings	Azimuths
Vary from 0° to 90°	Vary from 0° to 360°
Require two letters and a numerical value	Require only a numerical value
May be true, magnetic, grid, assumed, forward, or back	Same
Measured clockwise and counterclockwise	Measured clockwise only
Measured from north and south	Measured from north only in any one survey, or from south only

Example directions for lines in the four quadrants (azimuths from north):

Bearings		Azimuths	
N 54° E	....	54°	
S 68° E	....	112°	$(180° - 68°)$
S 51° W	....	231°	$(180° + 51°)$
N 15° W	....	345°	$(360° - 15°)$

6-8. CALCULATION OF BEARINGS. Many types of surveys, especially those for *traverses*, require computation of bearings (or azimuths). A traverse is a series of distances and angles, or distances and bearings, or distances and azimuths, connecting successive instrument points. The boundary lines of a piece of property form a "closed-polygon" type of traverse. A highway survey from one city to another normally is an "open" traverse, but if possible it should be closed by tying-in on points of known coordinates near the starting and finishing points. Traverses are described in detail in Chapter 9.

Computation of the bearing of a line is simplified by drawing a sketch, similar to those in Figs. 6-7 and 6-8, and showing all data. In Fig. 6-7, assume that the bearing of line AB is N 41°35′ E, and the angle at B turned to

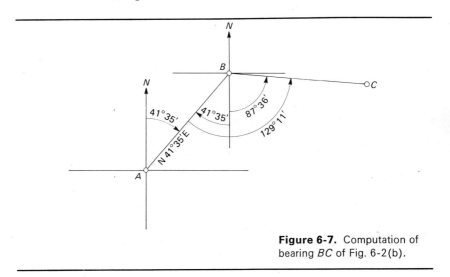

Figure 6-7. Computation of bearing BC of Fig. 6-2(b).

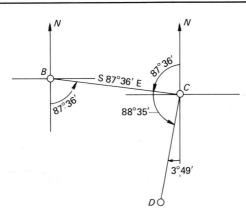

Figure 6-8. Computation of bearing CD of Fig. 6-2(b).

the left (counterclockwise) is 129°11'. Then the numerical value of the bearing of BC is 41°35' − 129°11' = −87°36'. By inspection of the sketch, the bearing of BC is S 87°36' E.

In Fig. 6-8, the bearing of CD is 180° − (87°36' + 88°35'), or S 03°49' W. By continuing with this technique, the bearings given in Table 6-2 have been determined for all lines in Figs. 6-2(a) and (b). Students should draw sketches similar to Figs. 6-7 and 6-8 for each of the remaining lines and verify the bearings given in the table.

TABLE 6-2. BEARINGS OF LINES IN FIGS. 6-2(a) AND (b)

Course	Fig. 6–2(a)	Fig. 6–2(b)
AB	N 41°35' E	N 41°35' E
BC	N 9°14' W	S 87°36' E
CD	S 79°21' W	S 3°49' W
DE	S 31°51' W	S 51°19' W
EF	S 12°27' E	N 84°23' W
FA	S 73°35' E	N 23°15' W
AB	N 41°35' E√	N 41°35' E√

The bearing of any starting course *must* be recomputed as a check, using the last angle. Any discrepancy shows an arithmetical error, or that the angles were not properly adjusted prior to computing bearings. In Table 6-2 note that the bearing of AB for Fig. 6-2(a), obtained using the angle 115°10' measured at A, yields a bearing of N 41°35' E and agrees with the starting bearing. A similar check was secured for the calculations of Fig. 6-2(b).

Traverse angles must be adjusted to the proper geometric total before bearings are computed. Since the interior angles of a closed polygon traverse equal $(n - 2)180°$, the original and computed check bearing of AB should be the same. If the traverse angles failed to close by, say, 2 min and were not adjusted prior to computing the bearings, the original and computed check bearing of AB will differ by the same 2 min, assuming there are no other calculation errors.

6-9. TABULAR METHOD OF CALCULATING BEARINGS.

If the bearings of a traverse having many sides are to be computed, a tabular form of the type shown in Illustration 6-1 may be preferable. In this shorthand arrangement, northeast bearings, southwest bearings, and other angles measured clockwise (to the right) are called plus; southeast bearings, northwest bearings, and other angles measured counterclockwise (to the left) are considered minus. Bearing letters are repeated and shown reversed in parentheses, to call attention to the fact that *the angles are turned from the back bearings.* For example, for Fig. 6-2(b), the bearing of AB is N 41°35' E, but at B the angle 129°11' is measured from the line BA, whose bearing is S 41°35' W. Since BA is 41°35' from south in a plus direction (Fig. 6-7) and angle ABC of 129°11' is turned in a minus direction from *BA*, then the *angular distance* representing the algebraic summation of these two angular values is −87°36′ measured from the *south*. The S is brought down from the (SW) in parentheses after bearing *AB* as indicated by the arrow in Illustration 6-1 to show the reference or starting line of the angular distance noted in Fig. 6-1, and completes the three necessary fundamentals—reference meridian, south; direction of turning, minus (counterclockwise); and angular distance, 87°36′.

Because the angular distance is less than 90°, line *BC* must fall in the southeast quadrant, and the bearing is therefore S 87°36′ E. When the algebraic summation gives an angular distance greater than 90°, the quadrant in which the line falls is determined and the bearing found from its known relation to the north or south direction. Several examples of angular distances over 90° are shown in Illustration 6-1.

The shorthand method is partially self-checking. If the back-bearing letters shown in parentheses are forgotten, the bearings of *BC*, *DE*, and *FA* would be wrong but those of *CD*, *EF*, and *AB* would be correct. Note that if deflection angles are used, the base line for turning the deflection angle is the traverse line extended so its bearing letters remain unchanged.

ILLUSTRATION 6-1. TABULAR METHOD OF COMPUTING BEARINGS

	Fig. 6-2(a) Clockwise (Right) Angles						Fig. 6-2(b) Counterclockwise (Left) Angles					
AB	N	41°35′	E	+	(SW)	*AB*	N	41°35′	E	+	(SW)
		129°11′		+				129°11′		−	
	S	170°46′		+		*BC*	S	87°36′	E	−	(NW)
BC	N	9°14′	W	−	(SE)			88°35′		−	
		88°35′		+			N	176°11′		−	
CD	S	79°21′	W	+	(NE)	*CD*	S	3°49′	W	+	(NE)
		132°30′		+				132°30′		−	
	N	211°51′		+			N	128°41′		−	
DE	S	31°51′	W	+	(NE)	*DE*	S	51°19′	W	+	(NE)
		135°42′		+				135°42′		−	
	N	167°33′		+		*EF*	N	84°23′	W	−	(SE)
EF	S	12°27′	E	−	(NW)			118°52′		−	
		118°52′		+			S	203°15′		−	
	N	106°25′		+		*FA*	N	23°15′	W	−	(SE)
FA	S	73°35′	E	−	(NW)			115°10′		−	
		115°10′		+			S	138°25′		−	
AB	N	41°35′	E			*AB*	N	41°35′	E		

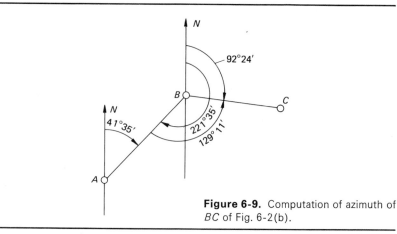

Figure 6-9. Computation of azimuth of *BC* of Fig. 6-2(b).

6-10. COMPUTING AZIMUTHS.   Many surveyors prefer azimuths over bearings for directions of lines because they are easier to work with, especially when computing traverses using electronic computers, since sines and cosines of azimuth angles automatically provide correct algebraic signs for latitudes and departures (see Chapter 10).

Azimuth calculations, like those for bearings, are best made with the aid of a sketch. Figure 6-9 illustrates the computations for azimuth *BC* of Fig. 6-2(b). Azimuth *BA* is obtained by adding 180° to azimuth *AB*, then counterclockwise angle *B*, 129°11′, is subtracted from azimuth *BA* to get azimuth *BC*. The calculations are conveniently handled in tabular form.

Illustration 6-2 lists the calculations for all azimuths of Fig. 6-2(a) and (b). Note again that a check is secured by recomputing the starting course azimuth using the last angle.

6-11. MISTAKES.   Some mistakes made in working with bearings and azimuths are:

1. Confusing magnetic and true bearings.
2. Mixing bearings and azimuths.
3. Failing to change the bearing letters when applying a direct angle at the forward end of a line.
4. Using the angle at the opposite end of a line in computing bearings, that is, using angle *A* when starting with line *AB*.
5. Not including the last angle to recompute the starting bearing as a check, for example, angle *A* in traverse *ABCDEA*.
6. Subtracting from 360°00′ as though it was 359°100′ instead of 359°60′, or using 90° instead of 180° in bearing computations.
7. Adopting an assumed reference line which is difficult to reproduce.
8. Forgetting to adjust traverse angles before computing bearings.
9. Orienting an instrument by resighting on magnetic north.

ILLUSTRATION 6-2. COMPUTATION OF AZIMUTHS (Azimuths from North)

Angles to the Right [Fig. 6-2 (a)]	Angles to the Left [Fig. 6-2 (b)]
$41°35' = AB$ $180°00'$	$41°35' = AB$ $180°00'$
$221°35' = BA$ $129°11'$	$221°35' = BA$ $-129°11'$
$350°46' = BC$ $180°00'$	$92°24' = BC$ $180°00'$
$170°46' = CB$ $88°35$	$272°24' = CB$ $-\ 88°35'$
$259°21' = CD$ $180°00'$	$183°49' = CD$ $180°00'$
$79°21' = DC$ $132°30'$	$363°49' = DC$ $-132°30'$
$211°51' = DE$ $180°00'$	$231°19' = DE$ $180°00'$
$31°51' = ED$ $135°42'$	$411°19' = ED$ $-135°42'$
$167°33' = EF$ $180°00'$	$275°37' = EF$ $180°00'$
$347°33' = FE$ $118°52'$	$455°37' = FE$ $-118°52'$
$466°25'$ $^a360°00'$	$336°45' = FA$ $180°00'$
$106°25' = FA$ $180°00'$	$156°45' = AF$ $-115°10'$
$286°25' = AF$ $115°10'$	$41°35' = AB\ \sqrt{}$
$401°35'$ $^a360°00'$	
$41°35' = AB\ \sqrt{}$	

^{a} When a computed azimuth exceeds 360°, the correct azimuth is obtained by merely subtracting 360°.

PROBLEMS

In problems 6–1 and 6–2 make the indicated unit conversions for the angles given.

6–1. Convert 127°15′ to radians, 114.24 grads to degrees-minutes-seconds, and 2400 mils to degrees-minutes-seconds.

6–2. Convert 238°41′18″ to radians, 48°29′37″ to grads, and 241.87 grads to degrees-minutes-seconds.

In problems 6–3 through 6–5 convert the azimuths (from north) to bearings.

6–3. 66°12′, 172°19′, 228°42′, 343°38′

6–4. 42°54′, 170°05′, 217°22′, 302°15′

6–5. 71°28′, 110°45′, 198°22′, 299°51′

Convert the bearings given in problems 6–6 through 6–8 to azimuths (from north) and compute the acute angle between each pair of successive bearings.

6–6. N 17°15′ E, S 26°34′ E, S 65°10′ W, N 76°30′ W

6–7. N 27°22′ E, S 87°54′ E, S 90°00′ W, N 8°06′ W

6–8. N 68°33′ E, S 90°00′ E, S 75°48′ W, N 20°53′ W

6–9. What is the difference between the true bearing and the magnetic bearing of a line?

6–10. Explain what is meant by the terms "back bearing" and "back azimuth."

What is the azimuth (from south) of line *CD* for the data in problems 6–11 through 6–14?

6–11. Azimuth (from south) $AB = 102°41′$, clockwise angles $ABC = 160°32′$ and $BCD = 73°52′$.

6–12. Azimuth (from south) $AB = 185°17′$, clockwise angles $ABC = 133°00′$ and $BCD = 221°24′$.

6–13. Bearing $AB = $ S 7°44′ W, clockwise angles $ABC = 35°26′$ and $BCD = 308°37′$.

6–14. Bearing $AB = $ S 44°18′ E, clockwise angles $ABC = 143°29′$ and $BCD = 193°09′$.

In problems 6–15 through 6–18, given the bearing of $DE = $ S 52°56′ E, and angles to the right DEF and EFG, compute the bearing of FG.

6–15. Angles *DEF* and *EFG* are 126°23′ and 189°35′, respectively.

6–16. Angles *DEF* and *EFG* are 87°36′ and 72°19′, respectively.

6–17. Angles *DEF* and *EFG* are 144°50′ and 71°51′, respectively.

6–18. Angles *DEF* and *EFG* are 172°24′ and 110°42′, respectively.

Side *AB* of a five-sided field runs due north. Station *C* is easterly from *B*. Compute and tabulate the bearings and azimuths (from north) of each side for the clockwise interior angles listed in problems 6–19 through 6–22.

6–19. $A = 141°16′, B = 110°31′, C = 86°01′, D = 51°46′, E = 150°26′$.

6–20. $A = 166°50′, B = 42°21′, C = 97°33′, D = 134°07′, E = 99°09′$.

6–21. $A = 62°10′, B = 136°27′, C = 130°52′, D = 81°35′, E = 128°56′$.

6–22. $A = 118°28′, B = 82°13′, C = 106°43′, D = 72°58′, E = 159°38′$.

In problems 6–23 and 6–24 compute and tabulate the bearings of a regular hexagon, given the starting bearing of side *AB*.

6–23. Bearing of $AB = $ S 45°16′ E. (Station *C* is easterly from *B*.)

6–24. Bearing of AB = N 23°52′ W. (Station C is westerly from B.)

6–25. Similar to problem 6–23, except for a regular pentagon.

6–26. Similar to problem 6–24, except for a regular octagon.

6–27. Calculate the bearings of lines, given the following deflection angles for an open traverse: At station 10+12.4, 12°27′ R; 25+89.4, 20°06′ R; 35+62.0, 17°41′ L. The beginning station is 0+00, the ending station 61+50.0, and the bearing of the line from 0+00 to 10+12.4 is S 56°16′ W. Sketch the traverse.

6–28. Similar to problem 6–27, except the bearing of the first line is N 32°19′ W.

Compute the bearings for a closed polygon traverse *ABCDEFGHIJA* with clockwise interior angles for the initial bearings as listed in problems 6–29 through 6–32. Similarly, compute azimuths (from north) for the initial azimuth recorded in problems 6–33 through 6–36.
A=183°18′; B=119°53′; C=177°36′; D=94°25′; E=152°59′; F=140°35′; G=162°49′; H=126°01′; I=98°16′; J=184°08′. (The deflection angle at A is 3°18′ L.)

6–29. Bearing AB = N 38°14′ E

6–30. Bearing DE = S 52°47′ E

6–31. Bearing HI = S 24°31′ W

6–32. Bearing IJ = N 36°38′ W

6–33. Azimuth AB = 346°42′

6–34. Azimuth CD = 210°18′

6–35. Azimuth EF = 53°49′

6–36. Azimuth GH = 137°09′

6–37. The sides of a certain traverse have the following bearings: AB = N 15°52′ E, BC = S 48°37′ E, CD = Due South, DE = S 79°46′ W, and EA = N 51°50′ W. For each line calculate the azimuth from north, and for each station determine (a) the deflection angle, (b) the angle to the right, and (c) the interior angle. Sketch the traverse.

6–38. The following information is known for a certain five-sided traverse $ABCDE$: the interior angle at E=96°12′; the deflection angles at C and D are 120°30′ R and 117°48′ R, respectively; and the bearings of lines AB and BC are S 72°28′ W and S 50°18′ E, respectively. Tabulate the interior angles and deflection angles for each station and the forward bearing, back bearing, and azimuth from south for each line. Sketch the traverse.

6–39. An angle AOB is measured at different times, using various instruments and procedures. The results, which are assigned certain weights, are as follows: 40°12′36″, wt. 4; 40°12′38″, wt. 3; 40°12′39″, wt. 1. What is the most probable value of the angle?

6–40. Similar to problem 6–31, but include an additional measurement of the angle which is 40°12′40″, wt. 2.

6–41. The true (geodetic) azimuth of a long line AB is 65°42′22″. The true azimuth of BA is 245°42′25″. Explain the discrepancy.

6–42. At what location will all bearings be south?

6–43. Explain three different methods of determining the azimuth of a line.

6–44. Why have azimuths been measured from the south by astronomers and the National Geodetic Survey?

7
THE COMPASS

7-1. GENERAL. The compass has been used by navigators and others for many centuries to determine directions. Prior to invention of the transit and sextant, the compass furnished surveyors with the only practical way to measure directions and horizontal angles.

The surveyor's compass, like the Gunter's chain, has now become little more than a museum piece. Nevertheless, an understanding of the compass and its vagaries is necessary to check work already done. Also, it is still used for rough engineering surveys and remains a valuable tool for geologists, foresters, and others.

Engineers' transits are equipped with a compass. In fact, the design of American transits was based upon the requirement of a long compass needle over the center of the instrument, and an erecting telescope. The small size of transits and theodolites now is due to the shorter inverting telescope and omission of the compass (which is available for mounting as an accessory).

7-2. THEORY OF THE COMPASS. A compass consists of a magnetized steel needle mounted on a pivot at the center of a graduated circle. The needle points toward *magnetic north.*

The north and south magnetic poles are located approximately 1000 miles and 1560 miles, respectively, from the true geographic poles. The magnetic lines of force of the earth, which align the needle, pull or dip one end of the needle below a horizontal position. The angle of *dip* varies from 0° at the equator to 90° at the magnetic poles.

In the northern hemisphere, to balance the effect of dip and keep the needle horizontal, the south end is weighted with a very small coil of wire. The position of the coil may be adjusted to conform to the latitude in which the compass is used. Weights on transit compasses are set for an average latitude of 40° N and usually do not have to be changed for any location in the United States.

As the compass box is turned, the needle continues to point toward magnetic north and gives a reading which is dependent upon the position of the graduated circle.

7-3. MAGNETIC DECLINATION.   *Declination* is the horizontal angle between the magnetic meridian and the true geographic meridian. Navigators call this angle the *variation* of the compass; the armed forces use the term *deviation*.

An east declination is obtained if the magnetic meridian is east of true north, and a west declination if it is west of true north. The value of the declination at any particular location can be obtained (if there is no local attraction) by establishing a true meridian from astronomical observations and then reading the compass while sighting along the true meridian.

A line connecting points having the same declination is called an *isogonic line*. The line made up of points having a zero declination is termed the *agonic line*; on it the magnetic needle defines true north as well as magnetic north.

Figure 7-1 is an isogonic chart covering the United States, for the year 1975.0. The agonic line cuts diagonally across the country through Michigan, Wisconsin, Indiana, Kentucky, Tennessee, Georgia, and Florida. Points to the west of the agonic line have an east declination, and points to the east of the line have a west declination. As a memory aid, the needle might be thought of as pointing *toward* the agonic line. Note that there is about a 42° difference in declination between Maine and Washington—a huge change if a pilot were flying by compass between the two states!

The *annual change* in declination shown on larger and more detailed isogonic charts aids in estimating the declination for a few years before and after the chart date. Secular change (see Section 7-4) for longer intervals should be computed from available tables which extend back to the earliest times likely to be significant in such problems. The best way to determine the declination at a given location on any date is to make an astronomical observation. If this is not possible, an approximate declination can be obtained from the National Geodetic Survey.

7-4. VARIATIONS IN MAGNETIC DECLINATION.   Magnetic declinations at any point vary with time. Variations may be categorized as secular, daily, annual, and irregular.

Secular variation. Because of its magnitude, this is the most important of the variations. Unfortunately, no general law or mathematical formula has been found to predict secular variation, and its past behavior can be described only by means of detailed tables and charts derived from observations. Records which have been kept at London for four centuries show a range in magnetic declination from 11° E in 1580, to 24° W in 1820, back to 8° W in 1960, and 6°58′ W in 1975. Secular variation changed the magnetic declination at Baltimore, Maryland, from 5°11′ W in 1640 to 5°41′ W in 1700, 0°35′ W in 1800, 5°19′ W in 1900, 7°25′ W in 1950, 7°43′ W in 1960, and 8°43′ W in 1975.

In retracing old property lines run by compass or based upon the magnetic meridian, it is necessary to allow for the difference in magnetic declination at the time of the orignal survey and at the present date. The difference is generally due mostly to secular variation.

Daily variation. Daily variation of the magnetic needle's declination causes it to swing through an arc averaging approximately 8′ for the United States. The needle reaches its extreme easterly position about 8 AM, and its most westerly reading about 1:30 PM. Mean declination occurs about 10:30 AM and 8 PM. These hours and the amount of the daily swing change with latitude and season of the year, but complete neglect of the daily variation is well within the range of error expected in compass readings. The term *diurnal variation* is often used in place of "daily variation."

Annual variation. This periodic swing amounts to less than 1′ of arc and can be neglected. It must not be confused with the annual change (the amount of the secular-variation change in one year), shown on some isogonic charts.

Irregular variations. Unpredictable magnetic disturbances and storms can cause short-term irregular variations of a degree or more.

7-5. LOCAL ATTRACTION. The magnetic field is affected by metallic objects and direct-current electricity, both of which cause a local attraction. If the source of an artificial disturbance is fixed, all bearings from a given station will be in error by the same amount. Angles calculated from bearings taken at the station will be correct, however.

Local attraction is present if the forward and back bearings of a line differ by more than the normal observational errors. Consider the following compass bearings read on a series of lines:

AB.............N 24°15′ W		*CD*.............N 60°00′ E
BA.............. S 24°10′ E		*DC*............. S 61°15′ W
BC.............N 76°40′ W		*DE*.............N 88°35′ E
CB.............. S 76°40′ E		*ED*............. S 87°25′ W

Forward bearing *AB* and back bearing *BA* agree reasonably well, indicating that local attraction does not exist at *A* or *B*. The same is true for

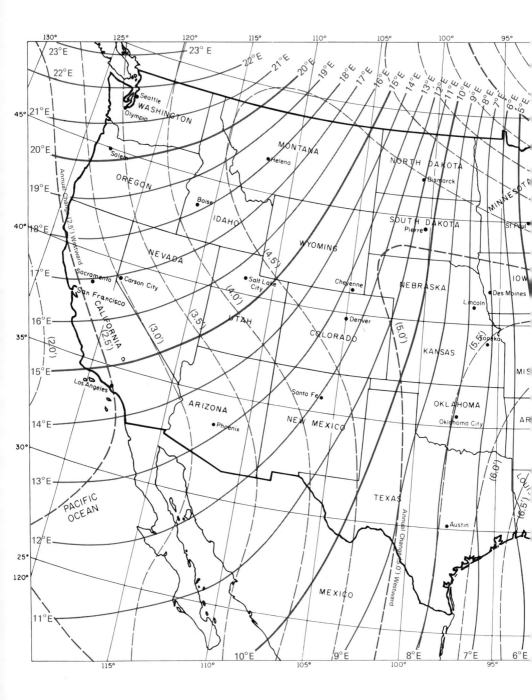

Figure 7-1. Distribution of magnetic declination in the United States for 1975.0. (Courtesy of United States Geological Survey.)

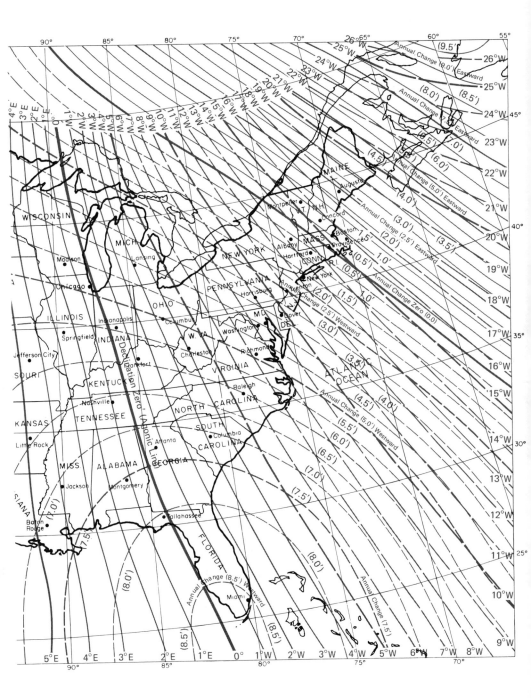

point C. However, the bearings at D differ from corresponding bearings taken at C and E by roughly $1°15'$. Local attraction therefore exists at point D and deflects the compass needle $1°15'$ to the west of north.

It is evident that to detect local attraction, successive stations on a compass traverse should be occupied, and forward and back bearings read, even though the directions of all lines could be determined by setting up the instrument only on alternate stations.

7-6. THE SURVEYOR'S COMPASS.   A surveyor's compass is shown in Figs. 7-2 and 7-3. George Washington, and thousands of surveyors who followed him, used this type of instrument to run land lines which still determine property holdings and therefore must be retraced. The circle is graduated in degrees or half-degrees, but can be read to perhaps $5'$ or $10'$ by estimation.

The instrument consists of a metal base plate A, Fig. 7-2, with two vertical sight vanes B placed at the ends and a round compass box C at the center. Two small level vials D are mounted on the plate. The sight vanes are strips of metal with vertical slits to define the line of sight.

The compass box, Fig. 7-3, has a conical point at its center to support the needle, and a glass cover to protect it. A circular scale at the outer rim

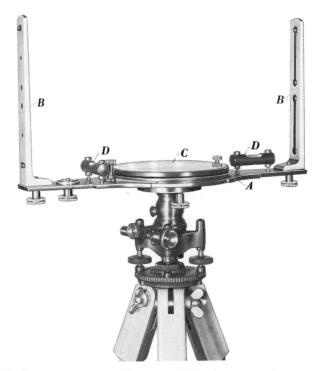

Figure 7-2. Surveyor's compass. (Courtesy of W. & L. E. Gurley.)

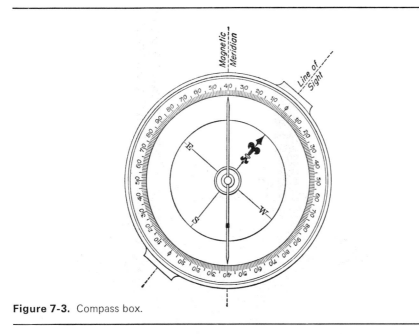

Figure 7-3. Compass box.

of the box is graduated in degrees or half-degrees. Zero marks are at the north and south points, and in line with the sight-vane slits. Graduations are numbered in multiples of 10°, clockwise and counterclockwise from 0° at the north and south, to 90° at the east and west. As the sight vanes and compass box are revolved, the needle shows the bearing of the line observed.

Note that letters E and W on the compass box are reversed from their normal position to give direct readings of bearings. Thus in Fig. 7-3, the sight line bearing through the vanes is N 40° E.

Accuracy of a compass depends upon sensitivity of the needle. A sensitive needle is readily attracted toward a small piece of iron held nearby, but settles in the original position each time the stimulus is removed. Sensitivity itself results from the needle having (a) proper shape and balance, (b) strong magnetism, (c) a sharp conical point, and (d) a smooth cup that bears on the pivot. Tapping the glass cover releases a needle which does not swing freely. Touching the cover with a moistened finger removes static electricity that may affect the needle.

Remagnetizing the needle is relatively easy, but reshaping the pivot difficult. To retain the conical shape of the pivot point and prevent blunting to a spherical or flat form which produces sluggishness, the needle should be lifted from the pivot when not in use. A lever arm is provided to raise the needle off the pivot and press it against the glass cover if the instrument is being moved or boxed.

Early compasses were supported by a single leg called a *Jacob staff.* A ball-and-socket joint and a clamp were used to level the instrument and set

Figure 7-4. Compass. (Courtesy of Keuffel & Esser Company.)

the plate in a horizontal position. Later-version compasses are mounted on a base with a four-screw leveling head, as shown in Fig. 7-2.

The compass box of a transit is similar in construction to the surveyor's compass. Zero marks at the north and south points are on a line parallel with and beneath the telescope. A special adjustment on some instruments swings the graduated circle through an arc to compensate for a given declination, thus permitting true bearings to be read from the needle.

7-7. THE FORESTER'S AND GEOLOGIST'S COMPASS. Figure 7-4 shows a type of compass employed by geologists and the United States Forest Service. It can be used as a hand-held instrument or supported on a staff or tripod.

This compass is made of aluminum and has brass sights. A declination adjustment is provided for the raised (upper) graduated compass ring. The beveled (lower) ring is used to turn right angles, or to measure vertical angles by placing an edge of the base on a level surface.

7-8. BRUNTON COMPASS. Figure 7-5 shows a Brunton pocket transit, which combines the main features of a sighting compass, a prismatic compass,

Figure 7-5. Brunton pocket transit. (Courtesy of Keuffel & Esser Company.)

a hand level, and a clinometer. It is an accurate and convenient device for topographic and preliminary surveys of all kinds. It can be used as a hand-held instrument, or mounted on a Jacob staff or tripod. Brunton compasses are widely used by geologists.

A Brunton compass consists of a brass case hinged on two sides. The cover at the left has a fine mirror and a center line on the inside face. A hinged sighting point at the extreme left, and the sighting vane at the far right, are folded outward when the instrument is in use. The bearing of a line is determined from the compass-needle reading while the point observed is reflected through the sight vane on a mirror.

A declination adjustment is made by revolving the raised compass ring. The clinometer (vertical-angle) arc inside the compass ring is graduated to degrees and can be read to the nearest 5' by a vernier on the clinometer arm. Another arc gives grade percentages for both elevation and depression. The compass is held vertically, instead of horizontally, to read vertical angles or grade percentages. It measures $2\frac{3}{4} \times 2\frac{3}{4} \times 1$ in. and weighs approximately 8 oz.

7-9. THE SUUNTO CLINOMETER. A new hand-held optical reading clinometer, the 3-in-1 Suunto, weighs only 4.2 oz, is $2\frac{3}{4} \times 2 \times \frac{5}{8}$ in., and has optical scales graduated in degrees from $0°$ to $\pm 90°$, and grade percentages from 0 to $\pm 150\%$. It can be read to $1°$ or 1%, and estimated to $10'$ or $\frac{1}{5}\%$ near the zero level. This device can be used by surveyors, engineers, architects, builders, geologists, foresters, and others.

7-10. TYPICAL PROBLEMS. Typical problems in compass surveys require the conversion of true bearings to magnetic bearings, magnetic bearings to true bearings, and magnetic bearings to magnetic bearings for the declinations existing at different dates.

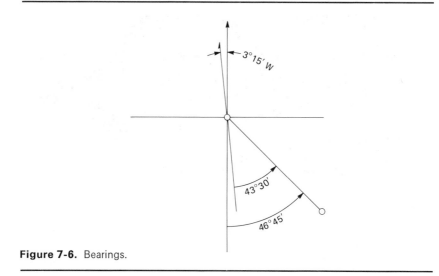

Figure 7-6. Bearings.

As an example, assume that the magnetic bearing of a property line was recorded as S 43°30′ E in 1862. The magnetic declination at the survey location was 3°15′ W. The true bearing is needed for inclusion in the subdivision plan of the property.

A sketch similar to Fig. 7-6 makes the relationship clear and should be used by beginners to avoid errors. True north is designated by a full-headed long arrow, and magnetic north by a half-headed shorter arrow. The true bearing is seen to be S 46°45′ E. Using different-colored pencils to show the directions of true north, magnetic north, and lines on the ground helps clarify the sketch.

As another example, assume that the magnetic bearing of a line AB read in 1878 was N 26°15′ E; the declination at that time and place was 7°15′ W; and in 1976 the declination is 4°30′ E. The magnetic bearing in 1976 is needed. The declination angles are shown in Fig. 7-7. The magnetic bearing of the line AB in 1976 is equal to the bearing at the earlier date minus the sum of the declination angles, or N 14°30′ E.

7-11. SOURCES OF ERROR IN COMPASS WORK. Some sources of error in using the compass are:

1. Compass out of level.
2. Pivot, needle, or sight vanes bent.
3. Magnetism of needle weak.
4. Magnetic variations.
5. Local attraction.
6. Chaining pins, metal range poles, axes, loose-leaf field books, a penknife, metal in a shirt pocket, power lines, or a parked car near the compass.

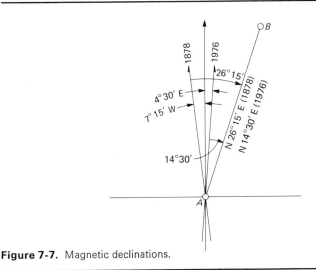

Figure 7-7. Magnetic declinations.

7-12. MISTAKES.   Some fairly typical mistakes in compass work include:

1. Reading the wrong end of the needle.
2. Setting the declination off on the wrong side of north.
3. Declination set off when reading magnetic bearings.
4. Parallax (reading while looking from the side of the needle instead of along it).
5. Failing to check the forward and back bearings when possible.
6. Not making a sketch showing known and desired items.

PROBLEMS

7-1. What is the total difference in magnetic declination between northeast Maine and northwest Washington?

7-2. At the present rate of change of declination shown in Figure 7–1, approximately how fast (in miles per year) is the agonic line moving in the United States, and in what general direction is it moving?

7-3. Determine from Figure 7–1 the approximate declination in 1975 at Seattle, Boston, Los Angeles, and Miami. What will be their approximate declinations in 1990?

7-4. Assuming the rate of annual change of declination shown in Figure 7–1 has been constant (although it has not been), compute the approximate declination for Atlanta in 1900. In your college library compare your result with the value shown on a 1900 isogonic chart in a surveying book of that time.

7–5. The magnetic declination at a given place is 4°50′ W. What is the magnetic bearing of true north ? Of true south ? Of true east ?

7–6. Explain why letters E and W on the compass of Figure 7–3 are reversed from their normal positions.

7–7. The magnetic bearing of a line of an old survey is recorded as N 11°30′ E. It is now N 3°45′ W. What has been the change in magnetic declination and its direction ?

7–8. The magnetic bearing of line AB in 1920 was S 89°47′ E, and the declination was 5°20′ W. If the declination today is 3°45′ E, what magnetic bearing would you use today to retrace the same line AB ? What is the true bearing of the line ?

7–9. At a certain location the declination was 3°10′ W in 1750, 1°30′ W in 1800, 0°35′ E in 1850, 1°15′ W in 1900, 3°50′ W in 1950, and 4°05′ W in 1975. If the line has a true bearing of N 2°40′ W, what was its magnetic bearing in the other years listed ?

7–10. Similar to problem 7–9, except that the true bearing in 1975 was N 1°30′ E.

In problems 7–11 through 7–14, convert the following magnetic bearings to true bearings.

7–11. N 74°35′ E, declination 12° W.

7–12. S 8°30′ E, declination 10°45′ W.

7–13. N 2°15′ W, declination 3°50′ E.

7–14. S 4°30′ W, declination 5°45′ E.

What magnetic bearing should be used to retrace a line AB for the conditions given in problems 7–15 through 7–18 ?

	1860 Magnetic Bearing	1860 Declination	Present Declination
7–15.	N 28°50′ W	7°15′ E	11°40′ E
7–16.	N 89°30′ W	4°50′ W	8°15′ E
7–17.	S 60°40′ E	2°10′ W	3°35′ W
7–18.	S 72°15′ W	12°25′ E	1°18′ W

7–19. Does local attraction at a point affect the size of an angle computed from magnetic bearings read at that point ? Explain.

7–20. After it was determined that no local attraction existed at point A, the following bearings were observed: $AB = $ N 42$^1/_2$° W, $BA = $ S 45$^1/_4$° E, and $BC = $ S 49° W. What is the angle (less than 180°) at B and the correct bearing of BC ?

In problems 7–21 through 7–24 compute the magnetic declination at line BC in 1845 based on the following data from an old survey record.

	1845 Mag. Bearing	Present Mag. Bearing	Present Mag. Decl.
7–21.	S 69°20′ W	S 58°35′ W	16°30′ E
7–22.	N 28°05′ E	N 32°20′ E	4°10′ E
7–23.	S 10°35′ E	S 9°20′ W	3°05′ W
7–24.	N 8°20′ W	N 10°35′ E	5°10′ W

7–25. The observed bearing of a line is N 87°25′ E, and its correct bearing is S 89°30′ E. Calculate the value and direction of the local attraction.

7–26. Determine the angle *ABC* and correct bearing of line *BC* from the following data : correct bearing of *AB* is N 89° E, observed bearing of *BA* is S 78° W, and observed bearing of *BC* is S 42° E.

Problems 7–27 through 7–29 list forward and back bearings. The correct bearing of *AB* is N 41° E. Compute the local attraction at each point possible, and the correct bearings of *BC* and *CD*.

7–27. *AB*=N 41° E ; *BA*=S 42° W ; *BC*=S 58° E ; *CB*=N 61° W ; *CD*=due S.

7–28. *AB*=N 41° E ; *BA*=S 38° W ; *BC*=N 22° W ; *CB*=S 17° E ; *CD*=S 31° W ; *DC*=N 30° E.

7–29. *AB*=N 41° E ; *BA*=S 39° W ; *BC*=N 65° E ; *CB*=S 58° W ; *CD*=S 87° E ; *DC*=due W.

7–30. The following bearings were observed by compass: *AB*=N 78°45′ E ; *BA*=S 80°30′ W ; *BC*=S 66°15′ W ; *CB*=N 65°45′ E ; *CD*=N 49°45′ W ; *DC*=S 49°45′ E. Find the magnetic bearing of *AB*. Where is the local attraction ? Which way is the needle deflected at each setup and how much ?

7–31. From what point of beginning is it possible for a person to travel due south along a meridian for 1 mile, due east along a parallel of latitude for 1 mile, and then due north along a meridian for 1 mile and be back at the starting point ?

7–32. Describe how you would determine in the field the magnetic declination at a given location.

7–33. Independent readings of a surveyor's compass to check the local declination were recorded : N 14°50′ E, N 14°55′ E, N 14°50′ E, N 14°55′ E, N 15°00′ E, and N 14°55′ E. What is the most probable value of the declination and its standard error ?

7–34. Where on the earth's surface is the direction of the earth's magnetic lines of force horizontal, and where vertical ? Why must an ordinary compass needle be balanced before it is used ?

7–35. Classify the kind of error resulting from local attraction.

7–36. Can local attraction be determined by setting up a compass at a single station ? Explain.

In problems 7–37 through 7–40, compute the interior angles of a five-sided traverse *ABCDEA* having the observed surveyor's compass bearings listed. Explain the closure.

	AB	*BC*	*CD*	*DE*	*EA*
7–37.	N 15°00′ E	N 59°45′ E	N 80°15′ W	S 34°30′ W	N 83°30′ E
7–38.	N 74°05′ E	S 31°15′ E	S 46°00′ W	N 79°45′ W	N 15°30′ W
7–39.	S 30°20′ W	S 52°15′ W	due E	N 42°55′ W	N 10°10′ W
7–40.	S 65°45′ E	S 14°00′ E	S 86°15′ W	N 35°10′ W	N 44°30′ E

8
THE TRANSIT
AND THEODOLITE

8-1. GENERAL. Transits and theodolites are perhaps the most universal of surveying instruments. Although their primary use is for accurate measurement or layout of horizontal and vertical angles, they are also commonly employed for a wide variety of other tasks such as determining horizontal and vertical distances by stadia (see Chapter 12), prolonging straight lines, and low-order differential leveling.

The main components of a transit or theodolite are a sighting telescope, two graduated circles mounted in mutually perpendicular planes, and level vials. Prior to measuring angles, the "horizontal" circle is oriented in a horizontal plane by means of level vials which automatically put the other circle in a vertical plane. Horizontal and vertical angles can then be measured directly in their respective planes of reference.

There is no internationally accepted understanding among surveyors on the exact difference denoted by the terms *transit* and *theodolite*. In Europe the term "transiting theodolite" was originally applied to this type of angle-measuring instrument. The word "transiting" meant the telescope could be *plunged, reversed,* or *inverted.* Europeans eventually dropped the adjective and retained the name *theodolite,* while Americans shortened the term to *transit.*

Throughout the years, as different names evolved for American and European angle-measuring instruments, divergent basic design characteristics emerged as well which now are the generally accepted criteria for distinguishing a transit from a theodolite. American transits have metal circles read by means of verniers; European theodolites employ glass circles, and readings are taken from either finely graduated glass scales or micrometers

171

Figure 8-1. Lietz 10-C optical transit and theodolite. (Courtesy Lietz/Sokkisha Co.)

which are viewed through internal microscopic optical systems. Other distinctions are described subsequently in Parts I and II of this chapter. A few instruments, such as the Lietz 10-C, Fig. 8-1, combine some design features of both the transit and theodolite, are called *optical reading transits*, and use glass circles but are read from glass verniers viewed through magnifying eyepieces.

In general, theodolites are capable of greater accuracy in angle measurements than transits, and because of this and other advantages are gradually replacing them in the United States. In spite of the differences between the two types of instruments, both operate on the same basic principles, and the parts and relationships described for transits are directly applicable to theodolites.

8-2. RELATIONSHIPS OF ANGLES AND DISTANCES. In making measurements, it is helpful to remember the relationship between angles and distances. Commonly used field conversions, shown in Fig. 8-2, are as follows:

$$\sin 1' = \tan 1' = 0.00029 \text{ (approx.)}$$
$$\sin 1° = \tan 1° = 0.01745 = 0.013\tfrac{3}{4} \text{ (approx.)}$$
1' of arc = 0.03 ft at 100 ft, or 3 cm at 100 m (approx.)
1' of arc = 1 in. at 300 ft (approx.; actually 340 ft)
1" of arc = 1 ft at 40 miles, or 0.5 m at 100 km (approx.)

In accordance with the relationships listed, a theodolite reading to the nearest 0.1" is theoretically capable of measuring the angle between two points 1 in. apart and 40 miles away.

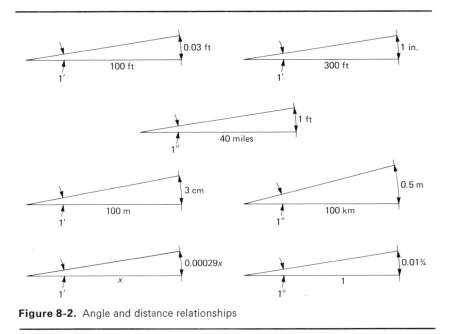

Figure 8-2. Angle and distance relationships

If a hand calculator or trig table is not handy, approximate results good enough for some stadia and other work (see Section 8-19) can be obtained readily by noting that for small angles, the sine function (and to a lesser extent the tangent relationship) is practically a straight line. Thus sin $1°$ = 60 (sin $1'$) = $60 \times 0.00029 = 0.0174$ compared with the true tabular value to five places of 0.01745. Sin $5° = 5 \times 0.01745 = 0.08725$ versus the exact figure of 0.08716, a difference of only 0.10%. Even at $10°$ the error for the approximate sine value is less than 5%—far too high for most surveying but frequently closer than temperatures judged without a thermometer, some rod readings on the ground in cross sectioning, and actual loads that may occur on structures can be estimated prior to design.

PART I. THE TRANSIT

8-3. PARTS OF THE TRANSIT. Transits are manufactured for general and special uses but all have three main parts: (1) upper plate, (2) lower plate, and (3) leveling head. These are shown in their relative positions in Fig. 8-3, and assembled in Fig. 8-4.

The various parts of a transit and its operation can best be learned by actually examining and handling an instrument. Once a transit has been taken apart and assembled, even though it be an old or damaged one retired from service, the precise machining and construction are certain to increase respect for such fine equipment.

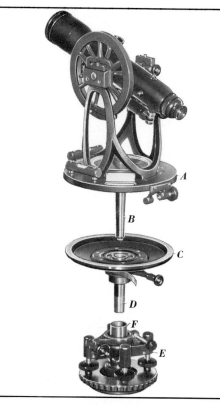

Figure 8-3. Transit parts. *A*, upper plate; *B*, inner spindle; *C*, lower plate; *D*, outer spindle; *E*, leveling head; *F*, socket. (Courtesy W. & L . E. Gurley.)

8-4. UPPER PLATE. The upper plate, Figs. 8-3 and 8-4, is a horizontal circular plate combined with a vertical *spindle* upon which it revolves about a vertical axis. The tapered design of American transit spindles assures that despite wear, unless damaged by dirt or an accident, they will still seat and center properly. Attached to the plate are two level vials, one parallel with the telescope (altitude bubble) and the other at right angles to it (azimuth bubble), and two *verniers* set 180° apart. Provisions are made for adjusting the verniers and level vials

Two vertical *standards*, either the A or U type, are cast as an integral part of the upper plate to support the horizontal *cross arms* of the telescope in bearings. The telescope revolves in a vertical plane about the center line through arms called the *horizontal (or transverse) axis.*

The telescope, similar to that of a dumpy level (see Section 5-7), contains an eyepiece, a reticle with one vertical and three horizontal lines, and an objective-lens system; it has a magnification range of 18 to 28 diam. A sensitive vial is attached to the telescope tube so the transit can be used as a leveling instrument on work where lower magnification and lesser sensitivity of the telescope vial are satisfactory.

The telescope is said to be in the *normal* or *direct* position when the level vial is below it. Turning the telescope on its horizontal axis puts the

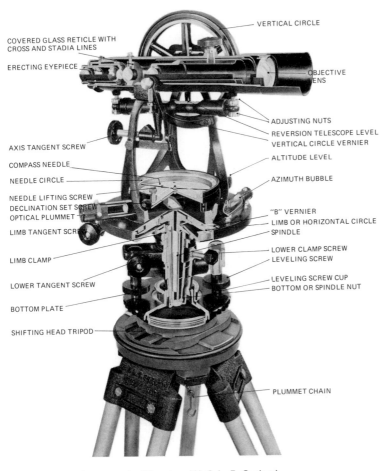

Figure 8-4. American transit. (Courtesy W. & L. E. Gurley.)

level vial above, and the instrument is said to be in a *plunged, inverted,* or *reversed* position. To permit use of the telescope for leveling in either the normal or inverted position, a reversion vial is desirable.

A *clamp screw* for the horizontal axis is tightened to hold the telescope horizontal, or at any desired inclination. After the clamp screw is set, a limiting range of vertical movement can be obtained by manipulating the *vertical-axis tangent screw* (also called the *slow-motion screw*).

A *vertical circle* or *arc* supported by a cross arm turns with the telescope as it is revolved. The arc normally is divided into $\frac{1}{2}°$ spaces with readings to the nearest minute obtained from a vernier having 30 divisions. The vernier is mounted on one standard with provisions for adjustment. If set properly, it should read zero when the telescope bubble is centered. If out of adjustment, a constant *index error* is read from the arc with the bubble centered and must be applied to all vertical angles, with appropriate sign, to get correct values.

The upper plate also contains the *compass box*, and holds the *upper tangent screw*.

8-5. LOWER PLATE.   The lower plate, *C* in Fig. 8-3, is a horizontal circular plate graduated on its upper face. Its underside is attached to a vertical, hollow, tapered spindle *D* into which the upper plate fits precisely. The upper plate completely covers the lower plate, except for two openings where the verniers exactly meet the graduated circle.

The upper (limb) clamp screw, Fig. 8-4, fastens the upper and lower plates together. A small range of movement is possible after clamping by using the upper (limb) tangent screw.

8-6. LEVELING HEAD.   The leveling head consists of a bottom horizontal plate and a "spider," with four leveling screws between them. Leveling screws, set in cups to prevent scoring the bottom plate, are partly or completely enclosed for protection against dirt and injury. The bottom plate has a collar threaded to fit upon the tripod head.

A socket *F*, Fig. 8-3, of the leveling head includes a lower clamp screw, Fig. 8-4, to fasten the lower plate. The lower tangent screw is used to make precise settings after the lower clamp screw is tightened. The base of the socket is fitted into a ball-and-socket joint resting on the bottom plate of the leveling head, on which it slides horizontally. A plummet chain attached to the center of the spindle holds the plumb-bob string. An optical plummet, which is a telescope through the vertical center (spindle), is available on some transits and points vertically when the plates are level. It is viewed at right angles by means of a prism for ease of observation.

A recapitulation of the use of the various clamps and tangent screws may be helpful to the beginner (see also Section 8-16). The clamp and tangent screw on one standard controls the movement of the telescope in the vertical plane. The upper clamp fastens the upper and lower plates together, and an upper tangent screw permits a small differential movement between them. The lower clamp fastens the lower plate to the socket, after which a lower tangent screw turns the plate through a small angle. If the upper and lower plates are clamped together, they will of course move freely as a unit until the lower clamp is tightened.

Tripods for transits, either fixed- or adjustable-leg types, are used interchangeably for levels.

8-7. SCALES.   The horizontal limb of a lower plate may be divided in various ways, but generally the circle is graduated into 30′ or 20′ spaces. For convenience in measuring angles to the right or the left, graduations are numbered from 0° to 360° both clockwise and counterclockwise. Figure 8-5 shows these arrangements. On newer transits, the numbers are slanted to show the direction in which the circle should be read. Different-length lines mark the 10°, 5°, 1°, and other major graduations.

The circles of more precise instruments are graduated in divisions of 10′ or 15′. The outer set of numbers on some old transits runs from 0° to 180° and back to 0°. Obsolete instruments had the circle divided into quadrants like a compass box. Graduations from 0° to 360° facilitate reading azimuths and direct angles and have therefore replaced the quadrant system of numbers which was used for bearings.

Transit circles are graduated automatically by means of a precise dividing machine. After each line is cut by a sharp tool, a precision gear moves the tool ahead for the next cut. Any small error in the gears is adjusted by a compensating cam. Under a microscope, the division slashes look somewhat rough, but to the naked eye they are smooth. The marks are painted to make them stand out clearly. Graduations on transit scales are correct to within about 2″.

8-8. VERNIERS. Vernier principles were demonstrated in Section 5-19, and the least count given by the following relation:

$$\text{least count} = \frac{\text{value of the smallest division on the scale}}{\text{number of divisions on the vernier}}$$

The combinations of scale graduations and vernier divisions generally used on transits are shown in Table 8-1.

TABLE 8-1. TRANSIT SCALES AND VERNIERS

Scale Graduations	Vernier Divisions	Least Count	Fig. No.
30′	30	1′	8-5(a)
20′	40	30″	8-5(b)
30′	60	30″	8-5(c)
15′	45	20″	
10′	60	10″	8-5(d)

Three types of verniers used on transits are shown in Fig. 8-5:

Direct, or single, vernier, Fig. 8-5(d). This is read in only one direction and must therefore be set with the graduations ahead of the zero (index) mark in the direction to be turned.

Double vernier, Fig. 8-5(a), (b), and (c). A double vernier can be read either clockwise or counterclockwise, only one half being used at a time.

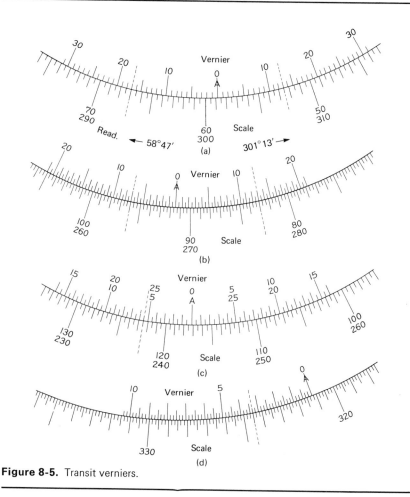

Figure 8-5. Transit verniers.

Once the index mark is set coincident with 0°00′ on the circle, or any known value, an observer is not limited to turning angles in one direction only.

Folded vernier, Fig. 8-5(c). This type avoids the long vernier plate required by the normal double vernier. Its length is that of a direct vernier with half of the graduations placed on each side of the index mark. Except possibly for vertical arcs, the use of folded verniers is not justified by space or cost savings and is likely to cause reading errors.

8-9. METHOD OF READING VERNIERS.   A vernier is read by finding a graduation on it which coincides with *any* division on the circle scale. There will be two such matching lines on a double vernier, one for a clockwise angle and the other for a counterclockwise angle. A vernier index shows

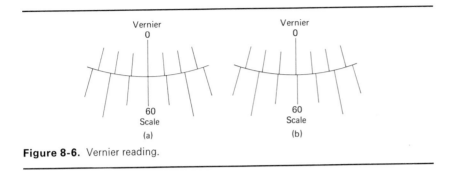

Figure 8-6. Vernier reading.

the number of degrees (and sometimes the multiple of 10', 15', 20', or 30'.) passed over on the scale. The coincident vernier graduation gives directly the additional part of a degree. The second divisions on each side of the apparently matching lines should be checked for symmetry of pattern.

In Fig. 8-6(a), the vernier index (zero) mark is set exactly opposite a graduation on the scale since the distances between the second vernier and second scale division on both sides of zero are equal. If two sets of lines appear to be almost coincident and a symmetrical pattern is formed, as in Fig. 8-6(b) by 0 and the first division on the left, a reading halfway between them can be interpolated.

Figure 8-5(a) shows a double vernier and two sets of numbers on the circle. The reading for the inner set is $58°30' + 17' = 58°47'$. For the outer circle it is $301° 00' + 13' = 301°13'$. Note that *the vernier is always read in the same direction from zero as the numbering of the circle, that is, on the side of the double vernier in the direction of the increasing angle.*

The reading of the inner set of numbers from the double vernier in Fig. 8-5(b) is $91°20' + 07' = 91°27'$; for the outer set it is $268°20' + 13' = 268°33'$.

The folded vernier of Fig. 8-5(c) reads $117°05'30''$ on the inner row of numbers and $242°54'30''$ on the outer set.

A direct vernier, Fig. 8-5(d), is the type used on transits or repeating theodolites and reads $321°13'20''$ for a clockwise angle.

An understanding of verniers is best obtained by practice in reading various types and by calculating and sketching the least count for different combinations of scale and vernier divisions. Typical mistakes in reading minutes and seconds from verniers result from:

1. Not using a magnifying glass.
2. Reading in the wrong direction from zero, or on the wrong side of a double vernier.
3. Failing to determine the least count correctly.
4. Omitting 10', 15', 20', or 30' when the index is beyond those marks.

8-10. PROPERTIES OF THE TRANSIT.   Transits are designed to have a proper balance between magnification and resolution of the telescope, least count of the vernier, and sensitivity of the plate and telescope bubbles. An average length of sight of about 300 ft is assumed in design. Thus a standard 1′ instrument has the following properties:

Magnification, 18 to 28 diam.
Field of view, 1° to 1°30′.
Resolution, 4″ to 5″.
Minimum focus, about 5 to 7 ft.
Sensitivity of plate levels per 2-mm division, 70″ to 100″.
Sensitivity of telescope vial per 2-mm division, 30″ to 60″.
Weight of instrument head without tripod, 11 to 16½ lb.

Cross hairs usually include vertical and horizontal center hairs and two stadia hairs, as shown in Fig. 8-7(b) and Fig. 8-7(c). Short stadia lines, used on glass reticles [Fig. 8-7(c)], avoid confusion between the center and stadia hairs.

A quarter hair, located halfway between the upper and middle hairs [Fig. 8-7(d)], is sometimes used to increase the range of stadia readings, as noted in Chapter 12.

The X pattern [Fig. 8-7(e)] is incorporated in precise instruments to prevent a rod or object seen at a long distance from being completely hidden behind the vertical hair. It also permits the observer to balance distances between the rod and hairs on both sides of the upper and lower sections to ensure centering, a task the human eye does in a highly efficient manner. The arrangement shown in Fig. 8-7(f), or one of the variations in Figs. 8-7(g) and 8-7(h), likewise avoids covering the object sighted and aids in centering.

A transit is a *repeating instrument* because angles can be measured by repetition any number of times and their total added on the plates. Advan-

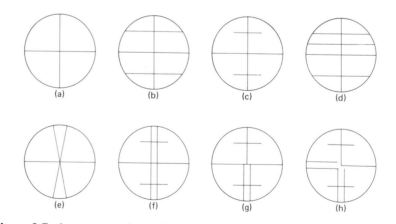

Figure 8-7. Arrangement of cross hairs.

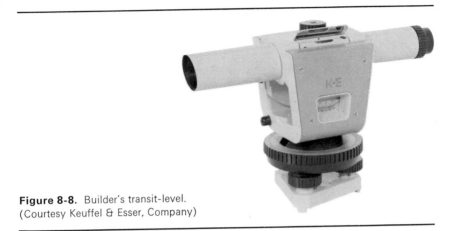

Figure 8-8. Builder's transit-level.
(Courtesy Keuffel & Esser, Company)

tages of the repeating procedure are (1) better accuracy obtained through averaging, and (2) disclosure of errors by comparing values of the single and multiple readings.

A *builder's transit-level* is a lower-priced instrument for use on work requiring only short sights and moderate precision. The model shown in Fig. 8-8 has a telescope with magnification of 20 diam, resolution of 4.7″, telescope level vial with sensitivity of 90″/2-mm division, and a horizontal circle and vertical arc reading to 5′. The cost is approximately one-third that of a standard transit.

8-11. HANDLING AND SETTING UP THE TRANSIT. A transit is taken from its box by holding the leveling head, the underside of the lower plate, or the standards (*not* lifting by the telescope). It should be screwed securely on the tripod. A transit carried indoors should be balanced in a horizontal position under one arm, with the instrument-head forward. The same method is suitable in areas covered with brush. In open terrain the instrument may be balanced on a shoulder. When one carries a transit, the telescope should be clamped lightly in a position perpendicular to the plates. The plate clamps should be set lightly to prevent swinging, while still permitting ready movement if the instrument is bumped.

The wing nuts on the tripod must be tight, to prevent slippage and rotation of the head. They are correctly adjusted if each tripod leg falls slowly of its own weight when placed in a horizontal position. If the wing nuts are overly tight, or if pressure is applied to the legs crosswise (which can break them) instead of lengthwise to fix them in the ground, the tripod is in a strained position. The result may be an unnoticed movement of the instrument head after observations have begun. Tripod legs should be well spread to furnish stability and place the telescope at a height convenient for the observer. Tripod shoes must be tight. Proper field procedures can eliminate most instrument inadjustments, but there is no way to take care of a poor tripod with dried-out wooden legs, except to discard or repair it.

A plumb-bob string hung on a hook at the bottom of the spindle using a slipknot permits raising or lowering the bob without retying, and avoids knots. A small slide attachment is also useful in accomplishing this purpose. The plumb bob must be brought directly over a definite point such as a tack in a wooden stake, and the plates leveled. The tripod legs can be moved in, out, or sideways, to approximately level the plates before the leveling screws are used. Shifting the legs affects the position of the plumb bob and makes setting up a transit more difficult than for a level.

Two methods are used to bring the plumb bob within about $\frac{1}{4}$ in. of the proper point. In the first method, the transit is set over the mark and one or more legs moved to bring the plumb bob into position. One leg may be moved circumferentially, to level the plates without greatly disturbing the plummet. Beginners sometimes have difficulty with this method because at the start the center of the transit is too far off the point, or the plates are badly out of level. Several movements of the tripod legs may then fail to both level the plates and center the plumb bob while maintaining a convenient height of instrument. If an adjustable-leg tripod is used, one or two legs can be lengthened or shortened to bring the bob directly over the point.

In the second method, which is particularly suited to level or uniformly sloping ground, the transit is set up near the point and the plates approximately leveled by moving the tripod legs as necessary. Then, with one tripod leg held in the left hand, another under the left armpit, and the third held in the right hand, the transit is lifted and placed over the mark. A slight shifting of one leg should bring the plumb bob within perhaps $\frac{1}{4}$ in. of the proper position and leave the plates practically level.

The plummet is centered exactly by loosening all four leveling screws and sliding them on the bottom plate using the ball-and-socket shifting-head device, which permits a limited movement. To assure mobility in any direction, the shifting head should be approximately centered on the bottom plate before setting up the instrument, and when boxing it.

A transit is accurately leveled by means of the four leveling screws in somewhat the same manner described for a level. However, each level vial on the upper plate is first set over a pair of opposite screws, and because there are two vials available, the telescope position need not be changed in the leveling process. After the bubbles are carefully centered and the telescope rotated, if they run very far off center, it may be necessary or desirable to adjust the vials as described in Section A-5.

If the plumb bob is still over the mark after leveling, the instrument is ready for use. But if the plates were badly out of level, or the leveling screws not uniformly set, the plummet moves off the mark during leveling. The screws must then be loosened, shifted again, and the transit releveled. It is evident that time can be saved by starting with the plates reasonably level to avoid excessive manipulation and possible binding of the screws.

PART II. THE THEODOLITE

8-12. CHARACTERISTICS OF THEODOLITES. Theodolites differ from American transits in general appearance (they are compact, lightweight, and "streamlined"), and in design by a number of features, the more important of which are as follows:

1. *Telescopes* are short, have reticles etched on glass, and are equipped with rifle sights for rough pointing.

2. *Horizontal and vertical circles* are made of glass with graduation lines and numerals etched on the circles' surface. The lines are very thin (0.004 mm), short (0.05 to 0.10 mm), and more sharply defined than can be achieved by scribing them on metal. Precisely graduated circles with small diameters can be obtained, and this is one reason the instruments are so compact. Circles are divided into conventional sexagesimal degrees and fractions (360°), or into centesimal "grads" or "grades" (full circle divided into 400^g).

3. The *vertical circle* of most theodolites is precisely indexed with respect to the direction of gravity in one of two ways: (a) by an *automatic compensator* or (b) by a *collimation level* or *index level*, usually the coincidence type connected to the reading system of the vertical circle. Both provide a more accurate plane of reference for measuring vertical angles than the plate levels used on transits.

4. *Circle reading systems* consist basically of a microscope having optics situated inside the instrument. A reading eyepiece is generally adjacent to the telescope eyepiece or located on one of the standards. Some instruments have optical micrometers for fractional reading of circle intervals (micrometer scale visible through reading microscope); others are "direct-reading." A mirror located on one standard can be adjusted to reflect light into the instrument and brighten the circles. The reading systems of most theodolites can also be illuminated electrically for night or underground work.

5. The *vertical axis* is cylindrical, or a precision ball bearing, or a combination of both, and generally made of steel.

6. The *leveling head* consists of three screws or *cams*.

7. *Bases* or *tribrachs* of theodolites are often designed to permit interchange of instrument and accessories (targets, EDM instruments, subtense bar, and so on), without disturbing centering over the survey point. Fig. 8-9, for example, shows the placement of a sighting target and an EDM reflector on a theodolite tribrach.

8. An *optical plummet*, built into the base or alidade of most theodolites, replaces the plumb bob and permits centering with great accuracy.

9. *Carrying cases* for theodolites are made of steel, lightweight alloy, or heavy plastic. They are generally compact, watertight, and can be locked.

10. *Distance-measuring devices* may be permanent and integral parts of theodolites. Tacheometers, for example, are theodolites that measure slope distance by the stadia principle and automatically convert them to horizontal and vertical components. Some theodolites have built-in EDM devices

Figure 8-9. Standard tribrachs for most theodolites are designed for interchanging various accessories. Here tribrachs are shown to be compatible with a sighting target (left) and an EDM reflector (right). (Courtesy Wild Heerbrugg Instruments, Inc.)

which permit measuring slope distances, and horizontal and vertical angles from a single setup.

11. Various *accessories* increase the versatility of theodolites, adapting them for special applications such as astronomical observations. The compass is an accessory rather than an integral part of the theodolite. A gyroscopic attachment is very expensive but valuable for certain applications.

12. *Tripods* are the wide-frame type. Some are all-metallic and feature devices for preliminary leveling of the tripod head and mechanical centering ("plumbing") to eliminate the need for a plumb bob or optical plummet.

8-13. REPEATING THEODOLITES.

Theodolites are divided into two basic categories: the *repeating* (or *double center*) type and the *directional* (or *triangulation*) model. Repeating theodolites are equipped with a double vertical axis (similar to that of American transits, but usually cylindrical in shape) or a repetition clamp. As in the American transit, this design enables angles to be repeated any number of times and added directly on the circle of the instrument.

Figs. 8-10 and 8-11 illustrate examples of repeating-type theodolites. The optical reading system of each instrument is shown in the small inset figures. Each of these theodolites reads directly to the nearest minute, with estimation possible to 0.1′. Both instruments have optical plummets, and plate bubble sensitivity of 30″/2-mm division.

The reading systems of the Theo 020A theodolite, Fig. 8-10, consists of a graduated glass scale having a span of 1° which appears superimposed on the degree divisions of the main circle. This scale is read directly by means of a microscope whose eyepiece is beside the main telescope. To take a reading, it is simply necessary to observe which degree number lies within the 1° span of the glass scale and select the minute indicated by the index mark. The vertical and horizontal circle readings indicated for the Theo 020A of Fig. 8-10 are 256°52.0′ and 235°05.0′, respectively. Thus on this instrument the horizontal and vertical circles can be viewed and read simultaneously through the reading microscope.

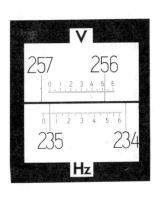

Figure 8-10. Theo 020 A
repeating theodolite.
(Courtesy Zena Company.)

The reading system of the T-1, Fig. 8-11, consists of an optical micrometer. To make a reading, the operator must first center the reference mark between the two bifilar lines of a degree mark by turning the micrometer knob. The micrometer spans 1° of the main circle and by centering the reference mark, the minutes portion of the angle can be read in the micrometer window on the right side of the reading microscope field of view. The horizontal angle indicated in Fig. 8-11 is 327°59.6′. The micrometer must be set again to read the vertical angle.

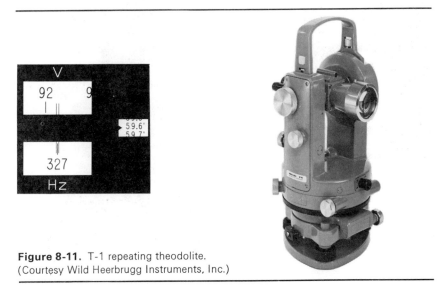

Figure 8-11. T-1 repeating theodolite.
(Courtesy Wild Heerbrugg Instruments, Inc.)

8-14. DIRECTIONAL THEODOLITES. A directional theodolite is a nonrepeating type of instrument which has no lower motion. "Directions" rather than angles are read. After a sight has been taken on a point, the direction of the line to the point is read on the circle. An observation on the next mark gives a new direction so the angle between the lines can be found by subtracting the first direction from the second.

Directional theodolites have a single vertical axis and therefore cannot measure angles by the repetition method. They do, however, have a *circle-orienting drive* to make a rough setting of the horizontal circle at any desired position.

On all directional theodolites each reading represents the *mean* of two diametrically opposed sides of the circle, made possible because the operator simultaneously views both sides of the circle through internal optics. This reading procedure, equivalent to averaging readings of the A and B verniers of a transit, automatically compensates for eccentricity errors (see Section 8-29).

Typical directional theodolites are shown in Figs. 8-12 and 8-13. Each has a micrometer, and can be read directly to 1″ with estimation possible to the nearest 0.1″. Both have 30-power sighting telescopes and plate bubbles with 20″/2-mm division sensitivity.

An inset for each figure illustrates the circle reading system of the instrument. The vertical and horizontal circles of the DKM2-A, Fig. 8-12,

Figure 8-12. DKM2-A directional theodolite. (Courtesy Kern Instruments, Inc.)

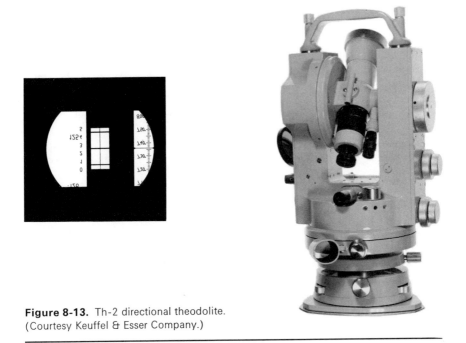

Figure 8-13. Th-2 directional theodolite.
(Courtesy Keuffel & Esser Company.)

carry two concentric scales, one with single-line graduations, the other with bifilar divisions. The circle-reading microscope shows a portion of one scale superimposed on the diametrically opposed portion of the other. In reading an angle, the operator turns the optical micrometer knob to shift the two scales until the single-line graduations appear centered within the bifilar lines. As the micrometer is revolved, there is a simultaneous movement of a *field stop* which frames the number of 10′ divisions in the reading. Centering with the microscope must be done separately for the horizontal and vertical circles.

In Fig. 8-12, the micrometer has been set to read the vertical circle so the single graduations are centered within the bifilar lines of the window labeled V. (Note they are not centered in the H window.) The reading is 85° (seen directly in the upper window), plus 3 × 10′ or 30′ (the three being taken from within the field stop frame of the same window), plus 5′14.0″ (from the lower window). Thus the vertical circle reading is 85°35′14.0″.

The reading system of the Th-2 shown in Fig. 8-13 is similar to that of the DKM2-A. A selector knob permits viewing either the horizontal or vertical circle through the microscope; both circles cannot be seen simultaneously. The center window of Fig. 8-13 shows the graduations on diametrically opposed parts of the circle. The micrometer has already been adjusted for reading by making opposite graduations coincide, and in that position the number corresponding to a multiple of 10′ in the reading is indicated in the

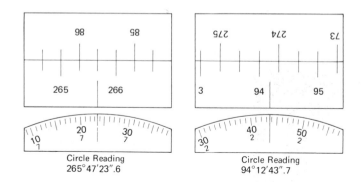

Figure 8-14. Reading system of horizontal circle of older version of T-2 directional theodolite.

left window directly beside the number of degrees. The additional minutes and seconds portions of the reading are taken from the rightmost window. The angle thus indicated in the Th-2 is 125°, plus 4 × 10′ (both from the left window), plus 7′36.0″ (in the right window), giving a final reading of 125°47′36.0″.

The reading system of a widely used older version T-2 directional theodolite is illustrated in Fig. 8-14. In this arrangement, the circles are divided into 20′ spaces and the whole-degree marks numbered.

A reading is obtained by turning the micrometer knob to make the division lines (which move in opposite directions) coincident. Since an average reading of the two sides of the circle is secured, each graduation is counted as 10′ to save a later division by 2. The micrometer range is limited to 10 min. The set of numbers seen upside down is on the opposite side of the circle.

In Fig. 8-14, a direction of 265°40′ is read by counting the number of divisions (4) between 265° and its diametrically opposite graduation, 85°. A micrometer scale gives the additional minutes and seconds, in this example 7′23.6″. The vertical circle, read in the same manner, furnishes the zenith distance (the complement of the vertical angle) to avoid the need for signs.

An additional extremely precise directional instrument used for first-order triangulation, the DKM-3, is shown in Fig. 18-7.

8-15. HANDLING AND SETTING UP A THEODOLITE. Theodolites should be carefully lifted from their carrying cases by grasping the standards (some newer instruments are equipped with handles for this purpose), and the instrument securely fastened to the tripod by means of a tribrach. The tripod with instrument is placed over the ground point in the manner described for transit setups (see Section 8-11). Beginners can use a plumb bob to approximate the required setup position. Exact centering over the point is done by means of an optical plummet which provides a line of sight directed downward collinear with the vertical axis of the theodolite. The instrument must be level for the optical plummet to define a vertical line. Most theodolite tribrachs have a relatively insensitive bull's-eye bubble to facilitate rough preliminary leveling before beginning final leveling with the plate bubble. Some tribrachs also contain an optical plummet.

The setup process is a trial-and-error one in which rough level is accomplished using the bull's-eye bubble, the optical plummet checked, and the instrument moved sideways in position as necessary to center over the point. More exact leveling is then performed using the plate bubble, the optical plummet sighted again, and the instrument position readjusted as necessary. Final careful leveling is performed by repeating the procedures.

It was noted earlier that theodolites have a three-screw leveling head and a single plate bubble. To level the instrument, the plate bubble is placed parallel to the line through any two foot screws, centered by turning these two screws, then rotated 90° and centered again using the third screw only. This process is repeated and carefully checked to ensure that the bubble remains centered. (As with the transit and level, the bubble moves in the direction of the left thumb when the foot screws are turned.) A solid tripod setup is essential for theodolites having very sensitive bubbles, and the instrument must be shaded if set up in bright sunshine; otherwise the bubble will expand and run toward the warmer end as the instrument is heated.

PART III. FIELD OPERATIONS WITH TRANSITS AND THEODOLITES

8-16. OPERATION OF THE TRANSIT.   Horizontal angles are measured with a transit by operating the upper clamp, lower clamp, and tangent screws. The telescope clamp and tangent screw are utilized to bring the object sighted to the center of the field of view.

Beginners may find it helpful to remember the following rules covering the use of the upper and lower clamps:

1. The lower clamp is used for backsighting only.
2. The upper clamp is used for setting the plates to zero, or any desired angle, and for foresighting.

Expressed in a different way, the lower clamp and tangent screw are used to bring the line of sight along a reference line from which an angle is to be measured. The upper clamp and tangent screw are used to set 0°00′ on the plates before sighting along the reference line, and to obtain a differential movement between the plates when foresighting. The step-by-step procedure for measuring a *direct* (interior) angle *ABC* in Fig. 8-15 is outlined to illustrate operation of the upper and lower motions:

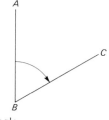

Figure 8-15. Measuring an angle.

1. Set up the instrument over point *B* and level it. Loosen both motions. Estimate the size of the angle as a check on the value to be obtained.
2. Set the plates to read approximately zero by holding the upper plate while turning the lower by tangential pressure on its underside. Tighten the upper clamp (snug but not wrench-tight). The upper and lower plates are now locked together.
3. Bring the vernier zero exactly opposite the plate zero by means of the upper tangent screw. Always use a positive (clockwise direction) turn for final setting of any tangent screw. If the zero is run beyond the point, back off and always finish with a positive motion. This prevents *backlash* (release of the spring tension, which can change the plate position).
4. Sight point *A* through the telescope. Set the vertical cross hair on, or almost on, the center line of the range pole or other object marking *A*, by turning the instrument with both hands on the plate edge or on the standards (*not* on the telescope).
5. Tighten the lower clamp. The lower plate is now fastened to the socket.
6. Set the cross hair exactly on the mark by means of the lower tangent screw, finishing with a positive motion. Both motions are now clamped together and thus to the socket, the plates read zero, and the telescope is pointing to *A*. The transit is therefore *oriented*, since the line of sight is in a known direction with the proper value (0°00′) on the plates. Read the compass bearing for line *BA*.
7. Loosen the upper clamp and turn the plate until the vertical hair is on, or almost on, point *C*. The lower plate containing the graduated circle is still clamped to the socket, and the zero graduation continues to point toward *A*. Tighten the upper clamp.
8. Set the vertical hair exactly on mark *C* by means of the upper tangent screw.
9. Read the angle on the plates, using the vernier ahead of the zero mark (in the same clockwise direction as the angle was turned). Read the compass bearing for line *BC*. Check the angle by comparing the measured value with the angle computed from the bearings.

Since the instrument setup, line clearing, objects to be sighted, and so on, are ready, little extra time is required to get a check and more reliable results by making a repeat measurement, even though a single reading may provide sufficient accuracy.

8-17. MEASURING ANGLES BY REPETITION WITH A REPEATING INSTRUMENT. If an angle is to be measured by repetition (turned two or more times), the method just described is followed for the first reading. Then, with the reading for the first angle left on the plates, a backsight is taken on A, as before, by using only the lower clamp and tangent screw to retain the angle setting. The transit is now oriented in the starting position, but the single angle value is on the plates, instead of 0°00′.

The upper clamp is loosened, point C sighted again, the upper clamp tightened, and the cross hair brought exactly on the mark with the upper tangent screw. The sum of the first two turnings of the angle is now on the plates. This process can be continued for the number of repetitions desired. A transit should be releveled if necessary after turning the angle, but the *leveling screws must not be used between the backsight and foresight* as required in differential leveling. If an even number of repetitions is taken, half should be obtained with the telescope normal, and half with the telescope plunged, to eliminate by reversion the effects of some possible inadjustments of the instrument described in Appendix A.

The total angle accumulated on the plates, divided by the number of repetitions, gives an average value. The total angle may be greater than 360°, making it requisite to add a multiple of 360° to the reading before dividing. It is always desirable, therefore, to record the approximate (single) angle after the first foresight.

It might be assumed that turning an angle 10, 50, or 100 times would give an increasingly better answer, but this supposition is not true. Experience shows that with a 1′ transit having the usual properties, an average observer can point the instrument (align the vertical wire) within about 2″ to 5″.

A 1′ vernier can be read to within 30″. An angle on the plates of, say, 42°11′29″ would theoretically be called 42°11′ by an experienced observer using a magnifying glass. If the angle on the plates is 42°11′31″, presumably a reading to the nearest minute of 42°12′ would be obtained. In either case, the recorded value would be within 30″ of the correct angle.

If the transit is in adjustment, leveled, exactly centered, and operated by an experienced observer under suitable conditions, there are only two sources of error in measuring an angle—pointing the telescope and reading the plates. For a 5″ average pointing error, and a maximum discrepency of 30″ in setting to zero and 30″ in reading a 1′ vernier scale, the number of repetitions needed to strike a balance between readings and pointings is approximately 7. Since an even number should be measured to have equal repetitions of normal and plunged sights, 6 or 8 turnings are usually made.

A general formula for computing the maximum random error can be developed from Eq. (2-7) as

$$E = \frac{1}{N}\sqrt{E_0^2 + 2NE_p^2 + E_R^2}$$ (8-1)

where E_0 is the error in setting to zero, N is the number of repetitions of the angle, E_p is the error in pointing, and E_R is the error in reading equal to one-half the least count of the vernier or reading system.

Neglecting small plate-graduation errors, using a 1' transit the maximum random error in measuring an angle by repetition, two direct and two reversed (2 D, 2 R) pointings, can be computed by noting that there are only two readings—initial and final—but eight pointings. Then, from Eq. (8-1), for zero and reading error 30", and pointing errors of 3", the maximum random error is

$$\tfrac{1}{4}\sqrt{(30)^2 + 8(3)^2 + (30)^2} = \tfrac{1}{4}(43.3) = 10.8''$$

If measured four times independently and the results averaged, the maximum random error, from Eq. (2-10), would be

$$\frac{1}{\sqrt{4}}\sqrt{(30)^2 + 2(3)^2 + (30)^2} = 21.3''$$

showing the advantage of the repetition method.

Direct angles, measured singly or by repetition, are commonly used in boundary surveys, hydrographic work, and building construction.

8-18. CLOSING THE HORIZON.   Closing the horizon is the process of measuring the angles around a point to obtain a check on their sum, which should equal 360°00'. For example, if in Fig. 8-16 only angles x and y are needed, it is desirable also to turn angle z to close the horizon at A. The method provides an easy way for a beginner to test his readings and pointings. Fig. 8-17 shows the left page of notes covering measurement of the angles

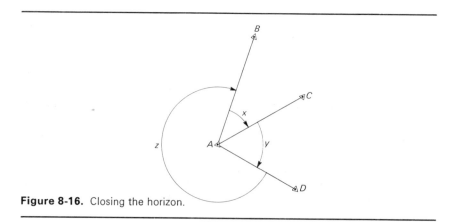

Figure 8-16. Closing the horizon.

Point Sighted	Plate Reading	Angle	Mag. Bearing	Angle Comp. from Bear.	
\multicolumn{6}{c}{CLOSING THE HORIZON}					

Point Sighted	Plate Reading	Angle	Mag. Bearing	Angle Comp. from Bear.	
\multicolumn{6}{l}{π at point A}					
B	3°26'		N22°15'E		
C	45°38'	42°12'		42°15'	
C	47°08' ~~42°08.~~		N64°30'E		
D	107°04	59°56'		60°00'	
D	110°35'		S55°30'E		
B	8°29'	257°54'		257°45'	
		360°02'			
	Closure	0°02'			

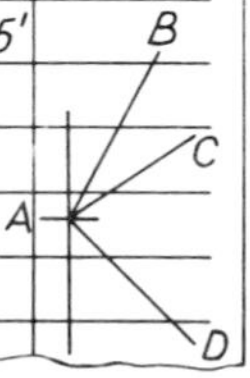

Figure 8-17. Field notes for closing the horizon.

in Fig. 8-16. The plate readings are changed slightly for each backsight to provide practice in reading the instrument, and for checking purposes.

The difference between 360° and the sum of angles x, y, and z is termed the *horizon closure*. Permissible values of this closure will determine whether the work must be repeated.

Plate A-7 shows a sample set of notes illustrating the measurement of angles by repetition to close the horizon. In this particular arrangement, the A vernier is set to read zero only at the beginning of the work and thereafter the final reading for each angle—for example, 253°13'00"—becomes the initial reading for the next angle. Both a *vernier closure* (difference between the initial and final vernier readings) and a horizon closure are obtained in this rigorous procedure.

8-19. LAYING OFF AN ANGLE WITH A REPEATING INSTRUMENT. To lay off an angle *BAC* equal to 25°30' with an instrument at point *A* (Fig. 8-18), the plates are set to zero and point *B* is sighted using the lower motion. The upper clamp is loosened, the telescope turned until the circle reads 25°30', and the upper clamp again tightened. The line of sight establishes *AC* at the proper angle with *AB*.

To lay off an angle *BAC* equal to 25°30'40" by repetition with a 1' instrument, an angle *BAC'* of 25°30' is laid out as previously described and

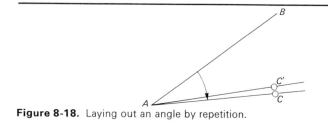

Figure 8-18. Laying out an angle by repetition.

point C' marked. The angle BAC' is then measured by repetition as many times as the desired precision requires. The difference between the angle BAC' and $25°30'40''$ can be marked off by measuring distance AC' and locating C by the following relation: distance $C'C = AC' \tan C'AC$. The angle BAC can then be turned by repetition as a check.

In Fig. 8-18, if angle BAC' is found by repetition to be $25°30'20''$, then $C'AC = 20''$. If distance AC' is 300 ft, then $C'C = 300 \tan 20'' = 300(0.00029/3) = 0.029$ ft.

8-20. DEFLECTION ANGLES. A deflection angle (described in Section 6-3) is a horizontal angle measured from the prolongation of the preceding line, right or left, to the following line. In Fig. 8-19(a), the deflection angle at F is $12°15'$ to the right ($12°15'$ R). At G the deflection angle is $16°20'$ L.

A straight line between terminal points is theoretically the most economical route to build and maintain for highways, railroads, pipelines, canals, and transmission lines. Practically, obstacles and conditions of terrain and land use require bends in the route, but deviations from a straight line are kept as small as possible. The use of deflection angles is therefore appropriate for easier visualization, sketching, and computation. Note that in the shorthand method of computing bearings from direct angles in Illustration 6-1, the letters for back bearings shown in parentheses are not needed for deflection angles, since these angles are turned from the extended line.

If an instrument is in *perfect* adjustment (which is unlikely), the deflection angle at F [Fig. 8-19(a)] is measured by setting the plates to zero and backsighting on point E with the telescope plunged (level vial above the telescope), then plunging again which puts the level vial beneath the telescope.

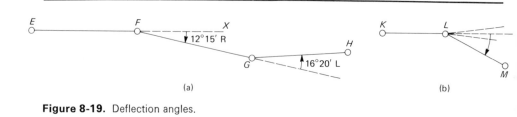

Figure 8-19. Deflection angles.

The line of sight is now on *EF* extended, and directed toward *X*. The upper clamp is loosened, point *G* sighted, the upper clamp tightened, and the vertical wire brought exactly on the mark by means of the upper tangent screw. The vernier will be under the eyepiece end of the telescope, so the observer can read the deflection angle without moving around the transit.

Deflection angles are subject to serious errors if the instrument is not in adjustment, and may be too large or too small depending upon whether the line of sight after plunging is to the right or left of the true prolongation [Fig. 8-19(b)].

To eliminate errors from this cause, angles are usually doubled or quadrupled by the following procedure: the first backsight is taken with the plates set to zero and the telescope in the normal position. After plunging, the angle is measured and kept on the plates. A second backsight is taken with the telescope plunged, the telescope transited back to the normal position for the foresight, and the angle remeasured. Dividing the total angle by two gives an average angle from which the adjustment errors have been eliminated by cancellation. In outline fashion the method is as follows:

Backsight with telescope normal. Plunge and measure angle.
Backsight with telescope plunged. Plunge again and measure angle.
Read total angle and divide by two for an average.

8-21. AZIMUTHS. Azimuths are measured from a reference direction which itself must be determined from (a) previous survey; (b) the magnetic needle; (c) a solar or star observation; or (d) assumed. Suppose that in Fig. 8-20 the azimuth of line *AB* connecting two triangulation stations is known to be 132°17′ from true north. To find the azimuth of any other line from *A*, such as *AC*, first set 132°17′ on the scale numbered in a clockwise direction and backsight on point *B*. The instrument is now oriented, since the line of sight is in a known direction with the appropriate angle on the plates. Loosen the

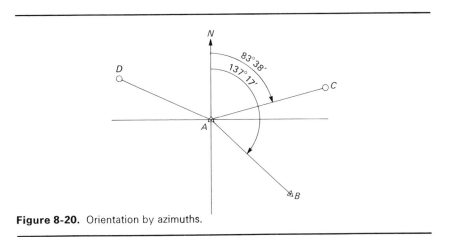

Figure 8-20. Orientation by azimuths.

AZIMUTH-TAPE TRAVERSE				
Point Occupied	Point Sighted	Distance	Azimuth	Mag. Bear.
A	Mag. N		0°00'	Due N
	B	126.24	23°32'	N 23°30'E
B	A		203°32'	S 23°30'W
	C	82.50	93°51'	S 86°15'E
C	B		273°51'	N 87°00'W
	D	122.58	137°39'	S 42°30'E
D	C		317°39'	N 43°00'W
	A	216.35	264°46'	S 84°45'W
A	D		84°46'	N 84°45'E
	B		23°34'	N 23°30'E
		Closure	0°02'	

Figure 8-21. Field notes for azimuth traverse (initial orientation on magnetic north).

upper motion and turn the telescope either clockwise or counterclockwise to C, but read the clockwise circle. In this case the reading would be, say, 83°38'.

Note that after the lower clamp and tangent screw are used to back-sight on point B, they are not disturbed regardless of the number of angles read from point A. When the plates read zero, the telescope is pointing true north. As a check, the compass needle can be lowered and read. If the telescope is pointing north, the needle should read the declination of the place (providing there is no local attraction at point A).

In Fig. 8-20, if the instrument is set up at point B instead of at A, the azimuth of BA (312°17') or back azimuth of AB is put on the plates and point A sighted. The upper plate is loosened and sights are taken on points whose azimuths from B are desired. Again, if the plates are turned to zero, the telescope points true north.

An alternative and shorter method of orienting the instrument at B if it plunges correctly is to leave the azimuth of AB (132°17') on the plates while backsighting on point A with the telescope plunged. The telescope is then transmitted to the normal position to bring the line of sight along line AB extended with its proper azimuth on the plates.

Figure 8-21 shows the left page of a sample set of notes for a traverse run by azimuths.

8-22. MEASURING WITH A DIRECTION INSTRUMENT. As noted in Section 8-14, directional theodolites can be used for determining horizontal angles, but the field procedures consist of measuring "directions" rather than angles. Directions are simply horizontal circle readings taken to successive stations sighted around the horizon. The difference in directions between any two stations is the angle.

Figure 8-22 shows a set of field notes for directions measured at station A of Fig. 8-16. The notes actually are the results of four "positions," each representing a reading at every station around the horizon with the instrument in both the direct and reversed modes.

Although there is no lower motion on a directional theodolite, the horizontal circle can be roughly indexed to selected values. To distribute readings around the entire circle, and hence minimize possible circle graduation errors, the initial sighting in the direct mode for the first position is set near 0°00′, then advanced approximately 180°/n for the first pointing of each

DIRECTIONS OBSERVED FROM STATION A

Position No. (1)	Station Sighted (2)	Reading Direct (3)	Reading Reversed (4)	Mean (5)	Reduced Direction (6)
		° ′ ″	° ′ ″	″	° ′ ″
1	B	0 00 05	180 00 04	04	0 00 00
	C	42 12 15	222 12 16	16	42 12 12
	D	102 08 33	282 08 28	30	102 08 26
2	B	45 00 03	225 00 06	04	0 00 00
	C	87 12 14 (12)	267 12 20	16	42 12 12
	D	147 08 35	327 08 28	32	102 08 28
3	B	90 00 08	270 00 05	06	0 00 00
	C	132 12 20	312 12 22	21	42 12 15
	D	192 08 28	12 08 31	30	102 08 24
4	B	135 00 07	315 00 05	06	0 00 00
	C	177 12 15	357 12 19	17	42 12 11
	D	237 08 30	57 08 34	32	102 08 26

Figure 8-22. Field notes for measuring directions.

successive position, where n is the number of positions being measured. For the field notes of Fig. 8-22, the initial readings for the four positions in the direct mode were indexed near 0°, 45°, 90°, and 135°, and the beginning readings with the telescope plunged therefore were 180°, 225°, 270°, and 315°, thus providing a uniform distribution of readings.

In the field notes of Fig. 8-22, the position number is in column 1, the station sighted in column 2, readings taken in the direct and reversed modes in columns 3 and 4, respectively, mean values of the seconds portion for the direct and reversed readings in column 5, and the reduced direction (obtained by subtracting the mean value for station B from all other mean directions) in column 6. Note at position number 2, column 6 values of 0°00′00″, 42°12′12″, and 102°08′28″ were obtained by subtracting the initial reading of 45°00′04″ from the other values in column 5 for that position.

The sets of values in column 6 should be compared for agreement and acceptance criteria before leaving the station occupied so that additional positions can be measured if necessary. Angles can be calculated from the directions, but in triangulation computations directions are often preferable.

8-23. SIGHTS AND MARKS.   Objects commonly used for sights on plane surveys include range poles, chaining pins, pencils, plumb-bob string, and tripod-mounted targets. For short sights, string is preferred to a range pole because the small diameter permits more accurate centering. Small red-and-white targets of thin-gauge metal or cardboard placed on the string extend the length of observation possible.

An error is introduced if the range pole sighted is not plumb. The observer must sight as low as possible on the pole when the mark itself is not visible, and the rodman has to take special precautions in plumbing the rod, perhaps employing a rod level or plumb bob.

In layout work on construction, and in topographic mapping, *permanent* backsights and foresights may be established. These can be marks on structures such as walls, steeples, water tanks, and bridges or can be fixed, artificial targets. They provide definite points on which the instrumentman can check his orientation without the help of a rodman.

8-24. PROLONGING A STRAIGHT LINE.   On route surveys, straight lines may be continued from one transit hub through several others. To prolong a straight line from a backsight, the vertical wire is aligned on the back point by means of the lower motion, the telescope plunged, and a point, or points, set ahead on line.

To eliminate the effects of instrument inadjustment, the same procedure used in making a number of adjustments, known as the *principle of reversion*, is employed. The method applied, actually *double reversion*, is termed *double centering*. Figure 8-23 shows a simple use of the principle in drawing a right angle with a defective triangle. Lines OX and OY are drawn with the triangle

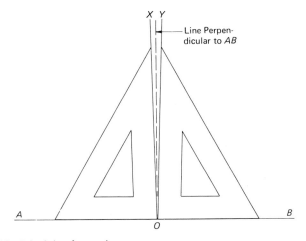

Figure 8-23. Principle of reversion.

in "normal" and "reversed" positions. Angle XOY represents twice the error in the triangle at the 90° corner, and its bisector establishes a line perpendicular to AB.

In practice, instruments should always be kept in good adjustment, but used as though they might not be.

In double centering, after the first point C' in Fig. 8-24 has been located with the telescope plunged, the lower motion is released and a second backsight taken on point A, this time with the telescope still plunged. The telescope is transited again to its normal position and point C'' marked. Distance $C'C''$ is bisected to get point C, on the line AB prolonged.

In outline form the procedure is as follows:

Backsight on point A with telescope normal. Plunge, and set point C'.
Backsight on point A with telescope plunged. Plunge to normal position, and set point C''.
Split the distance $C'C''$ to locate point C. Note that $C'C''$ represents twice the plunging error and, as described in Appendix A, four times the adjustment error.

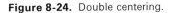

Figure 8-24. Double centering.

8-25. PROLONGING A LINE PAST AN OBSTACLE.   Buildings, trees, telephone poles, and other objects may block survey lines. Four of the various methods used for extending lines past an obstacle are the (1) equilateral-triangle method, (2) right-angle-offset method, (3) measured-offset method, and (4) equal-angle method. Short backsights can introduce and accumulate errors, so procedures using distant points should be followed.

Equilateral-triangle method. At point *B*, Fig. 8-25(a), a 120° angle is turned off from a backsight on *A*, and a distance *BC* of 80.00 ft (or any dis-

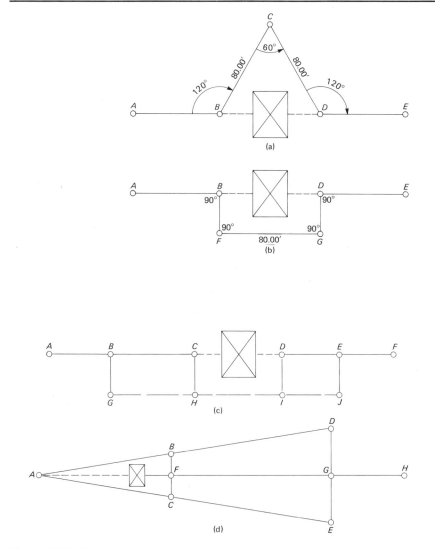

Figure 8-25. Prolonging line past an obstacle.

tance necessary, but not more than one tape length) is measured to locate point C. The transit is then moved to C; a backsight taken on B; an angle of 60°00′ put on the plates; and a distance $CD = BC = 80.00$ ft laid off to mark point D. The transit is moved to D, backsighted on C, and an angle of 120°00′ turned. The line of sight DE is now along AB prolonged if no errors have been made.

Right-angle-offset method. With transit setups at points B, F, G, and D, Fig. 8-25(b), 90°00′ angles are turned off at each hub. Distances FG, and BF, which is equal to GD, need be only large enough to clear the obstruction, but longer lengths provide more accurate sights.

The lengths shown in Figs. 25(a) and (b) permit students to check their taping and instrument manipulation by combining the two methods.

Measured-offset method. To avoid the four 90° angles with short sights and consequently possible large errors, measured offsets obtained by swinging arcs with the tape can be used [Fig. 8-25(c)]. A long base is established for check points on $GHIJ$ if desired.

Equal-angle method. This method is an excellent one when field conditions are suitable. Equal angles just large enough to clear the obstacles are turned from the line at point A, and equal distances $AB = AC$ and $AD = AE$ measured, Fig. 8-25(d). The line through points F and G at the midpoints of BC and DE, respectively, provides an extension of AH through the obstacle. Very little additional clearing is necessary using this method to bypass a large tree on line in wooded or brushy areas.

8-26. BALANCING IN.   Occasionally it is necessary to set up on a line between two points already established but not intervisible, for example, hubs A and B (Fig. 8-26). This process is called "balancing in," or "wiggling in."

Location of a point C on line is estimated and the transit set over it. A sight is taken on point A from trial point C', and the telescope plunged. If the line of sight does not pass through B, the instrument is moved laterally a distance CC' estimated from the proportion $CC' = BB' \times AC/AB$, and the process repeated. Several trials may be required to locate point C exactly, or

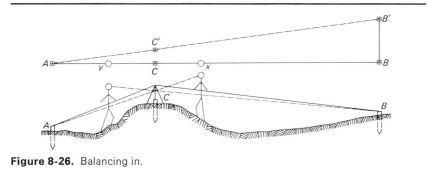

Figure 8-26. Balancing in.

close enough for the purpose at hand. The shifting head of the transit is used to make the final small adjustment.

Another method is to have two persons, X able to see hub A and Y having point B visible as shown in Fig. 8-26. Each lines the other in with the hub behind him in a series of adjustments, and two range poles are placed at least 20 ft apart on the course established. An instrument set at point C in line with the poles should be within a few tenths of a foot of the required location.

8-27. RANDOM LINE. On many surveys it is necessary to run a random line from a mark X to a nonvisible point Y, which is a known or indeterminate distance away. This problem arises repeatedly in property surveys.

On the basis of compass bearing or information from maps and other sources, a random line, such as XY' (Fig. 8-27), is run as close as possible by estimation to the true line XY. The distance XY', and the distance YY' by which the random line misses point Y, are measured and the angle YXY' found from its calculated sine or tangent. The correct line may then be run by turning off the computed angle $Y'XY$, or points on XY may be set by computed right-angle offsets from XY'.

8-28. MEASUREMENT OF A VERTICAL ANGLE. A vertical angle is the difference of direction between two intersecting lines measured in a vertical plane. As commonly used in surveying, it is the angle above or below a horizontal plane through the point of observation. Angles above the horizontal plane are called *plus angles*, or *angles of elevation*. Those below it are *minus angles*, or *angles of depression*. Vertical angles are measured in trigonometric leveling and in stadia work as an important part of the field procedure.

To measure a vertical angle with a transit, the instrument is set up over a point and carefully leveled. The bubble in the telescope level vial should remain centered when the telescope is clamped in a horizontal position and rotated 360° about its vertical axis. If the vernier on the vertical arc does not read 0°00′ when the bubble is centered, there is an *index error* which must be added to, or subtracted from, all readings. Confusion of signs is eliminated by placing in the field notes a statement such as "Index error is minus 2 min, to be subtracted from angles of depression and added to angles of elevation."

Figure 8-27. Random line.

The horizontal cross line is set approximately on the point to which a vertical angle is being measured, and the telescope clamped. Exact elevation or depression is obtained by using the telescope tangent screw. The vertical circle is read and any index error applied to get the true angle above or below the horizon. The observer calls out the uncorrected angle reading and any required adjustment is made later.

To eliminate the index error resulting from displacement of the vernier on the vertical arc, and lack of parallelism of the line of sight and telescope level vial, an average of two readings should be taken. One is secured with the telescope normal, the second with it inverted. This method requires a transit equipped with a complete vertical circle.

Measurement of vertical angles with a theodolite follows the same general procedure just described, except that the vertical circle is oriented by either an automatic compensator or an index level vial. If the latter is used, serious errors result if the index level bubble is not centered prior to reading angles. As with the transit, instrumental errors are compensated for by averaging an equal number of direct and reversed observations.

Note that a transit or theodolite can be employed as a level. The axis of sight is leveled by (1) centering the telescope bubble for a transit (although it is not as sensitive as the vial of a dumpy level) or (2) setting the vertical angle reading to exactly 90° on a theodolite. [Most theodolites read zero on the vertical circle when sighting the zenith, and 90° (or 270° in the reversed mode) when pointing horizontal.] If an index level vial is used to orient the vertical circle, the bubble must be centered before making the 90° setting.

8-29. SOURCES OF ERROR IN TRANSIT AND THEODOLITE WORK.

Errors in transit-theodolite surveys result from instrumental, natural, and personal sources. Normally it is impossible to determine the exact value of an angle, and therefore the error in its measured value. Precise results can be obtained, however, by (a) following specified procedures in the field, (b) manipulating the instrument carefully (for example, to eliminate parallax which can cause serious errors), and (c) checking measurements. Probable values of random errors and the degree of precision secured can be calculated from formulas given in Chapter 2.

INSTRUMENTAL ERRORS

Figure 8-28 shows the reference lines of a transit which are referred to in the following discussion of instrumental errors. (All of these lines also apply to theodolites with the exception of the telescope bubble axis.) For a properly adjusted transit, these reference lines must bear specific relationships to each other. If they become maladjusted, errors result in measured angles unless proper field procedures are observed. The principal sources of instrumental error follow:

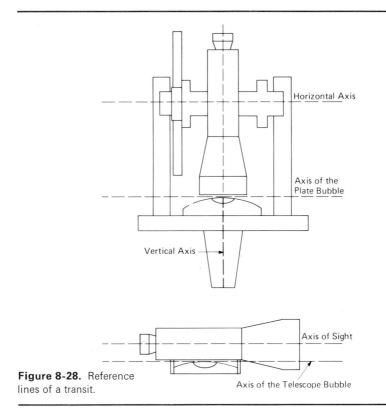

Figure 8-28. Reference lines of a transit.

1. *Plate bubbles out of adjustment.* If the axes of the plate bubbles are not perpendicular to the vertical axis, the latter will not be truly vertical when the plate bubbles are centered. This condition causes errors in measured horizontal and vertical angles, and they *cannot* be eliminated by averaging direct and reversed readings. Plate bubbles are out of adjustment, if, after centering them, they run when the instrument is rotated 180° in azimuth. The length of bubble run indicates double the tilt of the vertical axis, which is therefore made truly vertical by bringing the bubbles back *halfway* using the foot screws. With plate bubbles maladjusted, angles can be measured but it is inconvenient and time-consuming, so the required adjustment should be made. Procedures for making this and other transit and theodolite adjustments are described in Appendix A.

2. *Axis of sight not perpendicular to the horizontal axis.* If this condition exists, as the telescope is plunged the axis of sight generates a cone whose axis coincides with the horizontal axis of the instrument. The greatest error from this source occurs when plunging the telescope, as in prolonging a straight line or measuring deflection angles. Also, when the angle of inclination of the backsight is not equal to that of the foresight, measured horizontal angles will be incorrect. These errors are eliminated by double

centering, and by averaging equal numbers of direct and reversed readings.

3. *Horizontal axis not perpendicular to the vertical axis.* This situation causes the axis of sight to define an inclined plane as the telescope is plunged and, therefore, if the backsight and foresight have differing angles of inclination, fallacious horizontal angles will result. Errors from this origin can also be canceled by averaging an equal number of direct and reversed readings.

4. *Axis of the telescope bubble not parallel to the axis of sight.* For the transit, if this case exists, the axis of sight is inclined upward or downward when the telescope bubble is centered. It causes an error in vertical angles and rod readings when the transit is used as a level. The effect is eliminated in vertical angles by averaging equal numbers of direct and reversed readings, and in leveling by balancing backsight and foresight distances.

5. *Eccentricity of centers or verniers.* When the A and B transit vernier readings differ by exactly 180° for all positions, the circles are concentric and the verniers correctly set. If the readings disagree by a uniform number other than 180°, the verniers are offset and it is best to use only the A vernier, or take the mean of both verniers. If the difference is not constant, eccentricity of centers exists. Readings should be taken at several positions on the circle and the results of the A and B verniers averaged. Theodolites do not have verniers. Eccentricity of centers can be present, however, and errors from this source are minimized by taking readings at several positions on the circle so they are spaced around the entire arc and the results averaged.

Surveyors may adjust transits in the field by following the procedures outlined in Appendix A. Precise theodolites and damaged instruments, however, should be worked on by experienced craftsmen only.

NATURAL ERRORS

Wind. Wind vibrates a transit and deflects the plumb bob. Shielding the instrument, or even suspending observations on precise work, may be necessary on windy days. An optical plummet is a help in this situation.

Temperature changes. Temperature differentials cause unequal expansion of various parts of transits and theodolites. A level bubble is drawn toward the heated end of the vial as can be checked by blowing on one end of the vial and noting the movement of the bubble, then releveling and checking the position of the cross hairs on a target. Temperature effects are reduced by shielding instruments from sources of heat or cold.

Refraction. Unequal refraction bends the line of sight and may cause an apparent shimmering of the object observed. It is desirable to keep the line of sight well above the ground and avoid sights close to buildings, stacks, and even large individual bushes in generally open spaces. In some cases, observations may have to be postponed until atmospheric conditions have improved.

Settling of the tripod. The weight of an instrument may cause it to settle in soft ground. When a job involves crossing swampy terrain, stakes should be driven to support the tripod legs, and work at a given station completed as quickly as possible. Stepping near a tripod leg, or touching one while looking through the telescope, will demonstrate the effect of settlement upon the position of the bubble and cross hairs

PERSONAL ERRORS

Instrument not set up exactly over the point. The plumb bob or optical plummet position should be checked at intervals during the time a station is occupied, to be certain it remains centered, and the instrument is over the point.

Level bubbles not centered perfectly. The bubbles must be checked frequently, but NEVER releveled between a backsight and foresight—ONLY *before* starting, and *after* finishing, an angle measurement. Note that in leveling, or in measuring vertical angles with a transit, the level vials *parallel* to the telescope are the critical ones. For horizontal angles, the telescope can be elevated or depressed in the vertical plane without affecting measurements if the standards are properly adjusted. Hence the bubble *at right angles* to the telescope is the important one.

Vernier misinterpolated. Using a magnifying glass and exercising caution will help to reduce the size of these errors. Also, the number of minutes on the scale passed over by the vernier index should be estimated to check a reading.

Improper use of clamps and tangent screws. An observer must form good operational habits and be able to identify the various clamps and tangent screws by their touch without looking at them. Final setting of tangent screws is always made with a positive motion to avoid backlash. Clamps should be tightened just once and not checked again to be certain they are secure.

, *Poor focusing.* Correct focusing of the eyepiece on the cross hairs, and of the objective lens on the target, is necessary to prevent parallax. Objects sighted should be placed as near the center of the field of view as possible. Focusing affects pointing, which is an important source of error.

Overly careful sights. Checking and double checking the position of the cross-hair setting on a target is wasteful of time and actually produces poorer results than one fast observation. The cross hair should be aligned quickly and the next operation begun promptly.

Unsteady tripod. The tripod leg bolts must be tight so there is neither play nor strain (they can be tapped lightly to relieve any stress before taking the first sight), and the shoes set solidly in the ground. To eliminate strain, some surveyors loosen wing nuts and retighten after planting the legs and before leveling the instrument.

Careless plumbing and placement of the rod. One of the most common errors results from careless plumbing of a rod when only the top can be seen by the instrumentman because of brush or other obstacles in the way. Another is due to planting a pole off line behind a point to be sighted.

8-30. MISTAKES. Some common mistakes to guard against are (1) sighting on, or setting up over, the wrong point; (2) calling out or recording an incorrect value; (3) reading the wrong circle; (4) turning the wrong tangent screw; and (5) using haphazard field procedures.

PROBLEMS

Determine the angles subtended for the conditions given in problems 8–1 through 8–3.

8–1. Diameter of a 3-in. pipe sighted by theodolite from 1000 ft away.

8–2. Width of a 2-in. stake sighted by transit from 1 mile away.

8–3. A 5-mm diameter chaining pin seen by theodolite from 75 m away.

In problems 8–4 and 8–5 compute the natural sines and tangents of the angles listed using the conversion relationship for 1′ given in Section 8–2. Tabulate the answers beside exact values. If the conversion relationship is used, what are the approximate limiting sizes of angles for acceptable errors of 1, 2, 5, and 10%?

8–4. Angles of 0°10′, 0°20′, 0°45′, 1°00′, 2°00′, and 5°00′

8–5. Angles of 0°05′, 0°15′, 0°30′, 1°30′, 2°30′, and 4°00′

Problems 8–6 and 8–7 are similar to problems 8–4 and 8–5 but use the conversion relationship for 1°.

8–6. Angles of 2°, 4°, 6°, 8°, and 10°

8–7. Angles of 2°30′, 5°, 7°30′, 10°, and 15°

In problems 8–8 through 8–11 what is the error in a measured angle for the situations noted?

8–8. Setting a theodolite $1/2$ in. to the side of a tack on a 500-ft sight.

8–9. Lining in the edge (instead of center) of a 7-mm diameter pencil at 100 m.

8–10. Sighting the edge (instead of center) of a 1-in. diameter range pole 100 ft away.

8–11. Sighting a range pole that is 3 in. off line on a 1000-ft sight.

8–12. Intervening terrain obstructs the line of sight so only the top of an 8-ft range pole can be seen on a 1000-ft sight. If the range pole is out of plumb and leaning sidewise 1 in./vertical ft, what maximum angular error results?

8–13. Why are two plate level vials used on a transit instead of just one?

In problems 8–14 through 8–16 sketch a vernier and find the number of its divisions or least count.

8–14. A transit plate with 5′ spaces reading to 20″.

8–15. A transit plate divided into 1° spaces reading to 2′.

8–16. A protractor graduated to $1/2$° with 15 spaces on the vernier.

8–17. What is the purpose of loosening the wing nuts of a level or transit tripod before setting up?

8–18. Explain the procedure of leveling a theodolite having three leveling screws and a single plate bubble.

8–19. List the fundamental differences between a transit and a directional theodolite.

8–20. Explain the basic differences between repeating and directional theodolites.

8–21. What are the primary sources of error in measuring angles with a transit or theodolite, assuming it is properly leveled and centered?

8–22. Describe a method of reading angles with a transit or theodolite which will eliminate most instrumental errors caused by improper construction and poor adjustment.

8–23. Why are angles measured by repetition?

8–24. An angle is to be measured precisely with a transit. (a) What error is eliminated when both A and B verniers are read? (b) How is the error of graduations of the circle minimized? (c) What error is eliminated by measuring an angle the same number of times with the telescope normal and plunged?

8–25. In Figure 8–15, are the angles computed from bearings a reasonable check?

8–26. What are the advantages of closing the horizon around a point where only one angle is actually required?

8–27. In measuring an angle by repetition, readings after the first and second turnings in the direct position were 272°42.3′ and 185°24.9′. Readings after the third and fourth turnings in the reversed position were 98°07.6′ and 10°50.0′. Determine the angle.

8–28. Similar to problem 8–27, except that the first and second readings were 52°37.3′ and 105°14.8′, and the third and fourth readings 177°52.3′ and 230°29.9′.

8–29. An interior angle x and its explement y were turned to close the horizon. Each angle was measured once direct and once reversed using the repetition method. Starting with an initial backsight setting of 0°00′ for each angle, the readings after the first and second turning of angle x were 48°31.4′ and 97°03.0′, and the readings after the first and second turnings of angle y 311°28.7′ and 262°56.0′. Calculate each angle and the horizon closure.

8–30. Similar to problem 8–29, except that the readings for angle x were 126°43.3′ and 253°26.5′, and those for angle y 233°17.0′ and 106°33.8′.

Observed directions with a theodolite, normal and plunged from A to points B, C, and D, are listed in problems 8–31 and 8–32. Find the values of the three angles.

8–31. Normal: 37°29′21″, 103°57′44″, 267°09′27″. Plunged: 217°29′17″, 283°57′46″, and 87°09′25″.

8–32. Normal: 118°54′08″, 199°35′40″, 302°46′31″. Plunged: 298°54′07″, 19°35′43″, and 122°46′32″.

8–33. The angles at point X were measured with a 10″-theodolite, and based upon 12 readings, the standard error of the angle was 3.5″. If the same procedure is used in measuring the angles of a triangle, what is the standard error of the triangle closure?

8–34. Similar to problem 8–33, except that eight readings were taken with a standard error of 5.0″.

8–35. An angle $ABC=42°18'12''$ must be laid off with a 30'' transit. After a 400-ft backsight on point A, point C is marked 500 ft away with an angle of $42°18'$ set on the plates. Angle ABC, measured six times by repetition, gives a reading of $253°48'30''$. What offset at C will give the required angle?

8–36. Similar to problem 8–35, except that an angle of $24°40'50''$ is required and the repeated angle is $148°05'30''$.

8–37. How close to the true value should a horizontal angle be when read by repetition eight times with a 30'' transit?

8–38. Why is an assumed reference line not desirable for azimuths?

8–39. List the advantages and disadvantages of using azimuths for control traverses, property surveys, and surveys to locate topography.

8–40. The line of sight of a transit is out of adjustment by 15''. (a) In prolonging a line by plunging the telescope between the backsight and foresight, but not double centering, what angular error is introduced? (b) What linear error results on a foresight of 500 m?

A line PQ is prolonged to point R by double centering. Two foresight points R' and R'' are set. What is the angular error introduced in a single plunging based upon the following data in problems 8–41 through 8–43?

8–41. Length of QR is 745.50 ft and $R'R''$ is 0.44 ft.

8–42. Length of QR is 438.76 m and $R'R''$ is 4.5 cm.

8–43. Length of QR is 529.00 ft and $R'R''$ is $5^1/4$ in.

8–44. What is the index correction of a transit? How is its value obtained and the effect eliminated?

8–45. Describe the indexing systems used on theodolites to orient the vertical circle with respect to the direction of gravity.

8–46. With the transit telescope normal, the vertical angle to point A is $+2°28'$, and with the telescope plunged it is $+2°32'$. What is the index error? Compute the correct vertical angle to point B if the reading to it is $-4°17'$ with the telescope normal?

8–47. Similar to problem 8–46, except for readings of $-8°12'$ and $-8°06'$ on point A, and $-18°41'$ on point B.

8–48. Similar to problem 8–46, except for readings of $+0°10'$ and $+0°14'$ on point A, and $+0°22'$ on point B.

An instrument operator took a BS and a FS when the transit plumb bob was off the tack laterally. What maximum error in angle is introduced for the conditions noted in problems 8–49 through 8–51?

8–49. Plumb bob off $1/4$ in., 500-ft BS and 600-ft FS.

8–50. Plumb bob off 4 cm, 200-m BS and 350-m FS.

8–51. Plumb bob off $1/2$ in., 1000-ft BS and 200-ft FS.

8–52. Explain the difference between eccentricity and improper graduation of transit plates in their effect on measured angles.

If pointings can be made with a standard error of $\pm3''$, what is the maximum random error expected in measuring a horizontal angle by repetition for the situations given in problems 8–53 through 8–55?

8–53. 2 D and 2 R with transit reading and setting error of $\pm30''$.

8–54. 4 D and 4 R with theodolite reading and setting error of $\pm 0.1'$.

8–55. 8 D and 8 R with theodolite reading and setting error of $\pm 3''$.

8–56. What is the required number of repetitions to measure a horizontal angle to an accuracy of $10''$ with a $30''$ transit? Assume reasonable pointing and reading errors.

8–57. To reduce the effects of circle graduation errors in precise direction measurements with a directional theodolite, if eight positions are being measured, what should be the approximate circle readings for the initial sightings at each position with the telescope direct?

What error in horizontal angles is consistent with the linear precisions listed in problems 8–58 through 8–60? Check by Table B–11, Appendix B.

8–58. Linear precision: $1/200$, $1/800$, $1/1500$, $1/3000$, and $1/10,000$

8–59. Linear precision: $1/300$, $1/600$, $1/2000$, $1/5000$, and $1/15,000$

8–60. Linear precision: $1/400$, $1/1000$, $1/1800$, $1/2500$, and $1/12,000$

9
TRAVERSING

9-1. DEFINITION AND USES. A traverse is a series of consecutive lines whose lengths and directions have been determined from field measurements. *Traversing*, the act of establishing traverse stations and making the necessary measurements, is one of the most basic and widely practiced means of determining the relative locations of points.

There are two basic types of traverses: *closed* and *open*. In a closed traverse, (1) the lines either return to the starting point, thus forming a closed polygon (geometrically and mathematically closed), as shown in Fig. 9-1(a), or (2) they finish upon another station having a positional accuracy equal to or greater than that of the starting point. The second kind (geometrically open, mathematically closed), illustrated in Fig. 9-1(b), must have a closing reference direction, for example, line E-Az Mk_2. Closed traverses provide checks on the measured angles and distances, an extremely important consideration. They are used extensively in control, construction, property, and topographic surveys.

An open traverse (geometrically and mathematically open), Fig. 9-2, consists of a series of lines which are connected but do not return to the starting point or close upon a point of equal-or greater-order accuracy. Open traverses are sometimes used on route surveys, but generally should be avoided because they offer no means of checking for errors and mistakes. In open traverses, measurements *must* be repeated to guard against mistakes.

A *hub* (wooden stake with tack to mark the point) is set at each traverse station A, B, C, and so on in Figs. 9-1 and 9-2, where a change of direction occurs. The hubs are termed *angle points*, since an angle is measured at each one.

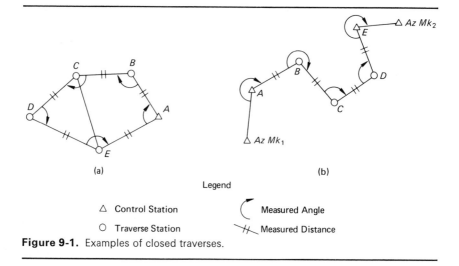

(a)   (b)

Legend

△ Control Station   (Measured Angle

○ Traverse Station   ⊬ Measured Distance

Figure 9-1. Examples of closed traverses.

9-2. METHODS OF MEASURING TRAVERSE ANGLES OR DIRECTIONS.
The methods used in measuring angles or directions of traverse lines vary, and include (a) compass bearings, (b) interior angles, (c) deflection angles, (d) angles to the right, and (e) azimuths.

9-3. TRAVERSING BY COMPASS BEARINGS.
The surveyor's compass was designed for use as a traversing instrument. Bearings are read directly on the compass as sights are taken along the lines (*courses*) of the traverse.

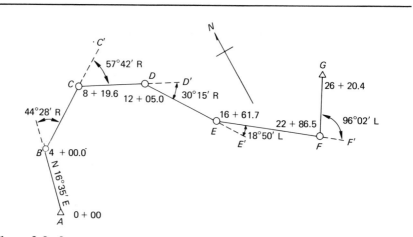

Figure 9-2. Open traverse.

Calculated bearings, rather than observed bearings, are normally used in compass traverses run with a transit. The instrument is oriented at each hub by backsighting on the previous point with the back bearing set on the plates. The angle to the foresight is then read and applied to the back bearing to get the succeeding bearing. Some older transit circles were subdivided into quadrants to permit direct reading of bearings. Calculated bearings are valuable in retracing old surveys but are more important in office computations and mapping.

9-4. TRAVERSING BY INTERIOR ANGLES. Interior angles, such as *ABC*, *BCD*, *CDE*, *DEA*, and *EAB*, Fig. 9-1(a), are used almost exclusively on property-survey traverses. They may be read either clockwise or counterclockwise, the survey party progressing around the traverse either to the right or to the left. It is good practice, however, to measure all angles clockwise. Consistently following one method prevents errors in reading, recording, and plotting. The exterior angles should be measured to close the horizon (see Section 8-18).

9-5. TRAVERSING BY DEFLECTION ANGLES. Route surveys are commonly run by deflection angles measured to the right or left from the lines extended, as indicated in Fig. 9-2. A deflection angle is not complete without a designation R or L, and of course it cannot exceed 180°. Each angle should be doubled or quadrupled to reduce instrument errors and an average value determined.

9-6. ANGLES TO THE RIGHT. Angles measured clockwise from a backsight on the previous line, Fig. 9-1(b), are called angles to the right, or azimuths from the back line. The procedure used in the method is similar to running an azimuth traverse except that the backsight is taken with the plates set to zero instead of to the back azimuth. The angles can be checked (and improved) by doubling, or roughly tested by means of compass readings. Always turning angles in the clockwise direction eliminates mix-ups in recording and plotting, and is suited to the arrangement of circle graduations on all transits and theodolites, including directional instruments.

9-7. TRAVERSING BY AZIMUTHS., Topographic surveys are often run by azimuths so that only one reference line, usually the true or magnetic north-south line, need be considered. In Fig. 9-3, azimuths are measured clockwise from the north end of the meridian through the angle points. The transit is oriented at each setup by sighting on the previous hub, one of the methods described in Section 8-21 being used.

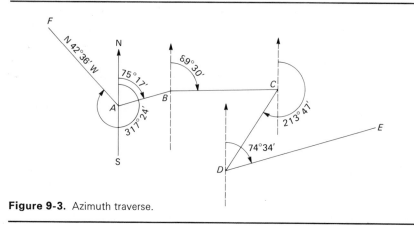

Figure 9-3. Azimuth traverse.

9-8. MEASUREMENT OF LENGTHS.

The length of each traverse line is usually obtained by the simplest and most economical method capable of satisfying the required precision on a given project. Electronic devices and taping are used most often, and provide the highest order of accuracy. When EDM is employed, the procedure is termed *electronic traversing*. For some geological and agricultural work, pacing may be accurate enough. Distances measured in both directions by stadia give control suitable for some types of work, such as low-precision topographic mapping.

The precision specified for a traverse to locate boundaries is based upon land values and survey costs. On construction work, allowable limits of closure depend upon use and extent of the traverse, and type of project. Bridge location, for example, demands a high degree of precision.

In closed traverses, each line is measured and recorded as a separate distance. On long open traverses for highways and railroads, distances are carried along continuously from the starting point. In Fig. 9-2, for example, beginning with station $0 + 00$ at point A, 100-ft stations ($1 + 00$, $2 + 00$, $3 + 00$, and $4 + 00$) are marked until hub B at station $4 + 00.0$ is reached. Then stations $5 + 00$, $6 + 00$, $7 + 00$, $8 + 00$, and $8 + 19.6$ are set along course BC to C, and so on. The length of an open-traverse line is the difference between stations of its ends, thus the length of line BC is $819.6 - 400.0 = 419.6$.

9-9. SELECTION OF TRAVERSE HUBS.

On property surveys, hubs are set at each corner if the actual boundary lines are not obstructed and can be occupied. If offset lines are necessary, a stake is set near each corner to simplify the measurements and computations. Long lines and rolling terrain may necessitate extra hubs.

On route surveys, hubs are set at each angle point and other locations where necessary to obtain topographic data or extend the survey. Usually

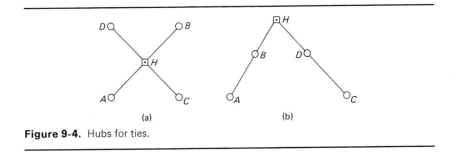

Figure 9-4. Hubs for ties.

the center line is run before construction begins, and again after it is completed. An offset traverse is necessary during the earth-moving and roadway-surfacing stages on a highway job.

A traverse run for control of topographic mapping serves as a skeleton upon which are hung such details as roads, buildings, streams, and hills. Locations of hubs must be selected to permit complete coverage of the area to be mapped. *Spurs* consisting of one or more lines may branch off as open (*stub*) traverses to reach vantage points. Their use should be discouraged, however, because a check on their positions cannot be made.

Traverse hubs, like bench marks, may be lost if not properly described and preserved. *Ties* are used to aid in finding a survey point, or to relocate one if it is destroyed. Figure 9-4(a) shows an arrangement of *straddle hubs* well suited to tying in a point on a highway or elsewhere. The traverse hub *H* may be found by intersecting strings stretched between diagonally opposite ties if the lengths are not too long. Hubs in the position illustrated by Fig. 9-4(b) are sometimes used but are not so desirable for stringing. In either configuration, the intersection of the lines of sight of two theodolites set up at *A* and *C*, and simultaneously aimed at *B* and *D*, respectively, will recover the point.

Figure 9-5 and Plate A-2 in Appendix A illustrate typical traverse ties. Short lengths (less than 100 ft) are convenient if using a steel tape, but of course the distance to definite and unique points is a controlling factor. Two ties, preferably about at right angles to each other, are sufficient, but three allow for the possibility that one reference mark may be destroyed. Ties to trees can be measured in hundredths of a foot if nails are driven into them.

Wooden and steel stakes, steel pins, pipes, and metal plates set in concrete are commonly used for hubs. Spikes, "P-K" nails, and nails driven through bottle caps are used on blacktop pavement, and chiseled or painted marks made on portland cement concrete.

9-10. ORGANIZATION OF FIELD PARTY. The type of survey and terrain determine the size of party needed. One person pacing distances can run a compass traverse alone; a transitman-notekeeper with one rodman

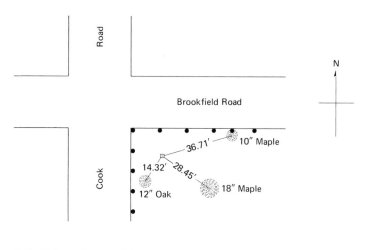

Figure 9-5. Referencing a point.

can lay out a stadia traverse; three people—an instrumentman and two tape-men who also serve as rodmen—are enough for a transit-tape survey; and a party of two is sufficient for electronic traversing. In most cases, additional personnel for notekeeping and rodding will speed the work, but the in-creased production must be balanced against greater cost of operating the crew. A head tapeman with energy and drive is more valuable than a fast instrumentman in keeping an engineering survey party moving.

On some surveys it is desirable to have a party chief who is free to move around and collect information on lines, hubs, reference marks, property-owners' names, and other items. The transitman or the head tapeman may serve as party chief, but his range of movement as chief is then limited.

In bush or wooded country, one or two axemen may be needed to open lines.

9-11. TRAVERSE NOTES. The importance of notekeeping was dis-cussed in Chapter 3. Since a traverse is the end itself on a property survey, and the basis for all other data in mapping, a single error or omission in recording is one too many. All possible field and office checks must therefore be made. Examples of field notes for interior-angle and azimuth traverses are shown in Plate A-8 and Fig. 8-19, respectively.

9-12. ANGLE CLOSURE. The closure in angle for an interior-angle traverse is the difference between the sum of the measured angles and the geometrically correct total for the polygon. The sum of the interior angles of a closed polygon is equal to

$$(n - 2)180°$$

where n is the number of sides, or angles.

This formula is easily derived from known facts. The sum of the angles in a triangle is 180°; in a rectangle, 360°; and in a pentagon, 540°. Thus each side added to the three required for a triangle increases the sum of the angles by 180°.

Figure 9-1(a) shows a five-sided figure in which, if the sum of the measured interior angles equals 540°02′, the angular closure is 2′. The permissible closure is based upon the occurrence of random errors that may increase or decrease the measured angles. It can be computed by the formula

$$c = K\sqrt{n}$$

where n is the number of angles and K is a fraction of the (a) least count of a transit vernier or (b) smallest graduation of a theodolite scale, in minutes or seconds. The fraction depends upon the number of repetitions used and the angular accuracy desired.

For ordinary transit work, a reasonable value of K is $\frac{1}{2}′$ to 1′, and the permissible closure for a pentagon 1′ to 2′.

The algebraic sum of the deflection angles in a closed-polygon traverse equals 360°, clockwise (right) deflections being considered plus and counterclockwise (left) deflections minus. This rule applies if lines do not criss-cross, or if they cross an even number of times. When lines in a traverse cross an odd number of times, the sum of right deflections equals the sum of left deflections.

If a transit is used, reading bearings aids in locating an angle turned left but mistakenly recorded to the right. Checks are available on the bearings computed from the deflection angles of an open traverse. The true direction or bearing of the first line may be determined from a sun or Polaris observation and the measured angles applied to calculate the true bearing of the last line, which may then be compared with the result obtained from another sun or Polaris shot. On long traverses, intermediate lines can be similarly checked. It is important to note the magnetic bearings for rough verification. Although they cannot be read closer than perhaps 15′, a serious mistake in an angle will be disclosed. In a closed traverse, the bearing of the first line should be recomputed, employing the last angle after progressing around the figure, as a check.

An azimuth traverse is checked by setting up on the starting point a second time after occupying the successive hubs around the traverse and orienting by back azimuths. The azimuth of the first side should be the same as the original value. Any difference is the closure. If the first point is not reoccupied, the interior angles computed from the azimuths will automatically check the proper geometric total even though one or more of the azimuths is incorrect.

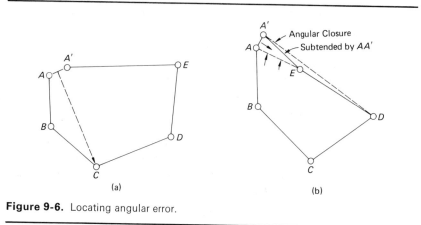

Figure 9-6. Locating angular error.

A *cutoff line*, such as *CE* in Fig. 9-1(a), run between two stations on a traverse, produces smaller closed figures to aid in checking and isolating errors.

One way to check an open traverse is to run a separate series of lines with the same or a lesser degree of precision to close the traverse. Long sights and stadia distances may be used, for example, to get a rough check.

Another check for an open traverse is to obtain the coordinates of the starting and closing points by tying in to marks of known position, thereby making it a closed traverse, and comparing the computed difference in coordinates with the actual values. Statewide coordinate systems have been devised by the National Geodetic Survey for every state (see Chapter 17), and permanent monuments have been set for the use of all surveyors. Computation of coordinates for traverse courses is discussed in Chapter 10.

A graphical analysis to determine the location of a mistake can save a lot of field time.[1] For example, if the sum of the interior angles of a five-sided traverse gives a bad closure—say, 10°03′—it is likely that one mistake of 10° and several small errors of 1′ have been made. A method of locating the station at which the mistake occurred, so that only one point need be reoccupied, will be illustrated. The procedure shown for a five-sided traverse can be used for traverses having any number of sides.

In Fig. 9-6(a) the traverse has been plotted roughly by using the measured lengths and angles but has a linear closing error *AA′*. The perpendicular bisector of line *AA′* points to the angle in error—in this case, *C*. A correction applied to this angle will swing the traverse through an arc to eliminate the linear error *AA′*.

If, as in Fig. 9-6(b), a second angle point lies near the perpendicular bisector of *AA′*, then the station at which the error has been made is the one

[1] See Dana E. Low, "Finding Angle-reading Errors in Long Traverses," *Civil Engineering*, Vol. 24 (1954), p. 738.

for which the angular closure, when plotted at that station, is subtended by AA'. Stated differently, if the angle of closure is AEA', E is the error station; if ADA', D is the error station.

If a mistake was made in one traverse line length, suspect the side parallel to the direction of the closing line.

9-13. SOURCES OF ERROR.   Some sources of error in running a traverse include:

1. Errors in measurement of angles and distances.
2. Poor selection of hubs, resulting in bad sighting conditions due to (a) alternate sun and shadow, (b) visibility of only the top of the rod, (c) line of sight passing too close to the ground, (d) lines that are too long or too short, and (e) sighting into the sun.
3. Failing to double-center, or to double deflection angles.

9-14. MISTAKES.   Some mistakes in traversing include:

1. Occupying or sighting on the wrong hub.
2. Incorrect orientation.
3. Confusing angles to the right and left.
4. Not taking extra precautions in measuring an angle having one short side (or two).

PROBLEMS

9–1. Explain the difference between closed and open traverses. Comment on the advisability of using open traverses.

9–2. Prepare a set of typical field notes for the closed interior angle traverse of Figure 9–1(a). Assume the bearing of AB is N 52°20′ W. Scale the lengths of lines, and measure the angles with a protractor.

9–3. Similar to problem 9–2, except for angles to the right in the traverse of Figure 9–1(b).

9–4. Similar to problem 9–2, except for deflection angles in the traverse of Figure 9–1(b).

9–5. Compute and tabulate bearings for the traverse of Figure 9–2, and prepare a set of field notes for the data shown.

9–6. Prepare a set of typical field notes for the closed traverse of Figure 6–2(a) using azimuths. Scale the lengths of lines, and measure the angles with a protractor.

9–7. What is the correct algebraic sum of the deflection angles, 10 R and 5 L, in a closed polygon traverse, assuming no lines criss-cross? Assuming lines criss-cross once?

9–8. If the bearings of all lines of a closed compass traverse *ABCDEFA* are given, how can the most westerly hub be readily identified without drawing a sketch ? The most northerly ?

9–9. Why is the method of placing reference hubs shown in Figure 9–4(b) generally not as good as that of Figure 9–4 (a) ?

9–10. List four pertinent considerations in selecting (a) hubs, (b) ties, and (c) stations.

9–11. What is the angular check on a closed interior angle traverse of 20 sides ? On a closed azimuth traverse of 10 sides ? On a closed azimuth traverse with a cutoff line ?

9–12. What are the two primary reasons for referencing traverse hubs ?

9–13. If the 95% error for each measurement of a traverse angle is 30″, what is the 95% error of the closure in angle for a five-sided traverse ?

9–14. If the angles of a traverse are turned so that the 90% error of any angle is 1′, prove that the 90% error of closure for a 10-sided traverse is equal to $1'\sqrt{10}$.

9–15. In running an azimuth traverse, if the plate bubbles on a transit run off center between the backsight and foresight readings, should they be recentered before taking the foresight reading ? Explain.

9–16. The true azimuth from north of a line *AB*, obtained from the coordinates of monuments at *A* and *B*, is 131 °08′. After a transit at station *A* has been oriented on this azimuth, point *C* is sighted and its azimuth found to be 165°42′. An open deflection angle traverse *ACDEFGHI* is then run, and the following angles read: *C* = 2°25′L; *D* = 8°46′L; *E* = 5°33′R; *F* = 1°16′ R; *G* = 4°50′ R; and *H* (to *I*) = 3°04′ L. The true bearing of *HI* determined by a Polaris observation is S 16°50′ E. Are the traverse angles acceptable for ordinary work ? Explain.

9–17. Similar to problem 9–16, except the azimuth of line *GH* is 166°05′ (from north).

9–18. Similar to problem 9–16, except the azimuth of line *FG* is 162°23′ (from north).

9–19. If hub *A* in problem 9–16 is at station 10 + 00 and hub *I* at station 85 + 50, what precision of linear measurements will be consistent with that of the angles ?

9–20. List a party organization suitable for "precise traversing" in hilly country using an Invar tape, a dumpy level for determining tape elevations, and a theodolite for alignment.

The recorded bearings and lengths for a traverse are listed in problems 9–21 through 9–24. If the lengths are assumed to be correct, which bearing is most likely to be wrong ?

9–21. *AB* = N 58°12′ E, 340 ft; *BC* = S 17°54′ E, 262 ft; *CD* = S 31°06′ W, 414 ft; and *DA* = N 14°48′ W, 378 ft.

9–22. *AB* = N 5°00′ E, 205 ft; *BC* = N 45°E, 150 ft; *CD* = S 40°E, 200 ft; *DA* = S 61°22′ W, 297 ft.

9–23. *AB* = N 15° W, 996 ft; *BC* = S 77°30′ W, 598 ft; *CD* = S 13°40′ E, 548 ft; *DE* = S 77°50′ W, 335 ft; *EF* = S 14°10′ E, 564 ft; and *FA* = N 60°35′ E, 956 ft.

9–24. *AB* = N 69°E, 437 ft; *BC* = S 19°E, 236 ft; *CD* = S 37°W, 244 ft; *DE* = N 71°W, 324 ft; and *EA* = N 19°W, 183 ft.

10
TRAVERSE
COMPUTATIONS

10-1. PURPOSE. Measured angles or directions of a closed traverse are readily investigated before leaving the field. Linear measurements, even though repeated, are a more likely source of error and must be checked by computations, usually in the office, to determine whether the traverse meets required precision. If specifications have been satisfied, the traverse is then adjusted to create perfect "closure" or geometric consistency among angles and lengths; if not, field measurements must be repeated until adequate results are obtained.

Investigation of precision, and acceptance or rejection of the field data, are extremely important in surveying. Adjustment for geometric closure is also crucial; in land surveying, for example, the law requires that property descriptions have exact geometric agreement.

10-2. BALANCING ANGLES. The first step in traverse calculations is to balance (adjust) the angles to the proper geometric total. This is readily done since the total error is known (see Section 9-12), although its exact distribution is not.

Angles of a closed traverse can be simply adjusted to the correct geometric total by applying one of the three following methods:

1. Arbitrary corrections to one or more angles.
2. Larger corrections to angles where poor observing conditions were present.
3. An average correction found by dividing total angle closure by the number of angles.

ILLUSTRATION 10-1. ADJUSTMENT OF ANGLES

		Method 1			Method 3		
Point	Measured Angle	Adjust-ment	Adjusted Angle	Multiples of Av. Corr.	Corr. Rounded to 30″	Succes-sive Diff.	Adjusted Angle
A	100°44′30″	30″	100°44′	18″	30″	30″	100°44′
B	101°35′	0	101°35′	36″	30″	0	101°35′
C	89°05′30″	30″	89°05′	54″	60″	30″	89°05′
D	17°12′	0	17°12′	72″	60″	0	17°12′
E	231°24′30″	30″	231°24′	90″	90″	30″	231°24′
Total	540°01′30″	90″	540°00′			90″	540°00′

Methods 1 and 3 are demonstrated in Illustration 10-1. For work of ordinary precision, it is reasonable to adopt corrections which are even multiples of (a) the least count of the transit vernier, (b) the smallest recorded digit or decimal place for theodolite readings, or (c) the smallest significant digit or decimal place when measuring angles by repetition.

If method 1 is used, corrections of 30″ may be subtracted from any three angles to give the proper geometric total for a five-sided traverse. Selection of the angles at A, C, and E simply rounds off all values to the nearest minute.

If only the top of the range pole was visible at C from the setup at B, or the angle at B has two short sides, method 2 might be used and the entire correction of 1′30″ subtracted from the angle at B. Or 1′ might be deducted from the angle at B and 30″ subtracted from another angle suspected of being slightly off because it has one short adjacent side.

Method 3 consists of subtracting 1′30″/5 = 18″ from each of the five angles. Since the angles were read in multiples of $\frac{1}{2}′$, applying corrections of 18″ gives a false impression of their precision. Therefore, it is desirable to establish a pattern of corrections, as shown on the right side of Illustration 10-1 for traverses of, say, 25 or more sides (not for a five-sided figure, which is used only as a simple illustration).

First a column consisting of multiples of the average correction of 18″ is tabulated beside the angles. In the next column, each of these multiples is rounded off to the nearest 30″. Successive differences (adjustments) are found by subtracting each value in the rounded-off column of corrections from the previous one. The adjusted angles obtained by using these adjustments must total exactly the true geometric value. The adjustments fall into a pattern form and thus distort the shape of the traverse less than when all of the closure is put into one angle.

It should be noted that although the adjusted angles satisfy the geometric condition of a closed figure, they may be no nearer the true values than before adjustment. Unlike corrections for linear measurements, *the adjustments applied to angles are independent of the size of an angle.*

10-3. COMPUTATION OF BEARINGS OR AZIMUTHS. Computation of bearings and azimuths was discussed in Chapter 6. Angles adjusted to the proper geometric total must be used; otherwise the bearing or azimuth of the first line will differ from its computed value (found by applying the successive angles around a closed traverse) by the angular closure.

10-4. LATITUDES AND DEPARTURES. Closure of a traverse is checked by computing the latitude and departure of each line (course). *The latitude of a course is its orthographic projection upon the north-south axis of the survey*, and is equal to the length of the course multiplied by the cosine of its bearing or azimuth. Latitude is also called *latitude difference*, and *northing* or *southing*.

The *departure of a course is its orthographic projection upon the east-west axis of the survey*, and is equal to the length of the course multiplied by the sine of its bearing or azimuth.

In equation form, the latitude and departure of a line are

$$\text{latitude} = L \cos \alpha \qquad\qquad (10\text{-}1)$$

$$\text{departure} = L \sin \alpha \qquad\qquad (10\text{-}2)$$

where L is the length and α is the bearing or azimuth of the course.

Departures and latitudes are merely the X and Y components of a line in the rectangular grid system, sometimes referred to as Δx and Δy. In traverse calculations, north latitudes and east departures are considered plus; south latitudes and west departures minus. For bearings, angles are always between $0°$ and $90°$; hence their cosines and sines are invariably positive. Proper algebraic signs of latitudes and departures are therefore assigned on the basis of the bearing angles' directions, so a NE bearing line has a plus latitude and departure, a SW bearing course gets a minus latitude and departure, and so on.

Azimuths used in computing latitudes and departures range from $0°$ to $360°$ and the algebraic signs of cosines and sines automatically produce proper algebraic signs of the latitudes and departures. Thus a line with an azimuth of $137°30'$ has a negative latitude and positive departure (its cosine is negative and its sine plus); a course of $323°18'$ azimuth has a positive latitude and negative departure. Electronic computers, and hand calculators with trigonometric functions, mechanically affix correct algebraic signs to latitudes and departures through those of their cosines and sines, and make azimuths convenient for traverse computations.

10-5. LATITUDE AND DEPARTURE CLOSURE CONDITIONS. In addition to the angular condition of traverse closure discussed in Section 10-2, other conditions enforced in traverse calculations are (1) the algebraic sum of all latitudes of closed polygons, Fig. 9-1(a), must equal zero [or the difference in latitude between the initial and final control points for traverses such as Fig. 9-1(b)]; and (2) the same applies to departures.

10-6. COMPUTATION OF LATITUDES AND DEPARTURES. Calculation of latitudes and departures, error of closure, and ratio of error for a closed polygon traverse will be described by an example. The interior angles of Illustration 10-1 have been used to compute the bearings shown in Fig. 10-1. Note that all bearings (which occupy more space) are lettered outside the traverse, and each length on the interior. This arrangement can be reversed, but a consistent policy should be followed. Arrows show the correct bearing directions for those courses where the bearings read from left to right but actually run from right to left.

Latitudes and departures are computed with the data and results usually inserted in a standard prepared form, arranged as shown in Illustration 10-2. The forms are printed with column headings and rulings to save time and simplify checking. Sine and cosine columns are generally omitted when computing with electronic calculators having trigonometric functions.

Latitudes and departures can be computed in a different type of prepared form similar to that shown in Illustration 10-3 (page 226). This is a combined

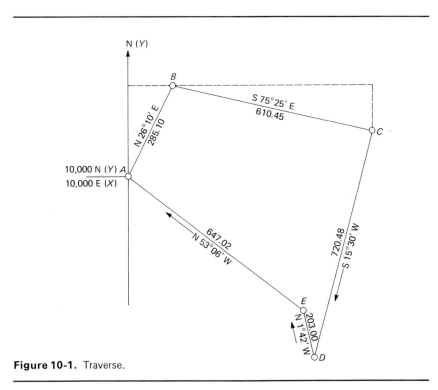

Figure 10-1. Traverse.

ILLUSTRATION 10-2. COMPUTATION OF LATITUDES AND DEPARTURES

Hub	Bearing	Length	Sine	Cosine	Departure	Latitude
A						
	N 26°10′ E	285.10	0.440984	0.897515	+125.72	+255.88
B						
	S 75°25′ E	610.45	0.967782	0.251788	+590.78	−153.70
C						
	S 15°30′ W	720.48	0.267238	0.963630	−192.54	−694.28
D						
	N 1°42′ W	203.00	0.029666	0.999560	− 6.02	+202.91
E						
	N 53°06′ W	647.02	0.799685	0.600420	−517.41	+388.48
A						
					Σ = +0.53	Σ = −0.71

table which also includes adjustment of the latitudes and departures. It is often preferred, especially when using electronic calculators.

Summing the north and south latitudes and subtracting the smaller total from the larger gives the closure in latitude, 0.71 ft, and a closure in departure of 0.53 ft. The *linear error of closure* is the hypotenuse of a small triangle with sides of 0.71 ft and 0.53 ft, and represents the distance from the starting point A to the computed point A' on the basis of the lengths and bearings used. In Illustration 10-3 the linear error of closure is 0.89 ft. The term "linear error of closure" may be shortened to *closure*, but it should not be called the error since the actual error is never known.

The *relative error of closure* (or precision) for a traverse is expressed by a fraction having the linear error of closure as the numerator, and the traverse perimeter length for the denominator, reduced to reciprocal form. For Illustration 10-3, this equals 0.89/2466 = 1/2800. The denominator is not carried beyond multiples of 100, or possibly 10. Note that random, and perhaps systematic, errors in *both* angles and distances affect the *computed* precision, so an exact answer of the actual precision is not obtained.

Various projects require different accuracies, and some surveys must rigidly meet specifications if the work is to be accepted and paid for. Relative accuracy requirements for control survey traverses are listed in Chapter 18. The required precisions for property surveys may be set by state law (for example a minimum of 1/7500 in Minnesota), and by cities and counties. A small city might decree 1/5000; a large metropolitan area 1/10,000.

10-7. METHODS FOR TRAVERSE ADJUSTMENT. For any closed traverse the linear error of closure must be distributed throughout the traverse to close the figure. This is true even though the closure is negligible in plotting

ILLUSTRATION 10-3. BALANCING LATITUDES AND DEPARTURES BY THE (BOWDITCH) COMPASS RULE

Pt.	Length	Bearing	Latitude North	Latitude South	Departure East	Departure West	Balanced Lat.	Balanced Dep.	Coordinates Y (Northing)	Coordinates X (Easting)
A									10,000.00	10,000.00
	285.10	N 26°10' E	*+0.08* 255.88		*−0.06* 125.72		N 255.96	E 125.66		
B									N 10,255.96	E 10,125.66
	610.45	S 75°25' E		*−0.18* 153.71	*−0.13* 590.78		S 153.53	E 590.65		
C									N 10,102.43	E 10,716.31
	720.48	S 15°30' W		*−0.21* 694.28		*+0.15* 192.54	S 694.07	W 192.69		
D									N 9408.36	E 10,523.62
	203.00	N 1°42' W	*+0.06* 202.91			*+0.05* 6.02	N 202.97	W 6.07		
E									N 9611.33	E 10,517.55
	647.02	N 53°06' W	*+0.18* 388.49			*+0.14* 517.41	N 388.67	W 517.55		
A									10,000.00	10,000.00
	2466.05		847.28	847.99 847.28	716.50 715.97	715.97	0.00	0.00		
				0.71	0.53					

Linear error of closure $= \sqrt{0.71^2 + 0.53^2} = 0.89$ ft

$$\text{Precision} = \frac{0.89}{2466} = \frac{1}{2800}$$

the traverse at map scale. There are five basic methods for traverse adjust-ment: (1) the arbitrary method, (2) the transit rule, (3) the compass or Bow-ditch rule, (4) the Crandall method, and (5) the method of least squares.

ARBITRARY METHOD

The arbitrary method of traverse adjustment does not conform to fixed rules or equations. Rather, the linear error of closure is distributed ar-bitrarily according to the surveyor's analysis of prevailing field conditions. For example, courses taped over rough terrain necessitating frequent plumb-ing and breaking tape will likely contain bigger errors than courses on level ground; therefore, they are given larger corrections. The total error of closure is distributed in this discretionary fashion to close the figure mathe-matically, that is, make the algebraic sum of the latitudes and the algebraic sum of the departures equal zero. This method of traverse adjustment is simple to perform and provides a logical assignment of weights based upon the expected accuracy of individual measurements.

TRANSIT RULE

The transit rule theoretically is better for surveys where the angles are measured with greater accuracy than the distances, such as stadia surveys, but it seldom is employed in practice because different results are obtained for every possible meridian. Corrections are made by the following rules:

$$\frac{\text{correction in latitude for } AB}{\text{closure in latitude}} = \frac{\text{latitude of } AB}{\text{arithmetical sum of all latitudes}} \quad (10\text{-}3)$$

$$\frac{\text{correction in departure for } AB}{\text{closure in departure}} = \frac{\text{departure of } AB}{\text{arithmetical sum of all departures}} \quad (10\text{-}4)$$

COMPASS (BOWDITCH) RULE

The compass or Bowditch rule, suitable for surveys where the angles and distances are measured with equal precision, is the rule most commonly used in practice. It is appropriate for a transit-tape survey on which angles are measured to the nearest $1'$ or $\frac{1}{2}'$ and distances taped to 0.01 ft, and for electronic traverses where distances are measured by EDM and angles by theodolite. Corrections are made by the following rules:

$$\frac{\text{correction in latitude for } AB}{\text{closure in latitude}} = \frac{\text{length of } AB}{\text{perimeter of traverse}} \quad (10\text{-}5)$$

$$\frac{\text{correction in departure for } AB}{\text{closure in departure}} = \frac{\text{length of } AB}{\text{perimeter of traverse}} \quad (10\text{-}6)$$

Application of both the transit and compass rules assumes that all lines were measured with equal care, and all angles taken with the same pre-cision. Otherwise, suitable weights must be given to individual angles or distances. Small errors of closure can be apportioned by inspection.

The compass rule will be used to distribute the closures in latitude and departure for the traverse of Fig. 10-1. The equations were given in a form easy to remember. In applying them, however, it is simpler to use the following arrangement:

$$\text{correction in latitude for } AB = \frac{\text{closure in latitude}}{\text{perimeter}} \times \text{length of } AB$$

The other corrections are likewise found by multiplying a constant—the ratio of the closure in latitude (or departure) to the perimeter—by the successive course lengths. The computations can be done mentally if the total error is small. Since the adjustments are made by an arbitrary rule, it is a waste of time to split hairs or carry values beyond the number of decimal places in the original measurements.

In Illustration 10-3 the correction in latitude for AB is

$$\frac{0.71}{2466} \times 285 = 0.08 \text{ ft}$$

and that for BC is

$$\frac{0.71}{2466} \times 610 = 0.18 \text{ ft}$$

Each correction is generally lettered in different-colored ink or pencil above the latitude or departure to which it will be applied. In Illustration 10-3, the corrections are shown in small italic numbers. In this example the adjustments are added to the north latitudes and subtracted from the south latitudes, to bring the totals of the north and south latitudes to the same corrected value.

The corrections applied to the tabular values should produce a perfect closure. In rounding off, an excess or deficiency of 0.01 ft may result, but this is eliminated by revising one of the corrections.

CRANDALL METHOD

In the Crandall method of traverse adjustment, the angular error of closure is first distributed in equal portions to all of the measured angles. The adjusted angles are then held fixed and all remaining corrections placed in the linear measurements through a weighted least-squares procedure. The Crandall method is more time-consuming than the transit and compass rule procedures but suitable for adjusting traverses where the linear measurements contain larger random errors than the angular measurements, for example, stadia traverses.

LEAST-SQUARES METHOD

The method of least squares, based upon the theory of probability, simultaneously adjusts the angular and linear measurements to make the sum of the squares of the residuals a minimum. The method is valid for any type of traverse survey regardless of the relative precision of angle and distance measurements, since each measured quantity can be assigned a relative weight. It logically provides the best possible traverse adjustment method but has not been widely used because of the lengthy computations required. Invention of the electronic computer has now made these calculations routine and consequently the least-squares method has gained popularity.

10-8. TRAVERSE COMPUTATION USING ELECTRONIC DEVICES.
Electronic calculators and computers have become commonplace in surveying computations, and a modern textbook is incomplete without some discussion of them.

As noted in Section 2-7, there are three general classifications of electronic computing devices: (1) pocket calculators, (2) programmable desk-top calculators, and (3) large-capacity computers. All are used extensively in traverse calculations.

Pocket calculators, especially those with trigonometric functions, are now almost indispensible to a modern surveyor. They have the advantage of portability, thus enabling the surveyor to make traverse computations and verify field data for closure before returning to his office.

Various programmable desk-top calculators of the type shown in Fig. 10-2 have been developed specifically for surveying work. Manufac-

Figure 10-2. 9830A Programmable desk-top calculator. (Courtesy Hewlett-Packard.)

turers supply traverse computation and other standard programs for use with their machines. These devices are capable of handling large traverses, and some can be interfaced with an accessory to plot traverses automatically at any selected scale.

Few surveying firms actually own large-capacity computers, but many have access to such facilities on a time-sharing basis for solving lengthy and tedious calculations. Programs which guide the computer can be written in some standard computer language. FORTRAN is one universal language, among others, which has been devised and used to program surveying and engineering problems. The simple FORTRAN program presented in Illustration 10-4 performs the steps in Illustration 10-3, including computations of latitudes and departures, their adjustment by the compass (Bowditch) rule, and calculation of the linear error of closure and precision. In addition, the program computes the traverse point coordinates and area within the traverse using the method of coordinates discussed further in Sections 10-10 and 11-6, respectively.

It is beyond the scope of this book to describe in detail the FORTRAN language and computer programming procedures. Interested students are advised to secure a manual on the subject, but a few brief comments will be made regarding the program of Illustration 10-4. The FORTRAN statements listed comprise the *source program*, which is the means of conveying instructions to the computer for the particular problem in a language which the computer can understand. The source program is generally read into the computer on punched cards. It cannot be overemphasized that each card must be punched perfectly.

Cards containing the traverse input information (course lengths and azimuths) are also read into the computer directly after the source program. For this purpose, the input cards are prepared as follows:

Card 1: An integer is punched, right justified in column 5, representing the number of traverses being calculated this run.

Card 2: A title card is punched to identify the first traverse. Any alpha or numeric data may be entered within columns 2–79.

Card 3: An integer is punched, right justified in column 5, representing n, the number of sides in the traverse.

Cards 4 through $(3 + n)$: For each successive traverse line, beginning from station A, punch the course length (columns 1–10), the degrees-portion of the azimuth (columns 11–15), the minutes portion of the azimuth (columns 16–20), and the seconds portion of the azimuth columns 21–30). Note that decimal points must also be punched on these cards.

Card $(4 + n)$: The X and Y coordinates of station A are punched in columns 1–10 and 11–20, respectively.

For each additional traverse in the run, repeat all above cards except No. 1. The *output* (solution results) is printed by the computer in the format

ILLUSTRATION 10-4. A FORTRAN PROGRAM FOR TRAVERSE
COMPUTATIONS (FOLLOWING ILLUSTRATION 10-3)

```
      PI=4.*ATAN(1.)
      DO 5 I=1,N
      READ 15,DIST(I),DEG(I),AMIN(I),SEC(I)
      RAD(I)=(DEG(I)+AMIN(I)/60.+SEC(I)/3600.)/(180./PI)
      SRAD(I)=SIN(RAD(I))
      CRAD(I)=COS(RAD(I))
      X(I)=DIST(I)*SRAD(I)
      Y(I)=DIST(I)*CRAD(I)
      IAZD(I)=DEG(I)
      IAZM(I)=AMIN(I)
    5 CONTINUE
      DX=0.
      DY=0.
      PER=0.
      DO 20 I=1,N
      DX=DX+X(I)
      DY=DY+Y(I)
   20 PER=PER+DIST(I)
      CLOS=SQRT(DX*DX+DY*DY)
      PREC=PER/CLOS
      IPREC=PREC
      READ 16,XCOR(1),YCOR(1)
      DO 30 I=1,N
      J=I+1
      XC(I)=X(I)-(DIST(I)*DX)/PER
      YC(I)=Y(I)-(DIST(I)*DY)/PER
      XCOR(J)=XCOR(I)+XC(I)
      YCOR(J)=YCOR(I)+YC(I)
      IF(J-N)31,31,35
   35 J=1
   31 PRINT 40,I,J,DIST(I),IAZD(I),IAZM(I),SEC(I),CRAD(I),SRAD(I),Y(I),X
     1(I),YC(I),XC(I),I,YCOR(I),XCOR(I)
   30 CONTINUE
      PRINT 28,PER,DY,DX
      AC=0.
      DO 45 I=2,N
      J=I+1
   45 AC=AC+XCOR(I)*YCOR(J)-XCOR(J)*YCOR(I)
      AC=AC+XCOR(N+1)*YCOR(2)-XCOR(2)*YCOR(N+1)
      ACRES=ABS(AC)/(2.*43560.)
      PRINT 30
      PRINT 25,CLOS
      PRINT 26,IPREC
      PRINT 50,ACRES
   60 CONTINUE
   10 FORMAT(I5)
   15 FORMAT(F10.3,2F5.0,F10.2)
   16 FORMAT(2F10.3)
   25 FORMAT(/4X,10HCLOSURE  =,F8.3,4H FT/)
   26 FORMAT(4X,19HPRECISION  =  1  IN,I7/)
   27 FORMAT(34X,51HTRAVERSE COMPUTATION AND ADJUSTMENT BY COMPASS RULE/
     1/)
   28 FORMAT(F13.3,35X,2F10.3)
   40 FORMAT(I3,2H -,I2,F11.3,I5,I3,F5.1,2F11.8,4F10.3,3H  /,I4,2F10.3)
   50 FORMAT(4X,6HAREA =,F10.3,6H ACRES)
   55 FORMAT(1H1)
   65 FORMAT(1X,13A6)
   70 FORMAT(60X,10HUNBALANCED,10X,8HBALANCED,18X,11HCOORDINATES)
   71 FORMAT(118H COURSE     LENGTH      AZIMUTH      COS        SIN
     1   LAT        DEP      LAT      DEP     STA   NORTH     EAST/)
   80 FORMAT(//)
      STOP
      END
```

ILLUSTRATION 10-5. COMPUTER OUTPUT FOR
ILLUSTRATION 10-3

COURSE	LENGTH	AZIMUTH	COS	SIN	
1 - 2	285.100	26 10	.0	.89751508	.44098377
2 - 3	610.450	104 35	.0	-.25178785	.96778245
3 - 4	720.480	195 30	.0	-.96363045	-.26723839
4 - 5	203.000	358 13	.0	.99955986	-.02966625
5 - 1	647.020	306 54	.0	.60042021	-.79968467
	2466.050				

UNBALANCED		BALANCED			COORDINATES	
LAT	DEP	LAT	DEP	STA	NORTH	EAST
255.882	125.724	255.963	125.663	/ 1	10000.000	10000.000
-153.704	590.783	-153.530	590.651	/ 2	10255.963	10125.663
-694.276	-192.540	-694.071	-192.696	/ 3	10102.433	10716.313
202.911	-6.022	202.969	-6.066	/ 4	9408.363	10523.618
388.484	-517.412	388.669	-517.552	/ 5	9611.331	10517.552
-.704	.533					

CLOSURE   =   .883 FT

PRECISION = 1   IN   2791

AREA =   6.259 ACRES

shown in Illustration 10-5. The tabulated coordinates are based on assumed values at traverse point A of $X = 10,000$ and $Y = 10,000$. Note that in the output, courses 1–2, 2–3, etc., correspond to courses A–B, and B–C, of Illustration 10-3. This computer program is general and as presently dimensioned will accommodate any closed traverse containing up to 25 sides. The only input data required are the number of sides of the traverse to be computed and the length and azimuth of each course. Computation time was less than 1 sec for the traverse of Illustration 10-5.

Traverse computation is but one example of the application of computers to surveying problems; others include reduction of stadia notes, reduction of astronomical observations, circular and parabolic curve calculations, triangulation and trilateration calculation, adjustment computations, earthwork determination, and subdivision calculations.

10-9. LATITUDES AND DEPARTURES BY TRAVERSE TABLES.
Traverse tables, compilations of the natural sines and cosines of angles multiplied by integers 1·to 10, or perhaps 1 to 100, provide a rapid method of finding latitudes and departures in the field or office by using only addition. Since the advent of electronic computing devices, traverse tables have seldom been used.

10-10. RECTANGULAR COORDINATES. Rectangular X and Y coordinates of any point give its position with respect to an arbitrarily selected pair of mutually perpendicular reference axes. The X coordinate is the perpendicular distance, in feet or meters, from the point to the Y axis; the Y coordinate is the perpendicular distance to the X axis. Although the reference axes are discretionary in position, in surveying they are normally oriented so that the Y axis points north-south, with north the positive Y direction. The X axis runs east-west, positive X being easterly. Given the rectangular coordinates of a number of points, their relative positions are uniquely defined.

Coordinates are useful in a variety of computations including (1) determining the lengths and directions of lines (see Section 10-11); (2) calculating areas of land parcels (Section 11-6); (3) making certain curve calculations (Section 22-8), and (4) locating inaccessible points. Coordinates are also advantageous for plotting traverses on base maps (Section 14-13).

In practice, *state plane coordinate* systems, as described in Chapter 17, are most frequently used as the basis for rectangular coordinates in plane surveys. For calculations, however, any arbitrary system may be used. For example, one traverse hub can be arbitrarily taken as the origin of coordinates. To avoid negative values of X and Y, an origin can be assumed south and west of the traverse such that one hub has coordinates $X = 1000$, $Y = 1000$, or any other suitable values. In a closed traverse, assigning $Y = 0$ to the most southerly point and $X = 0$ to the most westerly hub saves time in calculations.

For Fig. 10-1, if the coordinates of point A are 10,000 and 10,000, then in Illustration 10-3 the Y coordinate of B is equal to 10,000 plus the latitude of AB, and the X coordinate of B is equal to 10,000 plus the departure of AB, and so on. Note that for closed polygon traverses, if the latitude and departure of the last course are also added, the coordinates of the initial station should be produced as a check.

Reversing the process, the latitude and departure of a line AB, expressed in terms of rectangular coordinates, are

$$\text{latitude}_{AB} = Y_B - Y_A = \Delta y \tag{10-7}$$

$$\text{departure}_{AB} = X_B - X_A = \Delta x \tag{10-8}$$

where X_A, Y_A and X_B, Y_B are the rectangular coordinates of A and B, respectively.

10-11. LENGTHS AND BEARINGS FROM LATITUDES AND DEPARTURES, OR COORDINATES (INVERSION). If the latitude and departure of a line are known, its length and bearing (or azimuth) are readily obtained from the following relationships:

$$\text{tan bearing (or azimuth)} = \frac{\text{departure}}{\text{latitude}} \tag{10-9}$$

$$\text{length} = \frac{\text{departure}}{\sin \text{ bearing (or azimuth)}} \tag{10-10}$$

$$= \frac{\text{latitude}}{\cos \text{ bearing (or azimuth)}} \tag{10-11}$$

$$= \sqrt{(\text{departure})^2 + (\text{latitude})^2} \tag{10-12}$$

Substituting Eqs. (10-7) and (10-8) into Eqs. (10-9) through (10-12), there results:

$$\text{tan bearing (or azimuth) } AB = \frac{X_B - X_A}{Y_B - Y_A} = \frac{\Delta x}{\Delta y} \tag{10-13}$$

$$\text{length } AB = \frac{X_B - X_A \text{ (or } \Delta x)}{\sin \text{ bearing (or azimuth) } AB} \tag{10-14}$$

330.9'

60°38.95'

$$= \frac{Y_B - Y_A \text{ (or } \Delta y)}{\cos \text{ bearing (or azimuth) } AB} \tag{10-15}$$

$$= \sqrt{-(X_B X_A)^2 + (Y_B - Y_A)^2} \tag{10-16a}$$

or

$$= \sqrt{(\Delta x)^2 + (\Delta y)^2} \tag{10-16b}$$

The above formulas can be applied to any line whose coordinates are known, whether or not it was actually measured in the survey. For example, suppose the length and bearing of a *cutoff* (or closing) line *BE* of Fig. 10-3 and

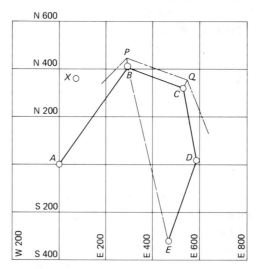

Figure 10-3. Plot of traverse.

Illustration 10-6 are required. The differences between the X and Y coordinates of hubs B and E are E 173.3 ft and S 719.2 ft, respectively. Then

$$\tan \text{bearing} = \frac{173.3}{719.2} \text{ and bearing } BE = \text{S } 13° \text{ } 33' \text{ E}$$

$$\text{length } BE = \frac{719.2}{\cos 13° \text{ } 33'} = \sqrt{173.3^2 + 719.2^2} = 739.8 \text{ ft}$$

ILLUSTRATION 10-6. COMPUTATIONS FOR A CLOSING LINE

Point	Length	Bearing	Latitude North	Latitude South	Departure East	Departure West	Coordinates Y	Coordinates X
A							0.0	0.0
	500.5	N 35°30′ E	407.5		290.6			
B							N 407.5	E 290.6
	251.6	S 70°10′ E		85.4	236.7			
C							N 322.1	E 527.3
	310.4	S 10°50′ E		304.9	58.3			
D							N 17.2	E 585.6
	350.7	S 20°18′ W		328.9		121.7		
E							S 311.7	E 463.9
							N 407.5	E 290.6
						Diff.	S 719.2	E 173.3

10-12. COORDINATE COMPUTATIONS IN BOUNDARY MEASURE-MENTS.
Computation of a bearing from the known coordinates of two points on a line is a common problem in boundary measurements. If the lengths and directions of lines from traverse points to the corners of a field are known, the coordinates of the corners can be determined and the lengths and bearings of all the sides calculated.

In Fig. 10-3, BC is a traverse line and PQ the property line which cannot be run directly because of obstructions. The measured lengths and azimuths are: for BP, 42.5 ft and 354°50′; for CQ, 34.6 ft and 26°40′. From the latitudes and departures of these lines the coordinates of P and Q are found as follows:

	Y	X		Y	X
B	N 407.5	E 290.6	C	N 322.1	E 527.3
BP	+ 42.3	− 3.8	CQ	+ 30.9	+ 15.5
P	N 449.8	E 286.8	Q	N 353.0	E 542.8

From the coordinates of P and Q, the length and bearing of line PQ are found in the following manner:

	Y	X
Q	+353.0	+542.8
P	+449.8	+286.8
PQ	S 96.8	E 256.0

$$\text{tan bearing } PQ = \frac{256.0}{96.8} \text{ and } PQ = \text{S } 69°17' \text{ E}$$

$$\text{length } PQ = \frac{256.0}{\sin 69°17'} = 273.7$$

By continuing this method around the field, coordinates of all corners and lengths and bearings of all the lines can be determined.

10-13. TRAVERSE ORIENTATION BY COORDINATES.

If the coordinates of one traverse hub, as A in Fig. 10-3, and a visible point X, are known, the direction of line AX can be computed and used to orient the transit or theodolite at A. In this way, azimuths and bearings of traverse lines are obtained without the necessity of making astronomical observations. This procedure is followed in various cities which have control monuments and coordinate systems.

State and federal mapping agencies will ultimately provide closely spaced permanent monuments whose coordinates are based upon precise control surveys. Such marks will permit the accurate location of the corners of any piece of property, either by coordinates or by lengths and true bearings.

10-14. STATE PLANE COORDINATE SYSTEMS.

Under ordinary circumstances, rectangular coordinate systems for plane surveys would be limited in size due to earth curvature. However, the National Geodetic Survey developed statewide coordinate systems for each of the United States which retain an accuracy of one part in 10,000 or better while fitting curved earth distances to plane grid lengths.

State plane coordinates are related to latitude and longitude, so control survey stations set by the NGS and others can be tied to the systems. As additional stations are set and their coordinates determined, they too become usable reference points. Ultimately, local surveys, and accurate restoration of obliterated or destroyed marks having known coordinates, will be simplified.

Some cities and counties have their own coordinate systems for use in locating street, sewer, property, and other lines. Because of their limited extent and the resultant discontinuity at city or county lines, such local systems are less desirable than a state-wide grid.

Military grids are used to pinpoint the locations of objects by coordinates for fire control and other purposes.

A more extended discussion of state plane coordinates is given in Chapter 17.

10-15. SOURCES OF ERROR IN TRAVERSE COMPUTATIONS. Some sources of error in traverse computations include:

1. Improper adjustment of angles, latitudes, and departures.
2. Carrying out corrections beyond the number of decimal places in the original measurements.
3. Poor selection of coordinate axes.

10-16. MISTAKES. Some more common mistakes in traverse computations are:

1. Failing to adjust the angles before computing bearings.
2. Applying angle adjustments in the wrong direction and failing to check the angle sum for proper geometric total.
3. Interchanging latitudes and departures, or their signs.
4. Confusing the signs of coordinates.

PROBLEMS

10–1. The sum of six interior angles of a closed traverse, each read to the nearest minute, is $719°56'$. Balance the angles by methods 1, 2, and 3, and state any assumptions made.

10–2. The closure of an eight-sided deflection-angle traverse $ABCDEFGHA$ with five left deflections and three right deflections is $+4'$. Balance the angles by methods 1, 2, and 3, and state any assumptions made.

10–3. Balance the angles in the following azimuth (from north) traverse by any method. Compute and tabulate the bearings, assuming azimuth AB is correct: $AB=163°23'$; $BC=25°32'$; $CD=55°25'$; $DE=165°41'$; $EF=86°36'$; $FA=277°09'$; and $AB=163°29'$. Explain the closure.

*10–4. Balance the following interior angles of a six-sided closed polygon traverse using method 3. If the bearing of side AB is fixed at N $85°18'$ E, calculate the bearings of the remaining sides. $A=88°10'$; $B=92°31'$; $C=100°23'$; $D=157°22'$; $E=195°35'$; and $F=86°05'$. (All angles measured to the right.)

---

* The asterisks indicate problems whose solutions are used again in problems for Chapter 11.

*10–5. Compute the latitudes and departures, linear error of closure, and precision for the traverse of problem 10–4 if lengths of the sides (in feet) are as follows: $AB=1835.01$; $BC=606.23$; $CD=460.46$; $DE=814.20$; $EF=593.65$; and $FA=628.97$.

*10–6. Using the compass (Bowditch) rule, adjust the latitudes and departures of the traverse in problem 10–5. If the coordinates of station A are $X=10,000$ and $Y=10,000$, calculate coordinates for the other stations, and then the lengths and bearings of lines AD and EB.

*10–7. Balance the following interior angles of a closed polygon traverse to the nearest 0.1′ using method 3. Compute the bearings assuming a correct bearing of S50°20.16′E for line HI. $A=126°43.3′$; $B=87°17.6′$; $C=179°30.7′$; $D=52°37.3′$; $E=311°28.4′$; $F=54°43.9′$; $G=260°38.3′$; $H=1°31.2′$; and $I=185°30.2′$. (All angles measured to the right.)

*10–8. Determine the latitudes and departures, linear error of closure, and precision for the traverse of problem 10–7 if the lengths of the sides (in feet) are as follows: $AB=299.36$; $BC=239.37$; $CD=273.73$; $DE=304.45$; $EF=906.05$; $FG=799.80$; $GH=653.90$; $HI=1091.05$; and $IA=540.58$.

*10–9. Using the compass (Bowditch) rule, adjust the latitudes and departures of the traverse in problem 10–8. If the coordinates of station H are $X=2,151,330.87$ and $Y=397,701.20$, calculate coordinates for the other stations, and from them the lengths and bearings of lines EA and BG.

*10–10. Compute and tabulate for the following traverse (a) bearings, (b) latitudes and departures, (c) linear error of closure, and (d) precision. For what type of survey is the accuracy satisfactory?

Line	Int. Angle (Right)	Bearing	Length (ft)
AB	$A=125°54′$	N 28°17′ E	542.0
BC	$B=135°00′$		846.6
CD	$C=114°27′$		845.4
DE	$D=121°52′$		1019.8
EF	$E=\ 88°59′$		1118.0
FA	$F=133°48′$		606.8

10–11. In problem 10–10, if one side and/or angle is responsible for most of the error of closure, which is it most likely to be?

10–12. Adjust the traverse of problem 10–10 using the compass (Bowditch) rule. If the coordinates of point B are 5000.0 N and 10,000.0 E, determine the coordinates of all other points. Find the length and bearing of line AE.

For the traverses given in problems 10–13 through 10–15, compute and tabulate (a) the unbalanced latitudes and departures, (b) latitudes and departures adjusted by both the compass and transit rules for comparison, (c) linear error of closure, and (d) precision (lengths are in feet).

Course	AB	BC	CD	DA
*10–13. Bearing	N 6°25′ E	N 85°10′ E	S 12°55′ W	N 70°35′ W
Length	319.0	491.2	515.7	435.0
*10–14. Bearing	N 35° E	S 55° E	S 80° W	N 55° W
Length	100.0	300.0	141.1	200.0
*10–15. Bearing	S 71°45′ E	N 22°00′ E	N 50°20′ W	S 22°02′ W
Length	295.4	778.0	308.6	891.2

10–16. Which of the traverse adjustment rules, compass or transit, swings the traverse around through a greater angle? Explain.

10–17. After adjustment of latitudes and departures by the compass (or transit) rule, does a traverse actually close? Explain.

*10–18. Compute the linear error of closure, precision, and new bearings for the sides after the latitudes and departures are balanced by the compass (Bowditch) rule in the following traverse.

Line	Length	Latitude	Departure
AB	187.01	N 58.27	W 177.70
BC	411.37	S 384.52	W 146.18
CA	459.93	N 326.41	E 324.02

Balance by the transit rule the latitudes and departures listed in problems 10–19 and 10–20. Calculate the linear error of closure, precision, and new bearings.

Line	AB	BC	CD	DA
*10–19. Latitude	N 38.11	S 79.47	S 30.44	N 71.83
Departure	E 18.35	W 173.34	W 7.70	E 162.93
*10–20. Latitude	N 323.64	N 138.27	S 315.76	S 146.35
Departure	E 58.26	W 164.06	W 180.21	E 286.14

10–21. If the coordinates of point F of Figure 9–2 are E 5000.00 and N 5000.00, determine the coordinates of point E, and the length and bearing of the line from F to E.

*10–22. Two measurements which presented unusual difficulty in the field were omitted in the survey of a closed boundary, as shown in the following field notes. Compute the missing data.

Line	Distance	Bearing	Line	Distance	Bearing
CD	814.11	N 81°16′ E	EF	339.28	S 18°16′ W
DE	721.38	S 86°36′ E	FC	——	——

*10–23. Similar to problem 10–22. Ascertain the missing field data indicated in the following field notes.

Line	Distance	Bearing	Line	Distance	Bearing
AB	309.72	N 86°41′ E	DE	178.48	——
BC	201.44	N 89°33′ E	EA	359.10	N 43°28′ W
CD	——	S 24°28′ W			

The bearings of a closed traverse are AB=N 43°10′ E; BC=N 88°45′ E; CD=S 1°05′ W; and DA=N 72°18′ W. Which course length is most likely responsible for the closure conditions given in problems 10–24 through 10–26 ? Is the course too long or too short ?

10–24. Algebraic sum of latitudes = +72.88 ft, of departures = +68.45 ft.

10–25. Algebraic sum of latitudes = −0.22 ft, of departures = −10.02 ft.

10–26. Algebraic sum of latitudes = −1.95 ft, of departures = −0.03 ft.

*10–27. Determine the lengths and bearings of the sides of a lot whose corners have the following X and Y coordinates: $A(0,0)$; $B(+125, +100)$; $C(+150, −70)$; $D(−50, −150)$.

*10–28. Compute the lengths and azimuths of the sides of a closed traverse whose corners have the following X and Y coordinates: $A(0,0)$; $B(+400, +100)$; $C(+300, +400)$; $D(+90, +470)$; $E(−60, +250)$.

10–29. Why shouldn't traverse closure precision be carried out to a reciprocal such as 1/9376.85 ?

10–30. What is the purpose of balancing the angles and latitudes and departures of a closed traverse ? After balancing latitudes and departures, will the angles close ?

10–31. In adjusting measured traverse angles, why aren't adjustments made in proportion to angle sizes ?

10–32. What uses are made of the precision of a closed traverse ?

10–33. Adjust the latitudes and departures of Illustration 10–3 if the co-ordinates of points B and C are fixed by a previous higher-order survey.

For problems 10–34 through 10–39, compute balanced latitudes and departures, linear error of closure, precision, and coordinates using the FORTRAN computer program of Illustration 10–4.

10–34. For the combined traverse data of problems 10–4 and 10–5.

10–35. For the combined traverse data of problems 10–7 and 10–8.

10–36. For the traverse data of problem 10–10.

10–37. For the traverse data of problem 10–13.

10–38. For the traverse data of problem 10–14.

10–39. For the traverse data of problem 10–15.

10–40. In searching for a record of the length and true bearing of a certain boundary line which is straight between A and B, the following notes of an old random traverse were found (survey by compass and Gunter's chain, declination 5°15′ E) :

Line	A–1	1–2	2–3	3–B
Mag. bear.	North	N 25° E	East	S 48° E
Dist. (ch)	6.20	18.52	10.49	4.10

Compute the true bearing and length of *BA*.

10–41. The interior angles of a four-sided closed travers *ABCD* were all measured by the same observer using the same equipment and procedures, except that the angles at *A* and *B* were turned four times (2 D, 2 R) and those at *C* and *D* were turned eight times (4 D, 4 R). If the mean values at *A*, *B*, *C*, and *D* were 37°28.3′, 96°20.1′, 72°43.6′, and 153°26.8′, respectively, adjust the angles for closure.

10–42. Similar to problem 10–41 except for a five-sided closed traverse with *A* and *C* turned eight times (4 D, 4 R), and the others repeated six times (3 D, 3 R) giving mean values at *A*, *B*, *C*, *D*, and *E* of 17°18.1′, 132°05.6′, 64°57.6′, 108°30.4′, and 217°06.3′, respectively.

11
AREA

11-1. GENERAL. One reason for making a property survey is to determine the tract area for inclusion with a description of the boundary lines and corners in a deed.

The most common unit of area for lots is the *square foot*; for large tracts it is the acre: 1 acre = 43,560 ft^2 = 10 ch^2 (Gunter's). An acre lot, if square, would thus be 208.71 ft on a side. In the metric system, area is given in square meters or *hectares*: 1 hectare = 10,000 m^2 = 2.471 acres.

11-2. METHODS OF MEASURING AREA. Both field and map measurements are employed to determine area. *Field measurement* methods include (1) division of the tract into simple figures (triangles, rectangles, and trapezoids), (2) offsets from a straight line, (3) double meridian distances, and (4) coordinates. The typical system of getting field data for procedures 3 or 4 is traversing with the property corners serving as hubs of a closed polygon figure. Before calculating area, the traverse is checked for closure and adjusted by one of the methods described in Section 10-7.

Map measurements are made by (1) division of the area into triangles, (2) coordinate squares, and (3) running a planimeter over the enclosing lines. Each of the processes listed will be described and illustrated in the topics which follow.

11-3. AREA BY DIVISION INTO TRIANGLES. A tract can be divided into simple geometric figures such as the triangles shown in Fig. 11-1. The

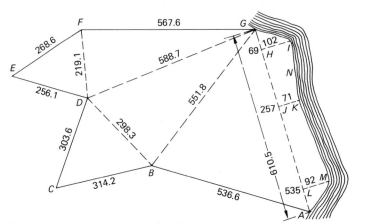

Figure 11-1. Area determination by triangles.

area of a triangle whose sides are known may be computed by the formula

$$\text{area} = \sqrt{s(s - a)(s - b)(s - c)} \qquad (11\text{-}1)$$

where a, b, and c are the sides of the triangle and

$$s = \tfrac{1}{2}(a + b + c)$$

Another formula for the area of a triangle is

$$\text{area} = \tfrac{1}{2}ab \sin C \qquad (11\text{-}2)$$

where C is the angle included between sides a and b.

The area of a field is the sum of the areas of all triangles. If Eq. (11-1) is used, each side and division line must be measured. This triangle method was used more often prior to the invention of the transit for measuring angles. Now, electronic distance measuring devices and the availability of computers make the method practical again.

11-4. AREA BY OFFSETS FROM STRAIGHT LINES.   Irregular tracts can be reduced to a series of trapezoids by right-angle offsets from points at regular intervals along a measured straight line, as indicated in Fig. 11-2.
Area is found by the formula

$$\text{area} = b\left(\frac{h_0}{2} + h_1 + h_2 + \cdots + \frac{h_n}{2}\right) \qquad (11\text{-}3)$$

where b is the length of a common interval between offsets and $h_0, h_1, \ldots h_n$ are the offsets.

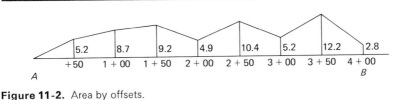

Figure 11-2. Area by offsets.

Offsets to an irregular boundary from a reference line AB are shown in Fig. 11-2. The enclosed area is

$$50\left(0 + 5.2 + 8.7 + 9.2 + 4.9 + 10.4 + 5.2 + 12.2 + \frac{2.8}{2}\right) = 2860 \text{ ft}^2$$

In the example, a summation of offsets (terms within parentheses) can be secured by the *paper strip method* in which each offset is successively added by placing tick marks on a long strip of paper. The total is then obtained by making a single measurement between the first and last tick mark.

For irregularly curved boundaries, Poncelet's rule and Francke's rule give somewhat better results more conveniently. For generally parabolic arcs, Simpson's one-third rule is applicable. Examples of the three rules are covered elsewhere.[1]

11-5. AREA BY DOUBLE-MERIDIAN-DISTANCE METHOD.

It is convenient to compute the area of a closed figure by the double-meridian-distance method when latitudes and departures of boundary lines are known. The meridian distance of a traverse course is the perpendicular distance from the center point of the course to the reference meridian. To ease the problem of signs, a reference meridian usually is placed through the most westerly traverse station.

In Fig. 11-3 the meridian distances of courses AB, BC, CD, DE, and EA are MM', PP', QQ', RR', and TT' respectively.

For the purpose of expressing PP' in terms of convenient distances, draw MF and BG perpendicular to PP'. Then

$PP' = P'F + FG + GP =$ meridian distance of AB
$\qquad\qquad\qquad\qquad + \frac{1}{2}$ departure of $AB + \frac{1}{2}$ departure of BC

Thus the meridian distance of any course of a traverse equals the meridian distance of the preceding course, plus one-half the departure of the preceding course, plus one-half the departure of the course itself. It is simpler to use full departures of courses. Therefore *double meridian distances* (DMD's) equal

[1] John C. Tracy, *Surveying Theory and Practice*. New York: John Wiley & Sons, Inc., 1947.

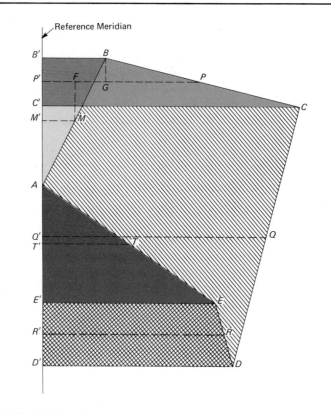

Figure 11-3. Meridian distances and traverse area computation by DMD method.

to twice the meridian distances are employed, and a single division by 2 made at the end of the computation. Based on the considerations described, the following general rule can be applied in calculating DMD's:

The DMD for any traverse course is equal to the DMD of the preceding course, plus the departure of the preceding course, plus the departure of the course itself. Signs of the departures, east plus and west minus, must be considered. When the reference meridian is taken through the most westerly station of a closed traverse and calculations of the DMD's started with a course through that station, *the DMD of the first course is its departure.* Applying these rules, for the traverse in Fig. 11-3,

   DMD of AB = departure of AB

   DMD of BC = DMD of AB + departure of AB + departure of BC

   A check on all computations is obtained if the DMD of the last course, after computing around the traverse, is also equal to its departure but of opposite sign. If there is a difference, the departures were not correctly adjusted before starting. or an error has been made in the computations.

The area enclosed by traverse $ABCDEA$ in Fig. 11-3 may be expressed in terms of the areas of trapezoids (shown with different crosshatchings) as:

$$B'BCC' + C'CDD' - (AB'B + DD'E'E + AEE') \qquad (11\text{-}4)$$

The area of each of these figures equals the meridian distance of a course times its balanced latitude. For example, the area of trapezoid $C'CDD' = Q'Q \times C'D'$, where $Q'Q$ and $C'D'$ are the meridian distance and latitude, respectively, of line CD. The DMD of a course multiplied by its latitude equals double the area. Algebraic summation of all double areas gives twice the area inside the entire traverse.

Signs of the products of DMD's and latitudes must be considered. If the reference line is passed through the most-westerly station, all DMD's are positive. The products of DMD's and north latitudes are therefore plus, and of DMD's and south latitudes minus.

To explain computational procedure, the traverse of Fig. 11-3 having the balanced departures in Illustration 11-2 will be used. Calculations of DMD's are shown in Illustration 11-1. The reference meridian is through station A.

Computations for area are generally arranged as in Illustration 11-2, although a combined form may be substituted. Individual sums of positive and negative double areas are obtained, and the absolute value of the smaller is subtracted from that of the larger. The result is divided by 2 to get the area ($272,610$ ft^2), and by $43,560$ to obtain the number of acres (6.258).

If the total of minus double areas is larger than the plus value, it signifies only that DMD's were computed by going around the traverse in a clockwise direction. If the route had been from A through E, D, C, and B and back to A,

ILLUSTRATION 11-1. COMPUTATION OF DMD's

Departure of AB = + 125.66 = DMD of AB
Departure of AB = + 125.66
Departure of BC = + 590.65

+ 841.97 = DMD of BC
Departure of BC = + 590.65
Departure of CD = − 192.69

+1239.93 = DMD of CD
Departure of CD = − 192.69
Departure of DE = −   6.07

+1041.17 = DMD of DE
Departure of DE = −   6.07
Departure of EA = − 517.55

+ 517.55 = DMD of EA Check

ILLUSTRATION 11-2. COMPUTATION OF AREA BY DMD's AND DPD's

Course	Balanced Latitude	Balanced Departure	DMD	Double Areas +	Double Areas −	DPD	Double Areas +	Double Areas −
AB	N 255.96	E 125.66	+ 125.66	32.164		+255.96	32,164	
BC	S 153.53	E 590.65	+ 841.97		129.268	+358.39	211,683	
CD	S 694.07	W 192.69	+1239.93		860.598	−489.21	94,266	
DE	N 202.97	W 6.07	+1041.17	211.326		−980.31	5,951	
EA	N 388.67	W 517.55	+ 517.55	201.156		−388.67	201,156	
Total	0.00	0.00		444,646	989.866		545,220	00
					444.646			

2)545.220

272.610 sq ft = 6.258 acres

the total plus double area would have been the greater. Areas carried out beyond the nearest square foot or 0.001 acre cannot be justified for a traverse on which distances were measured to the nearest 0.01 ft and angles read to 1′ or ½′.

As a check, the area can be computed by *double parallel distances* (DPD's).

The DPD for any traverse course is equal to the DPD of the preceding course, plus the latitude of the preceding course, plus the latitude of the course itself.

The last three columns in Illustration 11-2 show the area computation by DPD's for the traverse of Fig. 11-3. Again, signs of the latitudes, north plus and south minus, must be used in calculating DPD's.

All important engineering computations should be checked by using different methods, or by two persons who employ the same system. As an example of good practice, an individual working alone in an office could use a calculator to compute latitudes and departures and check by means of a traverse table. Or he might calculate areas by DMD's and check his results by DPD's. Experienced surveyors and engineers have learned that a half-hour spent checking computations in the field and office can eliminate later lengthy frustrations.

The area of a tract having a circular curve for one boundary, such as that in Fig. 11-4, can be found by dividing the figure into two parts: the polygon ABCDEGFA and the sector EGF. The radius R = EG = FG, and either the central angle EGF or the length EF must be known or computed to permit calculation of the area of sector EGF, which is then added to the area ABCDEGFA found by the DMD or coordinate method.

As a variation, the length and direction of EF can be calculated and the area of segment EF added to that of ABCDEFA. Note that angle XFE equals one-half of angle EGF.

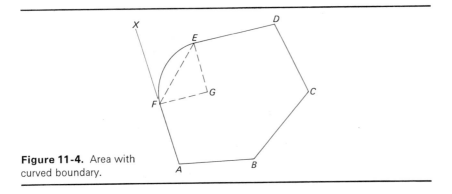

Figure 11-4. Area with curved boundary.

11-6. AREA BY COORDINATES. Computation of area from coordinates is a simple process for a closed polygon traverse with known values for each corner. The procedure can be readily developed by reference to Fig. 11-3. Since double the meridian distances $M'M$, and $P'P$ in coordinate terms are $(X_B + X_A)$, $(X_C + X_B)$, and the latitudes of lines AB and BC are $(Y_B - Y_A)$ and $(Y_C - Y_B)$, respectively, then based on the summation of trapezoidal areas, the following formula for double area can be written:

$$2(\text{area}) = (X_C + X_B)(Y_C - Y_B) + (X_D + X_C)(Y_D - Y_C)$$
$$+ (X_E + X_D)(Y_E - Y_D) + (X_A + X_E)(Y_A - Y_E)$$
$$+ (X_B + X_A)(Y_B - Y_A) \tag{11-5}$$

Equation (11-5) is equivalent to the trapezoid-area formula [Eq. (11-4)], except that the first two products are negative because $(Y_C - Y_B)$ and $(Y_D - Y_C)$ are negative, and the last three products are positive. Thus the double area resulting from Eq. (11-5) is negative but of no consequence because the absolute value is adopted. Expanding and rewriting, Eq. (11-5) is simplified to

$$2(\text{area}) = X_A Y_B + X_B Y_C + X_C Y_D + X_D Y_E + X_E Y_A - X_B Y_A - X_C Y_B$$
$$- X_D Y_C - X_E Y_D - X_A Y_E \tag{11-6}$$

Equation (11-6) can be reduced to an easily remembered form by listing the X and Y coordinates of each point in succession in two columns as shown in Eq. (11-7), with coordinates of the starting point repeated at the end. The products noted by diagonal arrows are ascertained, with solid arrows considered plus, the dashed ones minus. The algebraic summation of all products is computed and its absolute value divided by 2 to get area.

$$
\begin{array}{cc}
Y_A & X_A \\
Y_B & X_B \\
Y_C & X_C \\
Y_D & X_D \\
Y_E & X_E \\
Y_A & X_A
\end{array}
\tag{11-7}
$$

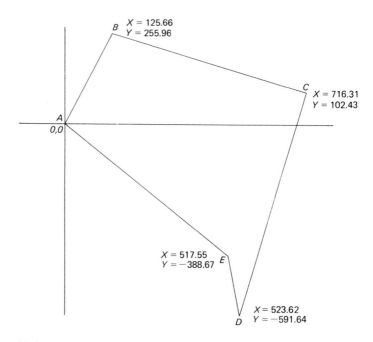

Figure 11-5. Area by coordinates.

The procedure indicated in Eq. (11-7) is applicable to calculating any size traverse. It is necessary only to consider the algebraic signs of the co-ordinates and an origin can be selected to make them all positive. Some surveyors assume $X = 0$ for the most westerly point, and $Y = 0$ for the most southerly station. Magnitudes of coordinates and products are thereby re-duced, and the amount of work lessened since four products will equal zero.

The coordinates of Illustration 11-3 (with 10,000 subtracted from each X and Y value) for the traverse of Fig. 11-5 will be used to demonstrate computation of area with point A as the origin. Illustration 11-3 shows the procedure and results. The method, readily adapted to electronic computers, is programmed in Illustration 10-4.

Another handy formula, easily derived, for calculating areas within closed polygon traverses is

$$\text{area} = \tfrac{1}{2}[X_A(Y_E - Y_B) + X_B(Y_A - Y_C) + X_C(Y_B - Y_D)$$
$$+ X_D(Y_C - Y_E) + X_E(Y_D - Y_A)] \tag{11-8}$$

11-7. AREA FROM A MAP BY TRIANGLES. A plotted traverse can be divided into triangles, the sides of each triangle scaled, and areas of the triangles found by Eq. (11-1).

ILLUSTRATION 11-3. COMPUTATION OF AREA BY COORDINATES

Point	Y	X	Double Area Plus	Double Area Minus
A	0.00	0.00		
B	+255.96	+125.66	0	0
C	+102.43	+716.31	+183,347	+ 12,871
D	−591.64	+523.62	+ 53,634	−423,798
E	−388.67	+517.55	−306,203	−203,515
A	0.00	0.00	0	0
			− 69,222	−614,442
			Subtract	− 69,222
				2) −545,220
				272,610 ft²

11-8. AREA BY COORDINATE SQUARES. To find the area within a plotted traverse by coordinate squares, the map is marked off in squares of unit area. The number of complete unit squares included in the traverse is counted and the sum of the partial units estimated. Areas of fractional units can be computed by treating them as trapezoids, but generally this refinement is not necessary.

A simpler method results from the use of transparent paper marked in squares to some scale. The paper is placed over the traverse and the number of squares and partial units counted.

A third method consists of plotting the traverse on coordinate paper and determining the number of units in the manner just described.

11-9. MEASUREMENT OF AREA BY PLANIMETER. A planimeter mechanically integrates area and records the answer on a drum and disk as a tracing point is moved over the outline of the figure to be measured.

There are two types of planimeters, mechanical and electronic. The major parts of the mechanical type are a scale bar, graduated drum and disk, vernier, tracing point and guard, and anchor arm, weight, and point. The scale bar may be fixed, or adjustable as in Fig. 11-6. For the standard fixed-arm planimeter, one revolution of the disk (dial) represents 100 in.² and one turn of the drum (wheel) represents 10 in.² The adjustable type can be set to read units of area directly for any particular map scale. The instrument touches the map at only three places—the anchor point, drum, and tracing-point guard.

An electronic planimeter, Fig. 11-7, operates similarly to the mechanical type, except that the results are given in digital form on a display console. Areas can be measured in units of square inches or square centimeters, and by setting an appropriate "scale factor" they can be obtained directly in

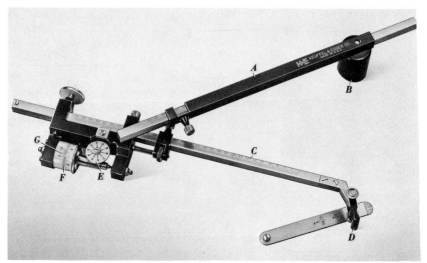

Figure 11-6. Mechanical planimeter: *A*, anchor arm; *B*, anchor point; *C*, scale bar; *D*, tracing point; *E*, disk; *F*, drum; *G*, vernier. (Courtesy of Keuffel & Esser Company.)

acres or hectares. Some instruments feature multipliers which can automatically compute and display volumes.

As an example of the use of a mechanical planimeter, suppose the area within the traverse of Fig. 11-3 is to be measured. The anchor point beneath

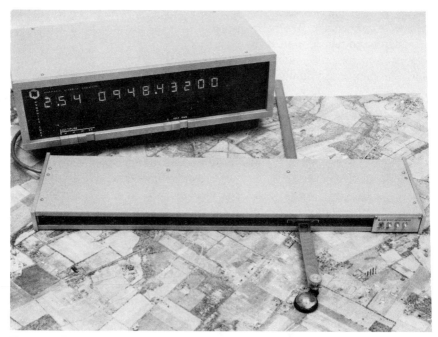

Figure 11-7. Electronic planimeter. (Courtesy Numonics Corporation.)

the weight is set in a position outside the traverse (if inside, a polar constant must be added), and the tracing point is brought over corner A. An initial reading—say, 7231—is taken, the 7 coming from the disk, 23 from the drum, and 1 from the vernier. The tracing point is moved along the traverse lines from A to B, C, D, and E and back to A. The point may be guided by a triangle or a straightedge, but normally it is steered freehand. A final reading, perhaps 8596, is made. The difference between the initial and final readings, or 1365, represents the area if the bar was set exactly to the scale of the map. Since the bar setting may not be perfect, it is best to check the planimeter constant by running over the perimeter of a carefully-laid-out square 5 in. on a side, with diagonals of 7.07 in.

Assume that the difference between the initial and final readings for the 5-in. square is 1250. Then

$$5in. \times 5in. = 25 \text{ in.}^2 = 1250 \text{ units}$$

or

$$1 \text{ unit} = {}^{25}\!/_{1250} = 0.020 \text{ in.}^2$$

and

$$1365 \text{ units} = 27.30 \text{ in.}^2$$

For a map scale of 1 in. = 100 ft, 1 in.^{2} = 10,000 ft^2 and the area measured is 273,000 ft^2.

As a check on planimeter operation, the outline may be traced in the opposite direction. The initial and final readings at point A should agree with a limit of perhaps 2 to 5 units.

The precision obtained in using the planimeter depends upon the skill of the operator, accuracy of the plotted map, type of paper, and other factors. Results correct within $\frac{1}{2}$ to 1% can be obtained by careful work.

A planimeter is most useful for irregular areas, such as that in Fig. 11-2, and has applications in many branches of engineering. Steam cutoff diagrams in mechanical engineering are readily investigated by planimetering. The planimeter has been widely used in highway offices for determining areas of cross sections, and is helpful in checking computed areas in property surveys.

11-10. SOURCES OF ERROR. Some sources of error in area computations include:

1. Poor selection of intervals and offsets to fit a given irregular boundary properly.
2. Incorrect setting of the planimeter scale bar.
3. Running off the edge of the map sheet with the planimeter drum.
4. Using different types of paper for the map and planimeter calibration sheet.
5. Not making adjustments of latitudes and departures in accordance with true conditions.
6. Using coordinate squares which are too large and therefore make estimation of areas of partial blocks difficult.

11-11. MISTAKES. In computing areas, common mistakes by students include:

1. Forgetting the division by 2 in the DMD and coordinate methods.
2. Confusing signs of DMD's coordinates, latitudes, departures, or areas.
3. Failing to check an area computation by a different method.
4. Not verifying the planimeter scale constant by tracing a known area.
5. Poor selection of the origin resulting in minus values for DMD's and coordinates.
6. Not drawing a sketch to scale or general proportion for visual checking.

PROBLEMS

11–1. Compute the area enclosed within polygon *BCDEFGB* of Fig. 11–1.

11–2. Calculate the area enclosed within polygon *BDFGAB* of Fig. 11–1.

11–3. Compute the area enclosed between line *GHJLA* and the shoreline of Fig. 11–1 using the offsets method.

11–4. Determine the area between the traverse line from station 5+42 to station 7+00 and Black Creek of Fig. 13–3 by the offsets method.

11–5. Ascertain the area between a lake and straight line from which offsets are taken at irregular intervals as follows (all distances in chains):

Offset point	A	B	C	D	E	F	G
Distance from A	0	1.05	2.61	3.82	4.67	6.38	8.50
Offset	0.53	1.28	3.11	2.85	2.27	1.69	0.28

11–6. Calculate by DMD's the area within the traverse of problem 10–13.

11–7. Compute by DMD's the area enclosed by the traverse of problem 10–14.

11–8. Calculate by DMD's the area within the traverse of problem 10–15.

11–9. Compute the area enclosed in the traverse of problem 10–13 using coordinates.

11–10. Determine the area within the traverse of problem 10–14 employing coordinates.

11–11. By the coordinate method, find the area enclosed by the traverse of problem 10–15.

11–12. Compute the area within the traverse of problem 10–22 using the DMD method. Check by DPD's.

11–13. Calculate the area inside the traverse of problem 10–23 by DMD's, and check by DPD's.

11–14. Calculate the area within the traverse of problem 10–6 using the coordinate method.

11–15. Determine the area inside the traverse of problem 10–9 by the coordinate method.

11–16. Compute the area enclosed by the traverse of problem 10–10 employing the DMD method. Check by coordinates.

11–17. Find the area within the traverse of problem 10–18 using the DMD method. Check by coordinates.

11–18. Ascertain the area of the lot of problem 10–27.

11–19. Calculate the area inside the traverse of problem 10–28.

11–20. Determine the area within the closed traverse of problem 10–19 by the DMD method. Check by DPD's.

11–21. Calculate the area enclosed by the traverse of problem 10–20 by the coordinate method. Check by DMD's.

11–22. Plot the traverse of problem 10–13 to a scale of 1 in. = 100 ft. Determine its surrounded area using a planimeter.

11–23. Similar to problem 11–22 except for the traverse of problem 10–14.

11–24. Plot the traverse of problem 10–15 to a scale of 1 in. = 200 ft and find its enclosed area by planimetering.

11–25. The latitudes and departures (in 100-ft tape lengths) for a closed polygon traverse *ABCDEFGA* follow. *AB*: N Lat. = 5, E Dep. = 5; *BC*: S Lat. = 8, W Dep. = 7; *CD*: S Lat. = 4, E Dep. = 5; *DE*: S Lat. = 6, W Dep. = 7; *EF*: N Lat. = 10, W Dep. = 2; *FG*: S Lat. = 0, W Dep. = 4. Calculate (a) the latitude and departure of line *GA*, (b) length of line *GA*, and (c) the area within the traverse in acres both by DMD's and coordinates.

11–26. Similar to problem 11–25 except that *AB* = N Lat. 6, E Dep. 10, and *DE* = S Lat. 5, W Dep. 12.

11–27. A closed polygon traverse *ABCDEFGHA* has courses with latitudes and departures (in hundreds of ft) as specified. *AB*: N Lat. = 4, E Dep. = 2; *BC*: N Lat. = 7, W Dep. = 3; *CD*: S Lat. = 2, W Dep. = 4; *DE*: S Lat. = 5, W Dep. = 5; *EF*: S Lat. = 1, E Dep. = 6; *FG*: S Lat. = 4, W Dep. = 3; *GH*: S Lat. = 2, E Dep. = 6; *HA*: N Lat. = 3, E Dep. = 1. (a) Which is the most westerly station? (b) The most southerly? (c) What are the length and bearing of the line connecting stations H and E? (d) Compute by DMD's the area enclosed in acres. (e) Check by DPD's and coordinates.

11–28. Similar to problem 11–27 except that *GH* = E Dep. 10, S Lat. 4 and *HA* = W Dep. 3, N Lat. 5.

11–29. Compute by DMD's the area in acres within a closed polygon traverse *ABCDEFA* by placing the axis through the most westerly station. Latitudes and departures (in engineer's chains) follow. *AB*: N Lat. = 5, E Dep. = 4; *BC*: N Lat. = 0, E Dep. = 6; *CD*: S Lat. = 4, E Dep. = 4; *DE*: S Lat. = 2, W Dep. = 6; *EF*: S Lat. = 5, W Dep. = 4; *FA*: N Lat. = 6; W Dep. = 4.

11–30. Similar to problem 11–29 except that *DE* = N Lat. 0, W Dep. 9, and *EF* = S Lat. 7, W Dep. 1.

11–31. For the following closed traverse (distances in Gunter's chains), (a) compute missing latitudes and departures, (b) plot the traverse by coordinates, and (c) calculate the area in acres by DMD's.

Line	Bearing	Distance	Latitude	Departure
AB	N 53°06′ E	5	+3	+4
BC	Due East	8		
CD	Due South	12	−12	
DA	N 53°06′ W	15		

Compute the area enclosed by the traverses of problems 11–32 and 11–33 selecting an axis so that there will be no negative DMD's.

11–32.

Course	AB	BC	CD	DA
Bearing	Due East	S 30°00′ W	Due West	N 45°00′ W
Length (ft)	304.9	150.0	100.0	Unknown

11–33.

Course	AB	BC	CD	DA
Bearing	N 60°00′ W	S 30°00′ W	N 60°00′ E	Unknown
Length (ft)	400.0	350.0	175.0	Unknown

11–34. Calculate the area of a piece of property bounded by a traverse and circular arc described as follows: *AB*, S 30°00′ W, 600.0 ft; *BC*, Due E, 600.0 ft; *CD*, N 45°00′ W, 300.0 ft; *DA*, a circular arc tangent to *CD* at point *D*.

11–35. Similar to problem 11–34, except that CD is 277.5 ft.

11–36. Divide the area of the lot in problem 11–34 into two equal parts by a line through point *B*. List in order the lengths and bearings of all sides for each parcel.

11–37. Partition the lot in problem 11–35 into two equal areas by means of a line parallel to *BC*. Tabulate in consecutive order clockwise the lengths and bearings of all sides.

11–38. Lot *ABCD* between two parallel street lines is 160.00 ft deep, has a 100-ft frontage (*AB*) on one street, and has a 140-ft frontage (*CD*) on the other. Interior angles at *A* and *B* are equal, as are those at *C* and *D*. What distances *AE* and *BF* should be laid off by a surveyor to divide the lot into two equal areas by means of a line *EF* parallel to *AB*?

11–39. The area of a field plotted on a map to a scale of 1 in. = 400 ft is measured with a fixed-arm planimeter, for which the constant is 10, and 4.157 revolutions of the wheel are recorded. What is the area of the field in square feet and in acres?

11–40. A planimeter tracing point, initial reading 1162, is run clockwise around the sides of a 5-in. square and gives a reading of 1287 when returned to the starting point. If the beginning reading on hub *A* of a plotted traverse is 1518, and 1883 when guided around the traverse back to *A*, compute the enclosed area in square feet.

11–41. Using the data of problem 11–40, suppose that after a planimeter reading of 1287 is obtained, a check run in the counterclockwise direction around the square brings the reading back to 1159, instead of 1162, on the first corner. What percent error does this result represent for the square? For the traverse? Is it satisfactory? What procedure is suggested?

11–42. In problem 11–25, if a tape assumed to be 100.00 ft long is found after standardization to be 100.10 ft long, how large an error in area is produced?

12
STADIA

12-1. GENERAL. The stadia method, referred to as *tacheometry* in Europe, is a rapid and efficient way to measure distances accurately enough for trigonometric leveling, some traverses, and the location of topographic details. Furthermore, a two- or three-man party can replace the three- or four-man party required in transit-tape surveys.

The term *stadia* comes from the Greek word for a unit of length originally applied in measuring distances for athletic contests; hence our modern "stadiums." The word denoted 600 of the Greek equivalent of "feet," or 606 ft 9 in. by present-day American standards.

The term "stadia" is now applied to the cross wires and rod used in making measurements, as well as to the stadia method itself. Stadia readings can be taken with transits, theodolites, alidades, and levels.

12-2. MEASUREMENT BY STADIA FOR HORIZONTAL SIGHTS.
Besides the center horizontal cross hair, a transit or theodolite reticle equipped for stadia work has two additional horizontal cross wires spaced equidistant from the center one, as illustrated in Fig. 8-7. The interval between stadia wires in most surveying instruments gives a vertical intercept of 1 ft on a rod held 100 ft away. Thus the distance to a rod decimally divided in feet, tenths, and hundredths can be read directly to the nearest foot. This is sufficiently precise for locating topographic details (such as rivers, bridges, and roads) which are to be plotted on a map having a scale smaller than 1 in. = 100 ft.

The stadia method is based upon the principle that in similar triangles corresponding sides are proportional. Thus in Fig. 12-1, which shows an

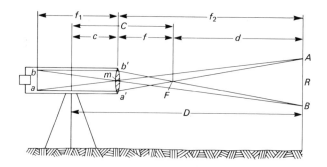

Figure 12-1. Principle of stadia: external-focusing telescope.

external-focusing telescope, light rays from points A and B passing through the center of the lens form a pair of similar triangles AmB and amb. Here $AB = R$ is the rod intercept (*stadia interval*) and ab is the interval between the stadia wires.

Standard symbols used in stadia measurements, and their definitions, are as follows:

$f = focal\ length$ of the lens (a constant for any particular compound objective lens). It can be determined by focusing upon a distant object and measuring the distance between the center (actually the *nodal point*) of the objective lens and the reticle.

f_1 = distance from the center (actually the nodal point) of the objective lens to the plane of the cross hairs when the telescope is focused on some definite point.

f_2 = distance from the center (actually the nodal point) of the objective lens to a definite point when the telescope is focused on that point. When f_2 is infinite, or very large, $f_1 = f$. (See Eq. 5-4.)

i = interval between the stadia wires (ab in Fig. 12-1).

f/i = stadia interval factor, usually 100.

c = distance from the center of the instrument (spindle) to the center of the objective lens. It varies slightly as the objective lens moves in and out for different sight lengths but is generally considered to be a constant.

$C = c + f.$ C is called the stadia constant although it varies slightly with c.

d = distance from the focal point in front of the telescope to the face of the rod.

$D = C + d =$ distance from the center of the instrument to the face of the rod.

Then from similar triangles of Fig. 12-1,

$$\frac{d}{f} = \frac{R}{i} \quad \text{or} \quad d = R\frac{f}{i}$$

and

$$D = R\left(\frac{f}{i}\right) + C \tag{12-1}$$

Fixed stadia wires in transits, theodolites, levels, and alidades are carefully spaced by instrument manufacturers to make the stadia interval factor f/i equal to 100. The stadia constant C ranges from about 0.75 to 1.25 ft for different external focusing telescopes, but is usually assumed to be equal to 1 ft. The only variable on the right side of the equation, then, is R, the rod intercept between stadia wires. In Fig. 12-1, if the intercept R is 4.27 ft, the distance from instrument to rod is $427 + 1 = 428$ ft.

An older type external-focusing telescope has been described, since a simple drawing correctly shows the relationships. The objective lens of an internal-focusing telescope remains fixed in position while a movable negative focusing lens between the objective lens and the plane of the cross wires changes the direction of the light rays. As a result, the stadia constant is so small (perhaps a few tenths of a foot) that *it can generally be assumed equal to zero.*

Disappearing stadia hairs were used in some older instruments to prevent confusion with the center horizontal hair. Modern glass reticles with short stadia lines and a full-length center line, Fig. 8-7(c), accomplish the same result more effectively.

The stadia interval factor should be determined the first time an instrument is used, although the exact value posted by the manufacturer on the inside of the carrying case will not change unless the cross hairs, reticle, or lenses are replaced. To determine the stadia interval factor, the rod interval R for a horizontal sight of known distance D is read. Then, in an alternate form of Eq. (12-1), the stadia interval factor is $f/i = (D - C)/R$. As an example, at a known distance of 300.0 ft, a rod interval of 3.01 was read. Values for f and c were measured as 0.65 and 0.45 ft, respectively; hence $C = 1.1$ ft. Then $f/i = (300.0 - 1.1)/3.01 = 99.3$. Accuracy of the determination of f/i can be increased by taking the average of values obtained from several lines whose measured lengths vary from about 100 to 500 ft by 100-ft increments.

12-3. MEASUREMENT BY STADIA FOR INCLINED SIGHTS.

Most stadia shots are inclined because of varying topography, but the intercept is read on a plumbed rod, and the slope length "reduced" to horizontal and vertical distances.

In Fig. 12-2, a transit is set over point M and the rod held at O. With the middle cross hair set on point D to make DO equal to the height of instrument EM, the vertical angle (angle of inclination) is a. Note that in

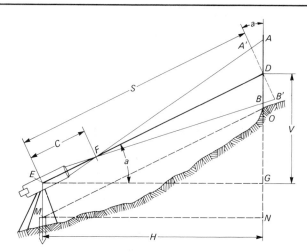

Figure 12-2. Inclined stadia measurement.

stadia work the height of instrument (h.i.) is defined as the height of the line of sight above the point occupied (*not* HI, height above the datum as in leveling).

Let S represent the slope distance ED; H, the horizontal distance $EG = MN$; and V, the vertical distance $DG = ON$. Then

$$H = S \cos a$$

and

$$V = S \sin a$$

If the rod could be held normal to the line of sight at point O, a reading $A'B'$, or R', would be obtained, making

$$S = R' \frac{f}{i} + C$$

Since it is not practical to hold the rod at an inclination angle a, it is plumbed and reading AB, or R, taken. For the small angle at D on most sights, it is sufficiently accurate to consider that angle $AA'D$ is a right angle. Therefore

$$R' = R \cos a$$

and

$$S = R \frac{f}{i} \cos a + C$$

or

$$H = R \frac{f}{i} \cos^2 a + C \cos a \tag{12-2}$$

For small angles and external focusing telescopes, $C = 1$ ft approximately, and

$$H = R \frac{f}{i} \cos^2 a + 1 \tag{12-3}$$

If $f/i = K$, then

$$H = KR \cos^2 a + 1 \tag{12-4}$$

To avoid multiplying R by $\cos^2 a$, which is a large decimal number, the formula for H can be rewritten for use in computation as

$$H = KR - KR \sin^2 a + C \tag{12-5}$$

The vertical distance is found by the formula

$$V = S \sin a = \left(R \frac{f}{i} \cos a + C \right) \sin a$$

or

$$V = R \frac{f}{i} \sin a \cos a + C \sin a \tag{12-6}$$

For small angles, sin a is very small and the quantity $C \sin a$ can be neglected. Substituting $\frac{1}{2} \sin 2a$, for sin a cos a, the formula becomes

$$V = KR(\tfrac{1}{2} \sin 2a) \tag{12-7}$$

In the final form generally used, K is taken as 100 and the formulas for reduction of inclined sights to horizontal and vertical distances are

$$H = 100R - 100R \sin^2 a + 1 \text{ (external focus)} \tag{12-8}$$

or

$$H = 100R - 100R \sin^2 a \text{ (internal focus)} \tag{12-8a}$$

and

$$V = 100R(\tfrac{1}{2} \sin 2a) \tag{12-9}$$

Tables, diagrams, special slides rules, and electronic calculators are used by surveyors to obtain quick solutions of these formulas. Table B-2, Appendix B, lists horizontal and vertical distances for a slope length of 100 ft and various vertical angles to expedite reduction of notes.

An unfamiliar table should always be investigated by substituting values in it which will give known answers. For example, angles of $5°$, $10°$, and $15°$ can be used to check tabular results. Assuming a vertical angle of $15°00'$, a rod intercept of 1.00 ft, and a stadia constant C of 1 ft, the following results are secured: by Table B-2,

$$H = 93.30 \times 1.00 + 1 = 94.3, \text{ say, } 94 \text{ ft}$$

By Eq. (12-8),

$$H = 100 \times 1.00 - 1.00 \times (0.259)^2 + 1 = 94.3, \text{ say, } 94 \text{ ft}$$

An example of a typical computation required in practice will be given. Assume that in Fig. 12-2 the elevation of M is 268.2 ft, the h.i. is $EM = 5.6$ ft, the rod intercept $AB = R = 5.28$ ft, the vertical angle a to point D at 5.6 ft on the rod is $+4°16'$, and $C = 1$ ft.

From Table B-2, for an angle of $+4°16'$ and a slope length of 100 ft, the horizontal and vertical distances are 99.45 and 7.42 ft, respectively. Then

$$H = (99.45 \times 5.28) + 1 = 525.1 + 1 = 526 \text{ ft}$$

and

$$V = (7.42 \times 5.28) + 0.08 = 39.18 + 0.08 = 39.3 \text{ ft}$$

The elevation of point O, then, is

$$268.2 + 5.6 + 39.3 - 5.6 = 307.5 \text{ ft}$$

The complete expression for determining the difference in elevation between M and O of Fig. 12-2 is

$$\text{Elev}_O - \text{Elev}_M = \text{h.i.} + V - \text{rod reading} \qquad (12\text{-}10)$$

From Eq. (12-10), the advantage of sighting on the h.i. is evident. Since the rod reading and h.i. are opposite in sign, if they are of equal magnitude they cancel each other and can be omitted from the elevation computation. If the h.i. cannot be seen because of obstructions, any rod reading can be sighted and Eq. (12-10) used, but setting the middle cross hair on a full foot mark just above or below the h.i. simplifies the arithmetic.

Determination of elevation differences by stadia can be compared with differential leveling. The h.i. corresponds to a plus sight, and the rod reading to a minus sight. On these is superimposed a vertical distance which may be either plus or minus, its sign depending upon the angle of inclination. On important sights to control points and hubs, instrumental errors should be reduced by good field procedures utilizing the principle of reversion, that is, reading vertical angles with the telescope in normal and plunged positions.

Direct rod readings with the line of sight horizontal (as in leveling), rather than vertical angles, are taken when possible to simplify the reduction of notes. Inspection of Table B-2 shows that for vertical angles less than about 4° the difference between the slope and horizontal distance is negligible except on long sights (where the distance-reading error is also greater). Hence inclining the telescope by several degrees is permissible for the stadia reading after taking a level "foresight."

12-4. STADIA RODS. Various types of markings are used on stadia rods but all have bold geometric figures designed for legibility at long distances. Most stadia rods have been graduated in feet and tenths (hundredths are interpolated), but metric ones will become common. Different colors aid in distinguishing the numbers and graduations.

One-piece, folding, and sectional rods having lengths of 10 or 12 feet are typical. Longer ones increase the sight-distance limit but are heavy and awkward to handle. Often the lower foot or two of a 12-ft rod will be obscured by weeds or brush, leaving perhaps only 10 ft visible. The maximum length of sight would then be about 1000 ft. On longer shots, the half-interval (intercept between the middle cross hair and upper or lower stadia hair) can be read and doubled for use in the standard stadia reduction equations. With a quarter-hair between the middle cross line and upper stadia hair, theoretically a distance of almost 4000 ft can be read. On short sights, ordinary leveling rods such as the Philadelphia type are satisfactory.

12-5. BEAMAN ARC.   The Beaman arc, Fig. 12-3, is a device placed on some transits and alidades to facilitate stadia computations. It may be part of the vertical circle or a separate plate. The H and V scales of the arc are graduated in percent. The V scale shows the difference of elevation per 100 ft of slope distance, whereas the H scale gives the *correction* per 100 ft to be subtracted from the stadia distance. Since V is proportional to $\frac{1}{2} \sin 2a$, and the correction for H depends upon $\sin^2 a$, spacing of the graduations decreases as the vertical angle increases. Therefore a vernier cannot be used, and an exact reading can be made only by setting the arc to read a whole number.

The indicator of the V scale is set to read 50 (or perhaps 30 on some instruments) when the telescope is horizontal to eliminate minus values. Readings greater than 50 are obtained for sights above the horizon, less than 50 below it. In Fig. 12-3 the V scale reads 80, and the H scale 10. The arithmetic required in using the Beaman arc is simplified by setting the V scale on a whole number and letting the middle cross hair fall somewhere near the h.i. The H scale generally will not then read a whole number and the value must be interpolated, but this is unimportant since the arithmetic remains simple.

The elevation of a point B sighted with the transit set up over point A is found by the following formula:

Elev. B = Elev. A + h.i. + (arc reading − 50)(rod intercept)

− rod reading of center cross hair   (12-11)

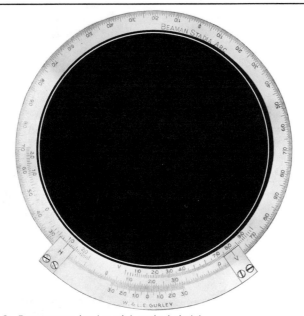

Figure 12-3. Beaman arc (and partial vertical circle).
(Courtesy W. & L. E. Gurley.)

Careful attention must be given to signs.

To illustrate the computation, assume that in Fig. 12-2 the V-scale reading is 56; H-scale reading 0.6; rod intercept 6.28 ft; h.i. = 4.2 ft; rod reading of the center wire 7.3 ft; $C = 0$; and the elevation of point M 101.5 ft. Then

$$\text{Elev. } O = 101.5 + 4.2 + (56 - 50)(6.28) - 7.3 = 136.1 \text{ ft}$$

and

$$H = (100)(6.28) - (0.6)(6.28) = 624 \text{ ft}$$

Other instruments have a similar arc called a stadia circle with the same V scale, but an H scale which gives a multiplier instead of a percent correction.

12-6. SELF-REDUCING TACHEOMETERS.

Self-reducing tacheometers, Fig. 12-4, and alidades have been developed in which curved stadia lines appear to move apart or closer together as the telescope is elevated or depressed. Actually, the lines are engraved on a glass plate which turns around a center (situated outside the telescope) as the telescope is transited.

In Fig. 12-5 the upper and lower lines (two outer lines) are curved to correspond to the variation in trigonometric function $\cos^2 a$ and are used for

Figure 12-4. Reduction tacheometer for use with vertical rod. (Courtesy Kern Instruments, Inc.)

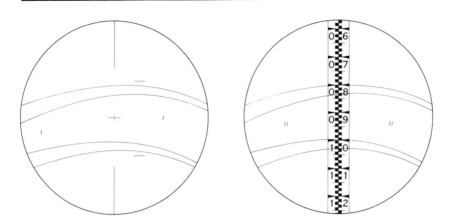

Figure 12-5. Curved stadia lines. Left: field of telescope without rod. Right: field of telescope with rod (horizontal distance = 100 × 0.227 = 22.7 m; difference in height = 20 × 0.167 = 3.30 m). (Courtesy Kern Instruments, Inc.)

distance measurements. The two inner lines are employed to determine differences in elevation and are curved to represent the function sin a cos a. A vertical line, center cross, and short stadia lines are marked on a second, but fixed, glass plate which is in focus simultaneously with the curved lines.

A constant stadia-interval factor of 100 is used for horizontal distances. A factor of 20, 50, or 100 is applied to measurements of elevation differences. Its value depends upon the angle of slope and is indicated by short lines placed between the elevation curves.

There are some other "diagram" tacheometers which basically work on the same principle in that the effect of the vertical angle is automatically compensated for by varying the stadia-hair separation. One self-reducing tacheometer utilizes a fixed horizontal line on one reticle, and another horizontal line on a movable second reticle geared to a cam that operates with changes in vertical angle. Most planetable alidades employ some type of rapid tacheometric reduction procedure.

12-7. FIELD NOTES. An example of stadia field notes is shown in Plate A-9. The transit is usually oriented by a meridional azimuth, and clockwise angles are taken to desired points.

In stadia work, many shots may be taken from one hub. *Orientation should therefore be checked by sighting on the control line after every* 10 *or* 20 *topographic points and before leaving the hub.*

As previously stated, on nearly level ground horizontal sights should be used in place of inclined ones if possible. Rod readings then become minus sights, as in profile leveling. This procedure reduces chances for mistakes and simplifies calculations.

Columns in the notes are arranged in the order of reading—point sighted, rod intercept, azimuth, and vertical angle. A sketch and pertinent data are placed on the right-hand page as usual. The numbering of topographic points begins with 1 at the first hub and continues successively through all hubs to eliminate possible duplication of numbers on any sketch. Note reduction is done in the office, unless information is needed immediately for control or plotting on a planetable sheet.

A newer method uses a tape recorder to expedite notekeeping.

12-8. FIELD PROCEDURE.   Proper field procedures save time and reduce the number of mistakes in all surveying operations. The order of taking readings best suited for *stadia work involving vertical angles* is as follows:

1. Bisect the rod with the vertical wire.
2. With the middle wire approximately on the h.i. set the lower wire at a full foot mark.
3. Read the upper wire, and subtract the reading of the lower wire from it to get the rod intercept. Record (or call out to the notekeeper) only the answer—the intercept.
4. Move the middle wire to the h.i. by using the tangent screw.
5. Release the rodman for movement to the next point by giving the proper signal.
6. Read and record the horizontal angle.
7. Read and record the vertical angle.

This procedure will enable an instrumentman to keep two or three rodmen busy in open terrain where points to be located are widely separated. The same order can be followed when the Beaman arc is used, but in step 4 the V scale is set to a whole number, and in step 7 the H- and V-scale readings are recorded.

12-9. STADIA TRAVERSES.   In a transit-stadia traverse, distances, horizontal angles, and vertical angles are measured at each point. Reduction of notes as the survey progresses provides elevations to be carried from hub to hub. Average values of stadia distances and differences in elevation are obtained from a foresight and backsight on each line. An elevation check should be secured by closing on the initial point, or nearby bench marks for an open traverse.

The horizontal angles should also be checked for closure. Any angular mis-closure should be adjusted, latitudes and departures computed, and traverse precision checked by the methods of Chapter 10.

12-10. TOPOGRAPHY.   The stadia method is most useful in locating numerous topographic details, both horizontally and vertically, by transit or planetable. In urban areas, angle and distance readings can be taken faster than a notekeeper is able to record the measurements and prepare a sketch.

Use of stadia in topographic work will be covered in more detail in the chapters on topography and the planetable.

12-11. STADIA LEVELING. The stadia method is adaptable to trigonometric leveling. The HI (height of instrument above datum) is determined by sighting on a station of known elevation, or by setting the instrument over such a point and measuring the height of the horizontal axis above it with a stadia rod. The elevation of any point can then be found by computation from the rod intercept and vertical angle. If desirable, a leveling circuit can be run to establish and check the elevations of two or more points.

12-12. PRECISION. A ratio of error of $\frac{1}{500}$ can be obtained for a transit-stadia traverse run with ordinary care. Short sights, a long traverse, and careful work may give ratios up to $\frac{1}{1000}$. Errors in stadia work are usually the result of poor rod readings rather than incorrect angles. An error of 1' in reading a vertical angle does not appreciably affect the horizontal distance. The same 1' error produces a difference in elevation of less than 0.1 ft on a 300-ft sight for any size vertical angle.

Figure 12-6 shows that if stadia distances are determined to the nearest foot (the usual case), horizontal angles *to topographic points* need be read only to within 5' or 6' for comparable precision on 300-ft sights. A stadia distance given to the nearest foot is assumed to be correct to within about $\frac{1}{2}$ ft. Allowing the same $\frac{1}{2}$-ft error laterally, the direction can be off about 5' (readily computed from sin 1' = 0.00029). If an American transit is used, angles therefore can be read without using the vernier merely by estimating the position of the vernier index.

Accuracy of trigonometric leveling by stadia depends upon the lengths of sights and size of the vertical angles required.

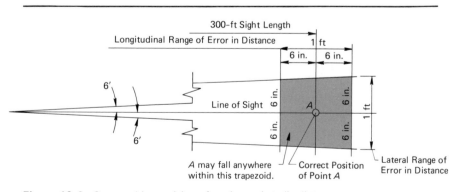

Figure 12-6. Comparable precision of angles and stadia distances.

12-13. SOURCES OF ERROR IN STADIA WORK.   Errors which occur in transit and theodolite operations are inherent in stadia work, too. Additional sources include the following:

Instrumental errors:
1. Improper spacing of the stadia wires.
2. Index error.
3. Incorrect length of rod graduations.
4. Axis of sight not parallel with the axis of the telescope bubble.

Personal errors:
1. Rod not held plumb.
2. Incorrect rod readings resulting from long sights.
3. Careless leveling for vertical-arc readings.

Most errors in stadia work can be eliminated by (a) careful manipulation of the instrument, (b) limiting the length of sights, (c) using a good rod and rod level, and (d) averaging readings in the forward and backward directions. Line-of-sight error cannot be corrected by field procedures—the instrument must be adjusted.

12-14. MISTAKES.   Some typical mistakes in stadia work are:

1. Index error applied with wrong sign.
2. Confusion of plus and minus vertical angles.
3. Arithmetic mistakes in computing the rod intercept.
4. Use of incorrect stadia interval factor.
5. Waving the rod. (The rod must always be held plumb. On inclined sights, waving produces readings on a tilted position.)

PROBLEMS

12–1. What is the advantage of using a transit as a level whenever possible in stadia operations?

12–2. When would a stadia interval factor of 1 : 132 be practical?

12–3. An external-focusing telescope has a focal length of 9 in. What error in spacing the stadia lines will raise the interval factor from 100.00 to 100.40?

12–4. On stadia measurements, why is it advisable to keep the line of sight through the lower crossline several feet above any intervening ground?

12–5. Explain why the stadia "constant" is almost zero in an internal-focusing telescope.

12–6. Why is it more difficult to obtain good elevation closures than satisfactory distance closures in transit-stadia surveying?

12–7. What assumption made in the stadia formula for inclined sights simplifies it?

12–8. Upon what principle is the stadia method based?

12–9. Why is it important in stadia work to have the line of sight of a transit or theodolite parallel with the telescope bubble axis?

12–10. Is the subtense bar method actually stadia in a horizontal plane? Explain.

12–11. What check should be made at intervals when many azimuths and distances are taken at one hub in a topographic survey?

12–12. Tally the advantages of the Beaman stadia arc in reading distances and elevation differences.

12–13. Is different-colored paint desirable for stadia rods used in varied field conditions?

Compute the stadia distances in problems 12–14 through 12–16.

12–14. Horizontal sight, rod intercept 4.62 ft, $K = 101.5$, $C = 1.0$ ft.

12–15. Horizontal sight, rod intercept 3.73 ft, $K = 99.2$, $C = 0.9$ ft.

12–16. Horizontal sight, rod intercept 2.41 m, $K = 98.4$, $C = 0.0$.

Compute the horizontal distance and difference in elevation for the data given in problems 12–17 through 12–20.

12–17. Rod intercept $= 2.12$ ft, $a = +3°16'$, $K = 100.0$, $C = 1.0$ ft.

12–18. Rod intercept $= 1.56$ m, $a = -5°04'$, $K = 99.2$, $C = 0.0$.

12–19. Rod intercept $= 7.82$ ft, $a = -8°36'$, $K = 101.6$, $C = 1.2$ ft.

12–20. Rod intercept $= 5.35$ ft, $a = +10°30'$, $K = 99.6$, $C = 0.6$ ft.

What is the rod intercept for the data given in problems 12–21 through 12–23.

12–21. Horizontal distance $= 124.0$ ft, $K = 101.6$, $a = +8°00'$, $C = 0.0$.

12–22. Horizontal distance $= 240.0$ ft, $K = 98.3$, $a = -4°15'$, $C = 0.0$.

12–23. Horizontal distance $= 160.0$ ft, $K = 99.4$, $a = +5°30'$, $C = 1.1$ ft.

12–24. A set of field notes from a stadia profile lists a slope reading of 300 ft, angle of $+5°16'$, rod reading on 12.0 ft, and h.i. $= 5.12$ ft. What is the correct difference in vertical elevation for this sight?

12–25. In running stadia traverses it is recommended that sights be taken both backward and forward on each course. Why?

12–26. Why is not usually necessary to read both the A and B verniers in stadia work? Explain.

12–27. Specifications for a certain stadia traverse require an accuracy not less than $1/600$. What is the lower limit for which it is necessary to reduce inclined sights to horizontal distances?

12–28. Same as problem 12–27 except for an accuracy of $1/400$.

*12–29. Calculate the ground elevations for the following stadia notes. The instrument is at station E, elevation 444.22 ft, h.i. $= 5.2$ ft, and $C = 1.0$. All sights are on the h.i. except as noted. (See table at top of p. 270.)

*12–30. Similar to problem 12–29 except the instrument is over hub M, elevation 568.2 ft, h.i. $= 4.9$ ft, and $C = 1.2$ ft. (See table at top of p. 270.)

* The asterisks indicate problems whose solutions are used in problems for Chapter 13.

	Problem 29				Problem 30		
Point	Inter- cept	Azimuth	Vert. Angle	Point	Inter- cept	Azimuth	Vert. Angle
B	1.75	98°15′	−0°56′	M	5.10	340°38′	−4°28′
8	0.36	110°20′	−1°12′	45	4.13	352°20′	+5°15′
9	0.72	149°40′	0°00′	46	3.19	6°35′	+5°40′
			on 9.26 ft				on 7.7 ft
10	0.87	166°10′	+3°37′	47	2.75	6°35′	+6°50′
11	0.61	197°45′	−8°16′	48	2.98	6°35′	4°22′

12–31. Same data as problem 12–29 but the transit has a +02′ index error.

12–32. Same data as problem 12–30 except the transit has a −03′ index error.

A sight is taken on the h.i. at BM Rock, elevation 558.8 ft, with a transit at hub A. In problems 12–33 through 12–36, compute the elevation of hub B.

12–33. Rod intercept = 3.85 ft, $a = -5°10′$, h.i. = 5.3 ft, and $C = 1.0$.

12–34. Rod intercept = 2.18 m, $a = +3°15′$, h.i. = 1.52 m, and $C = 0.0$.

12–35. Rod intercept = 8.06 ft, $a = -2°52′$, h.i. = 5.2 ft, and $C = 0.4$.

12–36. Rod intercept = 6.44 ft, $a = +1°44′$ to 6.8 ft on the rod, h.i. = 4.8 ft, and $C = 0.0$. (Use the approximate relationships of Section 8–2.)

At hub D, elevation 360.0 ft, a FS is taken on hub E, the instrument moved to hub E, and a BS read on D. In problems 12–37 through 12–39 determine the distance DE and the elevation of hub E. $K = 100.0$ and $C = 0.0$.

12–37. At D, $R = 2.48$, $a = -1°58′$ to 8.2 ft on the rod, h.i. = 4.8 ft.
At E, $R = 2.47$, $a = +1°50′$ to 0.9 ft on the rod, h.i. = 5.1 ft.

12–38. At D, $R = 4.84$, $a = +4°36′$ to 5.4 ft on the rod, h.i. = 5.0 ft.
At E, $R = 4.86$, $a = -4°50′$ to 2.4 ft on the rod, h.i. = 5.0 ft.

12–39. At D, $R = 1.85$, $a = +3°32′$ to 8.8 ft on the rod, h.i. = 4.9 ft.
At E, $R = 1.85$, $a = -3°21′$ to 2.2 ft on the rod, h.i. = 5.3 ft.

In problems 12–40 through 12–43 determine the horizontal distance AB and the elevation of point B for the Beaman-arc readings noted with the instrument at A, elevation 924.8 ft, and h.i. = 5.4 ft.

12–40. Rod intercept = 2.80 ft, V scale = 80 to 6.7 ft on the rod, and H scale = 10.

12–41. Rod intercept = 4.32 ft, V scale = 72 to 5.8 ft on rod, and H scale = 5.

12–42. Rod intercept = 5.48 ft, V scale = 33 to 5.6 ft on rod, and H scale = 3.

12–43. Rod intercept = 3.76 ft, V scale = 40 to 8.2 ft on rod, and H scale = 1.

For consistent precision of angles and distances in transit-stadia readings, how close must the angles be read under the conditions of problems 12–44 through 12–46?

12–44. Stadia constant = 0, a sight of 700 ft.

12–45. Stadia constant = 1 ft, a sight of 400 ft.

12–46. Stadia constant = 1.2 ft, a sight of 900 ft (estimated to nearest 5 ft).

12–47. In using a 1′ transit, at what distance does a 1 ft stadia constant become negligible?

12–48. What error in stadia distance results if, instead of being properly plumbed, the top of a 10-ft stadia rod is inclined 4 in. away from the instrument when a rod intercept of 9.00 ft is obtained on a horizontal sight?

12–49. Same as problem 12–48 except for a 12-ft rod inclined 8 in. away from the instrument on a rod intercept of 7.50 ft.

In problems 12–50 and 12–51 calculate the error of closure in elevation and adjust the azimuth-stadia traverses by distributing it in proportion to the differences in elevation between adjacent hubs. Elevation of point A is 425.70 ft. Stadia distances and vertical angles to the h.i. of 5.4 ft are the averages of foresights and backsights.

12–50 12–51

Course	Inter-cept	Azimuth	Vert. Angle	Course	Inter-cept	Azimuth	Vert. Angle
AB	3.40	68°12′	+3°15′	EF	2.96	106°12′	−4°22′
BC	2.62	172°06′	+2°42′	FG	7.78	19°57′	+2°50′
CD	4.13	231°05′	−1°36′	GH	3.09	307°40′	+6°33′
DA	3.78	355°12′	−3°06′	HE	8.90	199°58′	−3°21′

13
TOPOGRAPHIC SURVEYS

13-1. GENERAL. Topographic surveys are made to determine the configuration (relief) of the surface of the earth, and to locate the natural and cultural features thereon. By means of conventional symbols, topographic maps are produced from the survey data. A topographic map is a large-scale representation of a portion of the earth's surface, showing the *culture, relief, hydrography,* and perhaps the *vegetation.* Products of man, such as roads, trails, buildings, bridges, canals, and boundary lines, are termed *artificial features* (culture). Names and legends on maps identify the various features shown.

Topographic maps are made and used by engineers in determining the most desirable and economical location of highways, railroads, bridges, buildings, canals, pipelines, transmission lines, reservoirs, and other facilities; by geologists in investigating mineral, oil, water, and other resources; by foresters in locating fire-control roads and towers; by architects in housing and landscape design; by agriculturists in soil conservation; and by geographers and scientists in numerous fields.

A *planimetric map,* or *line map,* shows the natural and/or cultural features in plan only. A *hypsometric* map presents relief by conventions such as *contours, hachures, shading,* and *tinting.*

13-2. METHODS FOR TOPOGRAPHIC SURVEYING. Topographic surveys may be conducted by either *aerial* (photogrammetry) or *ground* (field) methods. Refined equipment and procedures available today have made photogrammetry very accurate and economical, and hence almost all topo-

273

graphic mapping projects covering large areas are done using this method. Ground surveys are still frequently used, however, especially for preparing large-scale maps of smaller areas. Even when photogrammetry is used, ground surveys are necessary to establish control and field-check mapped features for accuracy. This chapter concentrates on ground methods, and several field procedures for locating topographic features, both horizontally and vertically, will be discussed. The subject of photogrammetry is described in Chapter 25.

13-3. CONTROL FOR TOPOGRAPHIC SURVEYS. The first requirement of any topographic survey is good control. This is true whether the surveys are done by ground or aerial methods. Control, as discussed in Chapter 18, is classified as either horizontal or vertical.

Horizontal control is provided by two or more points on the ground, accurately fixed in position horizontally by distance and direction. It establishes scale of the map and also the basis for accurately showing map locations of features. Horizontal control is usually established by traversing, triangulation, or trilateration.

For small areas, horizontal control for topographic work is generally a traverse, although one line may suffice in some cases. Triangulation and trilateration furnish the most economical basic control for surveys extending over a state or the entire United States. Monuments of the state plane coordinate systems are excellent for all types of work, but unfortunately there are not enough of them available in most areas.

Vertical control is provided by bench marks in or near the area to be surveyed. It is used as the basis for accurately portraying relief on a map. A vertical control net is established by lines of levels starting from, and closing on, bench marks. Elevations are determined for the traverse hubs, with provision in some cases for marks set nearby and out of the way of construction. A lake surface is a continuous bench mark and may be utilized when possible. Even a gently flowing stream may serve as supplementary control. Barometric leveling is now employed to extend vertical control in rugged terrain.

Topographic details are usually built upon a framework of traverse hubs whose positions and elevations have been established. Any errors in the hub positions or their elevations are reflected in the location of topography. It is advisable, therefore, to run, check, and adjust the traverse and level circuits before the topographic detail survey is begun, rather than to carry on both processes simultaneously. This is particularly true in planetable work where an error in the elevation or position of an occupied station will displace the plotted locations of cultural features and contours.

The kind of control (traverse, triangulation, or trilateration) and method selected to obtain the topographic details govern the speed, cost, and efficiency of a topography survey.

13-4. TOPOGRAPHIC DETAILS.   Objects to be located in a survey may range from single points to meandering streams and complicated geological formations. The process of tying topographic details to the control net is called *detailing*.

13-5. METHODS OF LOCATING POINTS IN THE FIELD.   Seven methods used to locate a point *P* in the field are illustrated in Fig. 13-1. Resection is another method that is used with planetables. All are based on horizontal control. One line (distance *AB*) must be fixed in each of the first four methods. The positions of three points must be known or identifiable to apply the seventh method, which is called the *three-point problem*. Known distances are shown in the figure as heavy lines. The quantities to be measured in the respective diagrams are:

1. Two distances.
2. Two angles.
3. One angle and the adjacent distance.
4. One angle and the opposite distance (two possible points *P*).
5. One distance and a right-angle offset.
6. The intersection of string lines from straddle hubs.
7. Two angles at the point to be located.

Method 3 is used most often, but an experienced party chief employs whichever method is appropriate in a given situation. He must consider both field and office (computation and map) requirements.

13-6. LOCATION OF LINES.   Most objects can be located by considering them composed of straight lines, each line being determined by two points. Irregular or curved lines may be assumed straight between points sufficiently

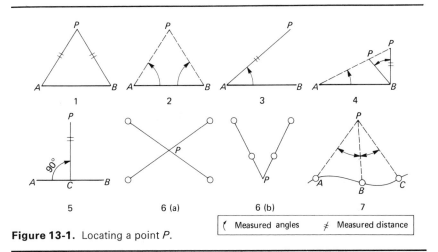

Figure 13-1. Locating a point *P*.

close together. Thus detailing becomes a process of locating points. Two examples will illustrate the measurements made to locate straight and curved lines.

In Fig. 13-2, the house *abcdea* is to be tied to traverse line *AB*. The building is so shaped that only two main corners, such as *a* and *e*, need be found. Corner *a* could be located by any of the first five methods of Fig. 13-1, but an angle and a distance are used as shown. It is good practice to locate a third corner, if possible, to provide a check. All sides of the house are measured by tape and the lengths recorded on a sketch. Location of the barn by measurements from the house is satisfactory if only a tape is available, but two angles and distances from the traverse hubs normally provide a quicker and independent result. Stations projected on the center-line traverse from the second house *q*, *r*, *s*, and *t* are practical in route surveys, but again angles and distances are a strong alternate.

Since a transit or theodolite is used to measure the angle, the distances to *a* and *e* could be measured by tape or stadia. All measurements can be shown on a sketch, but generally the angles and distances from traverse points are tabulated on the left page of the field book to avoid crowding the sketch. Topographic points are then identified by consecutive numbers, rather than letters, as on Plate A-9.

Location of a crooked stream by using the offset method is shown in Fig. 13-3. At intervals along the traverse line, offsets to the edges of the creek are measured. They can be taken at regular intervals or spaced at distances which permit the line to be considered straight between successive offsets.

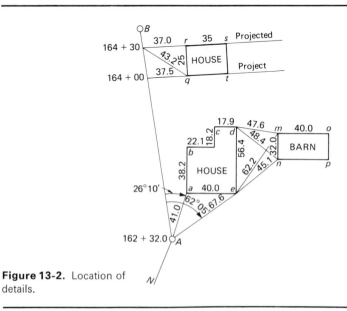

Figure 13-2. Location of details.

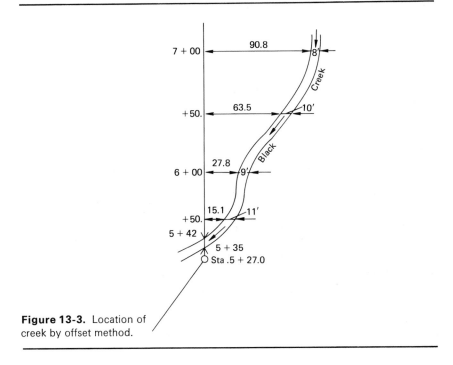

Figure 13-3. Location of creek by offset method.

13-7. LOCATION OF LINES FROM A SINGLE POINT.

The single-point method may be used to locate lines of a closed figure, such as the boundaries of a field. A point O is chosen from which all corners can be seen, as in Fig. 13-4(a). The direction to each corner is found by measuring all central angles, or by azimuths from point O. Lengths of all radiating lines, such as OA and OB, are determined by stadia, taping, or EDM, and the sides of the field computed by trigonometry since two sides and the included angle in each triangle are known. As a check, coordinates of each corner can be cal-

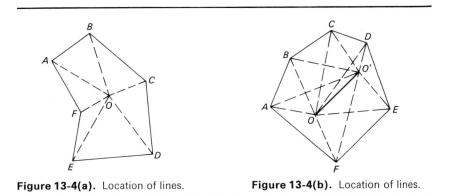

Figure 13-4(a). Location of lines.   **Figure 13-4(b).** Location of lines.

culated from the lengths and directions of the radiating lines and used to determine boundary lengths.

A more rigid solution of the boundary measurements can be obtained with the method shown in Fig. 13-4(b). A line *OO′* is chosen as the base and its length carefully measured. Angles are taken from each end of the base to all corners, and lengths of the radiating lines measured as in the single-point method.

13-8. CONTOURS. The best method of quantitatively representing hills, mountains, depressions, and ground-surface undulations on a two-dimensional sheet of paper is by contours. *A contour is a line connecting points of equal elevation.* Contours may be visible, as in the case of a lake shoreline, but usually on the ground, elevations of only a few points are defined and contours sketched between these controls.

Contours are shown on maps as the traces of level surfaces of different elevations, Fig. 13-5. Thus level surfaces cutting a vertical cone form circular contours and intersect a sloping cone to produce eliptical ones. On uniformly sloping surfaces, such as those in highway cuts, contours are straight lines.

Most contours are irregular lines like the closed loops for the hill in Fig. 13-5. The vertical distance between level surfaces forming the contours is called the *contour interval*. For topographic quadrangles at 1:24,000 scale, the United States Geological Survey uses one of the following contour intervals: 5, 10, 20, 40, or 80 ft. Contour intervals in meters will eventually replace foot units.

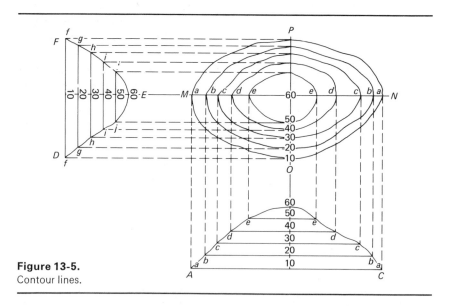

Figure 13-5.
Contour lines.

The contour interval selected depends upon the purpose of the map, its scale, and the amount of relief in the area mapped. Where extensive flat areas occur in mountainous regions, supplementary contours at one-half or one-fourth the basic interval are employed (and shown as dashed lines).

Figure 13-6 is a contour map showing 25-ft contours. *Spot elevations* are given for critical points such as peaks, sags, streams, and highway crossings. Sketching ridge, valley, and drainage lines (dashed) prior to drawing contours is desirable.

13-9. PROPERTIES OF CONTOURS. Certain properties of contours are fundamental in their location and plotting.

1. Since the earth is a continuous surface, all contours must close upon themselves. This closure may occur within the area being mapped, but often happens outside it and therefore will not appear on the map sheet.
2. Contours are perpendicular to the direction of maximum slope.
3. Evenly spaced parallel contours show a uniform slope, for example, on a highway cut or fill.
4. The distance between contours indicates the steepness of a slope. Wide spacing denotes gentle slopes; close spacing, steep slopes.
5. Concentric closed contours which increase in elevation represent hills. A contour forming a closed loop around lower ground is termed a *depression contour*. Hachures inside the lowest contour and pointing to the bottom of a hole or sink with no outlet make map reading easier. Contour elevations are shown on the uphill side of lines, or in breaks, to avoid confusion.
6. Irregular contours signify rough, rugged country. Smooth lines designate gradual slopes and changes.
7. Contours of different elevations never meet except on a vertical surface such as a wall or cliff. They cannot cross other than in the unusual case of a cave or overhanging shelf. Knife-edge conditions are seldom if ever found in natural formations.
8. A contour can never branch into two contours of the same elevation.
9. Contours cross sloping streets in typical U-shaped curves.
10. Valleys are usually characterized by V-shaped contours, and ridges by U-shaped contours.
11. The V's formed by contours crossing a stream point upstream.
12. The U's made by contours crossing a ridge line point down the ridge. Contours cross ridge and valley lines at right angles.
13. Contours tend to parallel streams and have an M shape just above stream junctions.
14. The shoreline of a small lake forms a contour if inflow, outflow, and wind effects are negligible.

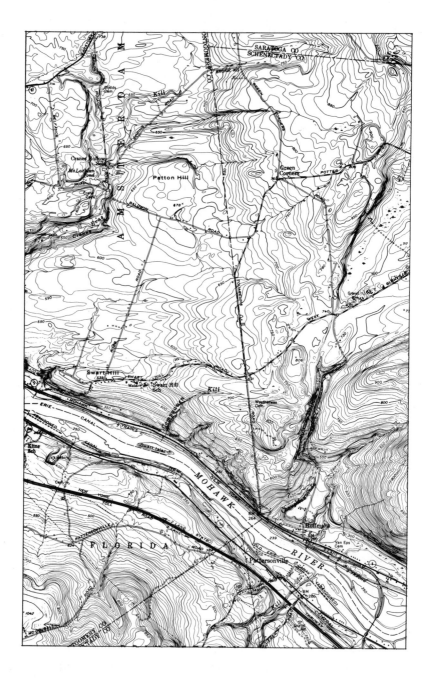

Figure 13-6. Contour map. (Courtesy U. S. Geological Survey.)

Keeping these principles in mind will make it easy to visualize contours when looking at an area, and prevent serious mistakes in sketching. Numerous points may be necessary to locate a contour in certain types of terrain. For example, in the unusual case of a level field which is at contour elevation, exact location of a single unique contour would be time-consuming or perhaps impossible.

13-10. DIRECT AND INDIRECT METHODS OF LOCATING CONTOURS.
Contours may be found by either the *direct method* (*trace-contour method*) or the *indirect method* (*controlling-point method*). In the direct method, the rod reading (foresight) which must be subtracted from the HI to give the contour elevation is determined. The rodman then selects trial points which he believes will give this minus sight and is directed uphill or downhill by the instrumentman until the required rod reading is actually secured (within 0.1 to 0.5 ft, the allowable discrepancy depending upon the terrain and the specified accuracy).

In Fig. 13-7 the transit is set up at point *A* whose elevation is 674.3 ft, h.i. of 4.9 ft, and HI equal 679.2 ft. If 5-ft contours are being located, a reading of 4.2 or 9.2 with the telescope level will place the rod on a contour point. For example, in Fig. 13-7, the 9.2-ft rod reading means that point *X* lies on the 670-ft contour. After this point has been located by trial, the distance and azimuth are read and the process repeated. Work is speeded by using a piece of red cloth perhaps 0.2 ft wide which can be moved up and down on the stadia rod to mark the required reading and eliminate searching for a number on any length sight.

The maximum distance between contour points is determined by the terrain and accuracy required. The tendency for beginners is to take more sights than necessary in ordinary terrain. Contours are sketched between the located points as a part of the drafting-room work, but they may also be drawn in the field book to clarify unusual conditions.

Unless the rod can be read by using the transit as a level, the direct method of locating contours is impractical. Too much time is wasted if the combination of a vertical angle and stadia distance must be juggled to get a required difference in elevation.

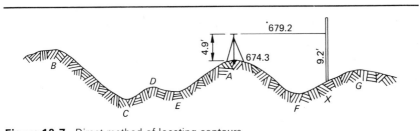

Figure 13-7. Direct method of locating contours.

For the indirect method, the rod is set on critical points where there are changes in ground slope, such as B, C, D, E, F, and G in Fig. 13-7. Elevations are obtained with the telescope level whenever possible, to save time in reducing notes and increase the accuracy. Points are selected at random, or along desired azimuth lines. The rodman moves clockwise to facilitate note-keeping and plotting. Contours are interpolated between the high and low points whose elevations are found.

The direct method is advantageous in gently rolling country. The indirect method is better in rough, rugged terrain.

13-11. FIELD METHODS OF OBTAINING TOPOGRAPHY. Location of topographic details is usually accomplished by one of the following methods: (a) radiation, (b) stadia, (c) planetable, (d) coordinate squares (grid), (e) offsets from a center line (cross sectioning, cross profile). A brief explanation of the use, advantages, and disadvantages of each will be given.

13-12. RADIATION METHOD. In the radiation method, traverse hubs are occupied with a transit or theodolite, and angles to the desired points measured. Distances are found by EDM or taping. After corners of buildings, bridges, and other features have been located, their lengths, widths, and projections are taped and sketched in the field book. The radiation procedure is accurate but also the slowest method and therefore often too costly for ordinary work.

13-13. STADIA METHOD. The stadia method is similar to the radiation process, except that distances are secured by stadia. The procedure is rapid and sufficiently accurate for most topographic surveys. Stadia distances, azimuths, and vertical angles are read for lines radiating from the transit, theodolite, or planetable to required points. Plate A-9 shows sample notes for a transit-stadia survey.

13-14. PLANETABLE METHOD. In the planetable method an alidade is sighted on a rod held at the point to be located, and the stadia distance and vertical angle (or Beaman arc) read. Direction of the line is drawn along the alidade ruler, thus eliminating the need to measure or record any horizontal angles. Vertical angles also are avoided, if possible, by using the alidade as a level.

The instrumentman sketches contours by either the direct or the indirect method while looking at the area. Since the map is plotted in the field, coverage can be checked by observation. Planetable usage is discussed in Chapter 15.

13-15. COORDINATE SQUARES.

The method of coordinate squares (grid method) is better adapted to locating contours than cultural features, but can be used for both. The area to be surveyed is staked in squares 10, 20, 50, or 100 ft on a side, the size depending upon the terrain and accuracy required. A transit or theodolite can be used to lay out lines at right angles to each other, such as AD and $D3$ in Fig. 13-8. Grid lengths are marked and the other corners staked by intersections of taped lines. Corners are identified by the number and letter of intersecting lines. If a transit is not available, all layout work can be done with a tape.

To obtain elevations of the corners, a level is set up in the middle of the area, or in a position from which level sights can be taken on each point. Contours are interpolated between the corner elevations (along the sides of the blocks) by estimation, or by calculated proportional distances. Except for plotting contours, this is the same procedure as that used in the borrow-pit problem, Section 5-27.

In plotting contours by the grid method, elevations obtained by interpolation along diagonals will generally not agree with those from interpolation along the four sides because of the ground's warped surface.

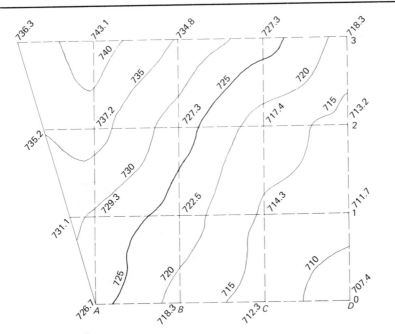

Figure 13-8. Coordinate squares.

13-16. OFFSETS FROM THE CENTER LINE. After the center line for a route survey has been established, a profile is taken to get elevations at regular stations and critical points. Details such as fences and buildings are located by right-angle offsets. The right angle can be measured by a *pentagonal prism* of the type shown in Fig. 13-9, or estimated by standing on the centerline, pointing the arms in opposite directions along the line, then bringing the palms of the hands together with arms outstretched in front of the body (eyes should be closed to prevent unconsciously aiming at a prominent object near the perpendicular line).

Cross sectioning consists in taking a vertical section of the surface of the ground at right angles to the center line of a route survey. In effect it is profiling normal to the center line. Rod readings are secured at all breaks in the ground surface and recorded with their respective distances out. Plate A-10 is a sample set of cross-section notes.

Cross sections are usually plotted on special paper that is most commonly ruled in 1-in. squares divided decimally with lighter lines 0.1 in. apart horizontally and vertically. Cross-section notes—when plotted along with the design template (base width and side slopes cut in a piece of plastic) for a proposed highway or canal—outline the areas of cuts and fills, which are readily measured by planimetering. Excavation quantities can be calculated from the areas of the cross sections and their known distances apart.

In recent years, electronic computers have generally eliminated the need to plot cross sections and planimeter the areas. Instead, the cross-section field notes and design-template values are read into a computer, together with an appropriate program, which calculates and lists the cut and fill areas as well as the excavation or fill volumes. Cross sections with superimposed design templates can be plotted automatically by the electronic computer if desired.

On some surveys, contour points are located along with any decided changes in slope of the ground. For example, if 5-ft contours are being de-

Figure 13-9. Double pentagonal prism (on side). (Courtesy Kern Instruments, Inc.)

lineated, a typical set of notes on the right-hand page of a field book would be in the following form:

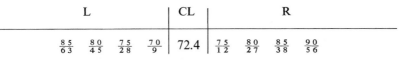

L				CL				R
$\frac{8\,5}{6\,3}$	$\frac{8\,0}{4\,5}$	$\frac{7\,5}{2\,8}$	$\frac{7\,0}{9}$	72.4	$\frac{7\,5}{1\,2}$	$\frac{8\,0}{2\,7}$	$\frac{8\,5}{3\,8}$	$\frac{9\,0}{5\,6}$

The numerator of a fraction represents the contour elevation, and the denominator the distance out from the center line.

Contour points can be plotted on cross-section paper to obtain the equivalent of a set of cross-section notes, or the contours might be drawn on the plan view of a proposed highway.

Readings are taken with a level, or, in some cases, a hand level.

13-17. CONTOURS BY HAND LEVEL. A hand level can be used for contouring when a high order of precision is not required. In this procedure, the observer first measures his HI (height of his eye above datum) by taking a plus sight on a point of known elevation, as in differential leveling. In going uphill, the point at which a level line of sight strikes the ground will have the same elevation as the observer's HI. After identifying this point on the ground, he moves there and uses the elevation to compute a new HI.

In leveling downhill, the observer finds by trial the point where he must stand to make a backsight strike the ground at the previously occupied position. The elevation of the trial point is then found by subtracting the observer's h.i., (the height of his eye above ground) and the process repeated. In locating 5-ft contours, adoption of an exact 5-ft h.i. by using a rod or forked stick is desirable to speed the work and simplify the arithmetic. Horizontal positions of contour points thus located must be determined by one of the methods described in previous sections.

13-18. SELECTION OF FIELD METHOD. Selection of the field method to be employed on any topographic survey depends upon the following considerations:

1. Purpose of the survey
2. Map use (accuracy required)
3. Map scale
4. Contour interval
5. Size and type of area involved
6. Cost
7. Equipment and time available
8. Experience of the personnel

Items 1, 2, 3, 4, and 5 are interdependent. The cost of course, will be a minimum if the most suitable method is chosen for a project. On large-scale work, personnel cost rather than equipment investment will govern (except perhaps in photogrammetric offices). A private surveyor making a topographic survey of 50 or 100 acres, however, may be governed in his choice of method by the equipment he owns.

Special training is necessary before the average surveyor can do photogrammetric work. Likewise, relatively few men have had enough planetable experience to become efficient in its operation.

13-19. SPECIFICATIONS FOR TOPOGRAPHIC SURVEYS. *National map standards of accuracy* specifications for the maximum errors permitted in horizontal positions and elevations shown on maps are as follows:

Horizontal accuracy. For maps to scales larger than 1 : 20,000, not more than 10% of the points tested shall be in error by more than $\frac{1}{30}$ in. On smaller-scale ones, the limit of error is $\frac{1}{50}$ in., or approximately 33 ft on the ground at a map scale of 1 : 20,000. These limits of accuracy shall apply in all cases to positions of well-defined points only such as monuments, bench marks, highway intersections, and corners of large buildings.

Vertical accuracy. Not more than 10% of the elevations tested shall be in error by more than one-half the contour interval.

The accuracy of any map may be tested by comparing the positions of points whose locations or elevations are shown upon it with corresponding positions determined by surveys of a higher accuracy.

Published maps meeting these accuracy requirements usually have noted in their legends that "This map complies with the National Map Accuracy Standards."

Plotted horizontal positions of objects are checked by an independent traverse, triangulation, or trilateration run to points selected by the person or organization for whom the survey is made. A profile run from any point, in any arbitrary direction, is compared with one made from the plotted contours. Thus both field work and map drafting are checked.

13-20. SOURCES OF ERROR IN TOPOGRAPHIC SURVEYS. Sources of error in topographic surveys include the following:

1. Control not established, checked, and adjusted before topography is taken.
2. Control points too far apart.
3. Control points poorly selected for proper coverage of area.
4. Poor selection of points for contour delineation.

13-21. MISTAKES.   Typical mistakes in topographic surveys are:

1. Improper selection of contour interval.
2. Unsatisfactory equipment or field method for the particular survey and terrain conditions.
3. Insufficient horizontal and vertical control of suitable precision.
4. Too few contour points taken.
5. Omission of some topographic details.

PROBLEMS

13-1. List six examples of topographic details classified as "cultural features."

13-2. Tabulate, in order of descending precision, the methods and/or equipment for establishing horizontal control for (a) large-area topographic surveys and (b) small-area topographic surveys. Do the same for vertical control.

13-3. In a topographic survey, what advantages does a lake have as a bench mark?

13-4. Describe the best method for determining the water-surface elevation of a lake disturbed by light winds.

13-5. Sketch and name the seven field methods for locating points, and give an example of the best application of each.

13-6. Prepare a set of field notes to locate the buildings and walks of Fig. 14–8 from the traverse shown by the most appropriate method.

13-7. Contours with a 1-m interval are spaced 20 cm apart on a map having a scale of 1 cm = 40 m. What is the average slope of the ground between contours?

13-8. On a map to a scale of 1 in. = 400 ft, how far apart would 2-ft contours be on a uniform slope (grade) of 5%?

13-9. List the relative advantages and disadvantages of each of the following methods of determining the locations and elevations of ground points: (a) grid; (b) controlling-point; (c) trace-contour; (d) cross-profile.

13-10. Give examples and sketch terrain conditions for which the best method of locating contours would be (a) the grid method, (b) the direct method, and (c) the indirect method.

13-11. Prepare a set of field notes for locating the topographic details shown in Fig. 13–2. Scale the distances and angles. Use different methods from those shown, including each of the first five methods of Section 13–5.

13-12. If the locations of contours for an area are to be based upon barometric readings, which method of location is best and why?

Draw contours with the intervals noted for problems 13–13 through 13–16.

13-13. 2-ft contours for problem 5–42.

13-14. 1-ft contours for problem 5–43.

13–15. 1-ft contours for problem 12–29.

13–16. 1-ft contours for problem 12–30.

13–17. List and give examples of the pertinent factors considered in selecting the proper scale for a transit-stadia topographic-mapping project.

13–18. Explain in detail how to test the accuracy of the map in Figure 13–6.

13–19. Discuss the reasons for immediately completing up-to-date topographic maps like that of Figure 13–6 for the entire United States.

13–20. In outline form, describe a method of making a topographic survey of a lot 50 × 60 m having a maximum difference of elevation of about 3 m. Assume that only a tape is available. Improvise your own equipment.

13–21. Sketch a contour which crosses a 50-ft wide street having a 4% grade, a 10-in. parabolic crown at the center line, and 6-in. deep curbs.

13–22. Draw a profile of the terrain alongside and parallel with the north side of Baldwin Road, Figure 13–6.

13–23. Same as for problem 13–22 but for the south side of Baldwin Road.

13–24. State any additional property of contours not given in Section 13–9.

13–25. In your opinion, which is the most important of the 14 properties of a contour listed in Section 13–9 ? Why ?

13–26. A city area has many details to be located by transit stadia. Which is the best method to make notekeeping and later plotting easier ?

13–27. If contour elevations are not shown on a map such as Fig. 13–5, what additional "symbol" could be used to verify that a hill, or a sump, is represented ?

13–28. Is the direct method of locating contours faster than the indirect method for ordinary terrain ? More accurate ?

13–29. Why is the offsets-from-the-center-line method used more than any other ground system on route surveys to locate points ?

13–30. Select two of the considerations listed in Section 13–18 and give examples of three situations in which the items chosen would govern the field method to be used.

14
MAPPING

14-1. GENERAL. Throughout the ages, maps have had a profound impact upon the activities of man, and today the demand for them is perhaps greater than ever before. They are of utmost importance in engineering, resource management, urban and regional planning, management of the environment, construction, conservation, geology, agriculture, and many other fields. Maps are made which show various features, for example, topography, property boundaries, transportation routes, soil types, vegetation, land ownership for tax purposes, mineral and resource locations, and so on. In engineering, maps are especially important. They are used in planning project locations, designing the facility, and estimating contract quantities.

The military services have always depended heavily upon a steady flow of up-to-date maps and charts. During World War II, the Army Map Service, now the Topographic Center, Defense Mapping Agency (DMA), prepared more than 40,000 maps of all types covering approximately 400,000 miles^2 of the earth's surface; 500 million copies were printed. The Normandy invasion alone required 70 million copies of 3000 different maps. In the first four weeks of the Korean Conflict, the Army Map Service and the Far East Command printed and distributed 10 million copies of maps—more than printed during all of World War I. Because of the size and dispersion of military forces in Viet Nam, the Army Map Service issued an estimated 500 million copies of maps to support that conflict. Complete country coverage was made in 1 : 50,000 scale maps, and most of the area also shown at 1 : 25,000. Numerous special products for riverine operations and photo-maps were used.

14-2. MAPPING AGENCIES. Maps are prepared by private surveyors, industries, cities, counties, states, and several agencies of the federal government. Unfortunately, these many mapping activities have not been coordinated; hence some duplication of effort has occurred, and the existence of much valuable information is unknown and thus unavailable to prospective users. A start has been made to improve this situation by setting up depositories in some cities and states, where every obtainable map of the area is filed for the use of interested persons. The National Cartographic Information Center[1] provides information helpful to surveyors, engineers, cartographers, and other technical map users, as well as the general public. This office, which is a central source of information on surveys and maps, provides comprehensive data on topographic maps, aerial photography, geodetic control surveys; basic facts needed for engineering and construction programs, such as irrigation projects, highways, and railroad location, urban and rural development, transmission and pipelines, airports, and the location of radio and television facilities.

Some of the federal agencies producing maps and charts on a national scale are the Geological Survey; Hydrographic Center, DMA; and the National Geodetic Survey (NGS).

The Geological Survey began publishing topographic maps in 1886 as an aid to scientific studies. Standard sheets cover $7\frac{1}{2}'$ or 15' quadrangles and show the works of man in black, contours in brown, water features in blue, urban regions in red, and woodland areas in green. An index map giving the status of topographic mapping in the United States and its territories and possessions is available free of charge from the Geological Survey. Other index maps giving the status of aerial photography and aerial mosaics in the United States are published by the same agency.

The NGS and National Ocean Survey (NOS) provide basic position and elevation control for mapping, and nautical and aeronautical charts which are fundamental tools in maintaining the nation's air and sea transportation systems, as well as tide and current surveys, seismological and geomagnetic surveys.

The DMA, Topographic Center, fulfills a key mission in an era when accurate mapping, charting, and geodesy products are essential to realize the full potential of new weapons. Technological advances in weaponry demand corresponding improvement in mapping, charting, and geodesy to obtain accuracies that were only dreams a few years ago.

14-3. MAP SCALE. The choice of map scale depends upon the purpose, size, and required precision of the finished map. Dimensions of a standard sheet, type and number of topographic symbols, and need for scaling distances from it are some of the considerations involved.

---

[1] Requests for information should be addressed to National Cartographic Information Center, U.S. National Center, Stop 507, Reston, Va. 22092.

Map scales are given in three ways: (a) by *ratio* or *representative fraction*, such as 1 : 2000 or $\frac{1}{2000}$; (b) by an *equivalence*, for example, 1 in. = 200 ft; and (c) *graphically*. Two graphical scales placed at right angles to each other and in diagonally opposite corners of a map sheet permit accurate measurements to be made even though the paper changes dimensions.

Map scales are generally classified as *large*, *medium*, and *small*. Their respective scale ranges are as follows:

Large scale, 1 in.   = 100 ft (1 : 1200) or larger.
Medium scale, 1 in. = 100 ft to 1000 ft (1 : 1200 to 1 : 12,000).
Small scale, 1 in.   = 1000 ft (1 : 12,000) or smaller.

Discussion in this chapter will be primarily confined to large-scale maps. A map drawn to any scale can be enlarged or reduced by means of a pantograph or an opaque projector, or photographically. However, it is important to note that for enlarged maps, the errors are also magnified and the resulting product may no longer meet accuracy standards.

14-4. MAP DRAFTING.   Map drafting generally consists of two steps: (1) preparing the manuscript and (2) drafting the final map. The manuscript is usually compiled in pencil. It should be carefully prepared to locate all features and contours as accurately as possible and to be complete in every detail, including placement of symbols and letters. Lettering on the manuscript need not be done with extreme care, for its major purpose is to ensure good overall map design and proper placement. A well-prepared manuscript goes a long way toward achieving a good-quality final map.

The completed version is drafted in ink, or *scribed*. Either process involves tracing from the manuscript. If inked, the manuscript is placed on a "light table" and features traced on a stable-base transparent overlay material. Lettering is usually done first, then planimetric features and contours are traced. Scribing is executed on sheets of transparent stable-base material coated with an opaque emulsion. Manuscript lines are transferred to the coating in a laboratory process. Special scribing tools are used to vary line weights and make standard symbols. Lines representing features and contours are prepared by cutting and scraping to remove the coating. Scribing is generally easier and faster than inking, and its use is increasing.

The process of preparing a pencil manuscript can be divided into four parts: (1) plotting the control; (2) plotting the details; (3) drawing the topography and special data; and (4) finishing the map, including labeling and lettering.

14-5. PLOTTING THE CONTROL.   The method selected for plotting control depends upon the surveying procedures employed to establish it and/or the form in which the control data are available. A traverse control survey can be plotted as a series of angles (using one of the methods described in Section 14-6) and distances laid out at the selected scale for the map (e.g. 1 in. = 10, 20, 40, 50, or 100 ft if the English system is employed, or 1 : 100, 1 : 200, 1 : 500, 1 : 1000, and so on, in metric units). An engineer's scale is satisfactory but supplemented by steel scales and dividers for marking control points accurately to perhaps 0.02 or 0.01 in., or better.

For a traverse plotted by angles and distances, bearings and lengths of the courses are placed parallel to the lines so they can be read easily when the user looks at the sheet *from the bottom or right-hand side*. Bearings are shown in the forward direction and continuous around the traverse. When a bearing is read from left to right, but actually runs from right to left, an arrow is used to note the correct direction, as in Fig. 14-8.

Instead of angles and distances, the coordinate method can be adopted for plotting traverses after calculating X and Y values for the hubs as described in Section 10-10. If control was established by triangulation or trilateration, point locations will probably be computed in coordinates ready for the most accurate and convenient method of plotting. The map sheet is first laid out precisely in a grid pattern with unit squares of appropriate size, such as 100, 400, 500, or 1000 ft, and checked by measuring the diagonals. Each grid line is labeled with its coordinate value. The origin of coordinates may be the most westerly or southerly station of the traverse, or somewhere off the sheet to assure all plus values.

Control points are plotted by measuring their X and Y coordinates from the ruled grid lines. Small circles, $\frac{1}{8}$ in. or less in diameter, are drawn to mark the hubs. Any errors in plotting are detected by comparing the scaled distance and bearing of each line with the length and direction measured in the field or computed. On most topographic maps, hub locations are omitted from the finished drawings. If shown, they may be drawn in light blue ink to make them less prominent on a print.

Special instruments called *coordinatographs* are also available for plotting points by coordinates. Index marks set to coordinate values on perpendicular graduated X and Y rails enable rapid and accurate plotting to be performed.

14-6. PLOTTING ANGLES.

14-6. PLOTTING ANGLES. Angles may be plotted by the tangent method, chord method, or by protractor. These procedures will be described.

TANGENT METHOD

To lay off an angle by the tangent method, a convenient distance is measured along the reference line to serve as a base. Thus, in Fig. 14-1, to plot a 12°14′ deflection angle at point A, length AB equal to 10 in. is first marked on the prolongation of the back line. A perpendicular with length equal to the distance AB times the natural tangent of 12°14′ (2.17 in.) is erected at B to locate point C. The line connecting A and C makes the desired angle

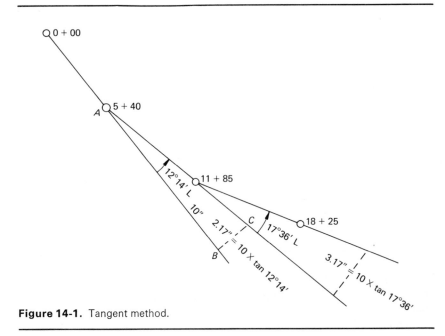

Figure 14-1. Tangent method.

with *AB*. Any length of base can be used, but a distance of 10 or 100 units requires only the movement of the decimal place in the natural tangent taken from a set of tables or a calculator.

The tangent method is employed extensively for plotting deflection angles. It is not so advantageous for large direct angles.

CHORD METHOD

To lay off an angle by the chord method, as indicated in Fig. 14-2, a convenient base length *BD* of 10 units is first marked on one side, *BA*, giving point *D*. With the vertex *B* as the center and a radius of 10 units, an arc is swung. Then with point *D* as the center, and a radius equal to the chord for

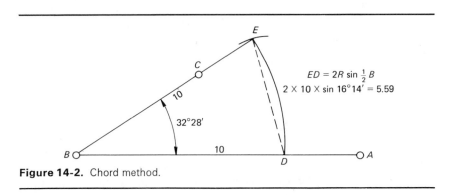

Figure 14-2. Chord method.

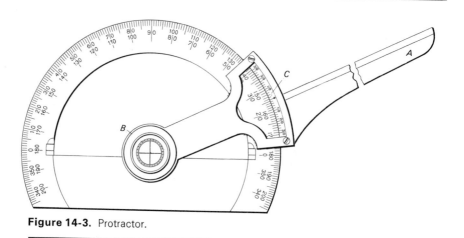

Figure 14-3. Protractor.

the desired angle, another arc is drawn. The intersection of the two arcs locates *E*. The line connecting points *B* and *E* forms the other side of the angle.

The chord for a desired angle may be found by multiplying twice the distance *BD* by the sine of half the angle. Thus in Fig. 14-2 the chord is $2 \times 10 \times \sin 16°14'$. By making the base length 10, 50, or 100 units to some scale, the chord is readily computed by using natural sines taken from a trigonometric table, or a calculator.

PROTRACTOR METHOD

A protractor is a device made of paper, plastic, or metal, cut in a full circle or a semicircle, with angle graduations along the circumference. A fine point identifies the center of the circle. The protractor is centered at the vertex of the angle, with the zero line along one side, and the proper angle point marked along the edge.

Protractors are available in sizes having radii from 2 to 8 in. A metal circle with a movable arm extending beyond the edge, as illustrated in Fig. 14-3, is often used. The arm *a* rotates about the center *b* and has a vernier *c* reading to minutes. A similar arrangement on drafting machines makes plotting fast and accurate.

Protractors are universally used for the plotting of details but are not suitable for high-precision work on traverses or control.

14-7. ADVANTAGES AND DISADVANTAGES OF THE DIFFERENT METHODS.
With the coordinate method, any large errors in plotting are readily found by scaling. Correction usually involves replotting only one point. For example, if the scaled lengths of lines *CD* and *DE* of a plotted tra-

verse are not equal to their field measurements, point *D* is off. The independence of each point in the plotting procedure is a definite advantage.

The tangent method is accurate and probably the best way to lay out a single angle precisely. In plotting a traverse, however, an error in any angle or distance is carried through the remainder of the traverse. If a traverse fails to close, each angle and line must be checked. If the closure is due to drafting rather than the field work, it may be necessary to rotate each line, except the first, slightly and progressively.

The chord method has the disadvantage that errors in any traverse line are passed along to succeeding courses. Erection of a perpendicular is eliminated but determination of the chord lengths is somewhat more laborious than finding perpendicular offsets.

Layout of angles by protractor is the fastest but least accurate of the methods.

14-8. PLOTTING DETAILS.   Boundary corners and important points upon which construction work may depend are plotted by coordinates or the tangent method, but the protractor is used for most details. Orientation of the protractor zero line is by meridian for details located by azimuths or bearings, and by the backsight line if direct angles were measured. Angles are marked along the edge of the protractor, and distances scaled from the vertex to plot details. To avoid obliterating the vertex, and to reduce erasures, the engineer's scale can be laid along the line through the plotted point and the distance marked. An alternative method consists of drawing a short line through the point at the approximate distance by estimation, and then marking along it. Some protractors available have a graduated scale along their arm to make detail plotting easier.

For greatest accuracy, the distance to a detail should be less than the radius of the protractor unless the extended-arm type is used.

14-9. CONTOUR INTERVAL.   As noted in Section 13-8, choice of contour interval to be used on a topographic map depends upon its intended use, required accuracy, type of terrain, and scale. If, according to National Standards of Map Accuracy, elevations can be interpolated from a map to within one-half the contour interval, then for an accuracy of 1 ft, a 2-ft interval is necessary. However, if only 10-ft accuracy is required, a 20-ft contour interval will suffice.

Terrain type and map scale combine to regulate the contour interval needed to produce a suitable density (spacing) of contours. Rugged terrain requires a larger contour interval than gently rolling country, and flat ground mandates a relatively small one to portray the surface adequately. Also, if map scale is reduced, the contour interval must be increased; otherwise lines are crowded, confuse the user, and possibly obscure other important details.

For average terrain, the following large and medium map scales and contour interval relationships generally provide suitable spacing:

English System		Metric System	
Scale (ft/in.)	Contour Interval (ft)	Scale	Contour Interval (m)
50	1	1 : 500	0.5
100	2	1 : 1000	1
200	5	1 : 2000	2
500	10	1 : 5000	5
1000	20	1 : 10,000	10

14-10. PLOTTING CONTOURS.   Points to be used in plotting contours are located in the same manner as those for details. Contours found by the *direct method* are sketched through the points. Interpolation between plotted points is necessary for the *indirect method*.

Interpolation to find contour points between points of known elevation can be done in several ways:

1. Estimating.
2. Scaling the distance between points of known elevation and locating the contour points by proportion.
3. Using a rubber band graduated to some scale and stretching it to make convenient marks fall on the known elevations. Special devices known as *variable scales* are available which contain a graduated spring. The spring may be stretched to make suitable marks fall on the known elevations.
4. Using a triangle and scale, as indicated in Fig. 14-4. To interpolate for the 420-ft contour between point *A* at elevation 415.2 and point *B* at elevation 423.6, first the 152 mark on any of the engineer's scales is set

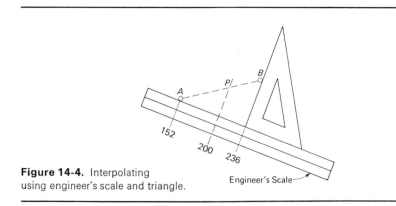

Figure 14-4. Interpolating using engineer's scale and triangle.

opposite *A*. Then with one side of the triangle against the scale and the 90° corner at 236, the scale and the triangle are pivoted together around *A* until the perpendicular edge of the triangle passes through point *B*. The triangle is then slid to the 200 mark and a dash drawn to intersect the line from *A* to *B*. This is the interpolated contour point *P*.

5. Using a converging-line device, such as that in Fig. 14-5, which can be pivoted and adjusted to fit the difference in elevation between any two points. The procedure is illustrated by the following example: Assume two plotted points have elevations of 17.6 and 25.9. Draw a straight line between these points. Determine the difference between the given elevations to the nearest whole number. Since $25.9 - 17.6 = 8.3$, use 8. Place the contour finder over the map so that its horizontal lines are parallel to the line drawn and eight intervals nearly fill the space between the plotted points. Adjust the finder until the 17.6 point lies 0.6 into the

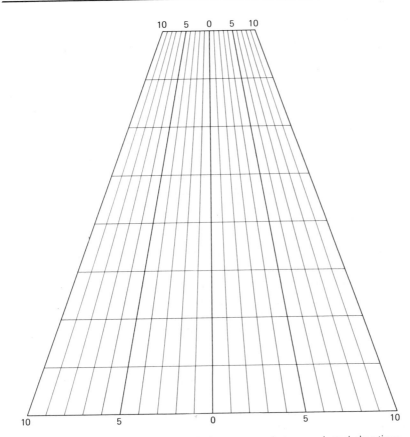

Figure 14-5. Contour finder for interpolating contours between plotted elevations, assuming uniform slope. (Courtesy Keuffel & Esser Company.)

first interval and the 25.9 point lies 0.9 beyond the eighth interval. With a needle point, punch through the contour finder at the contour points desired.

Contours are drawn only for elevations evenly divisible by the contour interval. Thus for a 20-ft interval, elevations of 800, 820, and 840 are shown, but 810, 830, and 850 are not. To improve legibility, every fifth line, evenly divisible by five times the contour interval, is made heavier. Thus for a 20-ft interval, the 800, 900, and 1000 lines would be heavier. The standard color for inked contour lines is sepia.

Hills, mountains, depressions, and ground-surface undulations can also be represented by hachures and other forms of hill shading. Hachures are short lines drawn in the direction of the slope. They are heavy and closely spaced for steep slopes; fine and widely separated for gentle slopes. They show the general shape of the ground rather than actual elevations and thus are not suitable for most engineering work.

14-11. COMPUTER MAPPING.   Electronic computers are used to plot maps automatically. The required input to the computer includes the control survey data, topographical detail information, map scale, and contour interval. Appropriate programs direct the computer to solve for the positions of points using the survey data, and plot the contours and various features. Advantages of the computer-driven systems are their speed, accuracy, and a consistently uniform final product. Moreover, all the data can be stored on magnetic tape with different numerical codes for the various kinds of features, and recalled later for plotting in total, or in parts for special-purpose maps. As an example, only roads and utilities might be needed by a city engineering department, whereas an assessor might want just the property boundaries mapped. Scale and contour interval can be readily varied, and either English or metric units called for.

With contour information stored in the computer, profiles along specified lines can be plotted automatically, and by giving grade lines and design templates, survey stakeout information and earthwork quantities obtained for projects such as highways and canals.

Figure 14-6 shows part of a planimetric map plotted automatically by a computer in less than 10 min using the Calcomp 7000 flatbed unit.

14-12. TOPOGRAPHIC SYMBOLS.   Standard symbols are used to represent special topographic features, thereby making it possible to show many details on a single sheet. Figure 14-7 gives a few of the hundreds of symbols employed on topographic maps. Considerable practice is required to draw these symbols well at a suitable scale. Before placing symbols on a map, such things as buildings, roads, and boundary lines are first plotted and

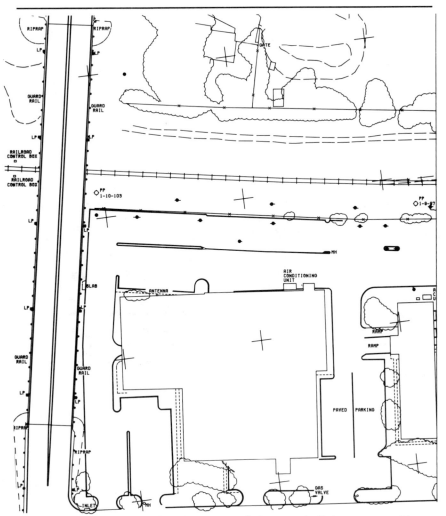

Figure 14-6. Portion of planimetric map compiled automatically by computer-driven plotter. (Courtesy California Computer Products, Inc.)

inked. The symbols are then drawn, or cut from standard sheets having an adhesive on the back and pasted on the map. A fully detailed map with coloring and shading is a work of art.

14-13. PLACING THE MAP ON A SHEET. The appearance of a finished map has considerable bearing on its acceptability and value. A map which is poorly arranged, carelessly lettered, and unfinished looking does not inspire confidence in its accuracy. A border line somewhat heavier than all other lines improves the appearance of the sheet.

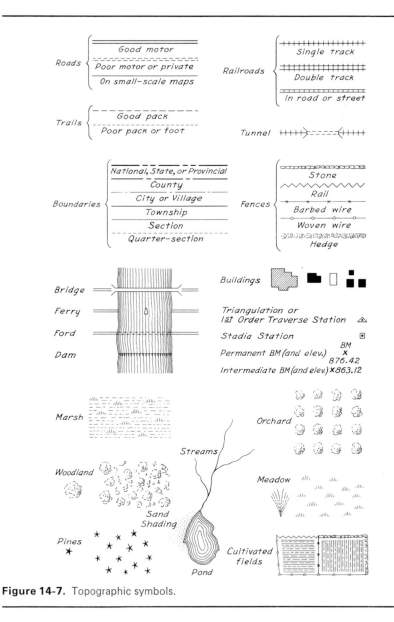

Figure 14-7. Topographic symbols.

The first step in map arrangement is to determine the position of the control and topography which will properly balance the sheet. Figure 14-8 shows a traverse (no topography outside it) suitably placed. Before any plotting is done, the proper scale for a sheet of given size must be determined.

Assume that an 18- × 24-in. sheet with a 1-in. border on the left (for possible binding), and a ½-in. border on the other three sides, is to be used. If the most westerly station *A* has been selected as the origin of coordinates,

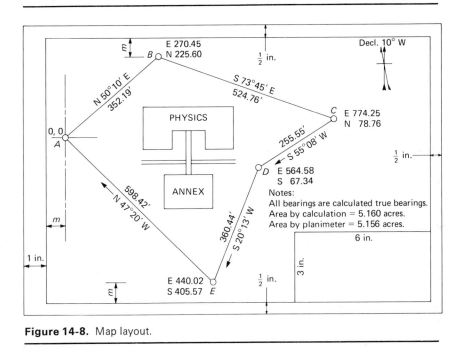

Figure 14-8. Map layout.

then divide the total departure to the most easterly point *C* by the number of inches available for plotting in the east-west direction. The maximum scale possible in Fig. 14-8 is 774.25 divided by 22.5, or 1 in. = 34 ft. The nearest standard scale which will fit is 1 in. = 40 ft.

This scale must be checked in the *Y*-direction by dividing the total *Y*-coordinate of 225.60 + 405.57 = 631.17 ft by 40 ft, giving 15.8 in. required in the north-south direction. Since 16½ in. is available, the scale of 1 in. = 40 ft is satisfactory, although 1 in. = 50 ft provides a better border margin.

In Fig. 14-8 the traverse is centered on the sheet in the *Y*-direction by making each distance *m* equal to ½[17 − (631.17/40)], or 0.61 in. The "weights" of the title, notes, and arrow compensate for the traverse being to the left of the center of the sheet.

If topography is to be plotted outside the traverse, the maximum north-south and east-west distances to topographic features must be added to the traverse coordinates before computations are made for the scale and centering distances.

On some types of maps it is permissible to skew the meridian with respect to the borders of the sheet in order to better accommodate a traverse relatively long in the NE–SW or NW–SE direction, or to make street lines parallel with the borders. When a traverse with topography is to be plotted by any means other than coordinates, it is advisable to first make a sketch showing controlling features. If this is done on tracing paper, orientation for the best fit and appearance is readily determined by rotating and shifting the tracing.

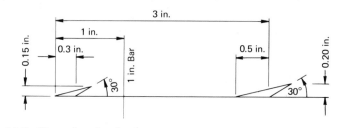

Figure 14-9. Dimensions for simple arrow.

14-14. MERIDIAN ARROW. Every map must display a meridian arrow for orientation purposes. It should preferably be near the top of the sheet, although it may be moved elsewhere for balance. An arrow should not be so large, elaborate, or heavily blacked in that it becomes the focal point of the sheet, as was true on maps of fifty years ago.

True, grid, or magnetic north, or all three may be shown. A true-meridian arrow is identified by a full head and full feather; a grid and/or magnetic arrow by a half-head and half-feather. The half-head and half-feather are put on the side away from the true north arrow to avoid bumping it. Figure 14-9 shows dimensions of an arrow that is suitable for routine maps. In practice, an arrow is traced from a sheet of standards, or cut out for pasting on the map.

14-15. TITLE. The title may be placed wherever it will better balance the sheet, but it is always kept outside the property lines on a boundary-survey sheet. Usually the title occupies the lower right-hand corner, with any pertinent notes just above or to the left of it. A search for a particular map in a bound set or in a loose pile of drawings is facilitated if all titles are in the same location. Since sheets are filed flat, bound on the left border, or hung from the top, the lower right-hand corner is the most convenient position.

The title should state the type of map; name of the property or project and its owner or user; location or area; date completed; scale; contour interval; horizontal and vertical datums used; and name of the surveyor. Additional data may be required on special-purpose maps. Lettering should be simple in style rather than ornate, and conform in size with the individual map sheet. Emphasis is placed on the most important parts of the title by increasing their height and using upper-case (capital) letters.

Perfect symmetry of outline about a vertical center line is necessary since the eye tends to exaggerate any defection. Also, an appearance of stability is obtained by having a full-width bottom line.

An example of a title and its arrangement for the 18- × 24-in. sheet of Fig. 14-8 is given in Fig. 14-10. Heights of letters in lines 1 and 2 could be ¼ in.; in line 3, 5⁄16 in.; and in the last two lines, ⅛ in.

No part of a map better portrays the artistic ability of a draftsman than a neat, well-arranged title.

UNIVERSITY OF HAWAII

CIVIL ENGINEERING DEPARTMENT

TRANSIT-STADIA SURVEY OF ENGINEERING CAMPUS

SCALE 1 INCH = 20 FEET   DATE 8 Nov. 1976

SURVEY BY L.HILL, T.HALL, A.AKER   MAP BY J. JONES

Figure 14-10. Title arrangement.

14-16. NOTES. Notes cover special features pertaining to the individual map, such as the following:

All bearings are true bearings (or magnetic, or grid, or calculated).
Area by calculation is X acres.
Area by planimeter is Y acres.
Legend (explanation of unusual symbols; for example, * represents cooling towers).

Notes must be in a prominent place where they are certain to be seen upon even a cursory examination of the map. The best location is just above or to the left of the title box in the lower right-hand corner of the map. A user then finds the desired map by title, and checks any special notes before examining the drawing.

14-17. PAPER. Drawing paper for surveying maps should be of excellent quality, take ink without spreading, stand erasures, and not deteriorate with age. Good brown detail paper and high-grade white drawing paper are commonly used. Cloth-backed white sheets and aluminum-backed paper are desirable for important work. They are expensive but more resistant to dimensional changes and rough handling.

Many maps are drawn or traced on transparent polyester materials such as Mylar, transparent paper, or fine linen so that blueprints can be made from them. Polyester sheets are commonly used because they are durable, dimensionally stable, and permit erasure of inking errors. An original paper drawing may be finished in pencil for printing, but maps of a permanent nature should be inked.

Blueprinted maps have the disadvantage of changing dimensions because of variations in temperature and humidity, and the printing process itself, so are less popular today. Surveys of city lots, normally drawn on small sheets, and other maps are now generally reproduced in the surveyor's office by an ozalid-type process which does not entail wetting and drying the printing paper.

14-18. SOURCES OF ERROR IN MAPPING. Sources of error in mapping include:

1. Not checking (scaling) distances when plotting by coordinates.
2. Plotting by protractor.
3. Using a soft pencil for plotting.
4. Variations in dimensions of map sheet.

14-19. MISTAKES. Some common mistakes in mapping are:

1. Improper orientation of topographic notes in field and office.
2. Using wrong edge of engineer's scale.
3. Making arrow too large, complex, or black.
4. Omitting the scale or necessary notes.
5. Failing to balance the sheet by making a preliminary sketch.

PROBLEMS

14–1. To keep plotting errors within 4 ft when using an engineer's scale, what is the smallest feasible map scale?

14–2. On a planetable sheet having a scale of 1 : 2400, what is the smallest distance that can be plotted with an engineer's scale?

14–3. How would the maps of Figs. 13–2, 13–3, and 13–6 be classified on the basis of scale?

14–4. List side by side the various methods of plotting traverses, and show under each its relative advantages and disadvantages.

14–5. Similar to problem 14–4, except for the methods of plotting topographic details.

14–6. Sketch the conventional symbols for a marsh, railroads, orchards, ponds, and woodland.

14–7. Draw the conventional symbols for a cultivated field, a meadow, a stream with a bridge, a vineyard, and cactus.

14–8. Draw 1-ft contours for the data in Plate A–7.

14–9. Sketch 5-ft contours for the data in Plate A–10.

14–10. Plot the topography in the notes of Plate A–9.

14–11. Using an $8^1/_2 \times 11$-in. quadrille sheet, plot in conformance with Section 14–5 the traverse of problem 10–13 to a suitable scale. Allow a $^1/_2$-in. border on the left side and a $^1/_4$-in. border on the other three sides.

14–12. Similar to problem 14–11, but assume that topography coverage extends about 300 ft to the north side of line BC.

14–13. Comparable to problem 14–11, but use the traverse of problem 10–15.

14–14. Similar to problem 14–13, but assume that topographic details are included for a distance out of approximately 300 ft perpendicular to line BC and for about 200 ft perpendicular to line CD.

14–15. Plot the traverse of problem 10–23 by bearings and distances. Check the positions of the corners by coordinates.

14–16. Plot the traverse of problem 12–50 by azimuths and distances; then check the positions of A, B, C, and D by coordinates.

14–17. Similar to problem 14–16 except use the data of problem 12–51.

14–18. Plot the following azimuth traverse by coordinates to a scale of 1 in. = 50 ft (distances in feet, azimuths from north): $AB=320.4$, $340°12'$; $BC=618.6$, $5°38'$; $CD=654.3$, $96°26'$; $DE=200.6$, $174°34'$; $EF=447.5$, $182°27'$; $FA=633.7$, $251°53'$.

14–19. In problem 14–18, azimuths and distances to a lake shore were taken from the traverse points as follows: A, $276°00'$, 352.2 ft; A, $300°54'$, 431.6 ft; B, $290°26'$, 216.3 ft; B, $340°12'$, 269.1 ft; C, $342°44'$, 241.5 ft; C, $289°06'$, 168.8 ft; C, $5°38'$, 171.0 ft; C, $55°30'$, 190.3 ft; D, $354°36'$, 255.7 ft. Plot these points and join them with lines to represent a lake shore. Finish the map, giving proper symbols, lengths and bearings of the fence lines, an arrow, notes, and a title. Show the land along the shoreline changing from marsh to pines to orchard.

14–20. What does a closed contour, hachured on the inside, depict?

14–21. If it is necessary to keep plotting errors within 10 ft on a map, using an engineer's scale, what is the smallest suitable map scale?

14–22. Why are traverse lines shown in light blue on a survey map? Should the hubs be light blue or black? Why?

14–23. List factors influencing the selection of contour interval.

14–24. According to National Map Accuracy Standards, if elevations must be interpolated from a map to ± 5 ft, what contour interval will be required?

14–25. For mapping of average terrain, state the contour intervals you would recommend for the following map scales: 100 ft/in., 500 ft/in., 1:500, and 1:2000?

14–26. List the advantages of computerized mapping systems.

14–27. A map is to be prepared of an area varying in elevation from 467 to 583 ft. Which contours will be shown if a 10-ft contour interval is used? Which lines will be drawn heavier?

14–28. Similar to problem 14–27 except the terrain varies between 861 and 908 ft and a 2-ft contour interval will be used.

14–29. List the important items usually designated by upper-case letters and those by lower-case letters (a) on a topographic map and (b) on a subdivision map of a property bordering a river or lake.

14–30. What is the first step in drawing a surveying map?

14–31. List statements that should be in the title of a profile map; of a property survey map.

14–32. Why are map titles usually placed in the lower right-hand corner of the sheet?

14–33. How do the features shown on a topographic map of a large area differ from those on a map of a small area?

14–34. Is there any difference between a map and a chart? Between a map and an aerial photograph?

14–35. Describe two mapping conditions where it might be desirable to skew the meridian with respect to the border, and one situation where the arrow must be parallel with the border.

14–36. Assume that only part of a building can be shown on a topographic map because of the sheet size and scale being used. Why should building lines be cut off and *not* run into the border line ?

14–37. List six topographic features that would be classified as relief and six that would be termed cultural.

14–38. What characterizes a contour map which "lacks expression" ?

14–39. Why are contours the best method of showing elevations on a map ?

14–40. Which one of the U.S. government agencies produces most of the topographic maps of the United States ?

PART B

THE PLANETABLE

15

15-1. GENERAL. The planetable is one of the oldest types of surveying instruments. In its modern form a planetable outfit consists of tripod, drawing board, alidade equipped with stadia wires, stadia rod, and tape. A sheet of drawing paper or Mylar is fastened to the board and a map made by plotting directions and distances obtained by sighting with the alidade.

Mapping topographic features while they are in full view is advantageous in many types of surveys in civil and mining engineering, forestry, geology, agriculture, archeology, and military operations. Geologists use the Brunton compass and planetable almost exclusively in their surveys. A small board, light tripod, and peep-sight alidade, collectively known as a *traverse table*, are standard equipment in military mapping. The table is leveled and oriented by movement of the tripod legs.

Although the planetable is considered obsolete by some people, and relatively few private surveyors own or have used one, it is a valuable piece of surveying equipment.

Photogrammetry is now the principal method used for large mapping projects, but the planetable is still needed for various classification and supplemental surveys. It is impossible to extract *everything* mapworthy from photographs. Extra surveys on the ground will always be required, therefore, although they may be called "ground-truth" surveys or something else. The USGS has indicated there is no real substitute for the alidade and planetable in surveying small tracts at large scales.

15-2. DESCRIPTION OF THE PLANETABLE. The drawing board of a planetable (usually 24 × 31 in.) is carefully made to resist warping and other damage from weathering. The upper side is smooth but has some means, such as brass screws, for attaching the paper to the board. At the center of the underside of the board is a socket with threads which fit a head fastened to the top of the tripod.

Two radically different tripod heads, the *Coast and Geodetic Survey type* and the *Johnson head*, are available for leveling and orienting the board. The Coast and Geodetic Survey type has four leveling screws, a clamp and a tangent screw like those of a transit. Leveling and orientation are accomplished easily.

The Johnson head, Fig. 15-1, has a ball-and-socket arrangement to hold the board in position after leveling and prevent its turning in a horizontal direction. Clamp *A* regulates the motion of the table as it moves on the larger ball joint. It is tightened after the board has been leveled by pressing or lifting on one side. The lower clamp *B* controls the movement of the board about the vertical axis and is fastened after orientation.

Keeping the table level is the most difficult part of planetable work for beginners. Even light pressure on an edge of the board applies a strong turning moment on the relatively small supporting area of the leveling head.

An alidade, Fig. 15-2, consists of a telescope supported by a pedestal rigidly attached to a base or blade that is up to 18 in. long on some instruments. The telescope is similar to that of a transit and is equipped with one vertical and three horizontal cross hairs. A sensitive level vial, bull's-eye level, vertical arc and/or Beaman arc, compass needle, and lifting knobs are provided. The telescope may be centered over the blade, or offset to place the line of sight along the edge.

Accessories used with the planetable include a scale, triangles, compass, magnifying glass, French curve, slide rule, erasers, protractor, declinator,

Figure 15-1. Johnson-type head.

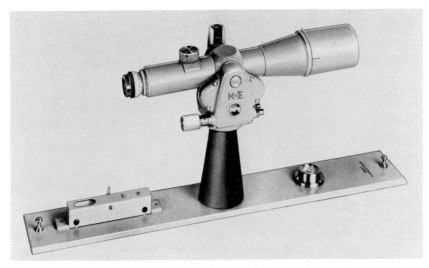

Figure 15-2. Planetable alidade. (Courtesy Keuffer & Esser, Company.)

and drafting tape. A *declinator* is a brass plate on which a compass box and one or two level vials are mounted. Two edges of the plate are parallel with the north-south line of the compass circle. The declinator is used, in the absence of a compass on the blade, to determine bearings and to orient the alidade by placing an edge against the base.

The alidade of European design shown in Fig. 15-3 is a self-reducing stadia instrument and has a parallel-ruler plotting device.

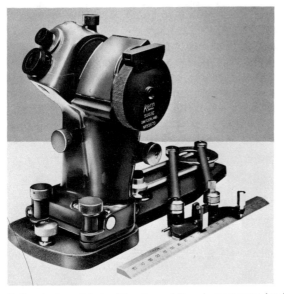

Figure 15-3. Self-reducing alidade. (Courtesy of Kern Instruments, Inc.)

15-3. USE OF THE PLANETABLE. The planetable is best suited for traversing and taking topography. It is seldom used to run boundary lines or route surveys, although some details may be added by planetable after transit-tape surveys have been made, or on an aerial photograph.

With a sheet of drawing paper firmly fastened on the board, the table is set up over any point such as A, Fig. 15-4, and leveled. The beveled edge of the alidade blade is then placed over the corresponding point a on the paper. This point may be selected in a convenient position on the board if not previously plotted. The direction to a point B is obtained by sighting through the telescope to align it and then drawing a line along the beveled edge. The stadia distance and vertical angle are read and reduced immediately, and b is located by scaling the horizontal distance on line ab. The difference in elevation computed from the stadia reading is applied to the elevation of A (assuming a reading on the h.i.) to obtain the elevation of B. This value is noted beside the plotted point for ready reference.

On precise work, horizontal control in the form of triangulation, trilateration, or traverse stations, and vertical control represented by bench

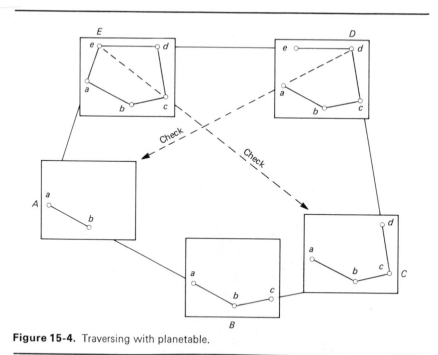

Figure 15-4. Traversing with planetable.

marks scattered over the area to be mapped, must be plotted carefully on the sheet in advance of any field work. Stadia readings are reduced and plotted as soon as taken, since notes are not recorded. *Sketching and interpolation for contours should be kept abreast of the plotting while the ground location of all mapped points is still fresh in the observer's mind.*

Obviously the drawing paper must be resistant to moisture and temperature changes, because the same sheet may be used in the field for extended periods. A hard pencil, 6-H or 8-H, is necessary to avoid smudges. The board may be covered with a waterproof material to protect the drawing. A small "window" is left open over the working area. Mylar sheets, which can be marked with a stylus, are often employed.

15-4. SETTING UP AND ORIENTING THE PLANETABLE.

After the board is screwed on the tripod head and the paper fastened, the tripod is set up with the plotted point over the corresponding hub on the ground. Generally this relationship is estimated by eye for small-scale maps. If greater accuracy is required, a plumb bob is used, or a pebble dropped from the underside of the board to check the position. The table must be carefully leveled by means of the leveling screws (or by the ball-and-socket movement of the Johnson head).

For convenience in drafting and to avoid pressure on the table which will disturb its level, the board should be placed at a height about 1 in. lower than the observer's elbows.

The table may be oriented by (1) compass, (2) backsighting, or (3) resection:

1. To orient by compass, the alidade is laid in the direction deemed most desirable for the north-south line, and the board turned until the compass on the blade, or the declinator against the ruler, reads north. The board is then clamped and a line drawn along the blade edge for future reference.

If a line AB of known bearing—say, S 28°30′ E—has already been plotted, the alidade is placed along AB, the table turned until the compass reads S 28°30′ E, and then clamped. Orientation by needle is not recommended if the backsighting or resection method can be employed readily.

2. The backsighting method is most commonly used in traversing, although the table may initially be oriented by compass to get north at the top or left side of the sheet. After a line AB has been drawn by sighting from a setup at A to point B, the table is moved to B, positioned, and leveled. With the alidade blade along BA, the table is rotated to line-in point A and the board clamped. Directions of other sights taken with the table in this position will automatically be referred to the same reference line or meridian as AB.

3. Resection will be discussed in Section 15-8.

After the table has been oriented by any of the three methods, prominent distant points should be sighted and short lines drawn near the edge of the sheet in their direction. At intervals the alidade can be laid on these lines and the occupied station point to recheck the orientation. Observing on these *permanent backsights* eliminates the need for the services of a rodman. The term *effective eccentricity* is used to describe the combined effects of both the rod and the planetable being off their corresponding ground points.

15-5. TRAVERSING.   To run a traverse, the table is set up over the initial point *A* of the survey, leveled, and clamped. Point *a* on the planetable sheet, Fig. 15-4, is marked to represent this hub. With the edge of the ruler on *a* and the alidade sighted at *B*, line *ab* is drawn. The distance *AB* may be determined by tape or stadia and its length marked off to map scale to locate *b*. It is essential that this first course be plotted accurately because it serves as the base line for all other measurements.

The table can now be moved to hub *B*, set up, and leveled. It is oriented by placing the edge of the blade on line *ba* and turning the board on its vertical axis until the alidade sights point *A*. Distance *BA* is measured and the average of *AB* and *BA* used in laying out *ab*. The next hub *C* is observed with the blade touching *b*, the distance *BC* determined, and length *bc* plotted. In similar fashion, succeeding points can be occupied and the traverse lines plotted. Whenever possible, check sights should be taken on previously occupied hubs. Small discrepancies are adjusted, but if a plotted point is missed by an appreciable distance, some or all of the measurements should be repeated.

Details can be located while the traverse is being run, or later. It is desirable to close and adjust the traverse before taking topography, inasmuch as all plotting done at an incorrectly located station will be offset. Two methods are used to obtain details—radiation and intersection.

15-6. RADIATION METHOD.   With the table oriented at any station of the traverse, radiating lines can be drawn to points whose locations are desired, as indicated in Fig. 15-5. Generally, distances are measured by stadia,

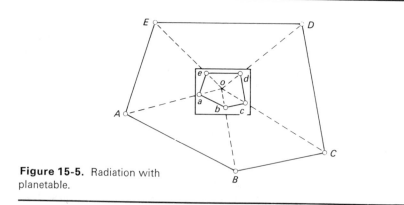

Figure 15-5. Radiation with planetable.

but a cloth tape is suitable for short sights. Radiating lines, or *rays*, are drawn along the edge of the blade and the distances scaled.

15-7. INTERSECTION, OR GRAPHICAL-TRIANGULATION, METHOD.

In the intersection method, shown in Fig. 15-6, rays of indefinite length are drawn toward the same point from at least two setups of the planetable. The intersection of the rays is the location of the point desired. One measured line serves as a base. No other distances are required.

The term graphical triangulation is sometimes applied to this method which corresponds to triangulation by transit intersections. *The method is particularly important in locating inaccessible and distant points.* In actual field practice, both radiation and intersection may be used on the same setup. Most shots are taken by radiation.

The elevation of an inaccessible point located by intersection can be found by reading the vertical angle with the middle cross hair on the point, scaling the plotted map distance to it, and computing the elevation by a trigonometric formula.

15-8. RESECTION.

Resection is a method of orientation employed when the table occupies a position not yet located on the map. Solutions for two field conditions will be described. In the first, called the *two-point problem*, the length of one line is known. In the second, the *three-point problem*, the locations of three fixed points are known.

15-9. THE TWO-POINT PROBLEM.

In Fig. 15-7, *ab* represents the known length of a line *AB* on the ground which is required in the two-point problem. With the table oriented at *B* and the alidade aligned on *C*, a line *bx* of indefinite length is drawn. The distance *bc* is not measured since the

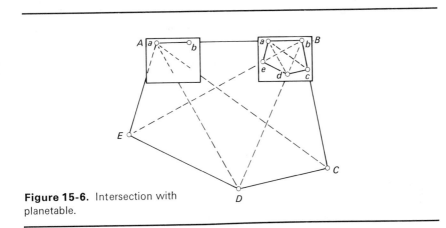

Figure 15-6. Intersection with planetable.

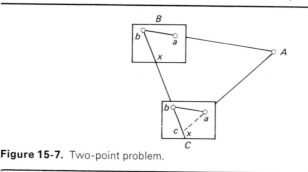

Figure 15-7. Two-point problem.

observer may wish to reserve judgment on the most advantageous position for his next instrument station, or he may wish the rodman to remain at point *A*. The table is moved to hub *C* (any point on line *bx*), oriented by backsighting along *xb*, and clamped. The alidade blade is set on *a* and pivoted around this point until the corresponding station *A* is sighted. A line drawn along the ruler from point *a* to intersect line *bx* gives the location *c* of the occupied point. Line *ac* is called a resection line.

15-10. THE THREE-POINT PROBLEM. The three-point method of location has many uses. It permits the topographer to set up the planetable at any favorable position for taking details and then determine its location on a map by sighting three plotted points such as church steeples, water towers, flagpoles, lone trees, radio masts, jutting cliff formations, or other prominent signals. Measurement of the three distances by electronic devices offers a new approach. The three-point method has long been employed in navigation to ascertain the position of a ship by observing on three shore features recognizable on a coastal chart.

The three-point problem is discussed frequently in technical literature. Trigonometric, mechanical, and graphical solutions have been devised. Only the tracing-paper and three-arm-protractor solutions will be described.

If the planetable is on a great circle through the three known points, its location is indeterminate. A strong solution results (a) when the table is well inside the *great triangle* formed by the three points (*A*, *B*, and *C* in Fig. 15-8), or (b) when the table is not near the great circle passing through the three points.

Tracing-paper method. A piece of transparent paper is fastened to the table as shown in Fig. 15-8. From any point *p'* on the paper, three radiating lines *p'a'*, *p'b'*, and *p'c'* are drawn toward hubs *A*, *B*, and *C*, which can be observed through the alidade. The tracing paper is then moved until the three radiating lines pass through the corresponding points *a*, *b*, and *c* previously plotted on the map. The vertex of these lines, *p''*, is the correct

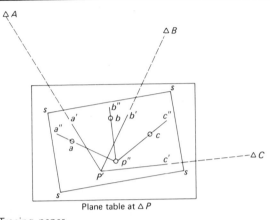

Figure 15-8. Tracing-paper
method of three-point resection.

location of the table. This point is marked and the board turned to make the lines radiate to the hubs *A*, *B*, and *C* on the ground. The board is then clamped.

Three-arm-protractor method. A similar solution can be obtained mechanically by means of a device called a three-arm protractor. This instrument has a center (somewhat like that of a drafting machine) around which two of the arms can be rotated. The desired angle between each rotating arm and the fixed arm is set by a vernier on a 360° graduated circle.

Angles *Ap'B* and *Bp'C* in Fig. 15-8 are read with a sextant or a transit. The protractor arms are clamped to these angles and then made to pass through the plotted points *a*, *b*, and *c* by trial. The three-arm protractor is not used on planetable work but is a valuable tool in hydrographic surveying and coastal navigation.

15-11. LEVELING. Elevations are obtained by using the alidade as a level, or by reading vertical angles and slope distances. After the alidade has been leveled carefully, a sight may be taken upon a rod set on a bench mark to obtain the HI. Or else, the HI is obtained by adding the h.i. (found by standing the rod beside the table and measuring the telescope's height above the point occupied) to the elevation of the occupied station. With the HI known, rod readings are taken as in ordinary leveling to determine the elevations of points.

Trigonometric leveling is commonly used where considerable difference of elevation exists. This method requires the use of vertical angles and stadia distances, from which differences of elevation are obtained by calculation. A Beaman arc on the alidade facilitates computations, but a stadia-reduction chart, slide rule, stadia table, or hand calculator can be used.

The *stepping method* of obtaining elevations is sufficiently accurate for some purposes, and in rough terrain it saves time and effort on the part of a rodman. In Fig. 15-9, assume that the elevation of point *k* at the bottom of a gorge is needed on a survey employing two rodmen, one on each side of the canyon. After the intercept on the rod between stadia hairs, *ab*, is found to be, say, 5.2 ft, the upper hair is set on the base of the rod at *c*. The position *d* where the lower cross hair strikes the ground is noted and the upper cross hair depressed to sight this point. The process is continued until point *h* is found, and the remaining drop to the lowest spot *k* estimated at perhaps 2 ft. The difference in elevation between *c* and *k* is therefore 28 ft.

Another version of the stepping method utilizes the fact that the axis of sight through the upper (or lower) cross hair is on a ½% grade from the axis through the middle hair.

Differences of elevation are generally computed in the field and plotted on the planetable map. The topographer may compute (if he does not have a self-reducing tacheometer) as well as plot, or he may have one member of the party make the stadia reductions. Contours are drawn through points established by the direct method, or interpolated if breaks in slope have been taken. Spot elevations are shown for grade crossings, peaks and depressions which do not fall at contour levels, and all other critical points.

The number of points taken need be only 50 to 60% of the total on a comparable transit-stadia survey to locate contours with the same degree of accuracy. Furthermore, features shown on the map can be compared with the terrain as work progresses, and any discrepancies readily discovered.

One of the greatest difficulties arising in the use of the planetable is keeping it level. Pressing on one corner of the board is a practical way to center the bubble and complete a few sights with the Johnson head. This procedure eliminates the necessity of loosening the ball-and-socket joint, which usually disturbs the orientation.

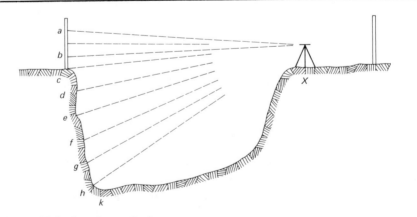

Figure 15-9. Stepping method.

15-12. ADVANTAGES AND DISADVANTAGES OF THE PLANE-TABLE. Some of the advantages of the planetable over the transit-stadia method follow:

1. The map is made while looking at the area.
2. Irregular lines, such as stream banks and contours, can be sketched.
3. Notes are not taken.
4. Fewer points are required for the same precision in locating contours.
5. A map is produced in less overall time (field plus office).

Some disadvantages of the planetable in comparison with the transit-stadia method are:

1. More field time is necessary.
2. Bad weather may halt field work.
3. Control must be plotted in advance for precise work.
4. More time is required to become proficient with the planetable than with the transit.
5. The table is set lower than a transit normally would be, thus providing less sight clearance.
6. Distances must be scaled if lengths are to be taken from the map and areas computed.
7. Many awkward items must be carried.
8. The planetable is unsuitable for wooded country.

15-13. PLANETABLE POINTERS. One of the troublesome problems in operating a planetable is to keep the alidade blade on the plotted position of the occupied point, such as P in Fig. 15-10. As the alidade is moved to sight a detail, the edge moves off point P. A solution sometimes tried is to use a pin at P and pivot around it, but a progressively larger hole is gouged in the paper with each sight.

Some alidades, such as that in Fig. 15-3, have a parallel ruler attached to the blade, and this provides the best answer. The next best is to place the alidade within an inch or two of the point P, pivot as necessary for a sight, and then transfer the line through P by using two triangles as shown in Fig. 15-10. The small error produced by the eccentric sight is no greater than that resulting from not being exactly over the ground point P, or even that caused by the telescope axis not being over the edge of the blade.

Other helpful pointers on use of the planetable are:

1. Use buff or green detail paper to lessen the glare.
2. Plot and ink the traverse in advance of the detailing, showing lengths of traverse lines, coordinates of triangulation stations, and useful signals available.
3. Have at least one vertical control point for each three hubs of a traverse, and show all known elevations.
4. Have all the accessories.

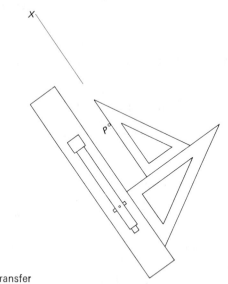

Figure 15-10. Transfer
of pivot point.

5. Cover the portion of the map not being used.
6. Set up the table slightly below elbow height.
7. Check the orientation on two or more lines if possible.
8. Check the distance and elevation difference in both directions when setting a new hub. Read vertical angles with the telescope in normal and
   plunged positions, if possible. Use the average value in plotting.
9. Read the distance first, then the vertical angle; or with a Beaman arc,
   read the H scale and then the V arc.
10. Lift the forward end of the alidade blade to pivot, instead of sliding the
    blade, to keep the paper cleaner.
11. Clean the blade frequently to remove graphite.
12. Reduce stadia readings in the following preferred order: self-reducing
    tacheometer, Beaman arc, hand calculator, slide rule, charts, tables,
    formulas.
13. Check the location of hubs by resection and by *cutting in* (sighting and
    plotting) prominent objects.
14. Draw short lines at the estimated distance on the map to plot points.
    Do not start lines at the hub occupied.
15. Keep in mind comparable limits of accuracy for direction (angle) and
    distance.
16. Identify points by consecutive numbers or names as they are plotted.
    Number the contours.
17. Have the rodman make independent sketches on long shots, for later
    transference to the planetable map.

18. Use walkie-talkie sets to enable the rodmen to describe topographic features when the observer cannot identify them because of distance and obstacles.
19. Use the same points to locate details and contours whenever possible.
20. Locate contours by the direct method in gently sloping and rolling terrain. Use the indirect method in rugged country and areas having uniform slopes.
21. Sketch contours after three points have been plotted. Points on the map lose their value if they cannot be identified on the ground.
22. Show spot elevations for summits, sags, bridges, road crossings, and all other critical points.
23. Tie a piece of colored cloth on the stadia rod at the required rod reading to speed work in locating contours by the direct method.
24. Employ the stepping method in areas where access is difficult.
25. Draw lines at 1-in. intervals on all four margins of the planetable sheet at the time the first plotting is done. The lines provide a means of determining the expansion and contraction of the paper.
26. Utilize vertical aerial photographs for planetable sheets. The planimetric details can be checked and contours added.
27. Use a 6-H or harder pencil to avoid smudging.

15-14. SOURCES OF ERROR IN PLANETABLE WORK. Sources of error in planetable operation include the following:

1. Table not level.
2. Orientation disturbed during the detailing.
3. Sights too long for accurate sketching.
4. Poor control.
5. Traversing and detailing simultaneously.
6. Too few points taken for good sketching.

15-15. MISTAKES. Some typical mistakes made in planetable work are as follow:

1. Detailing without proper control.
2. Table not level.
3. Orientation incorrect.

PROBLEMS

15–1. List side by side for comparison the respective advantages and disadvantages of the Johnson-type tripod head and the Coast and Geodetic Survey head.
15–2. Tabulate three methods of orienting a planetable, their advantages and disadvantages, and an example of the practical use of each method.

15–3. Upon what factors does accurate planetable orientation depend?

15–4. What is the danger of traversing with a planetable and locating details at the same time?

15–5. Why may it be difficult to measure a vertical angle of 40° with some planetable alidades?

15–6. For what field conditions is the planetable preferred to transit stadia in making a topographic survey?

15–7. Compare the radiation and intersection methods for general planetable operations, and give an example of the most desirable application of each.

15–8. Locate the position in a classroom of a point C on your desk by the two-point method. Mark point A on the blackboard and point B in a convenient manner on another desk. Measure the horizontal distance AB and plot it to scale as ab on a sheet of paper fastened to a drawing board. Then locate point c on the sheet over point C. Sight over one edge of an engineer's scale to get the resection line.

15–9. Locate your position in the classroom by the three-point tracing-paper method. Mark three points, A in one corner of the room and B and C on the blackboards. Measure the horizontal distances from A to points B and C. Plot the points to scale on a sheet $8^1/_2 \times 11$ in. Sight over an edge of an engineer's scale to obtain the resection lines.

15–10. Examine planetable literature and discuss the advantages of the Lehmann method of three-point location.

15–11. State two field situations that make the planetable preferable to photogrammetric mapping.

15–12. What are the three main methods of locating points with a planetable?

15–13. Given points C and D plotted on a planetable sheet. Describe the procedure in locating points E, F, and G with a nontelescopic alidade by making only two setups and without measuring any distances or setting up the table at D.

15–14. List the pertinent factors to be considered in selecting the proper scale for any specific planetable project.

15–15. On what maximum length of sight can the effects of curvature and refraction be neglected in determining elevations with a planetable?

15–16. How can the planetable be used in connection with topographic maps prepared photogrammetrically?

15–17. What is the purpose of a cover sheet (sheet mask) with a "window" on planetable work in the field?

15–18. Are spur traverses desirable with a planetable? Explain.

15–19. How is a planetable map checked for accuracy?

15–20. A planetable is oriented at hub A by compass only to start a survey and as a result the first line is off by 15′ from the assumed direction. If the line is extended 4 miles and a hub B set, what is its plotted position error if the scale being used is 1 in. = 2400 ft?

15–21. On a traverse 2 miles long, an experienced planetable man uses a typical alidade, Beaman arc, 45″/2-mm striding level vial, and stadia rod, and balances sights, limiting them to 400 ft. What maximum errors in distance and elevation are reasonable?

15–22. The alidade on a planetable is placed 2 in. off the proper point in sighting an object 120 ft away. The map scale is 1 in. = 50 ft. Is the error significant? Explain.

15–23. The telescope of an alidade is centered over a blade 3 in. wide. What error is introduced in plotting a shot 250 ft long if the map scale is 1 in. = 80 ft? If the sight is 500 ft and the map scale 1 in. = 100 ft? If the shot is 600 ft and map scale 1 in. = 400 ft?

15–24. The stepping method is employed to determine the elevation of a point k in a canyon (Fig. 15–9) from an instrument set up over X, elevation 760.0 ft. With the telescope level, an intercept $ab = 3.72$ ft is obtained on a rod held at c, and 5.4 ft read on the middle cross line. If six "steps" are taken from the bottom of the rod at c, and an estimated vertical distance of $1^1/_2$ ft remains to point k, what is the elevation of k? The h.i. is 5.1 ft.

15–25. Similar to problem 15–24 except that the rod intercept is 4.65 ft, five steps are taken, and the estimated vertical distance remaining to point k is 1 ft.

15–26. What assumptions and limitations are present in the stepping method?

15–27. The total length of a closed planetable traverse is 9600 ft. The plotted traverse fails to close by 0.06 in. If the map scale is 1 in. = 500 ft, what relative error of closure is obtained?

15–28. Similar to problem 15–27 except the linear closure is 0.08 in. and the scale 1 in. = 800 ft.

15–29. What are the main troubles which arise in using the planetable and how are they best corrected?

15–30. In leveling a planetable, which condition demands the most special care: when sights are short, vertical angles are large, or scale is small? Explain.

15–31. State two cases in which occupation of an eccentric station with a planetable might be necessary.

16
DETERMINATION OF MERIDIAN

16-1. GENERAL. To fix property lines and other survey courses, directions as well as lengths must be known. The direction of a course is determined by the horizontal angle between it and some reference line, usually a meridian, which can be assumed, a magnetic north-south line, or a true meridian through the celestial poles.

A magnetic needle furnishes one means of ascertaining the north-south line. Since magnetic forces are variable in direction throughout the earth, and a compass needle is sensitive to local attraction, its use is not reliable for accurate surveying. A true north-south direction can be found by observations on the sun or stars (or from known coordinates of two points) if locations of stations are to be permanently fixed.

North-seeking gyro attachments to be mounted above a theodolite are now made by two instrument manufacturers. True north can be quickly determined to an accuracy of $\pm 20''$ (standard deviation) with the gyro device shown in Fig. 16-1.

Standard error limits for geodetic control survey astronomical azimuths are as follows:

	First Order	Second Order		Third Order	
		Class I	Class II	Class I	Class II
Triangulation	0.45"	0.45"	0.6"	0.8"	3.0"
Trilateration	0.45"	0.45"	0.6"	0.8"	3.0"
Traverse	0.45"	0.45"	1.5"	3.0"	8.0"

Figure 16-1. TM-20C theodolite and GP-1 gyro attachment. (Courtesy Lietz Co.)

This chapter presents some fundamental facts of field astronomy applied to observations on the sun and Polaris (the North Star) for azimuth. Additional study will permit a person to sight any star whose position is given in an ephemeris or the *American Nautical Almanac*. Copies of an ephemeris are available at a small charge from companies manufacturing surveying instruments. More extensive tables are given in *Ephemeris of the Sun and Polaris* (prepared by the U.S. Naval Observatory for the Bureau of Land Management, BLM); *Apparent Places of Fundamental Stars*; and the *American Ephemeris and Nautical Almanac*.

Possession of an ephemeris will be assumed in the following discussion. The 1976 Keuffel and Esser (K & E) ephemeris with values carried out to the nearest 0.1′, far enough for ordinary work, has been used for reference in this chapter and the appropriate tables and page numbers noted for values taken from it. For 1977 and later years, the tabular values change slowly.

16-2. METHODS OF DETERMINING AZIMUTH. The following methods for determining an approximate north-south line will be examined briefly: (1) *Sun observations* by (a) shadow method, (b) equal-altitudes method, and (c) direct observations; (2) *circumpolar-star observations* at (a) culmination, (b) elongation, and (c) any hour angle.

Students usually find the study of field astronomy somewhat difficult because it requires many definitions, spherical trigonometry, and visualization in three dimensions. Several examples of simple methods which can be used for rough determinations of azimuth are given before discussing more-technical features.

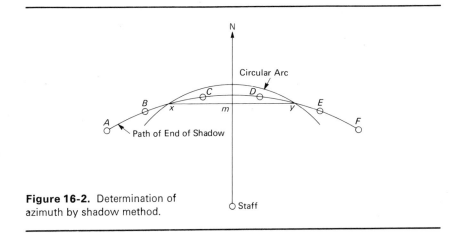

Figure 16-2. Determination of azimuth by shadow method.

16-3. SHADOW METHOD. It is possible to establish a meridian by the shadow method without any equipment except a piece of string. In Fig. 16-2, points *A*, *B*, *C*, *D*, *E*, and *F* mark the end of the shadow of a plumbed staff or a telephone pole at intervals of perhaps 30 min throughout the period from 9 AM to 3 PM. A smooth curve is sketched through the marks. With the staff or pole as a center, and any appropriate radius, a circular arc is swung to obtain two intersections, *x* and *y*, with the shadow curve. A line from the staff through *m*, the midpoint of *xy*, approximates the meridian.

If the ground is level, the pole is plumb, and the shadow points are carefully marked, the angle between the line established and the true meridian should not be larger than 30'. Since the sun moves diagonally across the equator instead of traveling along a perfect east-west path, some error is inherent in the method.

16-4. MERIDIAN BY EQUAL ALTITUDES OF THE SUN. Determination of the meridian by equal altitudes of the sun requires a transit, but the method is similar in principle to the shadow method. Assume that the meridian is to be passed through a point *P*, Fig. 16-3, over which the transit is set up. At some time between 8 AM and 10 AM, say about 9 AM—with a dark glass over the eyepiece or objective lens, the sun's disk is bisected by both the horizontal and vertical cross hairs. The vertical angle is read, the telescope depressed, and point *x* set at least 500 ft from the instrument. Shortly before 3 PM, with the vertical angle previously read placed on the arc, the sun is followed until the vertical and horizontal cross hairs again simultaneously bisect the sun. The telescope is depressed and a point *y* set at approximately the same distance from *P* as *x*. The bisector of angle *xPy* is the true meridian.

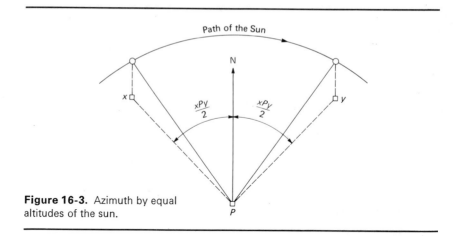

Figure 16-3. Azimuth by equal altitudes of the sun.

As in the shadow method, perfect results cannot be attained because the sun's changing declination gives it a diagonal path across the equator (instead of parallel with it). The declination of the sun is its distance north or south of the equator.

Other disadvantages of the method are the time and delay required, the possibility of clouds obscuring the second sight, and the difficulty of setting the vertical angle exactly (since most arcs read only to the nearest minute). The last problem can be eliminated by setting hub x first, then elevating the telescope to observe the sun as it passes over the point, and leaving the vertical angle on the arc until the afternoon sight has been taken.

16-5. MERIDIAN FROM POLARIS AT CULMINATION. Figure 16-4 shows the apparent motion of Polaris as seen from the earth on its path through culminations and elongations. The star moves in a counterclockwise direction around the north-south axis of the earth extended, but twice each day it is on the line of this axis for an observer at any location. The point at the upper limit of its travel is called *Upper Culmination* (U.C.), and the point at the lower extremity, *Lower Culmination* (L.C.). At *Eastern Elongation* (E.E.) and *Western Elongation* (W.E.) the star reaches its most distant position from the meridian.

If an observer at point O sights on Polaris at the exact instant of upper or lower culmination for his longitude, he need only depress the telescope and set a hub X on the ground to obtain a true north-south line, OX. If it is more convenient to do so, the horizontal angle from a mark to the star can be measured to give the azimuth of a desired line.

The exact time of culmination at Greenwich, England, for any date is available in an ephemeris. A few simple calculations are required to determine the time of culmination at any other location.

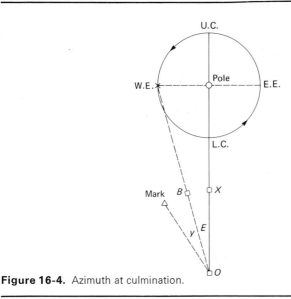

Figure 16-4. Azimuth at culmination.

Some basic principles of field astronomy will now be given, along with their use in observations.

16-6. DEFINITIONS. In observations upon heavenly bodies, the sun and stars are assumed to lie on the surface of a *celestial sphere* of infinite radius having the same center as the earth. All stars appear to move around centers which are on the north-south axis of the celestial sphere. Figure 16-5 illustrates some of the terms used in field astronomy. Here S represents a heavenly body, as the sun or a star. Students find it helpful to sketch the various features on a true sphere or globe.

The *zenith* is the point where the plumb line projected above the horizon meets the celestial sphere. On a diagram it is usually designated by Z. Stated differently, it is the point on the celestial sphere vertically above the observer.

The *nadir* is that point on the celestial sphere directly beneath the observer, and exactly opposite the zenith.

A *vertical circle* is any great circle of the celestial sphere passing through the zenith and nadir, and represents the line of intersection of a vertical plane with the celestial sphere.

An *hour circle* is any great circle on the celestial sphere whose plane is perpendicular to the plane of the celestial equator. Hour circles correspond to meridians and longitudinal lines, and are used to measure hour angles.

The *celestial equator* is the great circle on the celestial sphere whose plane is perpendicular to the axis of rotation of the earth. It corresponds to the earth's equator enlarged in diameter. Half of the equator is represented by $EWS''E'$ in Fig. 16-5.

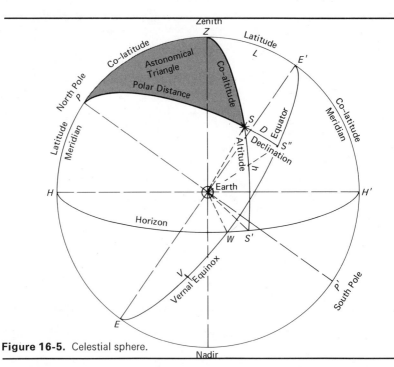

Figure 16-5. Celestial sphere.

A *celestial meridian* is the hour circle containing the zenith. It is also defined as the vertical circle passing through the celestial pole. The intersection of the plane of the celestial meridian with the plane of the horizon is the astronomic meridian line used in plane surveying.

The *horizon* is a great circle on the celestial sphere whose plane is perpendicular to the direction of the plumb line. In surveying, the plane of the horizon is determined by a spirit level. Half of the horizon is represented by $HWS'H'$.

An *hour angle* is the angle between the plane of the hour circle passing through a celestial body or point and the plane of the celestial meridian. It may be measured by the angle at the pole between an hour circle and the meridian, or by the arc of the equator intercepted by those circles.

The *Greenwich hour angle* of a heavenly body is the angle measured from the meridian of Greenwich westward to the meridian over which the body is passing at any moment. In the ephemeris it is designated by GHA.

The *declination* of a heavenly body is the angular distance measured along the hour circle between the body and the equator; it is plus when the body is north of the equator, and minus when south of it. Declination is usually denoted by D in formulas, and represented by $S''S$ in Fig. 16-5. About 22 June and 22 December the sun reaches its maximum declination north and south, respectively, of 23°26.5′ at the *solstices* or solsticial points.

The *position* of a heavenly body with respect to the earth, at any moment, may be given by its declination and Greenwich hour angle.

The *polar distance* of a body is the angular distance from the pole measured along an hour circle. It is equal to 90° minus the declination.

The *altitude* of a heavenly body is the angular distance measured along a vertical circle above the horizon, $S'S$ in Fig. 16-5. It is measured with the vertical arc of a transit, a theodolite, or sextant, and usually denoted in formulas by h.

The *co-altitude*, or *zenith distance*, equals 90° minus the altitude.

The *astronomical* or *PZS triangle* is the spherical triangle whose vertices are the pole (P), zenith (Z), and astronomical body (S).

The *azimuth* of a heavenly body is the arc of the horizon measured clockwise from either the north or south point to the vertical circle through the body. An azimuth from south is represented by $H'S'$. From Fig. 16-5, it is seen that $H'S'$ equals 180° minus the Z angle of the PZS triangle. Azimuth is measured as a horizontal angle with a transit or theodolite.

The *latitude* of an observer is the angular distance on his meridian between the equator and the zenith. It is also the angular distance between the polar axis and the horizon. Latitude is measured north or south of the equator. In formulas in this book it is denoted by L.

The *vernal equinox* is the point of intersection of the celestial equator and the ecliptic apparently traversed by the sun in passing from south to north in March. It is a fixed point on the celestial sphere (the astronomer's zero-zero point of coordinates in the sky) and moves with the celestial sphere just as the stars do. On Fig. 16-5 it is designated by V.

The *right ascension* of a heavenly body is the angular distance VS''. Right ascension frequently replaces Greenwich hour angle as a means of specifying the position of a star with respect to the earth. In this system, however, the Greenwich hour angle of the vernal equinox must also be given.

Refraction is the angular increase in the apparent altitude of a heavenly body due to bending of light rays passing obliquely through the earth's atmosphere. It varies from zero for an altitude of 90° to a maximum of about 35' at the horizon. The correction for refraction, in minutes, is roughly equal to the natural cotangent of the observed altitude. Small adjustments must also be made for temperature and pressure variations.

Refraction makes observations on heavenly bodies near the horizon less reliable than those taken at high altitudes. The correction is always subtracted from observed altitudes.

Parallax results from observations being made from the surface of the earth instead of at its center. It causes a small angular decrease in the apparent altitude; hence the correction is always added. Parallax is insignificant when observing a star but must be added on solar shots. The ephemeris contains tables listing refraction and parallax corrections.

16-7. TIME.   Four kinds of time are used in computing an observation.

Sidereal time. A sidereal day is the interval of time between two successive upper transits of the vernal equinox over the same meridian. Sidereal time is star time. At any instant it is equal to the hour angle of the vernal equinox.

Apparent solar time. An apparent solar day is the interval of time between two successive lower transits of the sun. Apparent solar time is sun time, and the length of a day varies somewhat. The average apparent solar day is 3 min 56 sec longer than a sidereal day of 23 hr 56.1 min, Fig. 16-6.

Mean solar, or civil, time. This is the time kept by a fictitious sun, called the "mean" sun, which is assumed to move at a uniform rate. It is the basis for watch time and the 24-hr day.

The *equation of time* is the difference between mean solar and apparent solar time. Its value changes continually as the sun gets ahead of, then falls behind the mean sun. Values for each day of the year are given in an ephemeris.

Standard time. This is the mean time at meridians 15° or 1 hr apart, measured eastward and westward from Greenwich. Eastern standard time (EST) at the 75th meridian differs from Greenwich civil time (GCT) by 5 hr (earlier, since the sun has not yet traveled from the meridian of Greenwich to the United States). Standard time was adopted in the United States in 1883, replacing some 100 local times previously used. Daylight saving time (DST) in any zone is equal to standard time in the zone to the *east.*

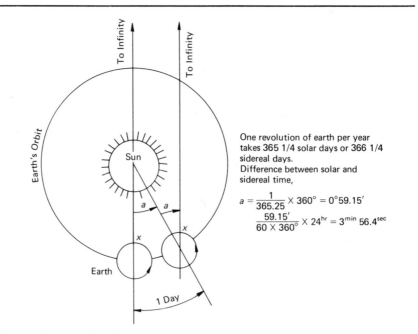

One revolution of earth per year takes 365 1/4 solar days or 366 1/4 sidereal days.
Difference between solar and sidereal time,

$$a = \frac{1}{365.25} \times 360° = 0°59.15'$$

$$\frac{59.15'}{60 \times 360°} \times 24^{hr} = 3^{min}\,56.4^{sec}$$

Figure 16-6. Earth's orbit.

In working with longitude and time zones it is helpful to remember the following relations:

$$360° \text{ of longitude} = 24 \text{ hours}$$
$$15° = 1 \text{ hour}$$
$$1° = 4 \text{ minutes (of time)}$$

16-8. STAR POSITIONS. If the pole could be seen as a definite point in the sky marked by a star a meridian observation would require only a simple sighting. Since the pole is not so marked, observations must be made on stars—preferably those close to the pole—whose radii of rotation and positions at given times are listed in a nautical almanac or ephemeris. Stars appear to move counterclockwise because of the earth's clockwise rotation.

The visible star nearest the north pole is Polaris, a part of the constellation Ursa Minor, also called the Little Dipper. The radius of rotation of Polaris, measured by a vertical angle along the meridian through the position of an observer, is its polar distance. The value of this angle changes slightly from year to year, but it was approximately 0°51' in 1976.

Polaris is located in the sky by first finding the Big Dipper, in Ursa Major. The two stars of the dipper farthest from the handle are the Pointers, as shown in Fig. 16-7. Polaris is the nearest bright star along the line through the Pointers distinguished by its location at the end of the handle of the Little Dipper, as well as on the line through the easternmost star of Cassiopeia and the end star of the Big Dipper handle. In 12,000 yr, however, it will have moved away from its present position (but will return in about 25,000

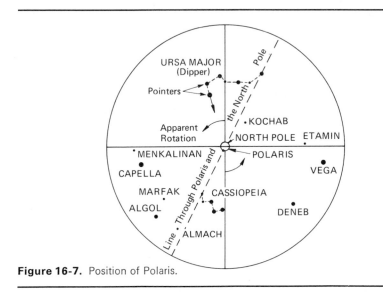

Figure 16-7. Position of Polaris.

yr!) and a new star come close to the pole. The Southern Cross is used for observations in the southern hemisphere since there is not a bright star near the pole.

16-9. OBSERVATION ON POLARIS AT CULMINATION. As previously noted, if Polaris can be observed at upper or lower culmination, the meridian is readily laid out on the ground. At culmination, however, the star appears to be moving most rapidly in the east-west or west-east direction (for an observer at 45° latitude, from Table 10, K&E Ephemeris,

$$\text{the average} = \text{approximately} \frac{6.3' \times 60''}{5° \times 4'^{/°}} = 19''/\text{min}$$

Accurate time is therefore required to obtain a precise meridian, and only a single sight is possible for each culmination.

Since the sidereal day is 23 hr 56.1 min and the mean solar (civil) day 24 hr, culmination occurs about 4 min earlier each day of the calendar year. Over a period of many years, however, there is very little difference in the time of culmination for the same date and location. In the example of Section 16-10, the time of upper culmination on 15 December 1968 was $20^h24.6^m$ or only 7.7 min different in the 8 yr to 1976. Thus an old ephemeris might be satisfactory for the approximate time of culmination if a meridian determination to the nearest few minutes is good enough.

Ephemerides list the time of culmination and elongation at Greenwich for every 10th or 15th day throughout the year. It is necessary to convert these tabulations to the standard time of the place of observation. The computational methods illustrated herein are believed to provide the easiest approach to field astronomy for beginners in the subject.

An observation at culmination is simple to compute. There are three important disadvantages, however: a small error in time causes a relatively large error in azimuth; both culminations may come at awkward hours—even during daylight in the summer; and with only a single pointing on the star, any instrumental inadjustments will cause an error in direction of the meridian when the telescope is transited.

16-10. COMPUTATIONS FOR TIME OF CULMINATION. Three computations (corrections) are made to convert the time of culmination listed in an ephemeris for Greenwich, England, to standard (watch) time for culmination at any other location. They will be illustrated for an observation on 18 December 1976 at latitude 46°42' N, longitude 93°18' W, using pertinent values from an ephemeris.

1. Correction to convert the time of upper culmination tabulated in the

ephemeris for Greenwich on certain dates, to the actual date of observation. The result from the table (the interpolated date or value is inset) follows:

1976 K&E Ephem.   15 December $20^h32.3^m$ GCT (Greenwich civil time)
Table 8, p. 75   18 December $\frac{3}{10} \times 39.5 = 11.8^m$ $20^h20.5^m$
                             25 December $19^h52.8^m$

2. Correction for longitude 93°18′ west of Greenwich. A place at longitude 93°18′ is approximately one-quarter of the way around the world from Greenwich, and therefore the time difference is ¼ day. The average change (decrease) in time of culmination per day (or per 360° of longitude) is 3.93 min over an entire year, but for the 10-day interval (Dec.15–25) being used, the change is 3.95 min/day. Correction for 93°18′ of west longitude is then

$$3.95 \text{ min} \times \frac{93.3°}{360°} = -1.0 \text{ min}$$

3. Correction for longitude west of the 90th (sixth time zone) meridian. The difference in time of culmination at longitude 90° and 93°18′ requires converting standard (watch) time to local time at the place of observation. Since 1° corresponds to 4 min of time, the correction is

$$3.30° \times 4 \text{ min/degree} = +13.2 \text{ min}$$

The plus indicates that culmination occurs later at longitude 93°18′ W than at the time-zone meridian. Note that standard time at the 90th meridian is 6 hr earlier than Greenwich time, but it takes Polaris approximately 6 hr to travel from the meridian of Greenwich to the 90th meridian.

The three computations show that when Polaris culminates over the meridian of the observer at longitude 93°18′, a watch set for the time zone of the 90th meridian should read

$$20^h20.5^m - 1.0^m + 13.2^m = 20^h32.7^m$$

Notice that for an observer on the 90th meridian, a correction of only 1 min would be necessary to get the local time of culmination after interpolating in the ephemeris.

Ephemeris tables are based on 40° latitude as an average for the United States. Since the star is on the meridian at culmination, latitude has no effect on the watch time.

16-11. OBSERVATION ON POLARIS AT ELONGATION.

Observing Polaris at elongation instead of at culmination has several advantages: (a) The star has a negligible east-west or west-east movement and appears to travel along the vertical wire for about 15 min before and after elongation. (b) Watch time therefore need not be precise. (c) Several sights can be taken with the telescope normal and plunged, and averaged to reduce instrumental and personal errors. ~~A minor disadvantage is the somewhat longer computation procedure.~~

An observation is made by first sighting on an illuminated fixed mark with the plates set to zero, and then loosening the upper motion to point on the star. The angle from mark to star, y in Fig. 16-4, is read, the telescope plunged, a second sight taken on the star, and the angle read again. This process is repeated for the desired number of repetitions. As a final step, the original mark should be resighted to be certain the plates still read zero.

An alternative method is to sight the star at elongation with zero on the plates, depress the telescope, and set a stake B, Fig. 16-4, at least several hundred feet from the instrument. The procedure is repeated after plunging as a check. A true north course can be laid off the next day after computing angle E.

16-12. COMPUTATIONS FOR AN OBSERVATION AT ELONGATION.

A computation for the time of western elongation and bearing of Polaris at elongation is given in Illustration 16-1. The data (except the date) are the same as in Section 16-10, but an additional (fourth) correction must be made for latitude other than 40°. Note that the time of western elongation tabulated opposite Dec. 15 is *for the next day* (see ephemeris statement below the table).

The star is 1°13.2′ to the west of north at elongation. This is the value of angle E, Fig. 16-4. Adding the angle y between the mark and the star produces the desired true bearing of the line from O to the mark.

ILLUSTRATION 16-1. COMPUTATION OF THE BEARING OF POLARIS
AT WESTERN ELONGATION

Longitude 93°18′ W   Latitude 46°42′ N   19 Dec. 1976

(Table 8, p. 75) Time of W. E. at Greenwich, 19 Dec. 1976	2ʰ16.7ᵐ
Correction for longitude west of Greenwich	− 1.0ᵐ
Correction for longitude west of 90th meridian	+ 13.2ᵐ
(Table 9, p. 75) Correction for latitude other than 40°	− 0.7ᵐ
Time of W.E. at observer's location	2ʰ28.2ᵐ

Polar distance of Polaris by interpolation from 1976 K&E ephemeris :
(Table 3, p. 67)

16 December		0°50.21′
19 December	³/₁₀ ×0.04=0.01	0°50.20′
26 December		0°50.17′

Bearing of Polaris at W.E. by double interpolation and extrapolation :

Polar distances	0°50.20′	0°50.30′	0°50.50′
(Table 7, p. 74) Latitude 46°		1°12.4′	1°12.7′
Latitude 46°42′	1°13.2′	1°13.4′	1°13.7′
Latitude 47°		1°13.8′	1°14.1′

Hence bearing of Polaris = N1°13.2′W

Another means of computing the angle E between Polaris at elongation and the meridian is by the formula

$$\sin E = \frac{\sin \text{ polar distance}}{\cos \text{ latitude}} \tag{16-1}$$

or

$$\text{bearing of Polaris (in minutes)} = \frac{\text{polar distance}}{\cos \text{ latitude}} \tag{16-1a}$$

In the example, $\sin E = \dfrac{\sin 0°50.20'}{\cos 46°42'} = 0.0212915, \qquad E = 1°13.2'$

or

$$E = \frac{0°50.20'}{\cos 46°42'} = \frac{0°50.20'}{0.6858184} = 73.2' = 1°13.2'$$

Mean polar distances for years 1975 through 1984 are listed in Table 16-1.

TABLE 16-1. MEAN POLAR DISTANCES FOR THE YEARS 1975–1984

Year	Mean Polar Distance	Year	Mean Polar Distance
1975	00°51'00"	1980	00°49'36"
1976	00°50'43"	1981	00°49'19"
1977	00°50'26"	1982	00°49'02"
1978	00°50'09"	1983	00°48'45"
1979	00°49'52"	1984	00°48'29"

For observations made less than 30 min before or after elongation, the correction to a bearing at elongation is computed by the formula

$$C = Kt^2 \tag{16-2}$$

where C is the correction to the angle in seconds of arc; t the time, in sidereal units, before or after elongation; and K a factor depending upon the bearing at elongation equal to $[(15)^2/2] \times (60)^2 \times \sin 1'' \times \tan Z$, where Z is the azimuth at greatest elongation. For t expressed in solar units,

$$K = \frac{(15)^2}{2} \times \left(60 \times \frac{366.2422}{365.2422}\right)^2 \times \sin 1'' \times \tan Z$$

Values of K (which do not change with time) are listed in Table 16-2.

For the values previously found and an observation 20 min after elongation, the correction is

$$C = 0.046(20)^2 = 18'' \text{ (less than } 1''/\text{min)}$$

The small value of the correction demonstrates the advantage of observing Polaris at or near elongation since a large error in watch time causes only a small error in the azimuth.

TABLE 16-2. CORRECTION FACTORS FOR
BEARINGS AT ELONGATION

Bearing at Elongation	K
1°00′	0.034
1°10′	0.040
1°20′	0.046
1°30′	0.051
1°40′	0.057
1°50′	0.063

16-13. OBSERVATION ON POLARIS AT ANY HOUR ANGLE. Frequently it is more convenient to make an observation on Polaris at *any* hour angle rather than at culmination or elongation. The local hour angle (difference between the time of observation and culmination) is computed, and the bearing of Polaris taken from an ephemeris table which gives values of the Z angle in the *PZS* triangle for listings of latitude and hour angle.

A sample set of field notes and computations for the bearing of a reference line are shown in Illustration 16-2. A second horizontal angle should always be obtained with the telescope plunged, and the watch time recorded, to permit computation of an average value of the bearing and compensate for instrumental error.

16-14. PRACTICAL SUGGESTIONS ON POLARIS OBSERVATIONS.
The following suggestions make observations on Polaris easier to perform:

1. During the late summer season in the United States, eastern elongation occurs at a convenient time.
2. Prepare the noteforms in advance of starting field work.
3. Have a watch, flashlight, reflector, and pencils. Note that the accuracy of vernier readings is lowered at night, because lighting from the side causes parallax if transit plates are not at the same level. Hold the flashlight over the compass box behind the ground-glass upright piece and let the light diffuse through it.
4. The mark must be visible at night, recognizable and definite in the daytime. It should be at least 1 mile away if possible to avoid instrumental errors in refocusing between mark and star, star and mark sights.
5. Set up the transit in daylight if possible. If the altitude of Polaris is known, observations can begin before dark.
6. The altitude of Polaris is equal to the latitude of the place when the star is at elongation. The star will be nearly a degree off and out of the telescope field of view near culmination for the latitude angle.

ILLUSTRATION 16-2.   OBSERVATION ON POLARIS AT ANY HOUR ANGLE

Data

△ at △ Cass.   Lat. 47°22'13"N   Long. 94°32'18"W   6 Sept. 1976

Tele-scope	Point Sighted	Watch Time	Watch Correction	Horizontal Angle (Clockwise)	Vertical Angle
	△ Snow			0°00'	
N	Polaris	5ʰ44ᵐ00ˢ	0ᵐ00ˢ	72°22'30"	48°08'
P	Polaris	5ʰ44ᵐ24ˢ		72°22'50"	
	△ Snow			0°00'	
		Ave. 5ʰ44ᵐ12ˢ		72°22'40"	

Hour Angle of Polaris

GCT of upper culmination 7 September 1976	3ʰ05.2ᵐ
Correction for 1 day at 3.91ᵐ/day	+ 3.9ᵐ
GCT of upper culmination 6 September 1976	3ʰ09.1ᵐ
Correction for longitude 94.54° west of Greenwich	− 1.0ᵐ
Local time of upper culmination	3ʰ08.1ᵐ
Correction for longitude 4.54° west of 90th meridian	+ 18.2ᵐ
CST of upper culmination at longitude 94°32.3'W	3ʰ26.3ᵐ
Actual time of observation	5ʰ44.2ᵐ
Time difference from culmination	2ʰ17.9ᵐ
Correction for 3.91ᵐ/day (approx. 10ˢ/hr)	+ 0.4ᵐ
Hour angle (west of upper culmination)	2ʰ18.3ᵐ

Bearing

(Table 10, p. 78, 1976 K&E ephem.) For latitude 47°22.2', tabular polar distance 0°50.50', and hour angle 2ʰ18.3ᵐ = 34.57° (in Table 5, use 2ʰ17.9ᵐ), by double interpolation, bearing of Polaris (west of north)	0°42.9'
(Table 11, p. 78) Correction (by double interpolation for polar distance 0°52.97' and bearing 0°46.8')	+ 0.2'
Bearing of Polaris	0°43.1'
Clockwise angle △ Snow to Polaris	72°22.7'
Clockwise angle △ Snow to North	73°05.8'
Bearing △ Cass to △ Snow	N 73°05.8'W

7. Use a paper reflector held on the telescope by a rubber band. The light must not be too bright or the star becomes invisible. It cannot be too dim or the cross hairs fade out. Most theodolites have a special receptacle to accommodate batteries and a bulb for lighting the cross wires, horizontal circle, micrometer scale, and vertical arc.

8. For pointings at high altitudes, the telescope objective lens may slide back and distort the focus in an older instrument.

9. Use a sketch to eliminate errors in the relationships between the mark, north, and star.

10. For short distances in the north-south direction, 1 mile is equal to slightly more than 1' of latitude. A difference of one mile in estimating latitude from a map thus causes an error in observed azimuth of approximately 1.5" at latitude 45°.

16-15. COMPARISON OF SOLAR AND POLARIS OBSERVATIONS.
Compared with Polaris observations, sights on the sun (a) are more convenient, (b) will not give as precise results, (c) can be made while a daytime survey is in progress, and (d) have a limiting accuracy of perhaps 1' with methods normally used.

16-16. METHODS OF OBSERVING THE SUN.
Observations on the sun can be made directly by placing an optically plane and parallel dark glass over the eyepiece, or indirectly by focusing the sun's image on an unlined white card held behind the eyepiece. The telescope is rotated in a horizontal plane until the shadow of transit standards and telescope axle (or theodolite outline) is symmetrical, then turning the telescope up and down until the sun's image is visible and sharp at infinite distance focus. *Looking at the sun directly through the telescope without a dark glass will result in permanent eye injury.* The best hours for observing are between 8 and 10 AM, and from 2 to 4 PM (or 9 to 11 and 3 to 5 for daylight saving time).

At least four observations on the sun, two normal and two plunged, should be made in a minimum of time on the sun's disk, which is not an easy target. The Roelof solar prism, when properly aligned, produces four intersecting suns, permitting bisection to within perhaps 5". The sun's path can be considered a straight line over a period of about 5 min, and an average value of the readings used in computations. Plotting vertical and horizontal angles against time for the four observations provides a good check, as in Fig. 16-8 for the data of Illustration 16-3 (p. 344). Observations in diagonally opposite quadrants produce a separation of the lines equal to the sun's diameter.

The diameter of the sun as viewed from the earth is approximately 32'. Bisecting such a large object moving both horizontally and vertically is difficult, but the average person can do it with an accuracy of perhaps 1'.

A better method is to sight on the sun's edges (limbs). In Fig. 16-9(a) the disk is brought tangent to both cross lines, first in one quadrant and then in the diagonally opposite one. Averaging the two readings eliminates consideration of the semidiameter.

To avoid coordinating the movement of both tangent screws with the sun, it is simpler to follow the disk by keeping the vertical cross hair tangent to it and letting the sun come tangent to the horizontal hair, as in Fig. 16-9(b).

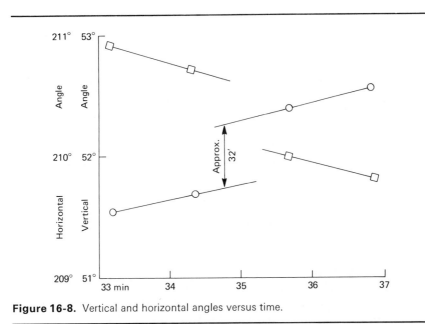

Figure 16-8. Vertical and horizontal angles versus time.

Since the altitude changes faster than the azimuth during observing hours, it is preferable to keep the vertical hair tangent.

The transit or theodolite is oriented with zero or a known value on the plates by sighting along a fixed line from the observer's position to a mark. After recording the times, and vertical and horizontal angles for four or more observations, the mark is resighted to be certain the plates still read the starting figure.

Before work is begun, the observer should have the (a) noteforms ready, (b) correct watch time and an ephemeris, (c) latitude and longitude of the place of observation, and (d) index error of the instrument.

16-17. REQUIRED QUANTITIES IN DETERMINING AZIMUTH BY DIRECT SOLAR OBSERVATION.
Five things must be known or determined in a solar observation for azimuth: the latitude, declination of the

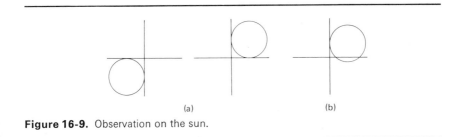

(a)   (b)

Figure 16-9. Observation on the sun.

sun, time of observation, altitude of the sun, and horizontal angle from some reference line to the sun.

Latitude can be taken from a map or found by a separate observation. North latitudes are considered plus in the standard formulas. For locations within the United States, an error of 1' in the (a) assumed latitude (that is, approximately 1 mile), (b) declination, or (c) measured altitude produces an error in the computed azimuth ranging from a few seconds to a maximum of about 3⅓', depending upon the time of year and declination on the date of observation, hour angle, and magnitude of the measured altitude.

Declination of the sun is given in ephemerides for each day of the year, along with the change per hour. Declination of the sun depends on its astronomical position and is independent of an observer's location. It is the same for all persons in any part of the world at the same instant. North declinations are always considered plus, regardless of the latitude of the observer.

The time of observation must be adjusted for the difference between watch time and Greenwich civil time. A correction is required only for the time zone, not for the exact longitude of the observer. Every manufacturer's ephemeris now lists the declination for Greenwich civil noon, rather than Greenwich apparent noon, to eliminate a correction for the equation of time. Greenwich noon is 12 hr Greenwich civil time.

The apparent altitude of the sun is its angular distance above the horizon as measured by a transit or theodolite. To obtain the true altitude, the observed value must be corrected for index error, for refraction and parallax as indicated in Fig. 16-10, and for the semidiameter of the sun if the border is sighted in only one quadrant. Errors of adjustment of the standards and cross hairs are eliminated by sighting with the telescope both normal and plunged. Careful leveling is required.

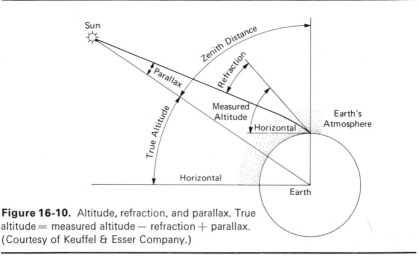

Figure 16-10. Altitude, refraction, and parallax. True altitude = measured altitude — refraction + parallax. (Courtesy of Keuffel & Esser Company.)

The horizontal angle to the sun's center is measured from some fixed line and combined with the computed bearing of the sun at any instant to get the bearing of a reference line.

A solar attachment which costs about the same amount as a transit or lower-order theodolite gives a mechanical solution of the *PZS* triangle. By setting the latitude, declination, and hour angle on three scales and sighting the sun, a mechanical procedure places the telescope in the north-south direction.

The special 30″ transit in Fig. 16-11 has a normal $\frac{1}{100}$ stadia interval instead of the $\frac{1}{32}$ used on much Bureau of Land Management (BLM) work, a Beaman arc, a solar reticle which allows accurate direct observations, and a Smith solar attachment; it gives $\pm20″$ azimuth determinations so is ideal for cadastral astronomy.

Figure 16-11. Gurley transit equipped with solar attachment.

ILLUSTRATION 16-3. SOLAR OBSERVATION FOR AZIMUTH

⊼ at △ Rover   Latitude 42°45′N   Longitude 73°56′W   30 July 1976

Point Sighted	Telescope	Watch Time (EDST)	Vertical Angle	Horizontal Angle (Clockwise)
△ Ridge				0°00′
☼ Sun	Direct	3ʰ33ᵐ10ˢ	52°54′	209°33′
☼ Sun	Direct	3ʰ34ᵐ20ˢ	52°43′	209°42′
⟟ Sun	Plunged	3ʰ35ᵐ37ˢ	52°00′	210°24′
⟟ Sun	Plunged	3ʰ36ᵐ49ˢ	51°47′	210°33′
△ Ridge				0°00′
Mean		3ʰ34ᵐ59ˢ	52°21.0′	210°03′

Index error	=	0°00.0′
(Tables 2, 2a, p. 65, 66) Refraction and parallax corr. (80°F, elev. 1200 ft) −0.74(0.97)(0.94)+0.09	= −	0.6′
True altitude	=	52°20.4′
Correction 0ʰ GCT to noon	= +	12ʰ
Correction To 5th time zone	= +	5ʰ
Correction For daylight saving	= −	1ʰ
EDST of observation	=	3ʰ34ᵐ59ˢ
Greenwich civil time of observation	=	19ʰ34ᵐ59ˢ = 19.58ʰ
(Table 1, p. 59, 1976 K & E ephem.)		
Declination 31 July 1976 0ʰ GCT	=	N 18°17.4′
Corr. for 4.42ʰ earlier = 0.61′ × 4.42ʰ	= +	02.7′
Declination	=	N 18°20.1′

$$\cos Z_n = \frac{\sin D}{\cos L \cos h} - \tan L \tan h$$

$$\cos Z_n = \frac{\sin 18°20.1′}{\cos 42°45′ \cos 52°20.4′} - \tan 42°45′ \tan 52°20.4′$$

$$= \frac{0.314572}{(0.734323)(0.610975)} \div (0.924390)(1.295717) = -0.496599$$

$$Z_n = 119°46.5′$$

Since the observation was made in the afternoon, this angle is counter-clockwise from north. The minus sign indicates an angle greater than 90°.

Azimuth of sun	= 240°13.5′
△ Ridge to sun	= 210°03′
Azimuth of △ Rover to △ Ridge	= 30°10′ (from north)

16-18. NOTES AND COMPUTATIONS FOR A SOLAR OBSERVA-TION. Determination of the azimuth of a line by observation on the sun requires solution of the *PZS* triangle defined previously, (see Fig. 16-5). The angle *PZS*, or Z_n, at the zenith is the bearing of the sun from the meridian through the place of observation.

Forms of the equation used in solving the *PZS* triangle are

$$\cos Z_n = \frac{\sin D}{\cos L \cos h} - \tan L \tan h \qquad (16\text{-}3)$$

or

$$\cos Z_n = \frac{\sin D - \sin L \sin h}{\cos L \cos h} \qquad (16\text{-}4)$$

and

$$\cos Z_n = \sin D \sec L \sec h - \tan L \tan h \qquad (16\text{-}5)$$

where Z_n is the angle from the meridian to the sun, measured clockwise in the morning and counterclockwise in the afternoon; *D* is the declination of the sun at the moment of observation; *L* is the latitude of the place; and *h* is the altitude of the center of the sun at the time of observation.

An example illustrating the field data and calculations for a solar observation is given in Illustration 16-3. The conditions are shown in Fig. 16-12.

16-19. SOURCES OF ERROR IN MERIDIAN OBSERVATIONS. Sources of error in meridian observations include:

1. Transit not perfectly leveled.
2. Horizontal axis of the instrument not truly horizontal.

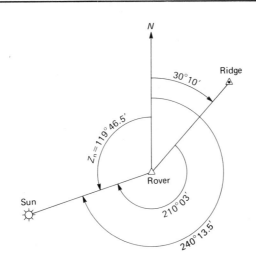

Figure 16-12. Relationship of sun, mark, and north.

3. Index error not corrected.
4. Sun not bisected by both cross hairs.
5. Time not correct, or not read exactly at the moment of observation.
6. Parallax in readings taken at night.

16-20. MISTAKES. Some more common mistakes that occur in observations for meridian are:

1. Sighting on the wrong star.
2. Using a poor signal on the reference line.
3. Computational errors.

PROBLEMS

16-1. Determine the direction of true north by the shadow method, using a flagpole or a telephone pole. Record the data obtained (times, and taped or paced distances) and include a sketch. Compare the result with a meridian established by an observation on the sun or Polaris. Check the local magnetic declination by reading the bearing of the line obtained.

16-2. Draw a revised Fig. 16-2 to show a true sketch of the sun's path for a determination of the meridian in the month of May if the observer is at latitude 30° and the shadow to the south.

16-3. The coordinates of a point on the earth's surface are latitude and longitude. What are the coordinates of the sun in the same system?

16-4. Why is sundial time not accurate?

16-5. What is the approximate date of the summer solstice?

16-6. When is the sun's declination 0°00'? When is it minus?

16-7. (a) What is the declination of a star as it passes through the zenith of an observer in latitude 32°12' S? (b) Of a star as it rises due east of an observer in latitude 26°30' N?

16-8. At what latitude are the altitude and declination of a celestial body equal?

16-9. Why is the moon not commonly used for meridian observations?

16-10. Is an observer's zenith always on his celestial meridian? Explain.

16-11. Do standard time zones follow 15° intervals exactly? Why?

16-12. When the GHA of Polaris is 152°15', what is the local hour angle (LHA) of Polaris for an observer at longitude 117°30' W?

16-13. Why does the calendar day start at midnight while the astronomer's day begins at noon?

16-14. Explain the gain or loss of one day in crossing the International Date Line.

16-15. Which is the central meridian for the Mountain Standard time zone?

16-16. What is the reason for having both apparent and mean solar time?

16-17. How often is apparent solar time the same as civil time?

16-18. What is the angular velocity of the earth per hour of civil or clock time and its direction of turning?

At Greenwich noon, what is the watch reading for the longitudes and conditions given in problems 16–19 through 16–22 ?

16–19. One hour DST, long. 168°10′ W   **16–20.** 2 hr DST, long. 110°20′ E

16–21. One hour DST, long. 92°45′ E   **16–22.** 2 hr DST, long. 78°30′ W

16–23. List the primary reference planes used in astronomical coordinate systems.

16–24. Express, in time, a difference of longitude of 62°47′28″.

16–25. At what local civil time will the center of the sun be on the meridian 30 April of this year at longitude 90° ?

16–26. Explain what is meant by the "Equation of Time" and how it is used.

16–27. List the hour angle of the (a) zenith, (b) south point, and (c) east point.

16–28. Tally the azimuth and altitude of the (a) celestial pole, (b) north point, and (c) west point.

16–29. Tabulate the right ascension and declination of the vernal equinox and autumnal equinox.

16–30. State the changes which take place in the azimuth and zenith distance of Polaris during 24 hr.

16–31. What is the watch time in New York City (longitude 73°57′30″) when it is 9^h03^m AM at San Francisco (longitude $8^h09^m43^s$) ?

16–32. Compute the time in Paris (longitude -09^m21^s) when it is 8 May, 9 PM, in New York (longitude $4^h55^m50^s$).

16–33. What is the watch time in Rome (longitude $0^h49^m50^s$ E) when the time in Chicago (longitude $5^h50^m27^s$) is $10^h57^m30^s$ PM on 8 September ?

16–34. The longitude of Cincinnati is 84°25′21″. What is the standard (Central) time when the local time is $4^h24^m17^s$ PM ? Determine the longitude of a place X where at the same instant the standard time is $9^h41^m10^s$.

16–35. Describe and show on a sketch a method for determining, without use of a table or any equipment, whether Polaris is on the meridian of the observer.

16–36. Which is the most accurate method of determining the true meridian that involves the least computational time ?

16–37. What maximum error in direction is possible if in a rough observation on Polaris at latitude 48°40′ N, the movement off culmination is neglected ?

16–38. Find the latitude of an observer if the altitude of Polaris at U.C. is 22°26′ and its declination 89°09.3′.

16–39. The vertical angle to the center of the sun measured as it crosses the observer's meridian is +44°55′ after all corrections have been made. If the sun's declination was −6°17′, what is the observer's latitude ?

16–40. Compute the hour angle of Polaris at 8^h30^m PM on 19 December of this year at latitude 35°00′ N and longitude 98°36′ W.

16–41. The latitude of an observer is 33°20′45″ and the declination of Polaris 89°09.4′. Compute the zenith distance of the star if it is on the observer's meridian (a) above the pole and (b) below the pole.

16–42. How much difference in the answer computed for the bearing of Polaris at elongation does the annual change in mean polar distance make ?

Compute for the current year, the four time conversions for azimuth observations on Polaris at U.C. from point P for the data in problems 16–43 through 16–46.

16–43. Latitude 38°30′ N, longitude $6^h00^m49^s$ W (St. Louis, Mo.), 19 April.

16–44. Latitude 32°18′ N, longitude 106°48′ W (Las Cruces, N.M.), 23 December.

16–45. Latitude 39°40′36″ N, longitude +6ʰ59ᵐ48ˢ (Denver, Colo.), 9 June.

16–46. Latitude 40°50′ N, longitude 73°57.5′ (New York, N.Y.), 28 September.

16–47. Similar to problem 16–43 except for E.E. on 22 February.

16–48. Similar to problem 16–44 except for W.E. on 17 January.

16–49. Similar to problem 16–45 except for E.E. on 7 May.

16–50. In problem 16–47, if the angle to the right from a line *PK* to Polaris is 63°18′, what is the true bearing of *PK*?

16–51. If the angle to the right from a line *PL* to Polaris is 191°06′ in problem 16–48, what is the true bearing of the line?

16–52. An observer at point *X* in latitude 35° N sights on Polaris 3 hr after E.E. and reads an angle to the right from *Y* to the star of 57°13′. What is the azimuth of *XY*?

16–53. Similar to problem 16–52, but for 2 hr after W.E.

16–54. At latitude 30° N, how long will Polaris appear to climb (or descend) the vertical cross line without departing more than 20″ in arc?

16–55. Similar to problem 16–54, except for 30″ at latitude 60°.

16–56. What error in azimuth is produced in an observation on Polaris at latitude 40° N if the time is off by 1 min and the star is at (a) U.C., (b) E.E., and (c) about midway between U.C. and W.E.

16–57. Why are the hours 8 to 10 and 2 to 4 best for solar observations?

16–58. What approximate error in azimuth results from a mistake of 1′ in reading the sun's altitude at 9ʰ45ᵐ AM, 8 September, latitude 45° N, longitude 80° E?

16–59. Determine the GHA of the sun and its declination in New York (longitude 73°57.5′ W) at 3ʰ35.5ᵐ PM on 13 June of this year.

16–60. What is the maximum declination of the sun at latitude 38° N and on what date of the current year does it occur?

16–61. What corrections must be made after recording time and vertical and horizontal angles in observing on the sun for azimuth?

16–62. List the sides of the *PZS* triangle used in computing a solar observation and the angles opposite them.

In problems 16–63 through 16–65 compute the azimuth for the current year, of line *AB* for the data given at hub *A*. The watch times, *H* angles to the right from *AB* to sun, and *V* angles in diagonally opposite quadrants are averages of four readings. Index error = 0°00′, elevation = 3000 ft, standard time.

	Date	Time	Temp.	Lat.	Long.	V Angle	H Angle
16–63.	10 Oct.	2ʰ54ᵐ PM	75°	39°41′ N	104°57′ W	28°24′	102°32′
16–64.	24 Sept.	2ʰ32ᵐ PM	80°	34°00′ N	118°21′ W	27°34′	79°42′
16–65.	16 April	10ʰ00ᵐ AM	65°	41°18′ N	73°02′ W	50°14′	64°10′

16–66. What order of accuracy should be expected for the data of problem 16–63?

16–67. How many checks are available for the data described in problems 16–63 through 16–65? Explain.

17
STATE PLANE COORDINATES

17-1. INTRODUCTION. Most surveys of small areas are based on the assumption that the earth's surface is a plane. For large-area surveys, however, it is necessary to consider the earth's curvature. In the past, horizontal positions of widely spaced geodetic stations were listed in terms of *geodetic positions* (latitude and longitude). Unfortunately, practicing surveyors often were not familiar with this convention. Clearly a system for specifying positions of geodetic stations using plane rectangular coordinates was required. The National Geodetic Survey fulfilled this need by developing a State Plane Coordinate System for each state. The first such system evolved in 1933 for the state of North Carolina.

A state plane coordinate system provides a common datum of reference for horizontal control of all surveys in a large area in the same way that mean sea level furnishes a single datum for vertical control. It eliminates having individual surveys based on different assumed coordinates, unrelated to those employed in other adjacent work. At present, state coordinates are widely used in all types of surveys, including those for photogrammetric mapping, highway construction projects, and property boundary delineation. In many states new subdivisions must include state coordinates. More extensive use is likely in the future because of the many advantages of the systems.

The earth's curved or mean sea level surface closely approximates a *spheroid* (derived by mathematically revolving an ellipse about the earth's polar axis). To convert geodetic positions of a portion of the earth's surface to plane rectangular coordinates, points are projected mathematically from the spheroid to some imaginary *developable surface*—a solid surface which can

349

be developed or "unrolled and laid out flat" without distortion of shape or size. A rectangular grid can be superimposed on the *developed* plane surface and the positions of points in the plane specified with respect to X and Y grid axes. A plane grid so developed is called a *map projection.*

Two basic projections are employed in state coordinate systems; the *Lambert conformal conic projection* and the *transverse Mercator projection.* The former utilizes an imaginary cone, the latter a fictitious cylinder, as their developable surfaces. These are shown in Fig. 17-1(a) and (b), respectively. The cone and cylinder are *secant* to the spheroid in the state coordinate systems; that is, they intersect the spheroid along two small circles AB and CD as shown. Figures 17-1(c) and (d) illustrate plane surfaces developed from the cone and cylinder, respectively.

In computing state plane coordinate systems, points are projected mathematically from the spheroid along radial lines from near the earth's

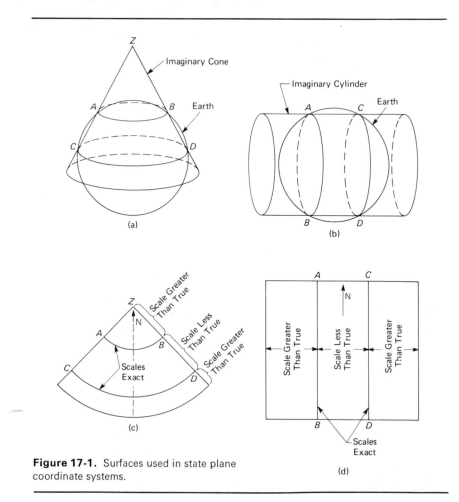

Figure 17-1. Surfaces used in state plane coordinate systems.

center to the surface of the imaginary cone or cylinder. Figure 17-2 illustrates this process diagrammatically, and displays the relationship between the length of a line on the spheroid and its extent when projected onto the surface of either a cone or a cylinder. Note that the distance $a'b'$ on the projection surface is greater than ab on the spheroid, and similarly $g'h'$ is longer than gh. From this observation it is clear that map projection scale is larger than true spheroid scale where the cone or cylinder is outside the spheroid. Conversely, distance $d'e'$ on the projection is shorter than de on the spheroid and thus map scale is smaller than true spheroid scale when the projection surface is inside the spheroid. Points c and f occur at the intersection of projection and spheroid surfaces and therefore map scale equals true spheroid scale along the lines of intersection. These relationships of map scale to true spheroid scale for various positions on the two projections are indicated in Figs. 17-1(c) and (d).

From the foregoing discussion, it should be clear that points cannot be projected from the spheroid to developable surfaces without introducing distortions in the lengths of lines or shapes of areas. These distortions are held to a minimum, however, by selected placement of the cone or cylinder secant, and also by limiting the zone size or extent of coverage of the earth's

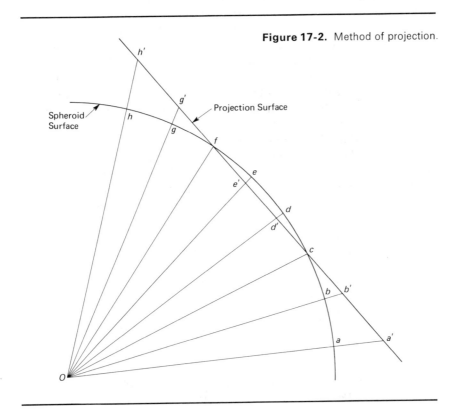

Figure 17-2. Method of projection.

surface for any one projection. If the width of zones is held to a maximum of 158 miles, and if two-thirds of this zone width is between the secant lines, distortions (differences in line lengths on the two surfaces) are kept to 1 part in 10,000 or less, which is the accuracy intended by the NGS in its development of the state coordinate systems. One zone is sufficient to cover an entire small state. Larger states require more zones, for example, California seven and Texas five.

17-2. THE LAMBERT CONFORMAL CONIC PROJECTION. The

Lambert conformal conic projection, as its name implies, is a projection onto the surface of an imaginary cone. The term *conformal* means that true angular relationships are retained around all points. This projection is used in 31 of the 50 states. The scale on a Lambert projection varies from north to south but not from east to west, as shown on Fig. 17-1(c). The projection is therefore ideal for mapping areas extending great distances in an east-west direction, for example, Kentucky, Pennsylvania, and Tennessee.

In the Lambert projection, as shown in Fig. 17-3, the cone intersects the spheroid along two parallels of latitude, called *standard parallels*, at one-sixth of the zone width from the north and south zone limits. On the projection, all meridians are straight lines converging at Z, the apex of the cone, and all parallels of latitude are arcs of concentric circles having centers at the apex of the cone. The projection is located in the zone in an east-west direction by selecting a *central meridian* whose longitude is near the middle of the area to be covered. The direction of the central meridian on the projection establishes *grid north*. All lines parallel with the central meridian point in the direction of grid north. Except at the central meridian, therefore, directions of true and grid north do not coincide.

Given the latitude and longitude of any point P, its X and Y state coordinates in the Lambert projection are readily calculated. Consider the developed plane of the Lambert projection illustrated in Fig. 17-3. Point Z is the apex of a cone, and point O the origin of rectangular coordinates. Line ZM is the central meridian of the projection. A constant C, usually 2,000,000, is adopted to offset the central meridian from the Y grid axis and make X coordinates of all points positive. Line ZP represents a portion of the meridian through point P with its length designated as R. Angle θ between the central meridian and the meridian ZP is termed the *mapping angle*.

The NGS has computed and published projection tables for every state.[1] For any point P, the value of R is listed in the tables versus the latitude of P, and θ recorded versus longitude P. A constant R_b (the Y coordinate of the cone's apex Z) is also given for any particular zone. From Fig. 17-3, and

---

[1] Projection tables for every state are available at a nominal fee from the Superintendent of Documents, Government Printing Office, Washington, D.C. 20402.

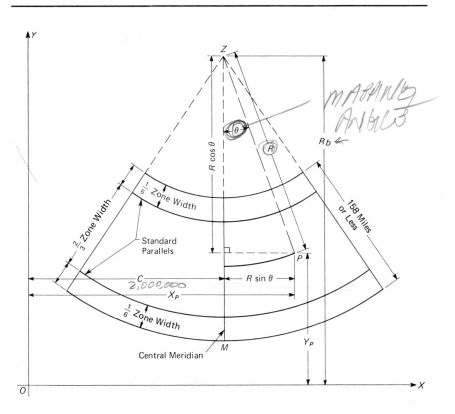

Figure 17-3. The Lambert conformal conic projection.

appropriate projection tables, the following equations can be solved for the X and Y coordinates of P:

$$X_p = R \sin \theta + C$$
$$Y_p = R_b - R \cos \theta$$

$$(17\text{-}1)$$

Note that if θ is to the left of the central meridian its sign is negative; if to the right it is positive. Except where a line of reference azimuth exceeds 5 miles in length, grid azimuth may be calculated with sufficient accuracy from geodetic azimuth using the following equation:

$$\text{grid azimuth} = \text{geodetic azimuth} - \theta \qquad (17\text{-}2)$$

17-3. THE TRANSVERSE MERCATOR PROJECTION.

The transverse Mercator projection is also a conformal projection based upon an imaginary secant cylinder as its developable surface. Because the scale varies in an east-west direction, but not from north to south, it is used to map areas of 22 states long in a north-south direction, such as Illinois and Indiana.[2]

The axis of the imaginary cylinder of a transverse Mercator projection lies in the plane of the earth's equator. The cylinder cuts the spheroid along two small circles equidistant from the central meridian. On the developed plane surface, Fig. 17-4, all parallels of latitude, and all meridians except the central meridian, are curves as shown in light broken lines. A central meridian establishes the direction of grid north and the X and Y coordinates of points are measured perpendicular and parallel to the central meridian, respectively.

Referring to Fig. 17-4 and appropriate transverse Mercator projection tables, the following equations may be solved for the X and Y coordinates of any point P:

$$X_p' = H \times \Delta\lambda'' \pm ab$$
$$X_p = X_p' + K \tag{17-3}$$
$$Y_p = Y_o + V\left[\frac{\Delta\lambda''}{100}\right]^2 \pm c$$

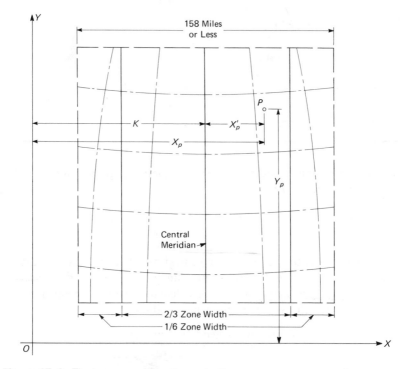

Figure 17-4. The transverse Mercator projection.

[2] Both the Lambert conformal conic and the transverse Mercator projections are used in Alaska, Florida, and New York.

In the equations, X_p' is the distance to point P either east or west of the central meridian. The difference in seconds between the longitudes of the central meridian and point P is $\Delta\lambda''$, its algebraic sign being negative if P is west, and positive if P is east, of the central meridian. Constant K offsets the Y axis from the central meridian so that all X coordinates are positive. Its value is 500,000 for most states. Values of H, a, Y_o, and V are tabulated versus the latitude of point P in projection tables, and b and c listed versus $\Delta\lambda''$. A negative sign for product ab decreases $H \times \Delta\lambda''$; a positive one increases it.

Except where a reference azimuth line exceeds 5 miles in length, grid azimuth can be calculated with sufficient accuracy from the geodetic azimuth using the following equation:

$$\text{grid azimuth} = \text{geodetic azimuth} - \Delta\alpha'' \qquad (17\text{-}4)$$

In the equation, $\Delta\alpha'' = \Delta\lambda'' \sin \phi_P + g$ (where g is listed versus $\Delta\lambda''$ in projection tables), and ϕ_P is the latitude of point P.

State coordinates and the grid azimuth to a nearby reference mark are published by the NGS for all stations of the U.S. network and therefore need not be computed (or, if necessary, are determined readily using projection tables and a calculator). In addition to the data described, the tables also provide detailed example problems. Projection tables for your state and adjacent ones should be obtained when working with state coordinates since a survey may cover several zones (double sets of coordinates are tabulated near zone edges).

A new general control adjustment currently being computed by the NGS will replace the last general adjustment of 1927, and thus produce new coordinates for all stations. In some localities computed positions may shift as much as 50 ft or more. New station descriptions will be published in the next five to 10 years with coordinates given in the metric system together with their foot equivalents.

17-4. COMPUTING STATE COORDINATES OF TRAVERSE STATIONS.

Placing a survey on the state coordinate grid normally requires traversing (or triangulating or trilaterating) to start and end on existing stations which have known state coordinates and from which known grid azimuth lines have been established. Generally these data are available for immediate use but if not they can be calculated as indicated when latitude and longitude are known.

It is important to note that if a survey begins with a given grid azimuth and ties into another, all intermediate ones will automatically be grid azimuths. Thus corrections for convergence of meridians are not necessary when the state coordinate system is used throughout the survey.

A simple two-sided traverse computation in the state coordinate system is presented in this section to illustrate its simplicity. As shown in Fig. 17-5, it starts at Irwin Triangulation Station in Ohio, which uses the Lambert

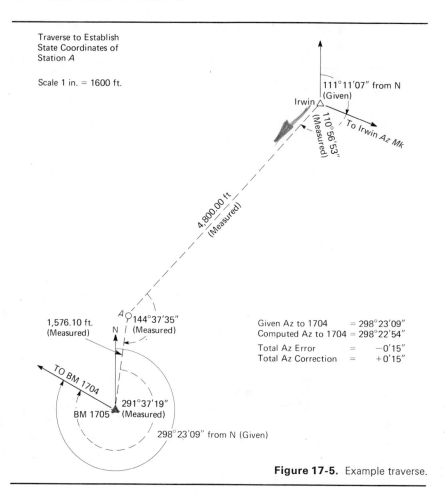

Traverse to Establish
State Coordinates of
Station *A*

Scale 1 in. = 1600 ft.

111°11'07" from N (Given)

Irwin

110°56'53" (Measured)

To Irwin Az Mk

4,800.00 ft (Measured)

1,576.10 ft. (Measured)

A 144°37'35" (Measured)

Given Az to 1704   = 298°23'09"
Computed Az to 1704 = 298°22'54"

Total Az Error   =   −0'15"
Total Az Correction   =   +0'15"

TO BM 1704

BM 1705

291°37'19" (Measured)

298°23'09" from N (Given)

Figure 17-5. Example traverse.

conformal conic projection, and ends at BM 1705. Station *A* in between is the only new point in the survey and its coordinates will be determined.

The first step is to reduce the traverse distances to mean sea level (spheroid surface),[3] and then to lengths according to their positions on the state coordinate grid. The following equation reduces measured lengths to mean sea level (MSL) distances:

$$L_s = L_m \frac{R_e}{R_e + h} \tag{17-5}$$

where L_s is the sea level length of the line, L_m the measured length of line, R_e the mean radius of the earth (approximately 20,906,000 ft or 6,372,200 m), and h the average elevation of the measured line above MSL.

The ratio $R_e/(R_e + h)$ is commonly called the *sea-level factor*. In this example problem, average elevation is 687 ft, and the factor is 0.999966.

[3] Michigan is the only exception, using lengths converted to the elevation of 800 ft.

The sea level length of line is next multiplied by a *scale factor* obtained from projection tables and corresponding to a particular area of the zone in which the line falls. The range of this reduction or increase in sea level length varies from zero along the two lines of exact scale, to maximum and minimum values determined by the zone size. In Connecticut, for example, the correction is never more than 1 part in 40,000, but it may reach 1 part in 10,000, or slightly more in a few cases for other states. For the illustrative problem, the average latitude of the traverse location obtained from published data on the two control stations is used as the argument to enter the table and find a scale factor of 0.999941.

The product of sea-level factor and scale factor is commonly called the *grid factor*—in this problem $0.999966 \times 0.999941 = 0.999907$.

If a traverse extent is so small that the scale factor does not change appreciably, and uniform elevations throughout the survey area permit applying a single sea-level factor, a common grid factor simplifies calculations. It may be ignored if near 1.000000. It should be checked if a measured ground distance disagrees slightly with the state plane coordinates.

Figure 17-5 shows the given or fixed stations and azimuth lines for the example traverse. Measured angles and courses were added with dashed lines. Published data for the two control stations are:

Station Irwin: E or $x = 1,367,887.24$ ft; N or $y = 442,126.54$ ft
  Azimuth to Irwin azimuth mark $= 111°11'07''$ from grid N
  Approximate elevation $= 883$ ft
BM 1705: E or $x = 1,364,481.50$ ft; N or $y = 437,001.53$ ft
  Azimuth to BM 1704 $= 298°23'09''$ from grid N
  Approximate elevation $= 492$ ft

The traverse computation has been performed in five steps:

1. Distribution of the angular error of closure to get corrected grid azimuths for all traverse sides. Clockwise angles were measured. Closing error (difference between given azimuth at BM 1705 and that computed by using the three measured angles and given azimuth at Irwin) is $-0°00'15''$. This error was distributed equally among the three angles as shown in Table 17-1. Final grid azimuths listed in the last column are converted to grid bearings in Table 17-2.
2. Reduction of measured distances to grid distances is done in Table 17-2 by multiplying values in the third column by those in the fourth column, or by subtracting a correction of 0.0093 ft/100 ft (which is less than 1 part in 10,000).
3. Computation of latitudes and departures.
4. Calculation of preliminary grid coordinates listed in the last column of Table 17-2. Errors of closure in the x and y directions are found by subtracting the given, or fixed, coordinates of BM 1705 from those obtained by traversing. The precision is 1 : 7,330.

KNOW THESE STEPS!

TABLE 17-1. ANGULAR CLOSURE AND ADJUSTMENT

Station	From	To	Prelim. Azimuth Angle to Right Prelim. Azimuth	Corr. Cum. Corr.	Final Azimuth Angle to Right Final Azimuth
	Irwin	Irwin Az.	111°11′07″		111°11′07″ (Given)
Irwin	Irwin Az.	A	110°56′53″	+5	110°56′58″
	Irwin	A	222°08′00″	+5	222°08′05″
	A	Irwin	42°08′00″		42°08′05″
A	Irwin	1705	144°37′35″	+5	144°37′40″
	A	1705	186°45′35″	+10	186°45′45″
	1705	A	6°45′35″		6°45′45″
BM 1705	A	1704	291°37′19″	+5	291°37′24″
	1705	1704	298°22′54″	+15	298°23′09″ (Given)

5. Traverse adjustment by the compass (Bowditch) rule. Corrections for preliminary coordinates are computed in proportion to the accumulated traverse distances up to any given station and applied in the last columns to get final state plane coordinates for station A. Full corrections (-0.27 and -0.83) applied at BM 1705, of course, give the fixed values written in previously.

17-5. SURVEYS EXTENDING FROM ONE ZONE TO ANOTHER.
Surveys in border areas often cross into different zones or even into different states. This presents no unusual problem, however, because adjacent zones overlap by approximately 50 miles.

To convert state plane coordinates of a point from one zone to another, it is necessary to calculate its latitude and longitude using the state plane coordinates from the zone where the survey originated. Then depending upon whether the coordinates are based on the Lambert conformal conic projection or the transverse Mercator projection, Eqs. (17-1) or (17-3) would be used, but solved in reverse to obtain latitude and longitude. From the latitude and longitude, state plane coordinates of the point are calculated using either Eqs. (17-1) or (17-3) as appropriate for the zone entered. The grid azimuth of a line in the zone entered can be obtained from the new state plane coordinates of the two points.

Suppose, for example, that a survey originates in southern Wisconsin and extends into northern Illinois. To convert a point to the Illinois system, latitude and longitude would be calculated by solving Eqs. (17-1) in reverse using data from the Wisconsin Lambert conformal conic projection tables. With latitude and longitude known, Eqs. (17-3) would be solved directly

TABLE 17-2. TRAVERSE CLOSURE AND ADJUSTMENT (COMPASS OR BOWDITCH RULE)

Station	Grid Bearing	Measured Distance	Grid Factor	Grid Distance	Sin Cosine	Departure	Latitude	Grid Coordinates Prelim. X Corr. Final X	Prelim. Y Corr. Final Y
Irwin							(Given) ⟶	1,367,887.24	442,126.54
	S 42°08′05″ W	4800.00	0.999907	4799.55	0.6708761 0.7415694	−3219.90	−3559.20	1,364,667.34 −0.20	438,567.34 −0.62
A								1,364,667.14	438,566.72
	S 6°45′45″ W	1576.10	0.999907	1575.95	0.1177540 0.9930428	− 185.57	−1564.98	1,364,481.77 −0.27	437,002.36 −0.83
BM 1705							(Given) ⟶	1,364,481.50	437,001.53
		6376.10					Error of closure =	+0.27	+0.83

Linear error of closure = $\sqrt{(0.27)^2 + (0.83)^2} = 0.87$ ft

Precision = 0.87/6376 = 1/7330

Compass (Bowditch) rule:

X correction = $-0.27/6.376 = -0.042$ ft/1000 ft of cumulative distance

Y correction = $-0.83/6.376 = -0.130$ ft/1000 ft of cumulative distance

using data from the Illinois transverse Mercator projection tables to get X and Y coordinates for the point. Sample calculations of this type are given in most of the published projection tables.

17-6. OTHER MAP PROJECTIONS.   The Lambert conformal conic and traverse Mercator map projections are designed to cover areas extensive in east-west or north-south directions, respectively. These systems do not, however, conveniently cover circular areas, or long strips of the earth that are skewed to the meridians. Two other systems, the *horizon stereographic* and *oblique Mercator*[4] projections, satisfy these problems.

The horizon stereographic projection can be divided into two classes, *tangent plane* and *secant plane*. In either class, as illustrated in Fig. 17-6, the projection point P is on the sphere where a line perpendicular to the map plane, and passing through the center point O, intersects the sphere. In the tangent plane sytem, spheroid points a and b are projected outward to a' and b', respectively, on the map plane. For the secant plane system, spheroid points c and d are projected inward (if they were outside of the secant points, projection would be outward) to c' and d' on the map plane. Horizon stereographic projections are not employed in the United States, but are used in Canada and other parts of the world. If point P is the north or south pole, the

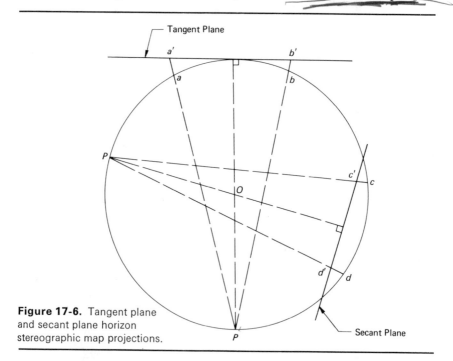

Figure 17-6. Tangent plane and secant plane horizon stereographic map projections.

---

[4] The oblique Mercator projection is also called the Hotine skew orthomorphic projection, named after the English geodesist Martin Hotine.

projection is called *polar stereographic*; if on the equator, *equatorial stereo-graphic.*

The oblique Mercator projection is designed for areas which run obliquely such as northwest to southeast. It has gained acceptance in the United States in recent years, and is currently employed as the state plane coordinate system for the southeast portion of the state of Alaska, and by the U.S. Lake Survey to cover the area of Lakes Ontario and Erie, and the St. Lawrence River.

The universal transverse Mercator (UTM) system is another important map projection. Originally developed by the military primarily for artillery use, it provides world-wide coverage from 80° S latitude, through the equator, to 80° N latitude (the polar caps are covered by polar stereographic systems). The UTM system is a modified transverse Mercator projection with zone widths of 6° longitude. Adjacent zones overlap by 30′. As with the state plane coordinate systems, a set of tables is available for converting from latitude and longitude to X and Y coordinates, and vice versa. The UTM system, or a modification of it, is currently under consideration for possible international adoption.

PROBLEMS

17–1. Discuss the advantages of placing surveys on state plane coordinate systems.

17–2. Name the two basic projections employed in state plane coordinate systems. Which one is preferred for states whose long dimensions are north-south? East-west?

17–3. Develop a table of sea-level factors for ground elevations ranging from sea level to 5000 ft above sea level. Use increments of 500 ft.

17–4. Similar to problem 17–3 except for ground elevations from sea level to 10,000 ft above sea level using 1000-ft increments.

17–5. Explain how surveys can be extended from one state plane coordinate zone to another, or from one state to another.

17–6. What accuracy in differences between spheroid and projection lengths was intended by the NGS in developing state plane coordinate systems? What maximum zone width is allowable in order to achieve the desired accuracy?

17–7. The state plane coordinates of points A and B are as follows:

Point	X	Y
A	2,283,381.32	763,274.12
B	2,279,528.05	766,680.44

Calculate the grid length and grid bearing of line AB.

17–8. Similar to problem 17–7 except points A and B have the following state plane coordinates.

Point	X	Y
A	421,823.18	875,209.97
B	423,002.79	873,627.39

17-9. Station A in Wisconsin's north zone (Lambert conformal conic) is at north latitude 45°21'20.698" and west longitude 89°44'39.878". Constants for this zone are C = 2,000,000 ft and R_b= 20,489,179.67 ft. R values tabulated for latitudes 45°21' and 45°22' are 20,422,328.19 ft and 20,416,250.84 ft, respectively, and θ values tabulated for longitudes 89°44' and 89°45' are +0°11'32.5160" and +0°10'49.2337", respectively. Compute the state plane coordinates for station A.

17-10. Point B, near station A of problem 17-9, has state plane coordinates X = 2,090,948.71 ft and Y = 77,053.28 ft. Calculate the grid length, grid azimuth, and geodetic azimuth of line AB.

17-11. Station Hill in Pennsylvania's south zone (Lambert conformal conic) has north latitude 40°10'53.275" and west longitude 79°43'26.054". Constants for this zone are C = 2,000,000.00 ft and R_b= 24,984,826.43 ft. R values tabulated for latitudes 40°10' and 40°11' are 24,681,260.43 ft and 24,675,189.10 ft, respectively, and θ values tabulated for longitudes 79°43' and 79°44' are −1°16'33.4556" and −1°17'12.3832", respectively. Determine the state plane coordinates for this point.

17-12. Station Vale, near station Hill of problem 17-11, has state plane coordinates X = 1,453,827.81 and Y = 1,771,840.09. Calculate the grid length, grid azimuth, and geodetic azimuth of line Hill-Vale.

17-13. A station in Indiana's west zone (transverse Mercator) has north latitude 39°25'18.371" and west longitude 87°41'20.075". Constant K for this zone is 500,000.00 ft, and the longitude of the central meridian is 87°05'00.000". Values for Y_o, H, V, and a tabulated for latitudes 39°25' and 39°26' are as follows:

Latitude	Y_o	H	V	a
39°25'	697,992.23	78.482017	1.208187	−0.730
39°26'	704,062.75	78.463323	1.208326	−0.727

Values for b and c listed versus $\Delta\lambda''$ are:

$\Delta\lambda''$	b	c
2100	+3.218	−0.085
2200	+3.293	−0.091

Compute the state plane coordinates of the point.

17-14. What corrections must be made to measured slope distances prior to computing in state plane coordinates?

17-15. Which state utilizes an oblique Mercator projection for its state plane coordinate system? Why is it used?

17-16. The horizontal ground lengths of a three-sided closed polygon traverse were measured as follows: AB = 1595.39, BC = 2127.48, and CA = 2861.40 ft. If the average elevation of the area is 1610 ft above sea level, calculate the sea-level lengths of the lines.

17-17. Assuming a scale factor for the traverse of problem 17-16 of 0.9999298, calculate grid lengths for the traverse lines.

17-18. For the traverse of problem 7-16, the grid azimuth of the line from A to a nearby azimuth mark was 340°21'03" and the clockwise angle measured at A from the azimuth mark to B was 56°30'18". The measured interior angles (to the right) were $A = 47°09'05"$, $B = 99°28'16"$, and $C = 33°23'03"$. Balance the angles and compute grid azimuths for the traverse lines.

17–19. Using grid lengths of problem 17–17 and grid azimuths from problem 17–18, calculate latitudes and departures, linear error of closure, and precision for the traverse.

17–20. Assuming station A has state plane coordinates $X = 1,516,036.50$ and $Y = 484,192.07$, balance the latitudes and departures computed in problem 17–19 using the compass (Bowditch) rule, and determine the state plane coordinates of stations B and C.

17–21. The horizontal ground lengths of a four-sided closed polygon traverse were measured as follows: $AB = 1154.12$, $BC = 1999.03$, $CD = 1571.39$, and $DA = 2027.94$ ft. If the average elevation of the area is 4825 ft above sea level, and the scale factor for the traverse is 1.0001047, calculate grid lengths of the lines.

17–22. For the traverse of problem 17–21 the grid bearing of the line BC is N 79°36'07" W. Interior angles (to the right) were measured as follows: $A = 117°27'57"$, $B = 74°49'56"$, $C = 100°25'59"$, and $D = 67°15'56"$. Balance the angles and compute grid bearings for the traverse lines.

17–23. Using grid lengths from problem 17–21 and grid bearings from problem 17–22, calculate latitudes and departures, linear error closure, and precision for the traverse. Balance the latitudes and departures by the compass (Bowditch) rule. If the state plane coordinates of point B are $X = 2,138,242.05$ ft and $Y = 538,924.70$ ft, calculate state plane coordinates for points C, D, and A.

18
CONTROL
SURVEYS

18-1. INTRODUCTION. Control surveys establish precise horizontal and vertical positions of a network of reference monuments to serve as the basis for originating or checking subordinate surveys for projects such as topographic and hydrographic mapping; property boundary delineation; and route and construction planning, design, and layout.

There are two general types of control surveys, *horizontal* and *vertical*. Horizontal control surveys establish either plane rectangular coordinates, usually in a state plane coordinate system (see Chapter 17), or the geodetic latitudes and longitudes of stations. The geodetic latitude, ϕ_A, and longitude, λ_A, for any point A on the spheroid are illustrated in Fig. 18-1. Great circles on the circumference of the spheroid which pass through the north and south poles are called *meridians*, and any plane containing a meridian and the polar axis is termed a *meridian* plane. Geodetic latitude is the angle, in the meridian plane containing A, between the equatorial plane and the normal to the spheroid at A. Geodetic longitude is the angle, in the equatorial plane, between the planes of the Greenwich Meridian and the meridian through A. Precise latitudes and longitudes are determined by employing geodetic surveying techniques and are useful for accurately specifying the relative positions of widely spaced points. Of course, as discussed in Chapter 17, if the geodetic latitude and longitude of a point are known, its state plane coordinates are readily computed.

Field procedures used in horizontal control surveying include *triangulation*, *precise traversing*, *trilateration*, or combinations of these basic methods. Terrain in the area, project requirements, available equipment, and relative economy normally dictate the system selected.

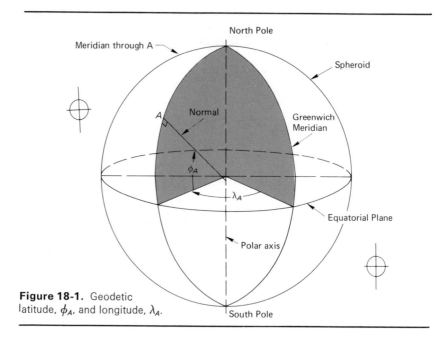

Figure 18-1. Geodetic latitude, ϕ_A, and longitude, λ_A.

Vertical control surveys establish elevations above a selected datum for a network of monuments called *bench marks*. In the United States this datum, known as the National Geodetic Vertical Datum of 1929, is based upon a mean sea level surface established from tidal observations. Depending upon accuracy requirements, vertical control surveys may be done by *barometric*, *trigonometric*, or *differential leveling*. The most accurate and widely applied method is precise differential leveling.

18-2. ACCURACY STANDARDS AND SPECIFICATIONS FOR CONTROL SURVEYS.

The required accuracy for a control survey depends primarily upon its purpose. Some major factors which affect accuracy are type and condition of equipment used, field procedures adopted, and the experience and capabilities of available personnel. To guide surveyors, the Federal Geodetic Control Committee, FGCC, has prepared and published a set of detailed classification standards of accuracy and specifications.[1] Rationale for them are twofold: (1) to provide a uniform set of standards specifying minimum acceptable accuracies of control surveys for various purposes, and (2) to establish specifications for instruments, field procedures, and closure checks to ensure getting the intended level of accuracy.

---

[1] "Classification, Standards of Accuracy, and General Specifications of Geodetic Control Surveys," dated May, 1974, is available from the Director, National Geodetic Survey, National Oceanic and Atmospheric Administration, U. S. Department of Commerce, Rockville, Maryland 20852.

Standards and specifications developed by the FGCC establish the following three distinct so-called *orders of accuracy*, given in descending order: *first-order*, *second-order*, and *third-order*. For horizontal control surveys, second-order and third-order each have two separate accuracy categories, *class I* and *class II*. For vertical surveys, first-order and second-order also each have class-I and class-II accuracy divisions. Thus a total of five levels are defined in the specifications for both horizontal and vertical control surveys.

Triangulation, traverse, and trilateration surveys are included in the FGCC horizontal control standards and specifications, but only differential leveling is covered in the vertical control section.

Tables 18-1 and 18-2 give relative accuracies required for the various orders and classes.

The ultimate success of any engineering or mapping project depends upon appropriate survey control. The higher the order of accuracy demanded, the more time and expense required. It is therefore important to select the

TABLE 18-1. HORIZONTAL CONTROL SURVEY ACCURACY STANDARDS

Order and Class	Relative Accuracy Required Between Directly Connected Adjacent Points
First-order	1 part in 100,000
Second-order:	
Class I	1 part in 50,000
Class II	1 part in 20,000
Third-order:	
Class I	1 part in 10,000
Class II	1 part in 5000

TABLE 18-2. VERTICAL CONTROL SURVEY ACCURACY STANDARDS

Order and Class	Relative Accuracy Required Between Directly Connected Bench Marks
First-order:	
Class I	$0.5 \text{ mm} \times \sqrt{K}$
Class II	$0.7 \text{ mm} \times \sqrt{K}$
Second-order:	
Class I	$1.0 \text{ mm} \times \sqrt{K}$
Class II	$1.3 \text{ mm} \times \sqrt{K}$
Third-order	$2.0 \text{ mm} \times \sqrt{K}$

where K is the distance between bench marks in kilometers.

proper order of accuracy for a given project, and carefully follow the specifications. Note that no matter how accurately a control survey is conducted, errors will exist in the computed positions of its stations, but a higher order of accuracy presumes smaller errors.

18-3. THE NATIONAL CONTROL NETWORK. In order to meet the various local needs of surveyors, engineers, and scientists, the federal government has established a national control network consisting of more than 500,000 monuments and bench marks located throughout the United States. The National Geodetic Survey (NGS) began control surveying operations as the Survey of the Coast in 1807, changed to Coast Survey in 1836, to Coast and Geodetic Survey in 1878, and to a division of the National Ocean Survey (NOS) in 1970. It continues to send field parties to all states to establish new control stations and upgrade and maintain existing ones.

The National Control Network is split into *horizontal* and *vertical* divisions. All control within each part is classified in a ranking scheme based on purpose and order of accuracy.

18-4. HIERARCHY OF THE NATIONAL HORIZONTAL NETWORK. The hierarchy of control within the National Horizontal Control Network, from highest to lowest order, follows.

Primary Control. Consists principally of east-west arcs of triangulation spaced at about 100 km, crossed by north-south arcs having similar spacing. In addition to triangulation, traverse and trilateration have been employed, and more recently *Doppler* methods (see Section 18-13) have been used. Primary control is established using first-order methods.

Secondary Control. Densifies the network within areas surrounded by primary control, especially in high-value land areas. Secondary-control surveys are executed to second-order, class-I standards; employ triangulation, traverse, and trilateration; and are adjusted simultaneously with, and thus strengthen, the primary network.

Supplemental Control. Serves in general to densify control between the primary network in lightly developed areas. It is also placed along coastlines and on extensive mapping or construction projects. Supplemental-control surveys originate at stations of the primary and, occasionally, secondary network, and are executed to second-order, class-II standards.

Local Control. Provides reference points for local construction projects and small-scale topographic mapping. These surveys are referenced to higher-order control monuments and, depending upon accuracy requirements, may be third-order, class I, or third-order, class II.

Figure 18-2 shows the locations of primary triangulation arcs and densifying secondary, supplemental surveys in Florida.

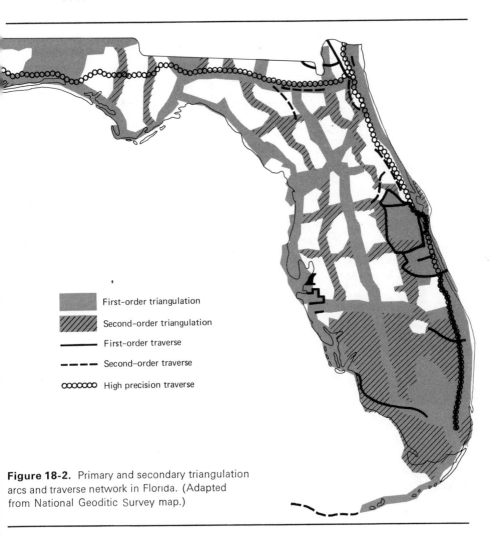

Figure 18-2. Primary and secondary triangulation arcs and traverse network in Florida. (Adapted from National Geoditic Survey map.)

First-order triangulation

Second-order triangulation

First-order traverse

Second-order traverse

High precision traverse

18-5. HIERARCHY OF THE NATIONAL VERTICAL CONTROL NETWORK.
The scheme of bench marks within the National Vertical Control Network may be classified as follows:

Basic Framework. A uniformly distributed nationwide network of bench marks whose elevations are determined to the highest order of accuracy. It consists of nets *A* and *B*. In net *A*, adjacent bench marks are spaced an average of about 100 to 300 km apart using first-order, class-I standards; in net *B* the average separation is about 50 to 100 km and first-order, class-II standards. are employed.

Secondary Network. Densifies the basic framework, especially in metropolitan areas and for large engineering projects. It is established to second-order, class-I standards.

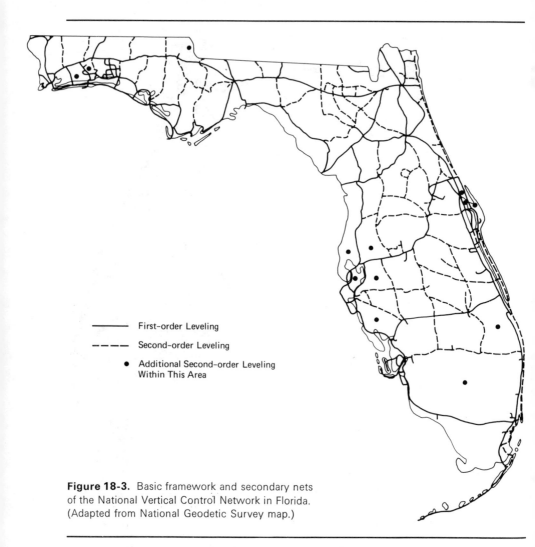

Figure 18-3. Basic framework and secondary nets of the National Vertical Control Network in Florida. (Adapted from National Geodetic Survey map.)

First-order Leveling

Second-order Leveling

● Additional Second-order Leveling Within This Area

General Area Control. Vertical control for local engineering, surveying, and mapping projects. It is established to second-order, class-II standards.

Local Control. Serves as vertical reference for minor engineering projects and small-scale topographic mapping. Bench marks in this category satisfy third-order standards.

Figure 18-3 shows the basic framework of the National Vertical Control Network in Florida.

18-6. CONTROL-POINT DESCRIPTIONS. To obtain maximum benefit from control surveys, all stations and bench marks are placed in locations favorable to their subsequent use, and adequate descriptions provided. They should be permanently monumented to ensure easy recovery by future potential users. National Control Network monuments placed by the NGS are marked by bronze disks about 3½ in. in diameter set in concrete or bedrock. Figure 18-4 shows two of these disks.

The NGS publishes and makes available to local surveyors location diagrams and complete descriptions of all their control, giving general placement in relation to nearby towns, and specific positions by means of distances and directions to several nearby reference monuments.[2] For horizontal control, the descriptions generally include the station's geodetic latitude and longitude, state plane coordinates, approximate elevation, and geodetic and plane azimuths to a nearby station or stations. Geodetic and plane azimuths differ as a result of convergence of meridians, and therefore the appropriate azimuth must be selected for the particular surveying methods being used. Published bench mark data include station locations and adjusted elevations both in meters and feet. All descriptions are likely to contain notes on successes or failures in earlier station recovery attempts.

Besides the control within the national network set by the NGS, additional marks have also been placed in various parts of the United States by other federal agencies such as the U.S. Geological Survey, the Corps of Engineers, and the Tennessee Valley Authority. Also state, county, and municipal organizations have added control. This work is frequently coordinated through the NGS, and descriptions of the stations are distributed by that agency.

18-7. TRIANGULATION. Prior to the emergence of electronic distance-measuring equipment, triangulation was the preferred and principal method

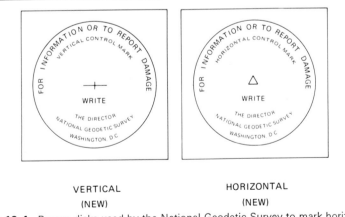

VERTICAL
(NEW)

HORIZONTAL
(NEW)

Figure 18-4. Bronze disks used by the National Geodetic Survey to mark horizontal and vertical control stations.

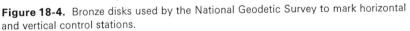

[2] Requests for control data in a given area should be made to the Director, National Geodetic Survey, NGS Information Center, C-18, Rockville, Maryland 20852.

for horizontal control surveys, especially if extensive areas were to be covered. Angles could be readily determined as compared to distances, particularly where long lines over rugged and forested terrain were involved, by erecting the very versatile Bilby towers. The method possessses a large number of inherent checks and closure conditions which help detect blunders and errors in field data, and increase the possibility of satisfying a high standard of accuracy.

As implied by its name, triangulation utilizes geometrical figures comprised of triangles. Horizontal angles and a limited number of sides called *base lines* are measured. Using the angles and base-line lengths, triangles are solved trigonometrically and positions of stations (vertices) calculated.

Different geometrical figures have been employed for control extension by triangulation, but chains of quadrilaterals called *arcs* (see Fig. 18-5) are most common. They are the simplest geometric figures permitting rigorous closure checks and adjustments of field observational errors, and enable point positions to be calculated by two independent routes for computational checks. More complicated figures like that illustrated in Fig. 18-6 are frequently used to establish horizontal control by triangulation in a metropolitan area.

Arcs of triangulation originate from one or more stations of known or fixed position and require the azimuth of at least one line. If two or more stations are fixed, azimuth orientation of the network is automatically determined. Today, fixed starting stations and initial azimuths are normally avail-

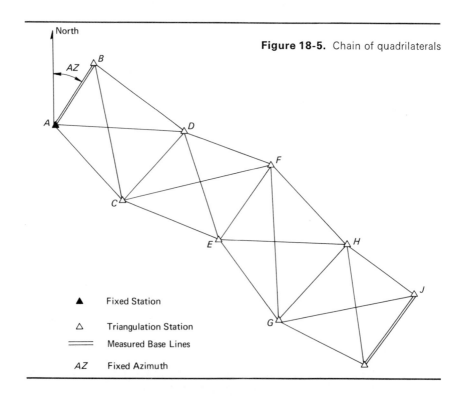

Figure 18-5. Chain of quadrilaterals

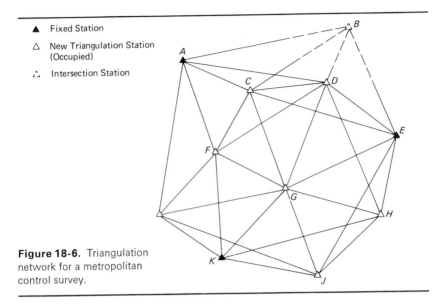

▲ Fixed Station

△ New Triangulation Station
   (Occupied)

⌂ Intersection Station

Figure 18-6. Triangulation network for a metropolitan control survey.

able from other previous higher-order control surveys. The NGS established beginning positions and azimuths for the national network from astronomical observations, which also are used at various intervals throughout extensive arcs to check and supplement angle and base-line measurements and to help maintain true azimuth orientation. In Fig. 18-5, the arc of triangulation originates from fixed station *A* and employs the known azimuth of line *AB*. All horizontal angles within the arc and base lines *AB* and *IJ* have been measured. From this information, positions of stations *B* through *J* were calculated.

In executing triangulation surveys, it is general practice to locate a number of *intersection stations* as part of the project. They can be tall prominent objects in the area, such as church spires, smokestacks, or water towers that are visible from several triangulation stations. Angles to them are measured from as many occupied points as possible, but the intersection stations themselves are not occupied. Their positions are calculated and thus become available as local reference points. An example is station B, Fig. 18-6.

18-8. TRIANGULATION RECONNAISSANCE.   One of the most important aspects of any triangulation survey is the reconnaissance and selection of station locations. Factors to be considered are (1) strength of figure, (2) station intervisibility, (3) station accessibility for the original triangulation observing party and surveyors who will subsequently use the stations, and (4) overall project efficiency. Careful attention must be given to each factor in planning and designing the optimum triangulation network for a given project.

Strength of figure deals with the relative accuracies of computed station positions that result from use of angles of various sizes in calculations. Triangulation computations are based upon the trigonometric *law of sines*. Since the sine function changes significantly for angles near 0° and 180°, a small observational error in an angle near these values produces a comparatively large difference in position calculations. Conversely, sines of angles near 90° change very slowly; thus a small observational error in that region causes little change in the computed position. Since similar observational errors are expected for each angle, design of triangulation figures having favorable angle sizes increases overall triangulation accuracy.

Rigorous procedures beyond the scope of this book have been developed for evaluating relative strengths of geometric figures used in triangulation. In general, angles near 90° are optimum, and if no angles smaller than 30° or larger than 150° are included in calculations, the figure should have sufficient strength. Locations of triangulation stations fix the angle sizes so they must be planned carefully for maximum strength of figure. If local terrain or other conditions preclude use of figures having strong angles, more frequent base-line measurements are necessary.

Station intervisibility is vital in triangulation because lines of sight to all stations within each figure must be clear for measuring angles. Preliminary decisions on station placement can be resolved from available topographic maps. Intervening ridges that might obstruct sight lines are checked by plotting profiles of the lines between stations. Trees on line, and, for long lengths, the combined effects of earth curvature and refraction, are additional factors affecting station intervisibility. After making a preliminary decision on station locations, a visual test should be made by visiting each proposed site. Stations are normally placed on the highest points in an area and, if necessary, towers erected to elevate the theodolite, observer, and targets above the ground stations. Because of the uncertainty of refraction near the ground, lines of sight should be kept at least 10 ft above it and not graze intervening ridges.

18-9. FIELD MEASUREMENTS FOR TRIANGULATION.

As previously stated, the basic field measurements for triangulation are horizontal angles and base-line lengths. Angles can be measured using a repeating instrument, or more likely a directional theodolite such as the Kern DKM-3, Fig. 18-7, having a plate bubble sensitivity of 10″/2-mm division, or the Wild T-3 with a 7″ bubble sensitivity. Both theodolites are suitable for first-order work and enable angles to be read by estimation to the nearest 0.1″. Other lower-order theodolites were discussed in Chapter 8.

To reduce effects of atmospheric refraction on high-order triangulation, observations are made at night with lights for targets. At each station, several "positions" are read—a position consists of angles or directions distributed around the horizontal circle of the instrument in both the direct and plunged mode. With directional theodolites, to compensate for possible circle gradua-

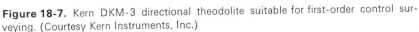

Figure 18-7. Kern DKM-3 directional theodolite suitable for first-order control surveying. (Courtesy Kern Instruments, Inc.)

tion errors, the circle is advanced by approximately $180°/n$ for each successive position (as described in Section 8-22), where n is the number of positions at the station. Angles should be computed in the field from the directions, checked for acceptable closure, and any rejected ones repeated before leaving the station. The average of all satisfactory values for each angle is used in the triangulation calculations.

Base lines now preferably are measured by electronic methods which produce excellent accuracies. Precise Invar tapes may also be used. Several measurements should be made in both directions. Slope distances must be reduced to horizontal and mean-sea-level lengths calculated. If computations involve state plane coordinates, sea-level distances must be converted to grid lengths by applying scale factors (see Section 17-4).

18-10. TRIANGULATION ADJUSTMENT. Errors that occur in angle measurement require that an adjustment be carried out prior to computing control-point positions. The most rigorous method utilizes least squares. In the procedure, all angle measurements plus distance or azimuth observations can be simultaneously included in the adjustment, and any configuration of quadrilaterals or more complicated figures handled to get station positions having maximum probability. The theory is beyond the scope of this text.

Other approximate methods for triangulation adjustment, easily applied to standard figures such as quadrilaterals, also give satisfactory results and are described in advanced surveying books.

After the angles have been adjusted, azimuths of the triangle sides are computed from the corrected angles and their lengths determined by the law of sines. With azimuths and lengths known, coordinates of the stations are calculated using two independent sets of triangles as a computational check.

18-11. PRECISE TRAVERSE. Employment of precise traversing is common among local surveyors for horizontal control extension, especially for projects of limited size. Field work consists of two basic parts—reading horizontal angles at the traverse hubs and measuring distances between stations. Angles can be secured with either a repeating or directional instrument, and distances measured with EDM equipment (*electronic traversing*) or by taping. Precise traverses are always the closed type.

The FGCC has defined standards and specifications for five orders of accuracy for traverses. First-order and second-order classes supplement the National Horizontal Control Network, particularly where a greater density of control is needed than that afforded by triangulation. Second- and third-order traverses are run extensively to solidify control in metropolitan areas for engineering and construction projects, property surveys, aerial photogrammetric surveys, and numerous other projects.

Unlike triangulation in which stations are normally widely separated and placed on the highest ridges and peaks in an area, traverse routes generally follow the cleared rights-of-way of highways and railroads with stations located relatively close together. Besides easing field work, this provides a secondary benefit in accessibility of the stations. Traverses lack the automatic checks inherent in triangulation, and extreme observational caution must therefore be applied to avoid blunders. Also, since traverses generally run along single lines, they are not as good as triangulation for establishing control over large areas.

Procedures for precise traverse computation vary, depending upon whether geodetic or plane procedures have been followed. In either case, it is necessary first to adjust angles and distances for observational errors. Closure conditions are enforced for (1) azimuths or angles, (2) latitudes, and (3) departures. The strictest process, the least-squares method, simultaneously satisfies all three conditions and gives residuals having the greatest likelihood according to the theory of probability. Other less precise systems such as the compass (Bowditch) rule method generally yield satisfactory results for small simple networks

In calculating state plane coordinates, it is necessary to reduce observed horizontal distances to their grid lengths before making the calculations, as described in Section 17-4.

In recent years the NGS has conducted special "ultra-high-accuracy transcontinental traverses" with results approaching one part per million. These surveys were originally begun to provide base lines for the worldwide satellite triangulation program (see Section 18-13) but will also be used in the future to upgrade the horizontal control network. Theodolites and EDM equipment of the highest precision are required for the transcontinental traverses, and rigorous field procedures adopted to meet the extremely stringent specifications. In addition to showing triangulation, Fig. 18-2 also illustrates locations of high-precision transcontinental traverses in part of Florida.

18-12. TRILATERATION.   Trilateration, a method for horizontal control surveys based exclusively on measured horizontal distances, has gained acceptance because of EDM instrumentation. Both triangulation and traversing require horizontal angle measurement; hence trilateration surveys often can be executed faster and produce equally acceptable accuracies.

The geometric figures used in trilateration, although not as standardized, are similar to those employed in triangulation. Stations should be intervisible and therefore placed on the highest peaks, perhaps with towers to elevate instruments and observers.

Strength of figure in trilateration is less quantified than for triangulation; however, slender figures are weakest in the direction transverse to their long dimensions. Hence networks covering essentially square areas are better since they give stronger overall uniform accuracy. Preliminary analyses indicate that a hexagon with 15 measurable lengths would approach the strength of a standard triangulation quadrilateral. Combinations of triangulation and trilateration will probably be the way of the future.

Because of intervisibility requirements and the desirability of having essentially square networks, trilateration is ideally suited to densify control in metropolitan areas and on large engineering projects. In special situations where topography or other conditions require elongated narrow figures, the network can be strengthened by reading some horizontal angles. Also, for long trilateration arcs, astronomic azimuth observations prevent the network from deforming in direction. A complete and accurate estimate of strength of figure for trilateration networks is secured by presurvey least-squares analysis of trial configurations, but the procedure is beyond the scope of this book.

As in triangulation, surveys by trilateration can be extended from one or more monuments of known position. If only a single station is fixed, at least one azimuth must be known or observed.

Trilateration computations consist of reducing measured slope distances to horizontal lengths; then to mean sea level equivalents; and finally to grid lengths if the calculations are being done in state plane coordinate systems. Observational errors in trilateration networks must be adjusted, preferably by the least-squares method. This process is relatively simple compared with

other methods, especially for larger networks, and it produces adjusted coordinates of the control stations directly.

18-13. WORLDWIDE CONTROL SURVEYING PROGRAMS. In recent years, the NGS, in cooperation with other federal agencies and host
foreign nations, has undertaken a worldwide control survey program. These
activities have established precise relative positions of the continents, various
ocean islands, and an extremely high-accuracy network of reference monuments which add considerable strength to those of the United States and
other cooperating nations.

Two global control survey activities are the *satellite triangulation* and
Doppler geodesy programs. The satellite triangulation program became
operational in 1963 and is now essentially completed. Field work consisted
of taking photographs of an orbiting satellite simultaneously from several
widely separated ground stations using large, precise *ballistic cameras*. From
measurements made on photographic plates, directions from ground stations
to the satellite were determined. Scale for the triangulation was obtained from
ultra-high-accuracy traverse surveys. As an indication of the vastness of
station spacing in the worldwide satellite triangulation network, one triangle
in North America consisted of points in northwestern Greenland and the
states of Maryland and Washington.

The Doppler geodesy program has supplanted the satellite triangulation
program for global control surveys because it is faster and more precise
(stations can be located to an accuracy of about 1 m). The Doppler program
also utilizes a satellite, but one which transmits radio waves as it orbits the
earth. By means of special receivers called *geoceivers* located at widely spaced
ground stations, changes in frequency (Doppler shift) of the radio waves
are recorded as the satellite approaches and moves away from ground stations.
With Doppler shift and precise time information, together with known
satellite orbital data, locations of the geoceivers can be accurately fixed.

18-14. INERTIAL SURVEYING SYSTEMS. New inertial surveying systems are currently being introduced which have the potential to completely
revolutionize current control surveying practices. These systems, carried in
aircraft or land vehicles, incorporate precise gyroscopes, accelerometers,
and a computer. They are spinoffs from the military guidance systems used
on aircraft and missiles, and can display latitude, longitude, and elevation
at any position.

Inertial surveying systems operate by a computer-controlled process
called *gyrocompassing*. Two gyros sense the earth's rotation and orient themselves orthogonally, one facing north-south, the other east-west. The gyros
maintain their orientation while accelerometers measure components of
movement in the cardinal directions, and in elevation, as they are moved from

point to point. The system starts at a point of known position and elevation· and by applying the components of change, positions and elevations of occupied points are determined

As inertial surveying equipment is refined, accuracies are improving. Tests to date, conducted over calibrated routes, show that position and elevation errors have averaged as low as $\frac{1}{2}$ m for short circuits, and precisions of up to 1/20,000 have been achieved on long courses. Inertial surveying systems do not require direct angle or distance measurements; thus towers and clear lines of sight are not necessary. They can operate day or night, rain or shine.

18-15. VERTICAL CONTROL SURVEYS. Vertical control surveys are run in a variety of ways, depending upon required accuracy. Barometric leveling, described in Section 5-4, is used to get approximate elevations suitable for reconnaissance surveys. Trigonometric leveling (see also Section 5-4) can provide a higher order of accuracy, suitable for controlling photogrammetric mapping. Differential leveling, described in Section 5-22, can supply different accuracies depending upon the precautions taken. In this section only *precise differential leveling* is considered.

As noted in Section 18-2 and Table 18-2, the FGCC has established accuracy standards and specifications for various orders of differential leveling, but the same basic principles are employed. To achieve higher orders, however, special care must be exercised to minimize errors.

For the most accurate work, precise tilting levels such as the Wild N-3 of Fig. 18-8 are used. This instrument has a split image or coincidence bubble

Figure 18-8. Wild N-3 precise tilting level. (Courtesy Wild Heerbrugg Instruments, Inc.)

with sensitivity of 10″ per 2-mm division that is centered by means of a tilting screw. It has a parallel-plate glass micrometer which can elevate or depress the line of sight parallel to itself to set precisely on the nearest rod graduation. A micrometer shows the amount raised or lowered and permits rod readings to about $\frac{1}{100}$ of the smallest graduation, instead of $\frac{1}{10}$ division by estimation. The instrument reticle is shown in Fig. 18-9. It has a single horizontal line on the right for making rod readings in the normal way, and two lines that form a wedge on the left to straddle a reading for utmost accuracy.

Special level rods are needed for precise work. They have scales graduated on Invar strips which are only slightly affected by temperature variations; nevertheless thermometers attached to the rod are read and corrections applied for any shrinkage or expansion of the scale. Precise level rods are equipped with rod bubbles to facilitate plumbing, and special braces aid in holding the rod steady. They usually have two separate graduated scales. One type is divided in centimeters on an Invar strip on the rod's front side, and a scale in feet painted on the back for checking readings and minimizing blunders. A second kind, shown in Fig. 18-9, has two sets of centimeter graduations on the Invar strip with the right one precisely offset from the left by a constant, thereby giving checks on readings.

Cloudy weather is preferable for precise leveling but an umbrella can be used on sunny days to shade the instrument and prevent uneven heating which causes the bubble to run (one design encases the vial in a styrofoam shield). Precise work should not be attempted on windy days. For best results, short equal backsight and foresight distances of a maximum of 250 ft (75 m) are recommended with their lengths balanced to within 6 ft (2 m) at each setup. Rodmen pace, or count rail or highway slab joints, to set sight distances which are checked for accuracy by three-wire stadia. Precise leveling demands good-quality turning points. Lines of sight should not pass closer than about 2 ft from the ground to avoid refraction. Readings at any setup must be completed in rapid succession; otherwise changes in atmospheric conditions might significantly change refraction characteristics between them.

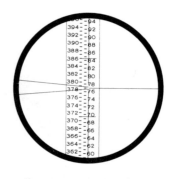

Figure 18-9. Reticle of the Wild N-3 precise level shown with dual metric-scale precise leveling rod. (Courtesy Wild Heerbrugg Instruments, Inc.),

Three-wire leveling has been employed for much precise surveying in the United States. The method has the advantages of (a) providing checks against rod reading blunders, (b) producing greater accuracy because averages of three readings are available, and (c) furnishing stadia measurements of sight lengths. In the three-wire procedure, rod readings at the upper, middle, and lower cross hairs are taken and recorded for each backsight and foresight. The difference between the upper and middle hair readings is compared with that for the middle and lower hair values, and must agree within one or two of the smallest units being recorded (usually 0.1 of the least count of the rod graduations); otherwise the readings are repeated. An average of the three readings is actually used, but as a computational check it must be very close to the middle hair figure. The difference between the upper and lower hair readings multiplied by the instrument stadia constant gives the sight distances.

A sample set of field notes for the three-wire method is illustrated in Fig. 18-10. Backsight readings on BM *A* of 0.718, 0.633, and 0.550 taken on

Sta.	+ Sight	Stadia	Sight	Stadia	Elev.
THREE-WIRE LEVELING					
TAYLOR LAKE ROAD					
BM A					103.8432
	0.718		1.131		
	0.633	8.5	1.051	8.0	+0.6337
	0.550	8.3	0.972	7.9	104.4769
	3)1.901	16.8	3)3.154	15.9	-1.0513
	+0.6337		-1.0513		
TP 1					103.4256
	1.151		1.041		
	1.082	6.9	0.969	7.2	+1.0820
	1.013	6.9	0.897	7.2	104.5076
	3)3.246	13.8	3)2.907	14.4	-0.9690
	+1.0820		-0.9690		
TP 2					103.5386
	1.908		1.264		
	1.841	6.7	1.194	7.0	+1.8410
	1.774	6.7	1.123	7.1	105.3796
	3)5.523	13.4	3)3.581	14.1	-1.1937
	+1.8410		-1.1937		
BM B					104.1859
	Σ +3.5567		Σ -3.2140		Check
Page Check :					
	103.8432 + 3.5567 - 3.2140 = 104.1859				

Fig. 18-10. Sample field notes for three-wire leveling.

the upper, middle, and lower hairs, respectively, give upper and lower differences (multiplied by 100) of 8.5 and 8.3 m, which agree within acceptable tolerance. Stadia measurement of the backsight length (the sum of the upper and lower differences) is 16.8 m. The average of the three backsight readings on BM *A*, 0.6337 m, agrees within 0.0007 m of the middle hair reading. The stadia foresight length of 15.9 m at this setup is within 0.9 m of the backsight length, and satisfactory. The HI for the first setup, if needed, is found by adding the average backsight reading to the elevation of BM *A*.

A second technique in precise leveling employs the parallel-plate micrometer attached to a precise leveling instrument, and a pair of precise rods like those described earlier. While this method has been used in Europe for over 50 years, it was not adopted in the United States until the late 1960s.

It is generally advisable to design large level networks so that several smaller circuits are interconnected to supply checks which isolate blunders or large errors. In Fig. 18-11, for example, it is required to determine the elevations of points *X*, *Y*, and *Z* by commencing from BM *A* and closing on BM *B*. As a minimum, this could be done by running level lines 1 through 4, but if an unacceptable closure were obtained at BM *B*, it would be impossible to discover in which lines the blunder occurred. If additional lines 5, 6, and 7 were run, calculating differences in elevation by other routes through the network might isolate the blunder. Furthermore, by including supplemental measurements, precision of the resulting elevations at *X*, *Y*, and *Z* is increased.

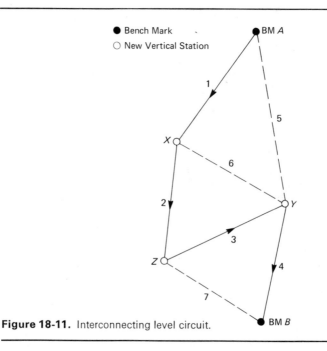

Figure 18-11. Interconnecting level circuit.

Regardless of precautions employed in field observations, errors accumulate in leveling and must be adjusted to provide perfect mathematical closure in all loops. For simple level circuits, adjustment procedures presented in Section 5-32 can be followed; for interconnected level networks such as that of Fig. 18-11, the method of least squares is preferable.

Precise leveling is very tedious and requires extreme care. Field personnel must heed minute details to minimize systematic errors which are always present. Probably no aspect of control surveying has been studied for so many years (over a century).

PROBLEMS

18-1. Describe what is meant by the terms "geodetic latitude" and "geodetic longitude."

18-2. What different field methods are used in horizontal control surveying? Which factors influence the choice of field method to use?

18-3. List the orders and classes of accuracy of horizontal control surveys and give their relative accuracy requirements.

18-4. Name the orders and classes of accuracy of vertical control surveys and give their relative accuracy requirements.

18-5. Describe the hierarchy of the National Horizontal Control Network.

18-6. Discuss the hierarchy of the National Vertical Control Network.

18-7. Explain why it is important to permanently monument and adequately describe control stations. Give the contents of a good control station description.

18-8. Why are quadrilaterals the most commonly used geometric figure in triangulation?

18-9. Analyze the factors that must be considered in triangulation reconnaissance.

18-10. Obtain a U.S. Geological Survey quadrangle map of your area. On the map, lay out a quadrilateral having sides from 3 to 5 miles in length. Check all lines for intervisibility by plotting their profiles, and revise station positions if necessary to provide unobstructed lines of sight.

18-11. Explain the reason for establishing triangulation figures that contain angles between 30° and 150°.

18-12. Discuss the special precautions that are taken in observing angles on high-order triangulation.

18-13. Outline the advantages and disadvantages of traverse control surveys as compared to triangulation for horizontal networks.

18-14. Explain the differences between triangulation and trilateration. List their similarities.

18-15. Name and describe two systems used for establishing worldwide control networks.

18-16. What is meant by the term "gyrocompassing"?

18-17. List the special precautions taken on high-order differential leveling.

18–18. Discuss the advantages of the three-wire leveling procedure.

18–19. A line of levels intended to be first-order, class-I was initiated at BM A, having elevation 281.471 m, and terminated at BM B, having elevation 281.537 m. The closure elevation obtained on BM B was 281.542 m. If the distance from BM A to BM B is 22 miles, does this leveling meet first-order, class-I standards ? Explain.

18–20. Prepare a set of three-wire leveling notes for the data given, and make the page check. The elevation of BM X is 161.281 m. The rod readings are: (H denotes upper cross hair reading, M middle hair, and L lower hair). BS on BM X : $H = 1.530$, $M = 1.321$, $L = 1.113$; FS on TP 1 : $H = 2.690$, $M = 2.461$, $L = 2.231$; BS on TP 1 : $H = 2.049$, $M = 1.867$, $L = 1.685$; FS on BM Y : $H = 0.921$, $M = 0.743$, $L = 0.564$.

19
BOUNDARY
SURVEYS

19-1. GENERAL. The earliest surveys were made to locate or relocate boundary lines of property. From Biblical times,[1] when the death penalty was assessed for destroying corners, to the colonial days of George Washington,[2] who was licensed as a land surveyor by William and Mary College of Virginia, and through the years to the present, trees and other natural objects, or stakes driven in the ground, have been used to identify corners.

As property increased in value and owners disputed rights to land, the importance of more accurate surveys, permanent monuments, and written records was obvious. "When Texas became a state in 1845, the public domain amounted to about 172,700,000 acres, which the United States government could have acquired by payment of approximately $13,000,000 in debts accumulated by the Republic of Texas. However, Congress allowed the Texans to retain their land and pay their own debts"[3]—a good bargain, even then, at roughly 7.6 cents/acre. Several years ago, land at Waikiki in Honolulu sold for over $100/ft² or $4,356,000/acre. In Tokyo property can be even more expensive.

Land titles now are transferred by written documents called *deeds* (grant, quit claim, agreement, or warranty) which contain a description of the property boundaries. The various methods of description include (a) metes and bounds, (b) block and lot number, (c) coordinate values for each

---

[1] "Cursed be he that removeth his neighbor's landmark. And all the people shall say Amen." Deut. 27:17.

[2] "Mark well the land, it is our most valuable asset." George Washington.

[3] Rupert F. Carroll, "Property Surveys Must Fit Their Titles," *ASCE Proceedings*, July 1949.

corner, and (d) township, section, and smaller subdivision. The first three methods are discussed briefly in this chapter, the last one in Chapter 20.

Most property surveys today are wholly or partly resurveys rather than originals. In retracing old lines, a surveyor must exercise acute judgment based on education, practical experience, and a knowledge of land laws, and be accurate in his measurements. The necessary mathematics and proper use of a transit, theodolite, level, tape, and EDM can be learned in a relatively short time. This background must be bolstered by tenacity in searching the records of all adjacent property as well as studying descriptions of the land in question. In field work, a surveyor must be untiring in his efforts to find points called for by the deed. Often it is necessary to obtain testimony from old settlers or others having knowledge of accepted land lines and the location of corners, reference points, fences, and other evidence of the correct lines.

A land surveyor may be confronted with defective surveys; incompatible descriptions and plats of common lines for adjacent tracts; lost or obliterated corners and reference marks; discordant stories by local residents; questions of riparian rights; and a multitude of legal decisions on cases involving property boundaries. His duty to a client is to sift all available evidence and try to obtain a meeting of minds among persons involved in any property-line dispute. In this task he is doing professional work although without any legal authority to force a compromise or settlement. Fixing title boundaries must be done by agreement of adjacent owners or court action. To serve as an expert witness in proceedings to establish boundaries, a surveyor has to be registered.

Many municipalities have rigid laws covering subdivisions. Regulations may specify the minimum size of lot; allowable closures for surveys; types of corner marks to be used; minimum width of streets, and the procedure for dedicating them; rules for registry of plats; and other matters. The mismatched street and highway layouts of today could have been eliminated by suitable subdivision regulations in past years.

The many problems associated with real estate titles and transfers have provided the impetus for research and development toward implementation of Modern Land Data Systems (MOLDS). Sometimes referred to as "Modern Cadastres," they will assemble computerized data banks at central locations. Information available for rapid retrieval may include parcel descriptions and identifiers, their geographic positions, records of ownership, easements, land use, soil types, and specialized data. Such systems can be invaluable to surveyors, lawyers, developers, planners, environmentalists, government officials, and others.

19-2. BASIS OF LAND TITLES.   In the eastern part of the United States, individuals acquired the first land titles by gift or purchase from the English Crown. Surveys and maps were completely lacking or inadequate, and descriptions could be given only in general terms. The remaining land in the Thirteen Colonies was transferred to the states at the close of the Revolutionary War. Later this land was parceled out to individuals, generally in irregular tracts. Boundary lines were described by metes and bounds (directions by magnetic bearings, and lengths in Gunter's chains, poles, or rods).

Many original transfers, and subsequent ownerships and subdivisions, were not recorded. Those that were legally registered usually had scanty or defective descriptions since land was cheap and abundant. Trees, rocks, and natural landmarks defining the corners, as in the first example metes-and-bounds description (see Section 19-3), were soon disturbed. The intersection of two property lines might be described only as "the place where John killed a bear," or "the bend in a footpath from Jones's cabin to the river."

Numerous problems in land surveying stem from the confusion engendered by early property titles, descriptions, and compass surveys. The locations of thousands of corners have been established by compromise after resurveys, or by court interpretation of all available evidence pertinent to their original or intended positions. Other corners have been fixed by *squatters' rights, adverse possession*, and *riparian changes*. Many boundaries still are in doubt, particularly in areas having marginal land where the cost of a good survey ("retracement of history") exceeds the value of the property.

The fact that four corners of a field can be found, and the distances between them agree with the calls in a description, does not necessarily mean they are in the proper place. Title or ownership is complete only when the land covered by a deed is positively identified and located on the ground.

Years of experience in a given area are needed by a land surveyor to become familiar with local conditions, basic reference points, and legal interpretations of boundary problems. The method used in one state for prorating differences between recorded and measured distances may not be acceptable in another. Different interpretations are given locally to the (a) superiority or definiteness of one distance over another associated with it; (b) position of boundaries shown by occupancy; (c) value of corners in place in a tract and its subdivisions; and (d) many other factors. Registration of land surveyors is therefore required in all states to protect the public interest.

19-3. PROPERTY DESCRIPTION BY METES AND BOUNDS. Descriptions by metes (to measure, or assign by measure) and bounds (boundary lines or property limits) have a *point of beginning* (POB), such as a stake, fence post, road intersection, or some natural feature. Lengths and bearings of successive lines from the point of beginning are given. Values in chains, poles, and rods are being replaced by distances in feet and decimals. A 1975 American Congress on Surveying and Mapping (ACSM) metric workshop recommended, among other things, that (a) surveyors immediately show equivalent values for areas in square meters or hectares, depending upon size of parcel, on all plans for recording; and (b) legal descriptions of existing deeds, record plans, or plans be converted to the metric system only if and when conveyancing or subdivision takes place.

Bearings may be magnetic or true, the latter being preferable. A West

Virginia survey regulation calls for exterior lines of new subdivisions to be based on the true meridian, thus requiring an astronomical observation by the surveyor for each subdivision unless it adjoins another where *he* made an astronomical observation.

In relocating an old survey, precedence (weight of importance) is commonly assigned as follows: (1) marks or monuments in place; (2) calls for boundaries of adjoining tracts; (3) courses and distances shown in the original notes or plat. If numbers are spelled out, and also given as figures, words control unless other proof is available. There is a greater likelihood of transposing than misspelling—and lawyers prefer words!

Property descriptions are written by surveyors and lawyers. A single error in transcribing a numerical value, or one incorrect or misplaced word or punctuation mark, may result in litigation for a generation or more, since the intentions of *grantor* (person selling property) and *grantee* (person buying property) are not clearly fulfilled.

The importance of permanent monuments is evident—in fact, some states require pipes, iron pins, and/or concrete markers long enough to reach below the frost line at all property corners before surveys will be accepted for recording. Actually, almost anything can be called for as a monument. A map attached to the description clarifies it, and scaling provides a rough check on the angles and distances.

To increase precision of property surveys, large cities and some states have established a network of control monuments to supplement triangulation stations of the NGS. Property corners can be tied to these control points and boundary lines relocated with assurance.

Description of land in a deed should always contain the following information in addition to the recital:

1. *Point of beginning (POB)*. This point must be identifiable, permanent, well-referenced, and near the property. Coordinates should be given if known or computable. Note that a POB is of no more importance than other corners and a called-for monument in place at the next corner establishes its position, even though bearing and distance calls to it do not agree.
2. *Definite corners*. Such corners are clearly defined points with coordinates if possible.
3. *Lengths and directions of the property sides*. All lengths in feet and decimals (or metric units), and directions by angles or true bearings, must be stated to permit computation of the closure error. Omitting the length or bearing of a closing line to the POB and substituting a phrase "and thence to the point of beginning" is no longer acceptable. Date of the survey is required and particularly important if bearings are referred to magnetic north.
4. *Names of adjoining property owners*. These are necessary to avoid claims in case an error in the description leaves a gap or creates an overlap.

5. *Area.* The included area is normally shown as an aid in valuation and identification of the property. Areas of rural land are given in acres; those of city lots in square feet at present. Depending upon the adjustment method used for a traverse (compass, transit, Crandall, etc.), one surveyor's calculated area, angles, and distances may differ somewhat from another's, so, unless only one rule is legally acceptable, the procedure employed should be stated.

A partial metes-and-bounds description for the tract shown in Fig. 19-1 is given as an example.

That part of the SW¼ of the NW¼ of Section 28, T 22 N, R 11 E, Town of Little Wolf, Brock County, Wisconsin, described as follows: Commencing at a stone monument at the W¼ corner of said Section 28; thence N 45°00′ E, 400.00 feet along the Southeasterly R/W line of Lake Street to a 1″ iron pipe at the point of beginning of this description, said point also being the point of curvature of a curve to the right having a central angle of 90°00′ and radius of 300.00 feet; thence Easterly, 471.24 feet along the arc of the curve, the long chord of which bears East, 424.26 feet, to a 1″ iron pipe at the point of tangency thereof, said arc also being the aforesaid Southerly R/W line of Lake Street; thence continuing along the Southwesterly R/W line of Lake Street, S 45°00′ E, 150.00 feet to a 1″ iron pipe; thence S 45°00′ W, 200.00 feet to a 1″ iron pipe located N 45°00″ E, 20 feet, more or less, from the water's edge of Green Lake, and is the beginning of the meander line along the lake; thence West 141.42 feet along the said meander line to a 1″ iron pipe at the end of the meander line; said pipe being located N 45°00′ W, 20 feet, more or less,

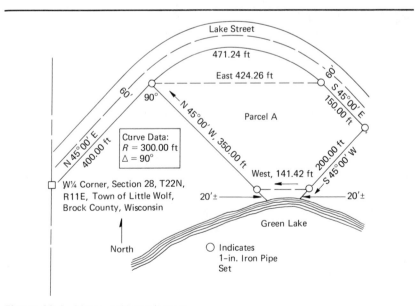

Figure 19-1. Metes and bounds tract.

from the said water's edge; thence N 45°00′ W, 350.00 feet to a 1″ iron pipe at the point of beginning . . . including all lands lying between the meander line herein described and the Northerly shore of Green Lake, which lie between true extensions of the Southeasterly and Southwesterly boundary lines of the parcel herein described, said parcel containing 2.54 acres. Bearings are based on astronomic north.

Two examples of *old* metes-and-bounds descriptions from the eastern United States will be given. The first, part of an early deed registered in Maine, is: "Beginning at an apple tree at about 5 minutes walk from Trefethens Landing thence easterly to an apple tree, thence southerly to a rock, thence westerly to an apple tree, thence northerly to the point of beginning." With numerous apple trees and an abundance of rocks in the area, the dilemma of a surveyor trying to retrace the boundaries many years later is obvious.

The second, a more typical old description of a city lot showing lack of comparable precision in angles and distances, follows:

Beginning at a point on the west side of Beech Street marked by a brass plug set in a concrete monument located one hundred twelve and five tenths (112.5) feet southerly from a city monument No. 27 at the intersection of Beech Street and West Avenue; thence along the west line of Beech Street S 15°14′30″ E fifty (50) feet to a brass plug in a concrete monument; thence at right angles to Beech Street S 74°45′30″ W one hundred fifty (150) feet to an iron pin; thence at right angles N 15°14′30″ W parallel to Beech Street fifty (50) feet to an iron pin; thence at right angles N 74°45′30″ E one hundred fifty (150) feet to place of beginning; bounded on the north by Norton, on the east by Beech Street, on the south by Stearns, and on the west by Weston.

19-4. PROPERTY DESCRIPTION BY BLOCK-AND-LOT SYSTEM.
In subdivisions and in large cities it is more convenient to identify individual lots by *block and lot number*, by *tract and lot number*, or by *subdivision name and lot number*. Examples are:

Lot 34 of Tract 12314 as per map recorded in book 232 pages 23 and 24 of maps, in the office of the county recorder of Los Angeles County.

Lot 9 except the North 12 feet thereof, and the East 26 feet of Lot 10, Broderick's Addition to Minneapolis. [Parts of two lots are included in the parcel described.]

That portion of Lot 306 of Tract 4178 in the City of Los Angeles, as per Map recorded in Book 75 pages 30 to 32 inclusive of maps in the office of the County Recorder of said County, lying Southeasterly of a line extending Southwesterly at right angles from the Northeasterly line of said Lot, from a point in said Northeasterly line distant Southeasterly 23.75 feet from the most Northerly corner of said Lot.

Map books in the city or county recorder's office give the location and dimensions of all the blocks and lots. It is now standard practice to require subdividers to file a map with the proper office showing the type and location of monuments, size of lots, and other pertinent information such as the dedication of streets. It is evident that if the boundary lines of a tract are in doubt, the individual lot lines must be questioned also.

The block-and-lot system is a short and unique means of describing property for tax purposes as well as for transfer. Identification by street and house number is satisfactory only for tax-assessment records.

Figure 19-2 is an example of a small block-and-lot subdivision.

19-5. PROPERTY DESCRIPTION BY COORDINATES. The advantages of state plane coordinate systems in improving the accuracy of local surveys, and in facilitating the relocation of lost and obliterated corners, have led to their legal acceptance in property descriptions. The coordinate description of corners may be used alone, but usually is prepared in conjunction with an alternative method. Wider use of the coordinate system will be made as more reference points become available to the local surveyor.

An example of a description by coordinates of a parcel in California follows.

A parcel of tide and submerged land, in the State-owned bed of Seven Mile Slough, Sacramento County, California, in projected Section 10, T 3 N, R 3 E, Mt. Diablo Meridian, more particularly described as follows:

BEGINNING at a point on the southerly bank of said Seven Mile Slough which bears S 62°37′ E, 860 feet from a California State Lands Commission brass cap set in concrete stamped "JACK 1969," said point having coordinates of $X = 2,106,973.68$ and $Y = 164,301.93$ as shown on Record of Survey of Owl Island, filed October 6, 1969, in Book 27 of Surveys Page 9, Sacramento County Records, thence to a point having coordinates of $X = 2,107,196.04$ and $Y = 164,285.08$; thence to a point having coordinates of $X = 2,107,205.56$, $Y = 164,410.72$: thence to a point having coordinates of $X = 2,106,983.20$, $Y = 164,427.57$; thence to the point of beginning.

Coordinates, bearings, and distances in the above description are based on the California Coordinate System, Zone II.

Earthquakes in Alaska, California, and Hawaii have caused ground shifts which move corner monuments and thereby change their coordinates. The monuments, rather than the coordinates, will then have greater weight in ownership rights.

19-6. SUBDIVISIONS.   A real estate *subdivision* is an unimproved tract of land surveyed and divided into lots for sale purposes. It may be synonymous in some localities with a *development*, which implies improvements are made before sales. Any of the four description methods listed in Section 19-1 can be applied to the parcels.

A small block-and-lot subdivision is shown in Fig. 19-2. (Some lot areas have been deleted so their calculations can become end-of-the-chapter problems.) Large electronic computers with appropriate available programs greatly reduce the labor of computing lot sizes and areas in subdivisions with curved streets. Automatic plotters using the printout results make platting simple and fast.

NO.	DELTA	TAN.	ARC	RADIUS	CHORD	CHORD BEAR.
1	12° 37'	67.00'	133.46'	606.07'	133.19'	N 65°00'30"E
2	5° 49' 40"	7.67'	15.33'	150.72'	15.32'	N 28°23'10"W
3	90°00'	25.00'	39.27'	25.00'	35.36'	N 13°42'E
4	12° 37'	103.57'	210.28'	954.93	209.85'	S 65°00'30"W
5	5° 50' 15"	33.59'	67.11'	658.72'	67.08'	N 68°23'30"E
6	97°40'27"	28.60	42.62'	25.00'	37.64'	S 65°41'05"E
7	75° 32' 50"	19.37'	32.96'	25.00'	30.63'	N 20°55'35"E
8	22° 20' 50"	19.75'	39.00'	100.00	38.76'	S 5° 40'25"E
9	67°39'10"	16.75'	29.52'	25.00'	27.83'	N 50°40'25"W
10	29°12'20"	36.38'	71.16'	139.62'	70.41'	S 80°53'50"W

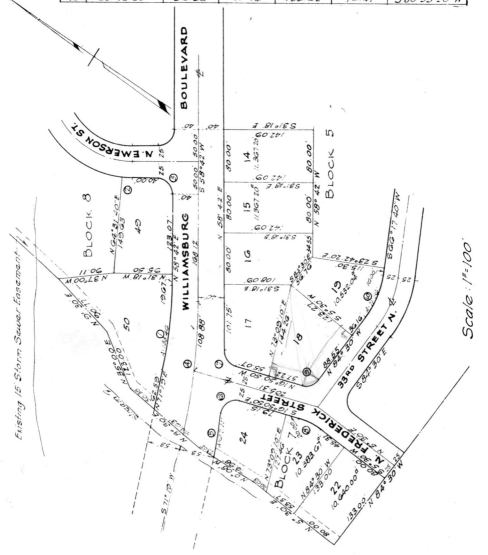

Figure 19-2. A small subdivision plat.

19-7. PARTITIONING LAND.   A common problem in property surveys is partitioning land into two or more pieces for sale, distribution to family members, heirs, and so on. A boundary survey is run; latitudes and departures computed; the traverse balanced; and total enclosed area calculated. Some parcel shapes and requirements permit formula solutions, often by using analytical geometry. Others require trial-and-error methods.

Figure 19-3 illustrates cutting off 12 acres by means of a line *EF* parallel to the base *AD*. The distances in this farm deed were given and balanced only to the nearest 0.1 ft and thus without exceeding the number of significant figures in the data, a "more-or-less" area of 12 acres = 522,720 ft² is obtained. Referring to Fig. 19-3,

$$\text{required area} = 522{,}720 = xy + \frac{y^2 \tan 8°17'}{2} = 790.7y + \frac{y^2(0.1455872)}{2}$$

then

$$0.0727936y^2 + 790.7y - 522{,}720 = 0$$

and

$$y = 625.1 \text{ ft}$$

$$z = y \tan 8°17' = 91.0 \text{ ft}$$

$$\text{base } EF = 790.7 + 91.0 = 881.7 \text{ ft}$$

$$CF = \frac{625.1}{\cos 8°17'} = 631.7 \text{ ft}$$

$$\text{area } EBCF = 625.1 \left(\frac{790.7 + 881.7}{2}\right) = 522{,}700 \text{ ft}^2$$

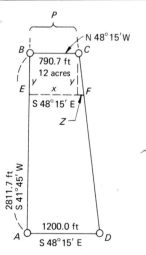

Figure 19-3. Land partitioning.

(with these lengths of sides measured to only tenths of a foot, a computed area to more than four significant figures is not justified).

Another approach is to extend AB and DC to meet at a point P, then use triangle EPF in which simple proportions are readily visualized.

Cutoff lines to separate a certain area from a parcel may have (1) a specified starting point (distance from one corner of the tract polygon, and run to the midpoint or any other location on the opposite side) or (2) a required direction (parallel with, perpendicular to, or on a designated bearing angle from a selected line). These cases usually require trial-and-error solutions involving an initial assumption such as the cutoff line direction or starting point.

Figure 19-4 shows that a statement "the southern half" of tract $ABCD$ can have a number of meanings—the *most* southerly half, half the frontage, or half the actual acreage. An important consideration is the final shape of each lot. Connecting midpoints G and H leaves the southerly "half" smaller than the northerly "half," but provides equal frontage for both parts on the two streets. Course EF, parallel with AD, produces one trapezoidal lot but a poorly shaped northerly parcel with meager frontage on Smith Street. The intent of the deed should therefore be clearly stated.

Before field work, a surveyor must spend considerable time searching courthouse records for descriptions, adjoiners, easements, and other pertinent facts.

19-8. FIELD WORK. The first field task is to locate the property corners. Here a most valuable piece of equipment to the land surveyor—the shovel— frequently comes into use along with a magnetic locator which is especially helpful if magnetized metal survey caps have been set. In many cases one or more lines must be run from control points some distance away to check or establish the location of a corner. If two points are available with known coordinates on a state or local system, a connecting line or traverse transfers true bearings or coordinates to the property boundaries, as indicated in Fig. 19-5.

Generally a closed traverse is run around the property, all corners being

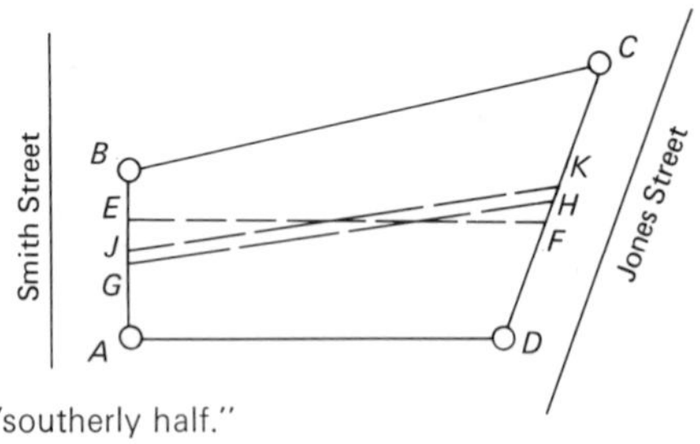

Figure 19-4. The "southerly half."

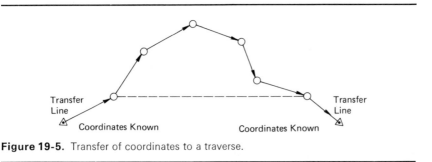

Figure 19-5. Transfer of coordinates to a traverse.

occupied if possible. Fences, trees, shrubbery, hedges, party walls, and other obstacles may necessitate a traverse that is inside or outside the property. From stub (side shot) measurements to the corners, their coordinates and the lengths and bearings of the sides are calculated (see Sections 10-11 and 10-12). All measurements should be made with a precision suited to the value of the land. If coordinates on a grid system are to be used in the description, the order of accuracy in the system itself should be maintained if possible.

Measurements made with an EDM, or a standardized tape corrected for temperature and tension, may not agree with distances on record or those between the marks. This provides a real test for the surveyor. Perhaps his tape is different in length from the one used in the original survey; the marks could have been disturbed, or be the wrong ones; monuments might not check with others in the vicinity believed or known to be correct; and perhaps several previous surveys disagree with each other.

Bearings, and angles between adjacent sides, may not fit those called for. The discrepancy could be due to a faulty original compass survey, incorrect corner marks, or other causes.

A surveyor's job is to relocate or establish boundary markers in the exact position where they were originally set. If differences exist between distances of record and measured values for found monuments, the data should be used to get a calibrated tape length which relates to the original surveyed distances. In relocating monuments, this calibration is employed to lay off the actual distances noted by the original surveyor.

19-9. REGISTRATION OF TITLE. To remedy difficulties arising from inaccurate descriptions and disputed boundary claims, some states provide for registration of property titles under rigid rules. The usual requirements include marking each corner with standardized monuments referenced to established points, and recording a plat drawn to scale and containing specified items. Titles are then guaranteed by the court under certain conditions.

A number of states have followed Massachusetts' example and maintain separate *land courts* dealing exclusively with land titles. As the practice spreads, accuracy of property surveys will be increased and transfer of property simplified.

A comparable service is offered by *title insurance companies*, which search, assemble, and interpret official records, laws, and court decisions affecting ownership of land. Title companies insure purchasers against loss by guaranteeing that its findings regarding defects, liens, encumbrances, restrictions, assessments, and easements are correct. Defense against lawsuits is provided by the company against these threats to a clear title from claims shown in the public records and not exempted in the policy. The location of corners and lines is not guaranteed; hence it is necessary to establish on the ground the exact boundaries called for by the deed and title policy.

Many technical and legal problems are considered before title insurance is granted. In some states, title companies refuse to issue a policy covering a lot if fences in place are not on the property line and exclude from the contract "all items that would be disclosed by a proper survey." Occupation and use of land belonging to a neighbor but outside his apparent boundary line as defined by a fence may lead to a claim of adverse possession.

Adverse rights are obtained against all except the public by occupying a parcel of land for a period of years specified by law, and performing certain acts. Possession must be (a) actual, (b) exclusive, (c) open and notorious, (d) hostile, (e) continuous, and (f) under color of title. In some states all taxes must be paid. The time required to establish a claim of adverse possession varies from a minimum of 7 years in Florida to a maximum of 60 years for urban property in New York. The customary period is 20 years.

The continuous use of a street, driveway, or footpath by an individual or the general public for a specified number of years results in establishment of a right-of-way privilege which cannot be withheld by the original owner.

Discussion of property surveys has necessarily been condensed in this text. For more extensive coverage, see the References, Appendix B.

19-10. SOURCES OF ERROR. Some sources of error in boundary surveys follow:

1. Corner not defined by a unique point.
2. Unequal precision of angles and distances.
3. Length measurements not made with a standardized tape nor corrected for tension, temperature, and slope.

19-11. MISTAKES. Typical mistakes in connection with boundary surveys are:

1. Use of wrong corner marks.
2. Failure to check deeds of adjacent property as well as the description of the parcel in question.

3. Ambiguous deed descriptions.
4. Omission of the length or bearing of the closing line.
5. Failure to close on known control.
6. Magnetic bearings not properly corrected to the date of the new survey.

PROBLEMS

19–1. Determine from one of the publications listed in the References, Appendix B, the meaning of eminent domain, riparian rights, escrow, color of title, deed ; quit claim deed, and prescription.

19–2. What is an aliquot ? An alloidal title ? An ambit ?

19–3. Determine, from the county courthouse or other local records, the number of types of property descriptions being used in your area. Copy one example of each type available.

19–4. What must the surveyor do in interpreting obscure descriptions ?

19–5. List the essential points covering the problem which arises when corners in place do not agree with deed descriptions.

19–6. What is the first job of a surveyor employed to survey a farm located in an unfamiliar area ?

19–7. List in their order of importance the following items used in legally interpreting deed descriptions: written and measured lengths ; written and measured bearings ; monuments ; witness corners and ties ; areas ; and testimony of living and dead witnesses. Justify your answer.

19–8. Submit a copy of a typical recital obtained from the deed description of a local piece of property.

19–9. Compute and plot the metes-and-bounds description of the city lot given in Section 19–3. Is the accuracy satisfactory today for an average town of 5000 people ?

19–10. Which of the four methods of property description do you consider the best ? Why ?

19–11. Starting with a house number and street name, get a copy of the deed description from the county courthouse. Can the property corners be located readily on the ground ?

19–12. Write a metes-and-bounds description for the house and lot where you live, assuming any necessary data. Draw a sketch map of the property showing all information which should appear on a plat to be filed with the deed at the registry office.

19–13. Determine how the assignment of block, tract, subdivision, and lot numbers is made, and by whom in your area.

19–14. In your area, can lots in a subdivision be designated by letters A, B, C, D, and so on instead of numbers ?

19–15. In your city's residential area, what are the required setbacks from property lines in the front, rear, and on the sides ?

19–16. In a description of land by metes and bounds, what purposes may be served by the statement "more or less" added to the acreage ?

19–17. Sketch the property described as part of lots 9 and 10 in Section 19–4.

19–18. Plat the portion of lot 306 described in Section 19–4.

19–19. Telephone poles are set on two corners of a rectangular lot. Explain how to survey the lot to locate boundaries and determine the area.

19–20. Outline the size of strip and form of easement used by your local telephone and utilities companies, and submit an example.

19–21. Secure a sample or make a copy of the pertinent features included in a title insurance company policy for a city lot.

19–22. A survey of a city block starting from proven corner monuments shows the block is 2.34 ft longer than the plat distance. Lot boundaries were never staked. Sketch how the excess is distributed. Explain.

19–23. In problem 19–22, what is the effect if lots have been staked for one-half the block?

19–24. Two neighbors having a boundary dispute employ a surveyor to check the line. Outline the surveyor's authority assuming (a) the line he establishes is satisfactory to his clients, and (b) it is not acceptable to one or both of them.

19–25. In establishing or reestablishing property lines or corners, what judicial authority does a licensed surveyor possess if his locations do not agree with those of another registered surveyor?

19–26. An error has been made on a subdivision plat and duly recorded. How can this defect be remedied and by whom?

19–27. List all types of pertinent information or data which should appear on a completed plat of a property survey.

19–28. What period of time is required to establish a claim for adverse rights in your city and state?

19–29. What is the purpose of the "hostile" requirement in the process of acquiring adverse rights to real property?

19–30. Lengths of the sides of a triangle are $AB=400.0$, $BC=620.0$, and $CA=430.0$ ft. The area is to be divided into two equal parts by a line perpendicular to the 400-ft side. Determine the distance x from point A where the cutoff line must start.

19–31. Side EF of lot $EFGH$ shown in the figure is parallel to a street. Compute the length of line GH parallel to EF which will cut off 20,000 ft², and the lengths of EH and FG.

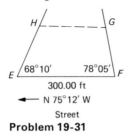

H — — — — — G

E 68°10'   78°05' F
300.00 ft
← N 75°12' W
Street

Problem 19-31

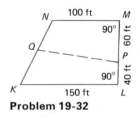

N   100 ft   M
90°
Q   P
90°
K   150 ft   L

Problem 19-32

19–32. Determine the length and direction of line PQ (see figure) which will cut off 6500 ft² for a new lot $KLPQK$, and the length of KQ.

19–33. Compute the area of lot 16 in Fig. 19–2.

19–34. Calculate the area of lot 18 in Fig. 19–2. (Radius = 25.00 ft, $I = 67°39'10''$, chord length = 27.83 ft, and chord bearing is N 50°40'25'' W).

19–35. Of the five items required in a deed description, as stated in Section 19–3, which do you consider the most important? The least important? Why? What else might well be included?

19–36. What is the main advantage of describing property by coordinate values for the corners?

19–37. Describe two obvious errors in the plat of Fig. 19–2. (A complete table of radii, arc lengths, and chords was included in the plat.)

19–38. A deed description contains the words "bounded on the north by Willow Creek." State how you would determine ownership limits.

19–39. Is a recorded deed to a tract of land proof of ownership by the grantee named therein? Explain.

19–40. With respect to land, what are the differences among "easement," "clear title," and "fee simple"?

20
SURVEYS OF THE PUBLIC LANDS

20-1. GENERAL. The term *public lands* is applied broadly to the areas which have been subject to administration, survey, and transfer of title under the public-land laws of the United States since 1785. These lands include those turned over to the federal government by the Colonial States, and the larger areas acquired by purchase from (or treaty with) the native Indians, or foreign powers that had previously exercised sovereignty.

Thirty states, including Alaska, comprise the *public domain* which has been, or will be, subdivided into rectangular tracts (see Fig. 20-1). The area represents approximately 72% of the United States.

The title to the vacant lands, therefore the direction over the surveys, within their own boundaries, was retained by the Colonial States, the other New England and Atlantic Coast States (excepting Florida), and later by the states of West Virginia, Kentucky, Tennessee, and Texas, in which areas the United States public land laws have not been applicable.

The beds of navigable bodies of water are not public domain and are not subject to survey and disposal by the United States. The sovereignty is in the individual states.

In 14 of the 30 states . . . the swamp and overflowed lands, through public domain, pass to the States upon identification by public land survey, and approved selection, the title being subject to the disposal by the States.[1]

Survey and disposition of the public lands was governed originally by two factors:

---

[1] *Manual of Surveying Instructions*, 1973 edition. Washington, DC.: Government Printing Office.

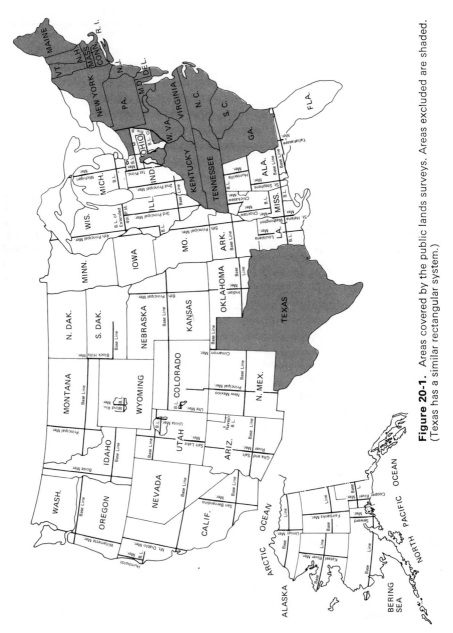

Figure 20-1. Areas covered by the public lands surveys. Areas excluded are shaded. (Texas has a similar rectangular system.)

1. A recognition of the value of a grid system of subdivision, based on experience in the Colonies and Europe.
2. The need of the Colonies for revenue from sale of the public lands. Monetary returns from their disposal were disappointing, but the planner's farsighted vision of a grid system of subdivision deserves commendation.

20-2. INSTRUCTIONS FOR SURVEY OF THE PUBLIC LANDS. The U.S. system of public-lands surveys was inaugurated in 1784, with the territory northwest of the Ohio River as a test area. Sets of instructions for the surveys were issued in 1785 and 1796. Manuals of instructions were issued in 1855, 1881, 1890, 1894, 1902, 1930, 1947, and 1973.

In 1796 a Surveyor General was appointed and the numbering of sections was changed to the system now in use (see Fig. 20-7). Supplementary rules were promulgated by each local Surveyor General "according to the dictates of his own judgment" until 1836, when the General Land Office was reorganized. Copies of changes and instructions for local use were not always preserved and sent to Washington. As a result, no office in the United States has a complete set of instructions under which the original surveys were supposed to have been made. Although the same general method of subdivision was followed, detailed procedures were altered in surveys made at different times in various areas of the country.

Most of the later public-land surveys have been run by the procedures to be described, or variations of them. The job of the present-day surveyor consists of retracing the original lines and perhaps further subdividing sections. To do so, he must be thoroughly familiar with the rules, laws, equipment, and field conditions governing the work of his predecessors in a given area.

Basically, the rules of survey stated in the 1973 *Manual of Surveying Instructions* are as follows:

The public lands shall be divided by north and south lines run according to the true meridian, and by others crossing them at right angles, so as to form townships six miles square. . . .

The corners of the townships must be marked with progressive numbers from the beginning; each distance of a mile between such corners must be also distinctly marked with marks different from those of the corners.

The township shall be subdivided into sections, containing as nearly as may be, six hundred and forty acres each, by running parallel lines through the same from east to west and from south to north at the distance of one mile from each other (originally at the end of every two miles but amended in 1800). and marking corners at the distance of each half mile. The sections shall be numbered, respectively, beginning with the number one in the northeast section, and proceeding west and east alternately through the township with progressive numbers until the thirty-six be completed.

Additional rules of survey covering field books, subdivision of sections, adjustment for excess and deficiency, and other matters are given in the manuals. Surveys were made by private surveyors, who were paid $2/mile of line run until 1796 and $3/mile run thereafter, on a contract basis. Sometimes the amount was adjusted in accordance with the importance of the line, the terrain, the location, and other factors. From his meager fee the surveyor had to pay and feed his party of at least four men while on the job, and in transit to and from distant points. He had to brush out and blaze the line, set corners and other marks, and provide satisfactory notes and one or more copies of completed plats. The contract system was completely discarded in 1910. Public-lands surveyors are now appointed.

Since meridians converge, it is evident the requirement that lines shall conform to the true meridians, and townships shall be 6 miles square, is mathematically impossible. An elaborate system of subdivision was therefore worked out as a practical solution.

It should be noted that two principles furnished the legal background for stabilizing land lines:

1. Boundaries of public lands established and returned by duly appointed surveyors are unchangeable.
2. Original township and section corners established by surveyors must stand as the true corners which they were intended to represent, whether in the place shown by the field notes or not.

In general, the procedure in surveying the public lands provides for the following subdivisions:

1. Division into quadrangles (tracts) approximately 24 miles on a side.
2. Division of tracts into townships (16), approximately 6 miles on a side.
3. Division of townships into sections (36), approximately 1 mile square.
4. Subdivision of sections (usually by the local surveyor).

It will be helpful to keep in mind that the purpose of the grid system was to obtain sections 1 mile on a side. To this end, all discrepancies were thrown into the sections bordering the north and west township boundaries to get as many *regular sections* as possible.

20-3. INITIAL POINT.

Subdivision of the public lands became necessary in any area as settlers moved in and mining or other land claims were filed. The early hope that surveys would precede settlement was not fulfilled.

In each area an initial point was established and located by astronomical observations. The manual of 1902 was the first to specify an indestructible monument, preferably a copper bolt, firmly set in a rock ledge if possible, and witnessed by rock bearings.

Thirty-seven initial points are available, five of them in Alaska.

A principal meridian and a base line were passed through each initial point, such as the one in the center of Fig. 20-2.

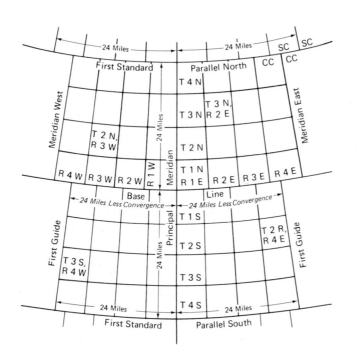

Figure 20-2. Survey of quadrangles. (Only a few of the standard corners and closing corners are identified.)

20-4. PRINCIPAL MERIDIAN. From each initial point, a true north-south line called a *principal meridian* (Prin. Mer. or P.M.) was run north and/or south to the limits of the area to be covered. Generally a solar attachment—a device for solving mechanically the mathematics of the astronomical triangle —was used. Monuments were set for section and quarter-section corners every 40 ch, and at the intersections with all meanderable bodies of water (streams 3 ch or more in width, and lakes covering 25 acres or more).

The line was supposed to be within 3' of the cardinal direction. Two independent sets of linear measurements were required to check within 20 links (13.2 ft)/80 ch, which corresponds to a precision ratio of only $\frac{1}{400}$. The allowable difference between sets of measurements is now limited to 7 links/80 ch.

20-5. BASE LINE. From the initial point, the base line was extended east and/or west as a true parallel of latitude to the limits of the area to be covered. As required for the principal meridian, monuments were set for section and quarter-section corners every 40 ch, and at the intersections with all meanderable bodies of water. Permissible closures were the same as those for the principal meridian.

Base lines were run as circular curves with chords of 40 ch by (a) the solar method, (b) tangent method, or (c) secant method.

Solar method. An observation is made with a solar attachment to determine the direction of true north. A right angle is then turned off and a line extended 40 ch, where the process is repeated. The series of lines so established, with a slight change in direction every half-mile, closely approaches a true parallel. Obviously if the sun is obscured, the method cannot be used.

Tangent method. This method of laying out a true parallel is illustrated in Fig. 20-3. A 90° angle is turned to the east or the west, as may be required from a true meridian, and corners set every 40 ch. At the same time, proper offsets are taken from tables and measured north from the tangent to the parallel. In the example shown, the offsets in links are 1, 2, 4, 6½,...37. The error resulting from taking right-angle offsets instead of offsets along the converging lines is negligible.

The main objection to the tangent method is that the parallel departs considerably from the tangent and therefore two lines must be brushed out.

Secant method. This method of laying out a true parallel is shown in Fig. 20-4. It actually is a modification of the tangent method in which a line parallel to the tangent at the 3-mile (center) point is passed through the 1-mile and 5-mile points to obtain minimum offsets, as shown in Tables B-4 and B-5.

Field work includes establishing a point on the true meridian, south of the beginning corner, at a distance taken from a table for the latitude of the

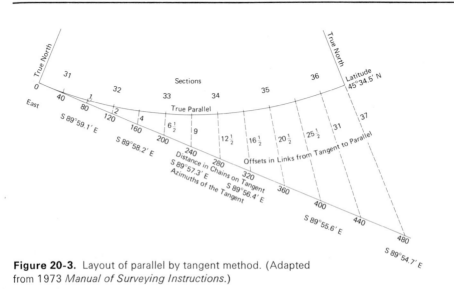

Figure 20-3. Layout of parallel by tangent method. (Adapted from 1973 *Manual of Surveying Instructions.*)

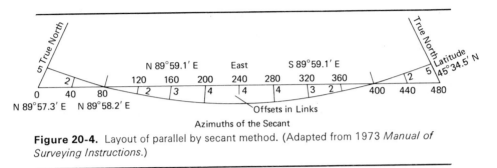

Figure 20-4. Layout of parallel by secant method. (Adapted from 1973 *Manual of Surveying Instructions*.)

desired parallel. The proper bearing angle from the same table is turned to the east or west from the true meridian to define the secant, which is then projected 6 miles. Offsets are measured north or south from the secant to the parallel.

Advantages of the secant method are its simplicity, the fact that the offsets are small and can be measured perpendicular to the secant without error, and the amount of clearing reduced.

20-6. STANDARD PARALLELS (CORRECTION LINES).

After the principal meridian and base line have been run, standard parallels (Stan. Par. or S.P.), also called correction lines, are run as true parallels of latitude 24 miles apart in the same manner as was the base line. All 40-ch corners are marked. In some of the early surveys, standard parallels were placed at intervals of 30 or 36 miles.

Standard parallels are numbered consecutively north and south of the base line; examples are First Standard Parallel North and Third Standard Parallel South.

20-7. GUIDE MERIDIANS.

Guide meridians (G.M.) are run due north from the base line and standard parallels at intervals of 24 miles east and west of the principal meridian, in the same manner as was the principal meridian, and with the same limits of error. Before the work is started, the chain or tape must be checked by measuring 1 mile on the base line or standard parallel. All 40-ch corners are marked.

Because of convergence of the meridians, a *closing corner* (CC) is set at the intersection of each guide meridian, standard parallel, or base line (see Fig. 20-2). The distance from closing corner to the *standard corner* (SC), which was set when the parallel was run, is measured and recorded in the notes as a check. Any error in the 24-mile length of the guide meridian is put in the northern-most half-mile.

Guide meridians are numbered consecutively east and west of the principal meridian; examples are First Guide Meridian West and Fourth Guide Meridian East.

20-8. TOWNSHIP EXTERIORS. MERIDIONAL (RANGE) LINES AND LATITUDINAL (TOWNSHIP) LINES.   Division of a quadrangle, or tract, into townships is accomplished by running range (R) and township (T or Tp) lines.

Range lines are true meridians through the standard township corners previously established at intervals of 6 miles on the base line and standard parallels. They are extended north to intersect the next standard parallel or base line, and closing corners are set (see Figs. 20-2 and 20-5).

Formulas for convergence of meridians (derived in various texts on geodesy, with results given in Table B-3) are as follows:

$$\theta = 52.13d \tan \phi \qquad (20\text{-}1)$$

$$c = \tfrac{4}{3} Ld \tan \phi \qquad \text{(slight approximation)} \qquad (20\text{-}2)$$

where θ is the angle of convergence, in seconds; d the distance between meridians, in miles, on a parallel; ϕ the mean latitude; c the linear convergence, in feet; and L the length of meridians, in miles.

Township lines connect township corners previously established at intervals of 6 miles on the principal meridian, guide meridians, and range lines.

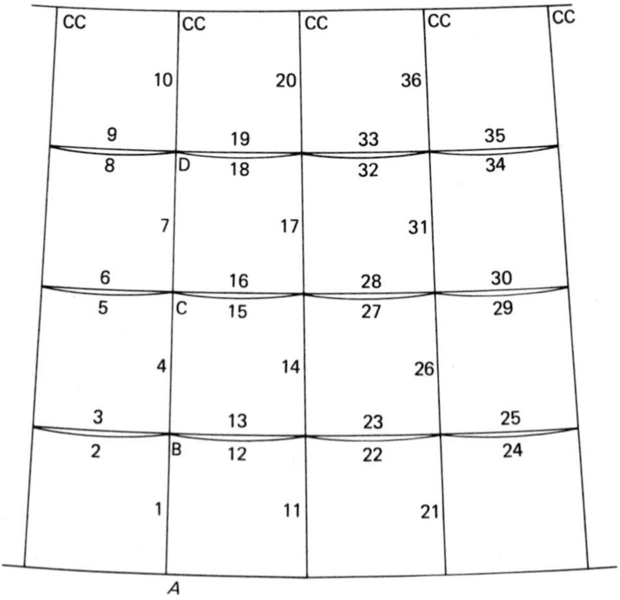

Figure 20-5. Order of running lines for the subdivision of a quadrangle into townships.

20-9. DESIGNATION OF TOWNSHIPS. A township is identified by a unique description based upon the principal meridian governing it.

North-and-south rows of townships are called *ranges*, and numbered in consecutive order east and west of the principal meridian as indicated in Fig. 20-2.

East-and-west rows of townships are named *tiers* and numbered in order north and south of the base line. By common practice, the term "tier" is usually replaced by "township" in designating the rows.

An individual township is identified by its number north or south of the base line, followed by the number east or west of the principal meridian. An example is Township 7 South, Range 19 East, of the Sixth Principal Meridian. Abbreviated, this becomes T 7 S, R 19 E, 6th P.M.

20-10. SUBDIVISION OF A QUADRANGLE INTO TOWNSHIPS. The method to be used in subdividing a quadrangle into townships is fixed by regulations in the *Manual of Surveying Instructions*. Under the old regulations, township boundaries were required to be within 21' of the cardinal direction. Later this was reduced to 14' in order to keep the interior lines within 21' of the cardinal direction.

The detailed procedure for subdividing a quadrangle into townships can best be described as a series of steps designed to ultimately produce the maximum number of regular sections with a minimum amount of unproductive travel by the field party. The order of running the lines is shown by consecutive numbers in Fig. 20-5. Some details are described in the following steps:

1. Begin at the southeast corner of the southwest township, point *A*, after checking the chain or tape against a 1-mile measurement on the standard parallel.
2. Run north on the true meridian for 6 miles (line 1), setting alternate section and quarter-section corners every 40 ch. Set township corner *B*.
3. From *B*, run a random line (line 2) due west to intersect the principal meridian. Set temporary corners every 40 ch.
4. If the random line has an excess or deficiency of 3 ch or less (allowing for convergence), and a falling north or south of 3 ch or less, the line is accepted. It is then corrected back (line 3) and all corners are set in their proper positions. Any excess or deficiency is thrown into the most westerly half-mile. The method of correcting a random line having an excess of 1 ch and a north falling of 2 ch is shown in Fig. 20-6.
5. If the random line misses the corner by more than the permissible 3 ch, all four sides of the township must be retraced.
6. The same procedure is followed until the southeast corner, *D*, of the most-northerly township is reached. From *D*, range line 10 is continued as a true meridian to intersect the standard parallel or base line, where a

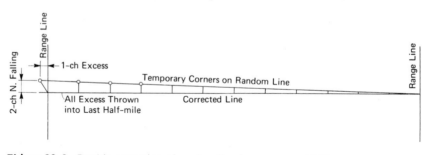

Figure 20-6. Double correction of random line for excess and falling.

closing corner is set. All of the excess or deficiency in the 24 miles is thrown into the most northerly half-mile.

7. The second and third ranges of townships are run in the same way, beginning at the south line of the quadrangle.

8. While the third range is being run, random lines are also projected to the east and corrected back, and any excess or deficiency is thrown into the most westerly half-mile. (All points may have to be moved diagonally to the corrected line, instead of just the last point as in Fig. 20-6.)

20-11. SUBDIVISION OF A TOWNSHIP INTO SECTIONS.   The method for subdividing a township can be described most readily as a series of steps to produce the maximum number of regular sections 1 mile on a side. Sections are now numbered from 1 to 36, beginning in the northeast corner of the township and ending in the southeast corner, as shown in Fig. 20-7.

1. Set up at the southeast corner of the township, point *A*, and observe the meridian. Retrace the range line northward and township line westward for 1 mile to compare the meridian, needle readings, and taped distances with those recorded.

2. From the southwest corner of Sec. 36, run north *parallel* with the east boundary of the township. Set quarter-section and section corners on line 1, Fig. 20-7.

3. From the section corner just set, run a random line *parallel* with the south boundary of the township eastward to the range line. Set a temporary quarter-corner at 40 ch.

4. If the 80-ch distance on the random line is within 50 links, falling or distance, the line is accepted. The correct line is calculated and the quarter-corner located at the *midpoint* of the line *BC* connecting the previously established corner *C* and the new section corner *B*.

5. If the random line misses the corner by more than the permissible 50 links, the township lines must be rechecked and the cause of the error determined.

6. The east range of sections is run in similar manner until the southwest

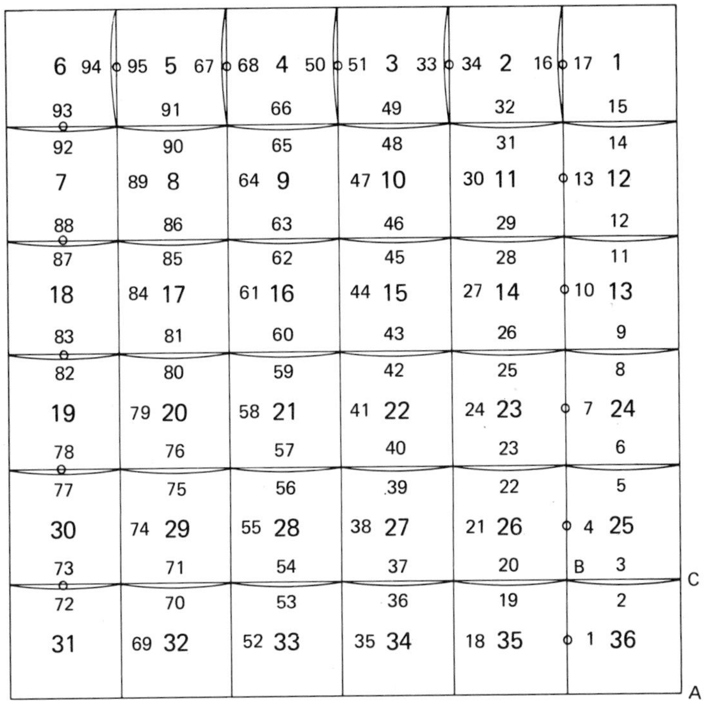

6 94	95 5 67	68 4 50	51 3 33	34 2 16	17 1
93	91	66	49	32	15
92	90	65	48	31	14
7	89 8	64 9	47 10	30 11	13 12
88	86	63	46	29	12
87	85	62	45	28	11
18	84 17	61 16	44 15	27 14	10 13
83	81	60	43	26	9
82	80	59	42	25	8
19	79 20	58 21	41 22	24 23	7 24
78	76	57	40	23	6
77	75	56	39	22	5
30	74 29	55 28	38 27	21 26	4 25
73	71	54	37	20	B 3
72	70	53	36	19	2
31	69 32	52 33	35 34	18 35	1 36

C (right side), A (bottom right corner)

Figure 20-7. Order of running lines for the subdivision of a township into sections.

corner of Section 1 is reached. From this point a random line is run northward to connect with the section corner on the north township line. The quarter-corner is set 40 ch from the south section corner (on line 17 corrected back by later manuals). All discrepancies in the 6 miles are thrown into the last half-mile.

7. Sucessive ranges of sections across the township are run until four have been completed. All meridional lines are parallel with the east side of the township, and all east-west lines are parallel with the south boundary.

8. When the fifth range is being run, random lines are projected to the west as well as to the east. The quarter-corners in the west range are set 40 ch from the east side of the section, all excess or deficiency resulting from errors and convergence being thrown into the most westerly half-mile.

9. If the north side of the township is a standard parallel, instead of running a random line to the north, lines parallel with the east township boundary are projected to the correction line and closing corners are set. The distance to the nearest standard corner is measured and recorded.

10. True bearings of the interior range lines for any latitude can be obtained by applying corrections from tables for the convergence at a given distance from the east boundary.

By throwing the effect of convergence of meridians into the western-most half-mile of the township and all errors to the north and west, 25 regular sections 1 mile^2 are obtained. Also, the south half of Sections 1, 2, 3, 4, and 5, and the east half of Sections 7, 18, 19, 30, and 31, are normal size.

20-12. SUBDIVISION OF SECTIONS.   To divide a section into quarter-sections, straight lines are run between opposite quarter-section corners previously established or re-established. This rule holds whether or not the quarter-section corners are equidistant from the adjacent section corners.

To divide a quarter-section into quarter-quarter-sections, straight lines are run between opposite quarter-quarter-section corners established at the midpoint of the four sides. The same procedure is followed to obtain smaller subdivisions.

If the quarter-sections are on the north or west side of the township, the quarter-quarter-section corners are placed 20 ch from the east or south quarter-section corners—or by single proportional measurement on line if the total length on the ground is not equal to that on record.

20-13. FRACTIONAL SECTIONS.   In sections made fractional by rivers, lakes, or other bodies of water, lots are formed bordering on the body of water and numbered consecutively through the section (see Sec. 8 in Fig. 20-8). Boundaries of lots usually follow the quarter-section and quarter-

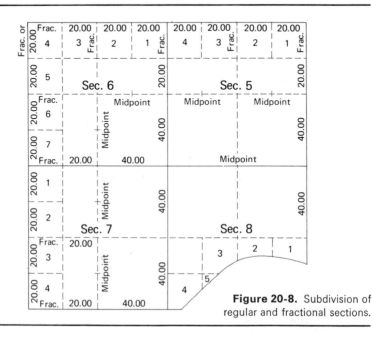

Figure 20-8. Subdivision of regular and fractional sections.

quarter-section lines, but extreme lengths and narrow widths are avoided, as are areas of less than 5 acres or more than 45 acres.

Quarter-sections along the north and west boundaries of a township made irregular by discrepancies of measurements and convergence of the range lines are usually numbered and sold as lots, as indicated in Fig. 20-8. One such quarter-section in a Wisconsin township contains 640 acres!

Lot lines are not actually run in the field. Like the quarter-section lines, they are merely indicated on the plats by protraction. Lot areas are computed from the plats.

20-14. NOTES. Specimen field notes for each of the several kinds of lines to be run are shown in various instruction manuals. Actual recording had to follow closely the model sets.

The original notes, or copies of them, are maintained in a land office in each state, for the benefit of all interested persons.

20-15. OUTLINE OF SUBDIVISION STEPS. Pertinent points in the subdivision of quadrangles into townships, and townships into sections, are summarized in Table 20-1.

TABLE 20-1. SUBDIVISION STEPS

Item	Subdivision of a Tract	Subdivision of a Township
Starting point	SE corner of SW township	SW corner of SE section (36)
Meridional lines		
Name	Range line	Section line
Direction	True north	North, parallel with east range line
Length	6 miles = 480 ch	1 mile = 80 ch
Corners set	Quarter-section and section corners at 40 and 80 ch alternately	Quarter-section corner at 40 ch. Section corner at 80 ch
Latitudinal lines		
Name	Township line	Section line
Direction of random	True east-west parallel	East, parallel with south side of section
Length	6 miles less convergence	1 mile
Permissible error	3 ch, length or falling	50 links, length or falling
Distribution of error		
Falling	Corners moved proportionately from random to true line	Corners moved proportionately from random to true line
Distance	All error thrown into west quarter-section	Error divided equally between quarter-sections

Table 20-1. (*continued*)

[*Work repeated until north side of area is reached. Subdivision of last area on the north of the range of townships and sections follows.*]

Case I.   When Line on the North Is a Standard Parallel

Item	Subdivision of a Tract	Subdivision of a Township
Direction of line	True north	North, parallel with east range line
Distribution of error in length	Placed in north quarter-section	Placed in north quarter-section
Corner placed at end	Closing corner	Closing corner
Permissible errors	Specified in *Manual of Surveying Instructions*	Specified in *Manual of Surveying Instructions*

Case II.   When Line on the North Is Not a Standard Parallel

Direction of line	No case	Random north and correct back to section corner already established
Distribution of error in length		Same as case I

[*Other ranges of townships and sections continued until all but two are laid out.*]

Location of last two ranges	On east side of tract	On west side of township
Next-to-last range subdivided	As before	As before
Last range		
Direction of random	True east	Westerly, parallel with south side of section
Nominal length	6 miles less convergence	1 mile less convergence
Correction for temporary corners	Corners moved proportionately from random to true line	Corners moved proportionately from random to true line
Distribution of error of closure	Corners moved westerly (or easterly) to place error in west quarter-section	Corner is placed on the true line so that error falls in west quarter-section

20-16. MARKING CORNERS.   Various materials were approved and used for monuments in the original surveys. These included pits and mounds; stones; posts; charcoal; and broken bottles. A zinc-coated, alloyed iron pipe 2½ in. outside diameter and 30 in. long is now standard except in rock outcrop, where a 3¼-in.-diameter brass tablet is specified.

Stones and posts were marked with one to six notches on one or two faces. The arrangements identify a monument as a particular section or township corner. Each notch represents 1 mile of distance to a township line or corner. Quarter-sections were marked with the fraction "¼" on a single face.

In prairie country, where large stones and trees were scarce, a system of pits and mounds was used to mark corners. Different groupings of pits and mounds, 12 in. deep and 18 in. square, designated corners of the several classes. Unless perpetuated by some other type of mark, these corners were lost in the first plowing.

20-17. WITNESS CORNERS.   Whenever possible, monuments were witnessed by several adjacent objects such as trees and rock outcrops. Bearing trees were blazed on the side facing the corner and marked with scribing tools.

When a regular corner fell in a creek, pond, swamp, or other place where it was impracticable to place a mark, *witness corners* (WC) were set on all lines leading to the corner. The letters WC were added to all other marks normally placed on the corner, and the corner in turn witnessed in the customary manner.

20-18. MEANDER CORNERS.   A meander corner (MC) was established on survey lines intersecting the bank of a stream having a width greater than 3 ch, or a lake, bayou, or other body of water of considerable extent. The distance to the nearest section corner or quarter-section corner was measured and recorded in the notes. A monument was set and marked MC on the side facing the water, and the usual witnesses noted. If practicable, the line was carried across the stream or other body of water by triangulation to another corner set in line on the farther bank.

A traverse joined successive meander corners along the banks of streams or lakes and followed as closely as practicable the sinuosities of the bank. The traverse was checked by calculating the position of the new meander corner and comparing it with its known position on a surveyed line.

Meander lines follow the mean high-water mark and are used for plotting and protraction of area only. They are *not* boundaries defining the limits of property adjacent to the water.

20-19. LOST AND OBLITERATED CORNERS.   A common problem in resurveys of the public lands is the replacement of lost or obliterated corners. This difficult task requires a combination of experience, hard work, and ample time to reestablish the location of a wooden stake or post monument incorrectly set 75 years ago on an undependable section line, and with all witness trees long-since cut or burned by apathetic owners.

An *obliterated corner* is one at whose point there are no remaining traces of the monument, or its accessories, but whose location has been perpetuated or can be recovered beyond reasonable doubt. The corner may be restored from the acts or testimony of interested landowners, surveyors, qualified local authorities, witnesses, or from written evidence. Satisfactory evidence has value in the following order:

1. Evidence of the corner itself.
2. Bearing trees or other witness marks.
3. Fences, walls, or other evidence showing occupation of the property to the lines or corners.
4. Testimony of living persons.

A *lost corner* is one whose position cannot be determined, beyond reasonable doubt, either from traces of the original marks or from acceptable evidence or testimony that bears on the original position. It can be restored only by rerunning lines from one or more independent corners (existing corners that were established at the same time, and with the same care as the lost corner). Usually single- or double-proportionate measurements are necessary, the latter being used for township corners common to four sections, and section corners common to four sections in a township interior. Thus the reliability of corner locations at the centers of sections and quarter-sections also depends upon these measurements.

Proportionate measurements allot the discrepancies between the original and later recordings among the several parts of a line in the proportions in which the original recorded measurements were distributed. The method should be used only as a last resort.

20-20. ACCURACY OF PUBLIC-LANDS SURVEYS.

The accuracy required in the early surveys was of a very low order. Frequently it fell below that which the notes showed. A small percentage of the surveys were made by men drawing upon their imagination in the comparative comfort of a tent. Obviously no monuments were set and the notes serve only to confuse the situation for present-day surveyors and landowners. Some surveyors threw in an extra chain length at intervals to assure a full measure.

The poor results obtained in many areas were due primarily to the following:

1. Lack of training of personnel. Some contracts were given to men without any technical background.
2. Poor equipment.
3. Surveys made in unsettled and apparently valueless areas.
4. Marauding Indians, swarms of insects, and dangerous animals.

5. Lack of appreciation for the need of accurate work.
6. Surveys made in piecemeal fashion as the Indian titles and other claims were extinguished.
7. Work done by contract at low prices.
8. Absence of control points.
9. Field inspection not provided until 1850, and not actually carried out until 1880.
10. Magnitude of the problem.

In general, considering the handicaps listed, the work was reasonably well done in most cases.

20-21. DESCRIPTIONS BY TOWNSHIP, SECTION, AND SMALLER SUBDIVISION.
Description by the sectional system offers a means of defining boundaries uniquely, clearly, and concisely. Several examples of acceptable descriptions are listed.

Sec. 6, T 7 S, R 19 E, 6th P.M.
Frac. Sec. 34, T 2 N, R 5 W, Ute Prin. Mer.
The SE¼ NE¼ Sec. 14, Tp. 3 S, Range 22 W, S.B.M. [San Bernardino Meridian.]
E½ of NE¼ of Sec. 20, T 15 N, R 10 E, Indian Prin. Mer.
E 80 acres of the NE¼ of Sec. 20, T 15 N, R 10 E, Indian Prin. Mer.

Note that the last two descriptions do not necessarily describe the same land. A California case in point occurred when the owner of a SW¼ section, nominally 160 acres but actually 162.3 acres, deeded the westerly portion as "the West 80 acres" and the easterly portion as "the East ½."

Sectional land which is privately owned may be partitioned in any manner at the option of the owner. The metes-and-bounds form is preferable for irregular parcels. In fact, metes and bounds are required to establish the boundaries of mineral claims, and various grants and reservations.

Differences between the physical and legal (or record) ground locations and areas may result because of departures from accepted procedures in description writing; loose and ambiguous statements; or dependence upon the accuracy of early surveys.

20-22. SOURCES OF ERROR.
Some of the many sources of error in retracing the public-lands surveys follow:

1. Discrepancy between the length of the early surveyor's chain and that of the modern tape.
2. Change in the magnetic declination or the local attraction, or both.
3. Lack of agreement between field notes and actual measurements.
4. Changes in watercourses.
5. Nonpermanent objects which were used for corner marks.
6. Loss of witness corners.

20-23. MISTAKES. Typical mistakes in the retracement of boundaries in public-land surveys are:

1. Failure to follow the general rules of procedure governing the original survey.
2. Neglecting to check the tape used against distances on record for marks in place.
3. Resetting corners without exhausting every means of relocating the original corners.

PROBLEMS

20–1. Why are the boundaries of public lands established by duly appointed surveyors unchangeable, even though set incorrectly in the first surveys?

20–2. What differences exist between the original and present instructions and practice in spacing corners and running section lines?

20–3. Describe the method of running a principal meridian. State the original and present accuracy required.

20–4. List the advantages and disadvantages of each of the three methods of running base lines and standard parallels.

Determine the offsets from, and the azimuths of, a secant to lay out a parallel at the latitudes listed in problems 20–5 through 20–7. Draw a sketch showing the values. (See Tables B–4, and B–5.)

20–5. At latitude 28°30′ N.

20–6. At latitude 37°00′ N.

20–7. At latitude 48°30′ N.

20–8. At latitude 46° N, what is the maximum (a) offset from the secant to the parallel and (b) difference of the azimuth of the secant from the cardinal direction?

What is the convergence in feet of two meridians for the conditions given in problems 20–9 through 20–11?

20–9. Originally 24 miles apart, after extending them 24 miles, latitude 47°00′.

20–10. Originally 18 miles apart, after extending them 14 miles, latitude 42°30′.

20–11. Originally 12 miles apart, after extending them 6 miles, latitude 34°00′.

Compute the nominal distance in miles between the points given in problems 20–12 through 20–14.

20–12. First Guide Meridian West and west range line of R 26 W.

20–13. Second Guide Meridian West and east range line of R 16 E.

20–14. Third Guide Meridian East and west range line of R 13 W.

20–15. In latitude 40°N, at what distance from the principal meridian will the quarter-quarter section corner of Sec. 36, T 1 N, theoretically fall exactly opposite a section corner of Sec. 6, T 1 S, due to convergence?

20–16. Show on a sketch where closing corners are located on township lines and the areas they govern.

20–17. What steps in public-lands subdivision are left to the local surveyor?

Sketch and label the principal meridian, base line, township lines, and so on; give distances if they are specified by law; and compute the nominal area of the parcels described in problems 20–18 through 20–21.

20–18. NW^1/$_4$ of NE^1/$_4$ of Sec. 21, T 6 S, R 6 E, Indian PM.

20–19. S^1/$_2$ of NW^1/$_4$ of SE^1/$_4$ of Sec. 17, T 8 N, R 4 E, Choctow PM.

20–20. NW^1/$_4$ of SW^1/$_4$ of SE^1/$_4$, Sec. 33, T 5 N, R 2 W, 2nd PM.

20–21. SE^1/$_4$ of SE^1/$_4$ of NE^1/$_4$ of SW^1/$_4$, Sec. 11, T 4 N, R 3 W, 5th PM.

In problems 20–22 (a) and (b), how many rods of fence are required to enclose the areas?

20–22. (a) Secs. 14, 15, 16, 21, and 22; (b) Secs. 9, 10, 15, 14, and 23.

20–23. What allowable error in distance is permitted in the location of the northeast corner of T 1 N, R 1 W?

20–24. Give the two causes for sections in a normal township being smaller than 640 acres. Which sections usually are not regular?

20–25. Name the section line which is run as a random line.

20–26. In the public-lands surveys which lines are laid out parallel to others?

20–27. Corners of the NW^1/$_4$ of the SW^1/$_4$ of Sec. 16 are to be monumented. Assume all section and quarter-section corners set originally by the public-lands surveyors are in place. Sketch all lines run and corners set.

20–28. The east line of the NE^1/$_4$ of Sec. 3 has a record distance of 40.28 ch, and field-measured length of 40.12 ch. Where should the SE corner of lot 1 be set? Explain.

20–29. The exterior dimensions of Sec. 6 on the west, north, east, and south sides are 78, 79, 80, and 81 ch, respectively. Explain, with a sketch, the distances and line directions to divide the section into quarters.

20–30. If you found a section corner set by the BLM and marked as shown in the figure, in which direction would you go to find the nearest established section corner, and how should it be marked?

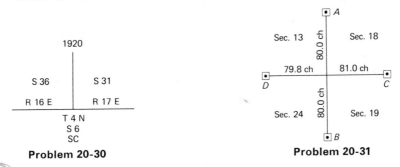

Problem 20-30

Problem 20-31

20–31. The distances given on the accompanying sketch are the original government survey distances. The southeast corner of Sec. 13 is lost. Corners A, B, C, and D are in. If the measured distance AB is 161.0 ch and DC is 164.2 ch, explain how to establish the location of the southeast corner of Sec. 13.

20–32. Section 6 is to be subdivided into quarters. The original survey distances in chains are shown on the sketch. Corners A, B, C, and D are found, but all other corners are lost. Measured resurvey distances are: $AB=82.4$ ch, $BC=78.4$ ch, $CD=81.6$ ch, and $DA=77.8$ ch. Explain how to subdivide the section into quarters, giving actual distances to be used.

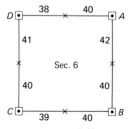

Problem 20-32

20–33. Using the data and figure of problem 20–32, explain how the $NW^1/_4$, $NW^1/_4$ of Sec. 6 would be staked out. Give actual distances to be used.

20–34. In a normal township, is lot 4 of Sec. 30 the $SW^1/_4$ of the $SW^1/_4$? Explain.

20–35. Show by a dimensioned sketch how a county surveyor would set the corners for the $NW^1/_4$ of the $SE^1/_4$ of Sec. 12.

20–36. The remeasured distance from the corner for Secs. 20, 21, 28, and 29 to the quarter-section corner between Secs. 28 and 29 is found to be 39.76 ch. Where should the quarter-quarter-section corner be set on this line in subdividing Sec. 29?

20–37. Which classes of corners are relocated by (a) single-proportionate measurement and (b) double proportionate-measurement?

Which method, single-proportion (two-way), or double-proportion (four-way), should be used to restore the corners in problems 20–38 through 20–40?

20–38. Township corners on guide meridians; section corners on range lines.

20–39. Section corners on section lines; township corners on township lines.

20–40. Quarter-section corners on range lines.

20–41. The southern boundary of a township lies on a standard parallel in latitude 44° N. What is the theoretical length of its north boundary?

20–42. Compute the difference between bearings of the east township boundary (N 0°06′ E) and the line separating Secs. 8 and 7 in latitude 41°. What should be the bearing of the section line?

20–43. Explain how metes and bounds can be used in areas covered by the public-lands surveys.

20–44. Why are meander lines not the boundaries defining the area of ownership of tracts adjacent to the water?

20–45. Are there any public-lands surveys which do not have an initial point as an origin for both township and range numbers? Explain.

20–46. What acreage limit determines whether a lake must be meandered?

20–47. Are lost meander corners, originally established on a line projected across the meanderable body of water, relocated by single- or double-proportionate measurement?

21
CONSTRUCTION SURVEYS

21-1. GENERAL. Construction is the largest industry in the United States, so surveying, as the basis for it, is extremely important. It is estimated that 60% of all surveying man-hours are spent on location-type work giving line and grade. Nevertheless, insufficient attention is frequently given to this type of survey.

An accurate topographic survey and site map are the first requirements in designing streets, sewer and water lines, and structures. Surveyors then lay out and position these elements for construction according to the design plan. A final "as built" map, incorporating any modifications made to the design plans, is prepared during and after construction and filed. Such maps are extremely important, especially where underground utilities are involved, to assure that they can be located quickly if trouble develops and will not be disturbed by later improvements.

The surveyor in charge should receive copies of the plans well in advance of construction to become familiar with the job and have time to "tie-out" or "transfer" any established control points that might be destroyed during building operations. The methods of Fig. 13-1, parts 6(a) and (b) particularly, can be used with intersection angles as close to 90° as possible. Differential levels should be run to set new bench marks well out of the construction area, but near enough for convenient reference.

New equipment now being employed to improve, simplify, and speed giving line and grade on various types of construction jobs includes self-leveling and visible-laser-beam instruments, and electronic short-distance measuring devices. Figure 21-1 shows one such model, a laser tracking level which automatically swings around to follow (track) a level rod equipped

421

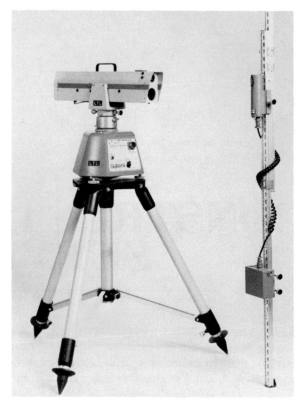

Figure 21-1. Laser tracking level and rod equipped with Trak-Tronic system. (Courtesy Construction Laser Division of Blount Industries, Inc.)

with a "Trak-Tronic system," and projects a red dot on it. The instrument can control elevations over a 1,000,000-ft² area from a single setup without requiring an operator, just a rodman, after the HI has been established.

A few common types of construction surveys, with which every surveyor, engineer, and architect should be familiar, will be described briefly. Construction surveying must be learned on the job by adapting fundamental principles to the undertaking at hand. Because each job involves individual problems, textbook coverage tends to be limited to introductory material.

21-2. HORIZONTAL AND VERTICAL CONTROL. The importance of a good framework of horizontal and vertical control in a project area cannot be overemphasized. It provides the basis for positioning structures, utilities, roads, and the like, in both the design and construction stages. Too often, attempts have been made to skimp on establishing proper marks and monumenting them for preservation.

On most projects, additional control is required to supplement any already available in the job area. The points must be:

1. Convenient for use by the contractor's craftsmen, that is, located sufficiently close to the item being built so that workers using relatively simple methods such as carpenters' levels and string lines can accurately transfer alignment and grade.
2. Far enough from the actual construction to ensure working room for the contractor and freedom from possible destruction of the stakes.
3. Clearly marked and understood by the contractor in the absence of a surveyor.
4. Supplemented by guard stakes to deter removal, and referenced to facilitate fixed procedures for restoring them. Contracts usually require the owner to pay the cost of setting initial control points and the contractor to replace damaged or removed ones.
5. Suitable for securing the accuracy agreed upon for construction layout (which may be to only the nearest foot for a manhole, 0.01 ft for an anchor bolt, or 0.001 ft for a critical feature).

21-3. STAKING OUT A PIPELINE. Flow in water lines is generally under pressure but most sewers have gravity flow. Alignment and grade must therefore be more accurate for the latter. Larger water lines also have definite grades because "blowoffs" are needed at low points and "air releases" at high spots. Grades are fixed by existing conditions, such as topography, which affects excavation depth of connecting lines, manholes, outfalls, and catch basins.

Construction stakes, sometimes set on the center line at 50-ft stations when the ground is reasonably uniform, disappear on the first pass of a ditcher or bulldozer, so parallel *offset lines* are necessary. Marks should be closer together on horizontal and vertical curves than on straight segments. For pipes of large diameter on horizontal curves, stakes may be placed for each pipe length, say, 6 or 8 ft (see Section 22-5).

When inflexible pipe lengths are laid as *chords*, they may not follow the trench properly. By installing big-diameter pipes (perhaps only 4-ft lengths) on relatively sharp-radius curves as *tangents*, tight joints and close adherence to desired alignment can be secured. Half of the first length should then precede the beginning of the curve (*BC*), and one-half of the last piece extend beyond the end of the curve (*EC*). See Section 22-5.

On hard surfaces where stakes cannot be driven, points are marked by paint, spikes, shiners (tin can top with nail through it), drill holes, or other means. A surveyor should know in advance approximately how much material will be deposited, on which side of the trench, and adjust offset staking accordingly.

Figure 21-2 shows the arrangement of *batter boards* for a sewer line. Batter boards are usually 1″ × 6″ boards nailed to 2″ × 4″ posts which have been pointed and driven into the ground. The top of the batter board is placed a full number of feet above the invert (lower inside surface), or above

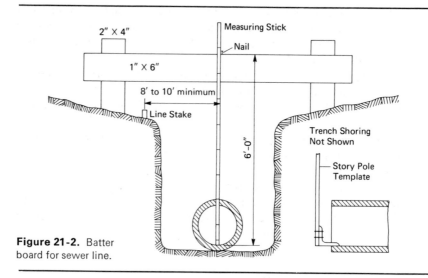

Figure 21-2. Batter board for sewer line.

the flow line, of the pipe. Nails are driven into the tops of the boards so that a string stretched tightly between them will define the pipe center line. A graduated stick or special rod is used to measure the required distance from the string to the pipe invert, or to the flow line. Thus the string gives both line and grade. It can be kept taut by hanging a weight on each end after wrapping it around the nails.

In Fig. 21-2, instead of a fixed batter board, a 2″ × 4″ carrying a level vial can be placed on top of the offset-line stake whose elevation is known. Measurement is made from the underside of a leveled 2″ × 4″ with a tape or graduated stick to establish the flow line.

On some jobs having a deep wide cut, a level or laser instrument is set up in the ditch to give line and grade. If the pipe is large enough, the laser device can be placed inside it.

Grades for trenches are designed to avoid excessive cut and fill, and permit connection to other facilities using a profile similar to that in Fig. 5-28.

21-4. STAKING PIPELINE GRADES. Staking grades is the reverse of running profiles, although in both operations the center line should first be marked and stationed in horizontal location. The actual profiling and staking are on an offset line with cut and fill values given from the offset hubs to pipe invert or flow line.

Grade elevations are computed, then fixed on the ground by a leveling process illustrated in noteform, Plate A-12, and summarized as follows:

1. Stake and profile stations on the pipeline are listed in columns 1 to 5 of noteform.

2. Calculate pipeline grade, if not previously determined.
3. Compute flow line or invert elevation at each station (column 6).
4. Subtract grade elevations from ground elevations (column 6 from 5) to get cut or fill, and mark the offset stake as stated in step 5 below.

A different approach, comparable with highway-slope staking described in Section 21-6, is also outlined, based upon Plate A-12.

1. Set up level and get HI (102.76) by reading a plus sight (2.11) on BM 16 (elevation 100.65).
2. The difference between the HI and grade elevation at any station is the *grade rod* ($102.76 - 95.34 = 7.42$ for Sta. $1 + 00$).
3. *Ground rod* at each station is obtained by holding the rod on successive stations and plusses (HI − ground elevation = $102.76 - 98.69 = 4.07$ at Sta. $1 + 00$).
4. Grade rod minus ground rod at any station equals cut $(+)$ or fill $(-)$, or $7.42 - 4.07 = $ C 3.35 ft at Sta. $1 + 00$. (Only under special circumstances are ground elevations feasible to 0.01 ft, so cuts and fills are normally to 0.1 ft.)
5. The cut or fill is marked with keel on the offset stake facing the center line; the station on the other side.

A level-rod target (or colored rubber band) can be set at the proper elevation to put the rod base at grade, or an even number of feet above or below it. Stakes are then driven until the level's horizontal line of sight coincides with the target center line as the rod is held on top of each stake.

Layout is expedited by using a Lenker direct-reading rod, Fig. 5-19(d), which eliminates all elevation computations. It has numbers on an endless graduated steel-band face strip 20 ft long that can be revolved on the rod's end rollers. Figures run down the rod and can be brought to a desired reading, for example, the elevation of a bench mark as the basis for sights to be taken, and thus give a direct answer without calculating an HI and subtracting a foresight.

Staking lines having $\frac{1}{2}\%$ or 1% grades is easy. Since the usual stadia interval factor is 100 to 1, sight lines through the middle and upper, or middle and lower, cross hairs of a level, transit, or theodolite differ by $\frac{1}{2}$ ft in 100 ft and define a $\frac{1}{2}\%$ grade. Between the upper and lower wires there is a 1% grade. After setting one cross wire on the grade-rod reading for any station, either a $\frac{1}{2}\%$ or 1% grade is readily established for succeeding points from that position even though the telescope is not level.

21-5. STAKING OUT A BUILDING.

The first task in staking out a building is to locate it properly on the correct lot by making measurements from the property lines. Most cities have an ordinance establishing setback lines from the street and between houses to improve appearance and provide fire protection.

Stakes may be set initially at the exact building corners as a visual check on positioning of the structure, but obviously such points are lost immediately when work is begun on the footings. A set of *batter boards* and reference stakes, placed as shown on Plate A-11, is therefore erected near each corner but out of the way of construction. The boards are nailed a full number of feet above the bottom of the footing, or at the first-floor elevation. Corner stakes and batter-board points for rectangular buildings are checked by measuring the diagonals for comparison with each other and the computed values. A bench mark (two or more on large projects) beyond the construction area but within easy sight distance is necessary to control elevations.

Nails are driven into the batter-board tops so that strings stretched tightly between them define the outside wall or form line of the building. Again, the boards give line and grade.

Permanent foresights are helpful in establishing principal lines of the structure. Targets or marks on nearby existing buildings can be used if movement due to thermal effects or settlement is considered negligible. On formed concrete structures such as retaining walls, offset lines are necessary because the outside wall face is obstructed.

Plate A-11 shows the location of batter boards and steps to be followed in setting them for a small structure. Positions of such things as interior footings, anchor bolts for columns, and special piping or equipment can first be marked by 2″ × 2″ stakes with tacks. Survey disks, scratches on bolts or concrete surfaces, and steel pins are also used. Batter boards set inside the building dimensions for column footings have to be removed as later construction develops.

Staking out a building can be a time-consuming and lengthy process if the surveyor does not give sufficient forethought to the basic control points required, and the best method for establishing them. The number of instrument setups should be minimized to conserve time, and calculations made in the office if possible, rather than in the field while a survey party waits.

One method of handling difficult jobs is to stake all (or many) points from a single instrument setup using precalculated angles and distances. Figure 21-3 sketches an unusual building shape which was laid out rapidly using only two setups by choosing an initial one to reach half the corners, and having the same calculated angles and distances (Fig. 21-4) for both ends of the building. In employing this method it is essential that enough building dimensions be checked by taping or an EDM after marking the corners to ensure no large errors or mistakes were made.

21-6. STAKING OUT A HIGHWAY. After suitable control has been instituted, the construction area limits are staked so the contractor can clear to them. Next, some contractors want points set on the right-of-way with subgrade elevations showing cut or fill to a given elevation for use in performing rough grading and preliminary excavation of excess material.

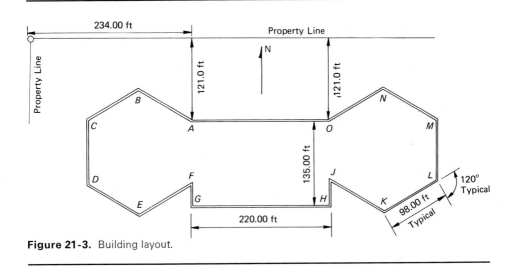

Figure 21-3. Building layout.

BUILDING LAYOUT

Sta.	Angle	To The	Distance
	⊼ @ Point A		
O	0°00'	Rt	220.00 ft
F	90°00'	Rt	98.00 ft
G	90°00'	Rt	139.00 ft
E	120°00'	Rt	169.74 ft
D	150°00'	Rt	196.00 ft
C	180°00'	Rt	169.74 ft
B	210°00'	Rt	98.00 ft
	⊼ @ Point O		
A	0°00'	Lt	220.00 ft
J	90°00'	Lt	98.00 ft
H	90°00'	Lt	135.00 ft
K	120°00'	Lt	169.74 ft
L	150°00'	Lt	196.00 ft
M	180°00'	Lt	169.74 ft
N	210°00'	Lt	98.00 ft

Figure 21-4. Precalculated angles and distances for building stakeout.

Location stakes for the highway are then placed on the center line or an offset line at full stations, the beginning and end of horizontal and vertical curves, and other critical points. A profile run on the center line determines the elevation at each stake.

To guide the contractor in making final excavations and embankment, *slope stakes* are driven at the intersection of the ground and each side slope, or offset a short distance, perhaps 4 ft, Fig. 21-5. The cut or fill at each location is marked on the slope stake. Note that actually there is *no* cut or fill at the slope stake—the figure given is the vertical distance from the slope-stake elevation to grade. Slope stakes are located by a trial-and-error method based upon mental calculations involving the HI, grade rod, ground rod, half-roadway width, and side slopes. One or two trials are generally sufficient to fix the stake position within an allowable error of 0.3 to 0.5 ft for rough grading. The infinite number of ground variations prohibits use of a standard formula in slope staking. An experienced surveyor employs only mental arithmetic, without scratch paper or hand calculator. Whether using the method to be described, or any other, systematic procedures must be followed to avoid confusion and errors. Computers and photogrammetric equipment are now employed to get cross sections and provide slope-stake distances, as well as cut and fill, on larger jobs.

Grade stakes are set at points having the same ground and grade elevation. Three transition sections occur in passing from cut to fill, and a grade stake is set at each one, Fig. 21-6. A line connecting grade stakes, perhaps scratched out on the ground, defines the change from cut to fill. Earthwork quantities *cannot* be correctly calculated going directly from cut to fill or vice versa—there *must* be one or more grade-point sections in between.

Steps to be taken in slope staking are listed in sequence, *assuming, for simplicity, academic conditions* of a 40-ft level roadway and side slopes of 1 to 1 in both cut and fill, Figs. 21-5 and 21-6. In practice, modern highways and shoulders have lateral slopes for drainage, then a steeper slope to a trapezoidal ditch in cut, and another slope up the hillside. Transition sections may have half-roadway widths of cuts different from those in fills to accommodate ditches, and flatter side slopes for fills which tend to be less stable than cuts. But the same basic steps listed still apply and can be extended by students after learning the fundamental approach.

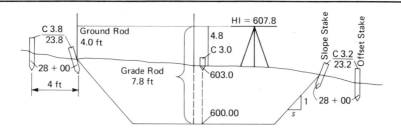

Figure 21-5. Slope stakes (shoulders and ditches not shown).

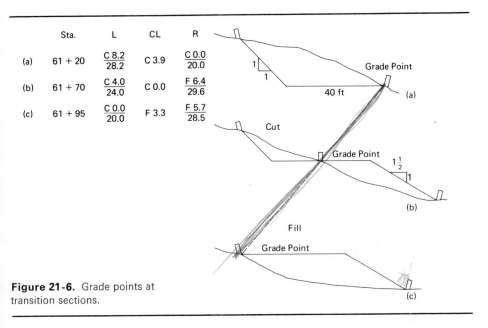

	Sta.	L	CL	R
(a)	61 + 20	$\frac{C\ 8.2}{28.2}$	C 3.9	$\frac{C\ 0.0}{20.0}$
(b)	61 + 70	$\frac{C\ 4.0}{24.0}$	C 0.0	$\frac{F\ 6.4}{29.6}$
(c)	61 + 95	$\frac{C\ 0.0}{20.0}$	F 3.3	$\frac{F\ 5.7}{28.5}$

Figure 21-6. Grade points at transition sections.

1. Compute the cut at the center line stake from profile and grade elevations ($603.0 - 600.0 = C\ 3.0$ in Fig. 21-5). Check in field by grade rod minus ground rod $= 7.8 - 4.8 = C\ 3.0$ ft. Mark the stake C 3.0/0.0.
2. Estimate the difference in elevation between the left-side slope stake point (20+ ft out) and the center stake. Apply the difference, say, +0.5 ft, to the center cut and get an estimated cut of 3.5 ft.
3. Mentally calculate the distance out to the slope stake, $20 + 1(3.5) = 23.5$ ft.
4. Hold zero end of a cloth tape at the center stake while the rodman goes out at right angles (turned by prism or extended-arm method) with the other end and holds the rod at 23.5 ft.
5. *Forget all previous calculations to avoid confusion of too many numbers, and remember only the grade-rod value.*
6. Read the rod with a level set anywhere, or by hand level while standing at center stake. Get cut from grade rod minus ground rod, perhaps $7.8 - 4.0 = C\ 3.8$ ft.
7. Compute required distance out for this cut, $20 + 1(3.8) = 23.8$ ft.
8. Check tape to see what is actually being held and find it is 23.5 ft.
9. Distance is within a few tenths of a foot and close enough. Move out to 23.8 ft if ground is level and drive stake. Move farther out if the ground slopes up, since a greater cut would result and thus the slope stake must be beyond the computed distance, or not so far if the ground has begun to slope down, which gives a smaller cut.
10. If the distance has been missed badly, make a better estimate of cut, compute a new distance out, take a reading to repeat the procedure.

11. In going out on the other side, the rodman lines up the center and left-hand slope stake to get his right-angle direction.
12. To locate grade stakes at road edge, one man carries the zero end of the tape along the center line while the rodman walks parallel with him holding the 20-ft mark until the required ground-rod reading is found by trial. Note that the grade rod changes during the movement but can be computed at 5- or 10-ft intervals. The notekeeper should have the grade rod listed in his book for quick reference at full stations and other points where slope stakes are to be set.
13. Grade points on the center line are located using a starting guess determined by comparing the cut and fill at back and forward stations.

Practice varies for different organizations but on transition sections, a peg may be set at the slope-stake point. A marker stake is also driven perhaps $\frac{1}{2}$ ft beyond, with the cut or fill distance out from the center line to the slope-stake point, side-slope ratio, and base half-width noted on the side facing the center line. Stationing is given on the back side. A reference stake placed 6 ft or more farther out of the way of clearing and grading has the same information repeated on it.

Slope staking using an EDM and vertical angles is now being carried out since the slope distance to a stake is readily measured. Slope-stake locations (and earthwork quantities) are also obtained from large-scale maps having small contour intervals.

After rough grading has shaped cuts and embankments to near final elevation, finished grade is set more accurately from *blue tops* (stakes whose tops are marked with blue keel and driven to grade elevation). These are not normally offset, but rather driven directly on center line. A tight string line stretched through notches in the blue tops can provide close control of the grading.

Highway and railroad grades can often be rounded off to multiples of 0.05 or 0.10% without appreciably increasing earthwork costs in cuts, or on fill where flat country requires elevating the roadway for good drainage. Streets need a minimum 0.05% grade for drainage from intersection to intersection, or from midblock both ways to the corners, and crowning for lateral flow to gutters.

Drainage profiles, prepared to verify or construct drainage cross sections, can be used to accurately locate drainage structures and easements. An experienced engineer, asked a question regarding the three most important items in highway work, replied "drainage, drainage, and drainage"! This requirement must be satisfied by good surveying and design.

Utility relocation surveys may be necessary in connection with highway construction; for example, manhole or valve-box covers have to be set at correct grade before earthwork begins to fit the center-line finished grade and differential elevation resulting from transverse surface slope. They are located by center-line station and offset distance.

A three-person field crew can handle most construction staking jobs. Grade and other calculations should be prepared in the office, in advance if possible, to save field time and its greater cost.

Location staking for railways and canals follows the methods outlined for highways.

21-7. OTHER CONSTRUCTION SURVEYS. Hydrographic surveys for causeways, bridges, and offshore oil platforms add the problem of establishing points and depths where it may be difficult or impossible to hold a rod or reflector. Triangulation, trilateration, EDM's, and sonar mapping devices are employed to plot dredging cross sections for underwater trenching and pipe laying. Today more pipelines are crossing wider rivers than ever before. The mammoth Alaskan program, for example, has introduced numerous new problems and solutions.

Large earthwork projects—dams, levees, superhighways—require widespread permanent control for quick setups and frequent replacement of slope stakes, all of which may disappear under fill in one day. Fixed signals for elevation and alignment painted or mounted on canyon walls or hillsides can mark important reference lines.

Underground surveys in tunnels and mines necessitate transferring line and elevations from the ground above, perhaps down shafts. Two heavy plumb bobs hung on wires (and damped in oil or water) from opposite sides of the surface opening can be aligned by theodolite there and in the tunnel. A vertical collimator will also provide two points on line below ground. Elevations are brought down by taping or other means. Bench marks and instrument stations are set on the roof, out of the way of equipment. A theodolite or laser is wiggled in on the short line defined by the two plumb-bob wires, a station mark set above the instrument, and the line extended. Later setups are made beneath *spads* (surveying nails with hooks) anchored in the roof.

Surveys are run at intervals on all large jobs to check progress for periodic payments to the contractor. And finally, an "as built" survey is made to determine compliance with plans and changes for the terminal contract payment.

21-8. SOURCES OF ERROR.   Two important sources of error in construction surveys are:

1. Movement of stakes and marks.
2. Failure to use tacks for proper line where justified.

21-9. MISTAKES.   Typical mistakes often made in construction surveys include:

1. Lack of foresight as to where construction will destroy points.

2. Notation for cut (or fill) and stationing on stake not checked.
3. Wrong datum for cuts, whether cut is to finished grade or subgrade.
4. Arithmetic mistakes, generally due to lack of a check.
5. Use of incorrect elevations, grades, and stations.
6. Failing to check the diagonals of a building.
7. Carrying out computed values beyond field accuracy possible (one good hundredth is worth all the bad thousandths).
8. Reading the rod on top of center-line stakes instead of on the ground beside them in profiling.
9. Failure to calculate midpoint grades by successive increments so that any error is evident if the last grade elevation does not check.

PROBLEMS

21–1. Name the orders of horizontal and vertical control needed for construction of a water line, sewer line, and long-span bridge.

21–2. How far apart should stakes be set on a sewer job having a relatively flat grade ? On a steep grade ? On a sharp curve ?

21–3. Grade stakes are to be set on a rolling sloping surface at stations 1+40, 1+84, and 2+18 on a uniform grade between station 0+00, elevation 335.72, and 2+66, elevation 340.02 ft. Prepare a set of notes in suitable form and compute rod settings for the grade points if the BS on 0+00 is 6.27 ft.

21–4. Sketch two different forms of story-pole templates not shown in Fig. 21–2.

21–5. State two conflicting requirements which enter the decision on how far offset stakes should be set beyond the construction line.

21–6. How are street grades arranged for drainage in a city with flat terrain ?

21–7. If a pipeline is parallel to and near the curb, would it be preferable to put the offset line on the curb or road surface ?

21–8. List the most important things to be considered in laying a grade line on a ground profile.

21–9. Are batter boards ever placed inside a building ? Explain.

21–10. By means of a sketch, show how and where batter boards should be located for a U-shaped building 80 × 60 ft, all wings being 20 ft wide.

21–11. Same as problem 21–10 except for an H-shaped structure 60×60 ft with wings 20 ft wide.

21–12. Describe two or more ways to still the swing of a plumb-bob line extending several stories outside a building wall.

21–13. Can the corner of a building be plumbed by running the vertical line of a transit telescope up and down the wall line ? Explain.

21–14. Specify a reasonable tolerance for plumbing elevator shafts.

21–15. Compare the accuracy required on a survey for a tall building with that for an ordinary property survey. What tolerances are reasonable for wall alignment and floor elevations ?

21–16. List suitable tolerances in positioning anchor bolts for a bridge; a steel column pier.

21–17. Describe a method to check deviations from the vertical of steel tubes driven to form cast-in-place piles.

21–18. Arrange in proper order the sequence of giving construction lines for (a) foundation, (b) excavation, (c) main structure, and (d) subdivisions of the structure.

21–19. Which building line of a structure is shown on a record plat, the outside or center line of a wall?

21–20. How are floor elevations controlled in high-rise steel and reinforced-concrete buildings?

21–21. Outline a suitable method for giving grade for a (a) parking lot, (b) reinforced-concrete culvert, and (c) footing for a bridge pier.

21–22. Discuss the suitability of a 0.00% grade for a street or highway.

21–23. List the advantages of a coordinate system for an overpass layout.

21–24. Are distances measured by stadia satisfactory for preliminary highway surveys?

21–25. Approximately how close should the levels check on a survey for a concrete-surfaced highway to be 1 mile long?

21–26. A highway survey is run by deflection angles. Which is the most important transit adjustment to check?

21–27. Why are side ditches sometimes extended into fill stations?

21–28. Does the Lenker level rod have any disadvantages in construction use?

21–29. State briefly the surveys you would make on which to base the layout of a ranch irrigation system.

21–30. What rule is used in some cities regarding responsibility of a contractor who breaks existing sewer or water lines during new construction?

21–31. On construction projects in your area, who is responsible for and pays the cost of setting initial control and survey stakes, the contractor or owner? For the replacement of stakes knocked out?

22
CIRCULAR
CURVES

22-1. GENERAL. Straight (tangent) sections of most types of transportation routes, such as highways, railroads, and pipelines, are connected by curves in both the horizontal and vertical planes. An exception is a transmission line, in which a series of straight lines is used with direct angular changes at tower locations.

Two types of horizontal curves are employed—circular arcs and spirals. A *simple curve*, Fig. 22-1(a), is a circular arc connecting two tangents. A *compound curve*, Fig. 22-1(b), is composed of two or more circular arcs of different radii tangent to each other, with their centers on the same side of the common tangent. The combination of a short length of tangent connecting two circular arcs having centers on the same side, as in Fig. 22-1(c), is called a *broken-back curve*. A *reverse curve*, Fig. 22-1(d), consists of two circular arcs tangent to each other, the centers being on opposite sides of the common tangent. Reverse, compound, and short-tangent (less than 100 ft) broken-back

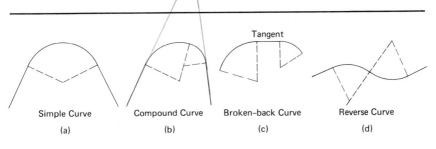

Simple Curve   Compound Curve   Broken–back Curve   Reverse Curve

(a)   (b)   (c)   (d)

Figure 22-1. Circular curves.

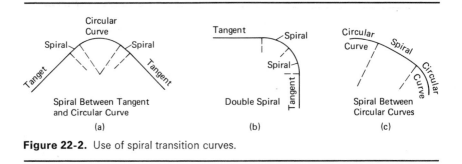

Figure 22-2. Use of spiral transition curves.

curves are unsuitable for modern high-speed highway, rapid transit, and railroad traffic.

Easement curves are desirable to lessen the sudden change in curvature at the junction of a tangent and a circular curve. A *spiral* makes an excellent easement curve because its radius decreases uniformly from infinity at the tangent to that of the curve it meets. Spirals are used to connect a tangent with a circular curve, a tangent with a tangent (double spiral), and a circular curve with a circular curve and compounded or reversed curves. Figure 22-2 illustrates most of these arrangements.

The effect of centrifugal force on a vehicle passing around a curve can be balanced by *superelevation* of the outer rail of a track and outer edge of a highway pavement. Correct superelevation on a spiral increases uniformly with the distance from the beginning of the spiral, and is in inverse proportion to the radius at any point. Properly superelevated spirals ensure smooth and safe riding qualities with less wear on equipment. For detailed coverage of the spiral and superelevation, the reader is referred to one of the books on route surveying listed in the References, Appendix B.

Circular arcs and spirals are used for curves in the horizontal plane because they are readily laid out in the field by transit and tape.

Grade lines are joined in the vertical plane by parabolic curves, discussed in Chapter 23. Elevations on parabolic curves are easily computed and can be established on the ground by leveling.

22-2. DEGREE OF CURVE. In European practice and the majority of American highway work, circular curves are designated by their radius; for example, "1500-m curve" and "1000-ft curve." American railroads and some highway departments prefer to identify curves by their *degree*, employing either chord or arc definition.

In railroad practice (and early highway construction), the degree of curve has been the angle at the center of a circular arc subtended by a chord of 100 ft. This is the *chord definition* shown in Fig. 22-3(a). In most highway work, degree of a curve is the central angle subtended by a circular arc of 100 ft,

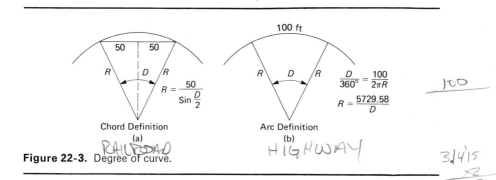

Figure 22-3. Degree of curve.

the *arc definition*, Fig. 22-3(b). Formulas relating the radius R and degree D are shown beside the illustrations.

Radii of chord- and arc-definition curves for values of D from 1° to 6° are given in Table B-6. Although the differences appear to be small in this range, they have some significance in computations.

A chord-definition curve is consistent in using chords for computation and layout with 100.00-ft tape lengths for full stations on large-radius curves. Its disadvantages are: (a) R is not directly proportional to the reciprocal of D; (b) the formula for length is slightly approximate; (c) small corrections must be added in using the "shortcut" formulas for tangent distance and external distance; and (d) greater difficulty is encountered in checking sharp curves.

The arc-definition curve has the disadvantage that most measurements between stations are less than a full tape length. Computations are facilitated since exact answers for the radius, tangent distance, and external distance are obtained by dividing tabular values for a 1° curve by the degree D. Also, the formula for length is exact, this being an advantage in preparing right-of-way descriptions.

Arc and chord definitions give practically the same result when applied to the flat curves common on modern highways and railroads.

Circular curves are usually laid out in the field by deflection angles and taped chords.

22-3. DERIVATION OF FORMULAS.   Circular-curve elements are shown in Fig. 22-4. The *point of intersection* of the tangents (PI) is also called the *vertex* (V). The *beginning of the curve* (BC) and the *end of the curve* (EC) are also termed the *point of curvature* (PC) and the *point of tangency* (PT). Other expressions for these points are *tangent to curve* (TC) and *curve to tangent* (CT).

The distance from the BC to the PI, and from the PI to the EC, is the *tangent distance* (T). A line connecting the BC and EC is the *long chord* (LC). *Length of curve* (L) is the distance from BC to EC measured along the curve for arc definition, or by 100-ft chords for the chord definition.

The *external distance* (E) is the length from vertex to curve on a radial line. *Middle ordinate* (M) is the (radial) distance from midpoint of the long chord to midpoint of the curve. Any *point on the curve* is a POC, on a *tangent*, POT. The degree of any curve is D_a (arc definition), or D_c (chord definition).

The change in direction of the two tangents is the intersection angle I, which is equal to the central angle.

By definition, and inspection of Fig. 22-4, relations for the *arc definition* follow:

$$\frac{D°}{360°} = \frac{100}{2\pi R} \quad \text{and} \quad R = \frac{100 \times 360}{2\pi D} = \frac{5729.58}{D} \tag{22-1}$$

$$T = R \tan \frac{I}{2} \tag{22-2}$$

$$T_a = \frac{T_{1°}}{D_a} \tag{22-3}$$

$$L = 100 \frac{I}{D} \tag{22-4a}$$

$$= RI \ (I \text{ in radians}) \tag{22-4b}$$

$$LC = 2R \sin \frac{I}{2} \tag{22-5}$$

$$\frac{R}{R + E} = \cos \frac{I}{2}; \ E = R\left(\sec \frac{I}{2} - 1\right) = R \operatorname{exsec} \frac{I}{2} \tag{22-6}$$

$$E_a = \frac{E_{1°}}{D_a} \tag{22-7}$$

$$\frac{R - M}{R} = \cos \frac{I}{2}; \ M = R\left(1 - \cos \frac{I}{2}\right) = R \operatorname{vers} \frac{I}{2} \tag{22-8}$$

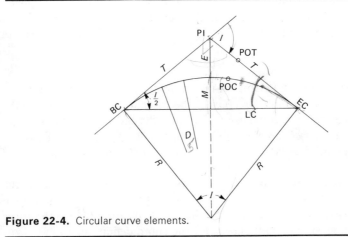

Figure 22-4. Circular curve elements.

In Eqs. (22-3) and (22-7), T_a and E_a are the tangent distance and external distance respectively for the given value of D_a, while $T_{1°}$ and $E_{1°}$ are their lengths (listed in tables) for a 1° curve and different values of I.

The formulas for T, L, E, and M apply also to a chord-definition curve. Small corrections must be added to the values of T_a and E_a found by Eqs. (22-3) and (22-7), respectively.

The formula relating R and D for a chord-definition curve is as follows:

$$R = \frac{50}{\sin D/2} \qquad (22\text{-}9)$$

22-4. SAMPLE COMPUTATION.   Assume that field measurements show $I = 8°24'$ and the station of the PI is $64 + 27.46$, and terrain conditions require use of the maximum degree of curve permitted by the specifications, which is, say, 2°00'. Then, for an *arc-definition* curve,

$$R = \frac{5729.58}{2} \qquad = 2864.79 \text{ ft}$$

$$T = 2864.79 \times 0.073435 = 210.38 \qquad \text{or} \qquad T = \frac{420.75}{2} = 210.38$$

$$L = 100 \times \frac{8.40}{2} \qquad = 420.00$$

$$E = 2864.79 \times 0.002693 = 7.71 \qquad \text{or} \qquad E_a = \frac{E_1}{D_a} = \frac{15.42}{2} = 7.71$$

$$M = 2864.79 \times 0.002686 = 7.69 \text{ ft}$$

$$
\begin{array}{rl}
\text{Station PI} = & 64 + 27.46 \\
- T = & 2 + 10.38 \\
\hline
\text{Station BC} = & 62 + 17.08 \\
+ L = & 4 + 20.00 \\
\hline
\text{Station EC} = & 66 + 37.08
\end{array}
$$

Calculations for the stations of the BC and EC should be arranged as shown. Note that the station of the EC *cannot* be obtained by adding the tangent distance to the station of the PI, although location of the EC on the ground is determined by measuring the tangent distance from the PI. Points representing the BC and EC must be carefully marked, and placed exactly on the tangent lines at the correct distance from the PI, so other computed values will fit their fixed positions on the ground. Field notes for this curve are given in Plate A-13. An instrument setup station on the curve is denoted by POC.

Since normally a route survey is a series of tangents having continuous stationing, an adjustment has to be made at each EC after curves have been inserted. Thus for preliminary stationing on the curves only, and final stationing at the EC, there is a "station equation" or an *equation of chainage*. For the example of this section, it would be 66 + 37.08 back = 66 + 37.84 ahead, that is, (PI 64 + 27.46) +(*T* = 2 + 10.38) along the forward tangent at EC before the curve was run in, which shortened the route .

22-5. CURVE LAYOUT. Except for unusual cases, such as street railways, the radii of curves in route surveys are generally too large to permit swinging an arc from the curve center. Circular curves are therefore laid out by (a) deflection angles and chords, (b) tangent offsets, (c) chord offsets, (d) middle ordinates, and (e) other methods. Layout by deflection angles from the tangents is the standard method and one of two procedures which will be discussed in this text.

In Fig. 22-5, assume that the instrument is set up over the BC (station 62 + 17.07 in the preceding example). The first point to be marked on the curve is station 63 + 00, since cross sections are normally taken, construction stakes set, and computations of earthwork made at full stations and critical points. From the BC to the next full station, a *subchord c* is required.

The *deflection angle* from a tangent for a full 100-ft arc is $D/2$, since an angle formed by a tangent and chord is equal to one-half the intercepted arc. The *subdeflection angle d/2* from the BC to station 63 + 00 can be computed by the proportion

$$\frac{d}{2} : \frac{D}{2} = c : 100; \text{ thus } \frac{d}{2} = \frac{cD}{200} \qquad (22\text{-}10)$$

A small subdeflection angle is expressed in minutes, rather than in degrees, and Eq. (22-10) then becomes

$$\frac{d}{2} = 0.3cD \qquad (22\text{-}11)$$

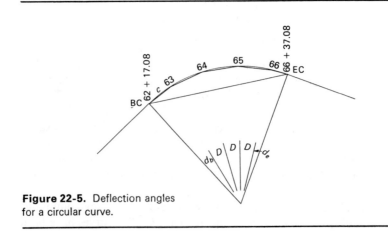

Figure 22-5. Deflection angles for a circular curve.

where D is in degrees and the subdeflection angle is in minutes.

In this example, the subchord is $(63 + 00) - (62 + 17.08) = 82.92^1$ and

$$\frac{d}{2} = 0.3 \times 82.92 \times 2 = 49.75' = 49'45''$$

Deflection angles are normally carried out to several decimal places for checking purposes, and to avoid accumulating small errors when D is an odd value, such as, perhaps, $3°17.24'$. In early railroad work with $1'$ transits, D was generally rounded off to a multiple of $2'$.

An alternate method of computing deflection angles is to multiply the deflection angle per foot of arc or chord by the length of arc or chord being laid out. In the present example, the deflection angle per foot of arc is $(D/2)/100 = 1°00'/100 = 0.60'/\text{ft}$. Then the deflection angle $d/2$ from the BC to station $63 + 00$ is $0.60' \times 82.92 = 49.75'$.

With a transit or theodolite set up over the BC, it is oriented by back-sighting on the PI, or on a point along the back tangent, with $0°00'$ on the circle. The subdeflection angle of $49'45''$ is then turned. Meanwhile, the 17-ft mark of the tape is held on the BC. The 100-ft end of the (subtracting) tape is swung until the line of sight hits the point 0.08 ft back from the 100-ft mark. This is station $63 + 00$.

Deflection angles to stations following 63 are found by adding $D/2 = 1°00'$ for each full chord. The rear tapeman next holds the zero mark on station 63, and the forward tapeman sets station 64 by direction from the instrumentman, who has placed an angle of $0°49'45'' + 1°00'00'' = 1°49'45''$ on the plates. An experienced forward tapeman will walk along the extended first full chord, know or estimate the chord offset, and from an outside-the-chord position be holding the tape end and a stake within a foot of the correct location when the instrumentman has the deflection angle ready.

The subdeflection angle $d/2$ for the final subchord equals $22.24'$. As a check, the deflection angle from the BC to the EC must equal $I/2$. In the field it is essential to read and check the deflection angle to the EC (when visible from the BC) before starting to run the curve. An error in I, T, L, or the stationing will then be discovered without wasting time running an impossible curve.

Field notes for the curve of this example are recorded in Plate A-13 as they would appear in a field book. Notes run up the page to simplify sketching in a forward direction.

---

[1] For up to $2°00'$ curve, lengths of arcs and chords are the same to two decimal places. On sharper curves the chords would be shorter than corresponding arc lengths. In these cases, c used in Eq. 22-11 is the difference in stationing, but chords for curve layout are calculated as $c = 2R \sin d/2$ for subchords, and $C = 2R \sin D/2$ for full chords. For example, the chord measurement to lay out a 100-ft arc for a $6°00'$ curve is $2(5729.58/6) \sin 3° = 99.95$ ft.

In many cases it is desirable to *back in* a curve by setting up over the EC instead of the BC. One setup is thereby eliminated and the long sights are taken on the first measurements. In precise work it is better to run in the curve from both ends to the center, where small errors can be adjusted more readily. On long or very sharp circular curves, or if obstacles block sights from the BC or EC, setups on the curve (POC's) are necessary.

Closure achieved in staking a curve is the "falling" of the EC located from the last deflection angle and chord, compared with the EC found by measuring distance T along the forward tangent from the PI. Field precision can be expressed as a numerical ratio like that used in traverse checks. Measured falling distance is the numerator, and $L + 2T$ the denominator. If closure of the example in Sections 22-4 and 22-5 was 0.25 ft, the precision would be $0.25/(420.00 + 2 \times 210.38) = \frac{1}{3360}$. Measuring the long chord permits investigating the curve layout as a traverse, and provides coordinates for right-of-way or other use.

The curve used in a particular situation is selected to fit ground conditions, and specification limitations on maximum D or minimum R. Normally the value of I and station of the PI are available from field measurements on the preliminary line. Then a value of D up to the maximum for a railroad line, or an R suitable for the highway type, is chosen. Sometimes the value of E or M required to miss a stream or steep slope outside or inside the PI is measured, and D or R computed. Tangent distance governs infrequently (one exception is to make a railroad, bus, or subway station fall on a tangent rather than a superelevated curve). Length of curve practically never governs.

22-6. CURVE LAYOUT BY OFFSETS.

For short curves, when a transit or theodolite is not available, or for checking purposes, one of four offset-type methods can be used for circular curves: tangent offsets, chord offsets, middle ordinates, and ordinates from the long chord. Figure 22-6 shows the relationship of chord offsets, tangent offsets, and middle ordinates. Visually and by formula comparison, the chord offset (chord definition) is

$$CO = 200 \sin \frac{D}{2} = \frac{(100)^2}{R} = 2 \text{ TO} = 8 \text{ MO (approx.)} \qquad (22\text{-}12)$$

Also, $CO : 100 = 100 : R$ and $CO = 100^2/R$. Furthermore, since $\sin 1° = 0.0175$ (approx.), $CO = 100(0.0175)D = 1\frac{3}{4}D$ (approx.) where D is in degrees and decimals. And m for any chord $= R$ vers $\frac{1}{2}d$ ($\frac{1}{2}d$ being the deflection angle for that chord).

A useful equation in laying out or checking curves in place is

$$D \text{ (in degrees)} = m \text{ (in inches) for a 62-ft chord (approx.)} \qquad (22\text{-}13)$$

A sample computation of tangent offsets for a circular curve laid out from the BC and EC to a common station near the midpoint—thereby avoiding long measurements and providing a check point where small adjustments can be made if necessary—is given in Illustration 22-1 for Fig. 22-7.

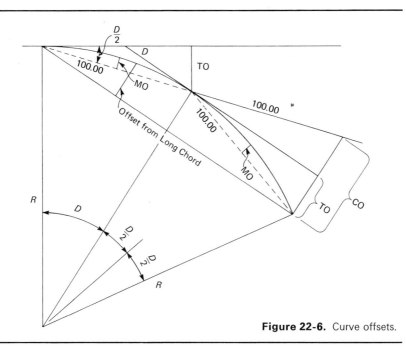

Figure 22-6. Curve offsets.

Ordinates and abscissas are computed from successive values of angle α where $\alpha = $ *central angle to the beginning of a chord + the deflection angle for that chord.*

Given data: $D = 5°00'$ (chord definition), $BC = 77 + 80.00$, and $EC = 80 + 00.00$. Then $L = 220.00$ ft, $I = LD/100 = 11°00'$, and $d_1/2 = \alpha_1 = 0.3 \times 20 \times 5 = 30'$. Angle α_2 to $78 + 50 = 1°00'$ (deflection angle for a 40-ft chord) $ + 1°15'$ (deflection angle for a 50-ft chord) $ = 2°15'$.

22-7. SETUPS ON THE CURVE. Obstacles and extremely long sight distances sometimes make it necessary to set up on the curve. The simplest

ILLUSTRATION 22-1. TANGENT OFFSETS FOR CIRULAR CURVE

Point	Station	α	$c \sin \alpha$	Total Ordinate	$c \cos \alpha$	Total Abscissa
EC	80 + 00	0°00′	0.000	0.000	0.000	0.00
	79 + 50	1°15′	1.090	1.09	49.998	50.00
	79 + 00	3°45′	3.270	4.36	49.893	99.89
	79 + 00	4°45′	4.140	6.28	49.828	119.79
	78 + 50	2°15′	1.963	2.14	49.961	69.96
	78 + 00	0°30′	0.1746	0.17	19.999	20.00
BC	77 + 80	0°00′	0.000	0.00	0.000	0.00

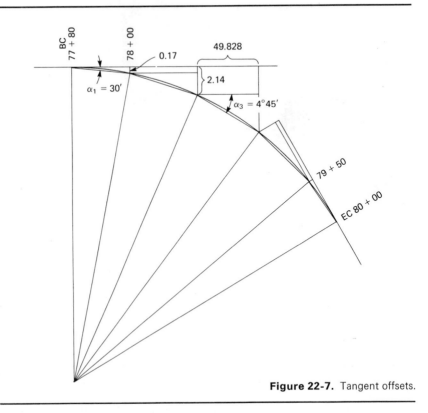

Figure 22-7. Tangent offsets.

procedure to follow is one which permits use of the same notes computed for running the curve from the BC.

In this method the instrument is backsighted on any curve station with the telescope inverted and the plates set to *the deflection angle for that station from the BC*. The telescope is plunged to the normal position, and the deflection angles previously computed for the various stations from the BC are used.

In the example of Sections 22-4 and 22-5, if a setup is required at station 65, place 0°00′ on the plates and sight to the BC with the telescope inverted. Plunge, set the plates to read the deflection angle 3°49′45″, and stake station 66. Or, if the BC is not visible, set 0°49′45″ on the plates, sight on station 63, plunge, set 3°49′45″ on the instrument, and locate station 66.

A simple sketch will make clear the geometry basic to this procedure.

22-8. INTERSECTION OF A CIRCULAR CURVE AND STRAIGHT LINE. Many problems in surveying requiring the point of intersection of a circular curve and a straight line are conveniently solved with coordinates, using analytic geometry equations. One form for a straight line in rectangular coordinates is

$$\frac{x_p - x_1}{y_p - y_1} = \frac{x_2 - x_1}{y_2 - y_1} \qquad (22\text{-}14)$$

where x_p and y_p are coordinates of any point P on the line where it intersects the circle; x_1, y_1 and x_2, y_2 are coordinates of points 1 and 2, respectively. Figure 22-8 shows a straight line superimposed on a rectangular coordinate system and illustrates these terms.

The comparable equation of a circular curve is

$$(x_p - x_o)^2 + (y_p - y_o)^2 = R^2 \qquad (22\text{-}15)$$

in which x_p, y_p are coordinates of any point on the circle; x_o, y_o the coordinates of the arc center; and R the curve radius.

Solution of straight line–circular curve intersection problems involves writing equations such as Eqs. (22-14) and (22-15). In typical cases, coordinates x_1, and y_1, x_2 and y_2, x_o and y_o, and radius R are known. Both equations contain x_p and y_p as unknowns and are solved to find them.

As an example of the computations required, assume the coordinates of the circle center are $x_o = 500.00$, $y_o = 200.00$; for points 1 and 2, $x_1 = 100.00$, $y_1 = 130.00$, and $x_2 = 300.00$, $y_2 = 200.00$; and $R = 150.00$ ft. Determine the coordinates of intersection point P.

From Eq. (22-14),

$$\frac{x_p - 100.00}{y_p - 130.00} = \frac{300.00 - 100.00}{200.00 - 130.00} \qquad (a)$$

and by Eq. (22-15),

$$(x_p - 500.00)^2 + (y_p - 200.00)^2 = (150.00)^2 \qquad (b)$$

Reducing Eq. (a), $x_p = 2.8571y_p - 271.43 \qquad (c)$

Substituting Eq. (c) in (b) and reducing,

$$y_p^2 - 524.73y_p + 66{,}856 = 0 \qquad (d)$$

so $y_p = \dfrac{524.73 \pm \sqrt{(524.73)^2 - 4(66{,}856)}}{2} = 217.87$

and $x_p = 2.8571(217.87) - 271.43 = 351.05$

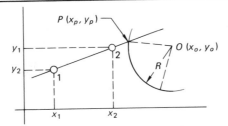

Figure 22-8. Intersection of circular curve and straight line.

In solving quadratic Eq. (d), the decision to add or subtract the value under the radical can be made on the basis of experience or use of a carefully constructed scaled diagram which also provides a check on the computations. One answer will be unreasonable and is discarded.

22-9. PASSING A CIRCULAR CURVE THROUGH A FIXED POINT.

Another special problem in practice is to determine the radius of a curve connecting two established tangents and going through a fixed point such as an underpass, overpass, or an existing bridge. A trial-and-error field or office process can be used, or Eq. (22-16) (derivation given in various route surveying books) applied with PV, x, and I in Fig. 22-9 known from field measurements, and angle o computed from relationships in triangle POV.

$$R = \frac{PV \sin (I + x)}{\text{vers} \left(\dfrac{I}{2} + o \right)} \tag{22-16}$$

22-10. COMPOUND AND REVERSE CURVES.
Compound and reverse curves are combinations of two or more circular curves. They should be used only for low-speed trafficways, and in terrain where simple curves cannot be fitted to the ground without excessive construction costs.

Special formulas have been derived to facilitate computations for such curves and are demonstrated in texts on route surveying. A compound curve is run at the BC and EC, or perhaps by one setup at the *point of compound curvature* (CC). Reverse curves are handled in similar fashion.

22-11. SIGHT DISTANCE ON HORIZONTAL CURVES.
Highway safety requires certain minimum sight distances in zones where passing is permitted, and in nonpassing areas to assure a reasonable stopping distance if

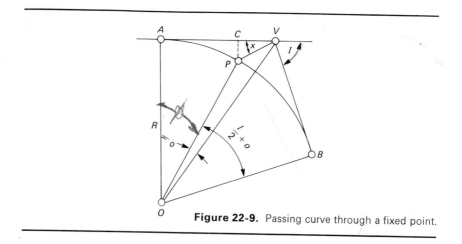

Figure 22-9. Passing curve through a fixed point.

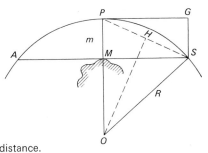

Figure 22-10. Sight distance.

there is an object on the roadway. Specifications and tables list suitable values based upon vehicular speeds, the perception and reaction times of an average individual, braking distance for a given coefficient of friction during deceleration, and type and condition of the pavement.

A minimum sight distance of 600 ft is desirable for speeds as low as 30 miles/hr.

An approximate formula for sight distance can be derived by referring to Fig. 22-10, in which the clear sight distance past an obstruction is the length of the long chord AS, denoted by C; and the required clearance is the middle ordinate PM, denoted by m. Then in triangles SPG and SOH,

$$m : SP = \frac{SP}{2} : R \quad \text{and} \quad m = \frac{(SP)^2}{2R}$$

Usually m is small compared with R, and SP may be assumed equal to $C/2$. Then

$$m = \frac{C^2}{8R} \tag{22-17}$$

If distance m from the center line of a highway to the obstruction is known or can be measured, the available sight distance C is calculated from the formula. Actually cars travel on either the inside or outside lane, so sight distance AS is not exactly the true stopping distance, but the computed length is on the safe side and satisfactory for practical use.

22-12. SOURCES OF ERROR. Some sources of error in curve computations and layout are:

1. Inability to set the transit plates to exact required subdivisions of a minute for deflection angles.
2. Poor intersections between some tape and sight lines (which may be almost parallel) on very flat curves.
3. Use of less than full 100.00-ft tape lengths on arc-definition curves.

22-13. MISTAKES. Typical mistakes that occur in laying out a curve in the field are the following:

1. Failure to take equal numbers of direct and reversed measurements of the deflection angle at the PI before computing or laying out the curve.
2. Adding the tangent distance to the PI station to get the EC station.
3. Using 100.00-ft chords to lay out arc-definition curves having D greater than 2°.
4. Taping subchords of nominal length for chord-definition curves having D greater than 5° (a *nominal* 50-ft subchord for a 6° curve requires a measurement of 50.02 ft).

PROBLEMS

22–1. A circular curve has an 1800-ft radius. What is its degree by (a) chord definition and (b) arc definition?

22–2. Similar to problem 22–1 but for a 3200–ft radius.

22–3. List the advantages and disadvantages of the chord and arc definitions for the degree of a circular curve in construction layout and land descriptions.

Compute T, L, R, or D, and stations of the BC and EC for a circular curve in problems 22–4 through 22–7. Distances are in feet. Use the chord definition for railroad curves, arc definitions for highways.

22–4. Railroad curve with $D=4°00'$, $I=20°00'$, and sta. $V=72+48.60$.

22–5. Highway curve with $R=1909.86$, $I=10°00'$, and sta. $V=80+10.50$.

22–6. Highway curve with $D=4°20'$, $I=22°10'$, and PI$=54+37.3$.

22–7. Railroad curve with $R=1910.08$, $I=15°00'$, and sta. $V=56+24.0$.

22–8. Compute E and M for problem 22–4.

22–9. Calculate E and M for problem 22–5.

22–10. Compute E and M for problem 22–6.

Calculate and tabulate the curve data R, D, T, L, E, M, BC, EC, and deflection angles to lay out the curves in problems 22–11 through 22–18.

22–11. Highway curve with $R=1432.39$, $I=34°42'$ R, sta. $V=87+64.0$.

22–12. Railroad curve with $D=3°00'$, $I=19°24'$, PI sta. $=78+64.22$.

22–13. Highway curve having $R=3000$ ft, $I=9°00'$, sta. $V=61+29.2$.

22–14. Railroad curve with $D=2°00'$, $I=10°40'$, PI sta. $=62+48.12$.

22–15. Highway curve with $L=500$ ft, $R=2864.79$, sta. $V=60+10.1$.

22–16. Railroad curve with $L=266.17$ ft, $D=4°30'$, PI sta. $=27+43.85$.

22–17. Highway curve having $T=283.5$ ft, $R=1322.2$, sta. $V=24+71.2$.

22–18. Railroad curve with $T=214.8$ ft, $D=2°20'$, and PI$=26+40.0$.

22–19. A street-car line on the center of an 80-ft street makes a 78°34' turn into another street of equal width. The corner curb line has $R=12$ ft. What is the largest R that can be given the track center line if the law requires it be at least 15 ft from the curb?

Compute and tabulate all data required to lay out the simple circular curves of problems 22–20 through 22–23.

22–20. The R for a highway curve will be rounded off to the nearest larger multiple of 100 ft. Field conditions require M to be approximately 15 ft to avoid an embankment. The PI=83+17.5 and I=11°00′.

22–21. The D for a highway curve will be rounded off to the nearest multiple of 20′. Field measurements show T should be approximately 182 ft to avoid an overpass. The PI=26+25.0, I=12°00′.

22–22. Similar to problem 20–21 except E should be at least 60 ft and D rounded off to the nearest 10′.

22–23. Similar to problem 22–20 except R must be rounded off to the nearest 50 ft and E is approximately 40 ft.

22–24. A highway survey PI falls in a pond, so a cutoff line AB=300.00 ft is run between tangents. In the triangle formed by points A, B, and vertex V, angle VAB=16°00′ and VBA=24°00′. The station of A is 36+47.18. Calculate and tabulate curve notes to run a 5°00′ curve to connect tangents AV and BV.

22–25. Similar to problem 22–24 except that angle VAB=16°00′ and angle VBA=20°00′.

22–26. A single circular curve will join tangents XV and VY, and also be tangent to BC. Calculate R, L, and stations of the BC and EC in Fig. 22–26.

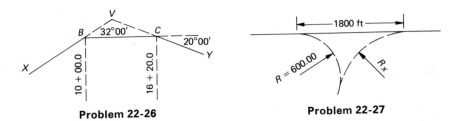

Problem 22-26   **Problem 22-27**

22–27. Compute R_x to fit the requirements in the figure.

In problems 22–28 through 22–30, after a BS on the BC with 0°00′ set on the instrument, what is the deflection angle to the curve point noted?

22–28. Setup at midpoint, deflection to the EC.

22–29. Instrument at midpoint of curve, deflection to the $^3/_4$ point.

22–30. Setup at $^5/_8$ point of curve, deflection to the $^1/_8$ point.

22–31. Why is the vertex angle usually measured by repetition?

22–32. List one advantage and one disadvantage of running circular curves by using single deflection angles.

For problems 22–33 through 22–35 compute and tabulate coordinates to stake out a circular railroad curve by tangent offsets. Regular and 50-ft stations are to be set, and approximately one-half the curve laid out from each tangent.

22–33. L=220.00 ft, D=5°00′, and station of the BC=77+80.00.

22–34. Station of PI=36+41.70, D=6°00′, and L=480.00 ft.

22–35. D=3°00′, I=9°45′, and EC=16+54.20.

22–36. Under what field conditions is layout of a circular curve by offsets from the LC an appropriate method ? What are its disadvantages ?

22–37. List in their order of importance the influence of R, D, L, T, E, M, and the LC in selecting curves to fit ground conditions. Explain.

22–38. Compute the length of chord (in feet) for which the middle ordinate (in inches) equals twice the degree of curve.

22–39. A running track must be exactly 1 mile along its center line with two semicircles and two tangents. The two curves are to comprise one-half its total length. Calculate $L, R,$ and D for the curves.

22–40. Similar to problem 22–39 except that 0.40 of the total length is in the two curves.

22–41. The coordinates of a circle center are $X_o = 1200.00$, $Y_o = 00.00$; for $A = 800.00$ and 0.00; and for $B = 400.00$ and 200.00. $R = 600.00$ ft. Compute the coordinates of a point P, the intersection of the curve and line AB.

22–42. Similar to problem 22–41 except $X_o = 300.00$, $Y_o = 600.00$; $A = 600.00$, 300.00; $R = 450.00$ ft; and bearing of $AB = S\ 45°00'\ W$.

What sight distance is available if there is an obstruction on a radial line through the vertex, inside the curve, in problems 22–43 through 22–45 ?

22–43. For problem 20–11, obstacle 18 ft from curve.

22–44. For problem 20–16, obstacle 24 ft from curve.

22–45. For problem 20–17, obstacle 25 ft from curve.

22–46. A compound curve consists of five equal-length circular curves of $D = 1°, 3°, 5°, 3°, 1°,$ in that sequence, and connects two tangents having an intersection angle of $65°00'$. If the beginning of compound curve (BCC) station is $49+27.7$, compute the stations of the compound curve (CC) and end of compound curve (ECC).

22–47. If the closure for the curve of problem 22–11 computed as described in Section 22–6 is 0.35 ft, what is the field layout precision? Do you think it would be acceptable for a farm road ?

22–48. Same as problem 42–47 but for the curve of problem 22–12 and a closure of 0.14 ft.

22–49. In laying out a road in a park, the center-line tangents are to be connected by the longest possible radius curve which will provide a 5-ft clearance between the north edge of a 20-ft road and a tree of historic value (see figure). Determine the roadway center-line radius,

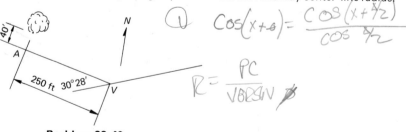

Problem 22-49

22–50. Same as problem 22–49 except $I = 40°20'$, $AC = 300.00$, and $CP = 50.00'$.

23
PARABOLIC
CURVES

23-1. GENERAL. Parabolic curves are normally used to provide a smooth transition between grade lines in the vertical plane on highways and railroads. They are also employed in the horizontal plane on landscaping work and for other functions which require a curve of pleasing appearance that can be laid out with a tape. The parabolic curves used in route-surveying practice differ only slightly on the ground from large-radius circular curves.

Parabolic curves can be computed by the *tangent-offset method* or the *chord-gradient method*. Both systems are based upon the following property of a parabola: *offsets from a tangent to a parabola are proportional to the squares of the distances from the point of tangency.*

In this brief treatment only tangent-offset methods will be demonstrated. They are applicable to curves having either equal or unequal tangents.

A vertical curve must (a) fit the grade lines it connects, (b) have a length sufficient to meet specification covering the maximum rate of change of grade per station (0.05 to 0.10% on railroads), and (c) provide the required sight distance. Generally the vertex is placed at a full station in railroad work, but it may be at a plus station on a highway layout.

23-2. COMPUTATIONS FOR AN EQUAL-TANGENT CURVE. An equal-tangent vertical curve is illustrated in Fig. 23-1. It has the property that the vertex (V) is midway between the beginning of the vertical curve (BVC) and its end (EVC). For an equal-tangent curve, two different tangent offset computational procedures are described herein: method A and method B.

451

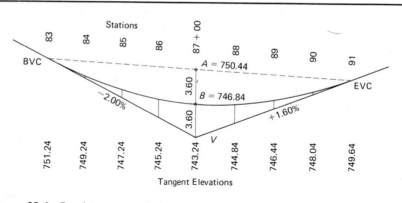

Figure 23-1. Equal-tangent vertical curve.

METHOD A

Another property of the parabola simplifies calculation in this system: *the center of a parabola is midway between the vertex and the long chord; that is, the external distance always equals the middle ordinate.*

This feature is shown in Fig. 23-1 where distances AB and BV are equal, and a -2.00% grade meets a $+1.60\%$ grade at vertex station $V = 87 + 00$ and elevation 743.24 ft. Assume an 800-ft curve fits ground conditions and satisfies the specifications.

Elevation of the BVC = elevation $V + L/2 \times$ grade $= 743.24 + 4(+2.00)$  $= 751.24$ ft; for the EVC $= 743.24 + 4(+1.60) = 749.64$. Grade elevations at the tangent stations are determined successively working backward and forward from V to BVC and EVC, respectively, thereby checking all arithmetic, if signs were correct, before proceeding further.

Elevation of point A (center of the long chord), found by averaging those of the BVC and EVC, is 750.44. Point B, curve midpoint, is halfway between A and the vertex V, at elevation $743.24 + 7.20/2 = 746.84$ ft. Then adding 3.60, the tangent offset at the curve center, equals the elevation of A as another check. All later results depend upon the correctness of values for BVC, EVC, A, and B; so, simple as these steps are, the process described at some length is strongly recommended for all calculations whenever possible.

Offsets from the tangents at full or plus stations are computed from the formula

$$\frac{\text{offset } a}{\text{offset at } V} = \left(\frac{x_a}{L/2}\right)^2 \tag{23-1}$$

where x_a is distance in feet or stations from BCV (or EVC) to point a on the tangent where the offset is desired; and $L/2$ is one-half the length of curve in the same units as x_a.

Offsets from the tangent for the full stations then are

$$(\tfrac{1}{4})^2 \times 3.60 = 0.225 \text{ ft}$$
$$(\tfrac{1}{2})^2 \times 3.60 = 0.90 \text{ ft}$$
$$(\tfrac{3}{4})^2 \times 3.60 = 2.025 \text{ ft}$$

ILLUSTRATION 23-1. EQUAL-TANGENT VERTICAL CURVE

Station	Point	Tangent Elevation	Tangent Offset	Elevation on Curve	First Diff. of Elevs.	Second Diff. of Elevs.
92		751.24				
91	EVC	749.64	0.00	749.64		
					1.38	
90		748.04	0.22	748.26		0.46
					0.92	
89		746.44	0.90	747.34		0.44
					0.48	
88		744.84	2.02	746.86		0.46
					0.02	
87	PVI	743.24	3.60	746.84		0.44
					−0.42	
86		745.24	2.02	747.26		0.46
					−0.88	
85		747.24	0.90	748.14		0.44
					−1.32	
84		749.24	0.22	749.46		0.46
					−1.78	
83	BVC	751.24	0.00	751.24		
82		753.24				

Final elevations on the curve are given in the usual form in Illustration 23-1. The entire curve can be computed from one tangent, but larger numbers are involved, and the advantage of calculating only half as many symmetrical offsets is lost.

A check on the curve elevations is obtained by computing the first and second differences between the elevations, as shown in the right-hand columns of Illustration 23-1. Unless disturbed by rounding off as in this example, all the second differences ("rate of change") should be equal.

METHOD B

The following general equation of a vertical parabola is convenient for computing tangent offsets with an electronic calculator:

$$Y = Y_{\text{BVC}} + g_1 x + \frac{r x^2}{2} \tag{23-2}$$

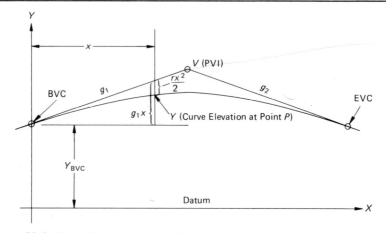

Figure 23-2. Parabolic curve relationships.

where Y is the curve elevation of any point P on the parabola; Y_{BVC} is the elevation of the BVC; g_1 the percent grade of the first or *back* tangent; g_2 the percent grade of the second or *forward* tangent; x the horizontal distance from the BVC to point P (in stations); r is equal to a constant that is the rate of change of grade, $(g_2 - g_1)/L$; and L is the length of the curve in stations.

Figure 23-2 illustrates a crest-type parabolic curve and shows the coordinate system and physical significance of terms in Eq. (23-2). For sag curves, such as Fig. 23-1, constant r is positive; for crest curves, it is negative.

The computational procedure for method **B** is given by an example in which grade $g_1 = +3.00\%$ intersects a grade $g_2 = -2.40\%$ at vertex station $46 + 70$ and elevation 853.48 ft. A 600-ft-long curve was selected. The calculations, arranged in tabular form, are shown in Illustration 23-2. Again, a check is obtained if the second differences of elevations between *full* stations are equal. (Note that they equal r.)

The grades shown in Figs. 23-1 through 23-3 are greatly exaggerated. Actually, there is no significant difference between vertical lines and offsets perpendicular to the tangents for the light grades used in practice. Verticals are more convenient and give a smooth curve.

23-3. COMPUTATIONS FOR AN UNEQUAL-TANGENT CURVE. In
Fig. 23-3, assume that for the two grades of Fig. 23-1 a 400-ft vertical curve is to be extended back from the vertex, and a 600-ft curve run in forward to better fit the ground conditions.

Connect the midpoints of the two curves, stations 85 and 90, to obtain line *AB*. Draw lines from the BVC and EVC to point CVC, station 87. Compute the elevation of the CVC, 747.56, by proportion from the known elevations of *A* and *B*.

ILLUSTRATION 23-2. PARABOLIC CURVE COMPUTATION BY METHOD B

$$r = \frac{-2.40 - 3.00}{6} = -0.90 \qquad Y_{BVC} = 853.48 - 3(3) = 844.48$$

PVI QV   R STA Y

630   BVC,

Station	x	$g_1 x$	$\frac{rx^2}{2}$	Curve Elevation	First Diff.	Second Diff.
49 + 70 (EVC)	6.0	18.00	−16.20	846.28		
49 + 00	5.3	15.90	−12.64	847.74		
					−1.32	
48 + 00	4.3	12.90	− 8.32	849.06		−0.90
					−0.42	
47 + 00	3.3	9.90	− 4.90	849.48		−0.90
					0.48	
46 + 00	2.3	6.90	− 2.38	849.00		−0.90
					1.38	
45 + 00	1.3	3.90	− 0.76	847.62		−0.90
					2.28	
44 + 00	0.3	0.90	− 0.04	845.34		
43 + 70 (BVC)	0.0	0.0	0.00	844.48		

Check: EVC = 853.48 − 2.40 (3) = 846.28

Now compute two vertical curves, one from the BVC to the CVC and another from the CVC to the EVC, by the methods of Section 23-2. Since both curves are tangent to the same line *AB* at point CVC, they will be tangent to each other and form a smooth curve. Critical elevations are shown in Fig. 23-3.

Vertical curve computations by themselves are quite simple, hardly a

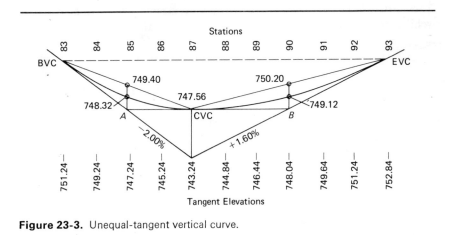

Figure 23-3. Unequal-tangent vertical curve.

challenge to the electronic computer. But when vertical curves are combined with horizontal curves, spirals, and superelevation on complex highway-interchange coordinate calculations, programming can save time.

23-4. HIGH OR LOW POINT ON A VERTICAL CURVE.   To investigate drainage conditions, clearance beneath overhead structures, cover over pipes, and sight distance, it may be necessary to determine the elevation and location of the low (or high) point on a vertical curve. At the low or high point, a tangent to the curve will be horizontal and its slope will be equal to zero. Based on this fact, the following formula is readily derived:

$$x = \frac{g_1 L}{g_1 - g_2} \qquad (23\text{-}3)$$

where x is the distance from the BVC to the high or low point of the curve, g_1 the tangent grade through the BVC, g_2 the tangent grade through the EVC, and L the length of the curve, in stations.

If g_2 is substituted for g_1 in the numerator, the distance x is measured from the EVC.

In the problem of Fig. 23-1, $g_1 = -2.00\%$, $g_2 = +1.60\%$, and $L = 8$ stations. Then

$$x = \frac{-2.00 \times 8}{-2.00 - (+1.60)} = 4.444 \text{ stations}$$

The elevation at this point (station $87 + 44.4$) is

$$(743.24 + 0.444 \times 1.60) + \left(\frac{3.56}{4}\right)^2 \times 3.60 = 746.80 \text{ ft}$$

23-5. SIGHT DISTANCE.   The formula for sight distance S with the vehicle on a vertical curve, and S less than the length L, is

$$S^2 = \frac{8Lh}{g_1 - g_2} \qquad (23\text{-}4)$$

where S is the sight distance, in stations; L the length of the curve, in stations; and h the height of the driver's eye, and the object sighted, above the roadway (by AASHTO[1] recommendation, 3.75 ft).

Then for a summit curve having a length of 800 ft, and grades of $+2.00\%$ and -1.60%, if $h = 3.75$ ft,

$$S = \sqrt{\frac{8 \times 8 \times 3.75}{2.00 - (-1.60)}} = 8.16 \text{ stations} = 816 \text{ ft}$$

[1] American Association of State Highway and Transportation Officials.

Since this distance is greater than the length of curve and thus not in agreement with the assumption used in deriving the formula, a different expression must be employed.

If the vehicle is off the curve and on the tangent to it, S is greater than L, and the applicable sight distance formula is

$$S = \frac{L}{2} + \frac{4h}{g_1 - g_2} \qquad (23\text{-}5)$$

In the preceding example, with $h = 3\,\frac{3}{4}$ ft,

$$S = \frac{8}{2} + \frac{4 \times 3.75}{2.00 - (-1.60)} = 8.17 \text{ stations}$$

For a combined horizontal and vertical curve, the sight distance is the smaller of the two values computed independently for each curve. (See Section 22-11 for horizontal sight distance discussion.)

23-6. SOURCES OF ERROR.   Some sources of error in vertical-curve work are:

1. Carrying out grade percentages beyond 0.01%. Multiples of 0.05% or 0.10% are desirable for highways.
2. Carrying out computed elevations to less than 0.01 ft.
3. Selecting the vertex at other than a full station.

23-7. MISTAKES.   Typical mistakes made in computations for vertical curves include the following:

1. Arithmetical errors.
2. Using an incorrect offset at the vertex.
3. Subtracting the offsets from the tangents for a sag curve, or adding them for a summit curve.
4. Failing to check the computed values for curve elevations, to be certain they fit those of the tangents, the PVI, the BVC, and the EVC.

PROBLEMS

23–1. A manhole is 15 ft from the center line of a 40-ft-wide street that has a 4-in. parabolic crown. The street center is at elevation 320.24 ft. What is the elevation of the manhole cover?

23–2. A 32-ft-wide street has an average parabolic crown from the center to each edge of $^1/_8$ in./ft. How much does the surface drop from the street center to a point 4 ft from the edge?

Tabulate elevations of the stations on an equal-tangent curve for the data given in problems 23–3 through 23–6.

23–3. A +4.00% grade meets a 0.00% grade at station 40+40 and elevation 300.00 ft; 800-ft curve.

23–4. A −1.20% grade meets a +0.40% grade at station 36+00, elevation 547.30; 1200-ft curve.

23–5. A 250-ft curve, 50-ft stations, grades of −2.00% and +1.00%, PVI at station 89+70, elevation 310.00 ft.

23–6. An 800-ft curve, grades of +2.00% and −4.00%, PVI at station 50+00, elevation 300.00 ft.

Field conditions require a highway curve to pass through a fixed point. Compute a suitable equal-tangent vertical curve and elevations for problems 23–7 through 23–9.

23–7. Grades of −2.00% and 0.00%, PVI elevation 220.00 ft, and station 15+00. Fixed point elevation 221.50 ft at station 15+00.

23–8. Grades of −3.00% and +1.00%, PVI elevation 400.00 at station 62+00. Fixed point elevation 404.00 ft at station 62+00.

23–9. Grades of +4.00% and +2.00%, PVI station 33+00, elevation 630.00 ft. Fixed point elevation 629.50 ft at station 33+00.

23–10. A −1.00% grade meets a 0.00% grade at station 46+00 and elevation 700.00 ft. The 0.00% grade then joins a +2.00% grade at station 49+00. Compute and tabulate the notes for a 1000-ft vertical curve to fit the stated conditions.

Compute and tabulate station elevations for an unequal-tangent vertical curve to fit the requirements noted in problems 23–11 through 23–14.

23–11. A +3.00% grade meets a −2.00% grade at station 50+00 and elevation 200.00 ft. Length of first curve 600 ft, second curve 400 ft.

23–12. Grade $g_1 = +2.00\%$, $g_2 = +4.00\%$, PVI at station 72+00 and elevation 300.00 ft, $L_1 = 800$ ft, and $L_2 = 400$ ft.

23–13. The PVI of +4.00% and −3.00% grades is at station 52+00 and elevation 222.24 ft. Lengths of curves are 400 and 600 ft.

23–14. A 0.00% grade meets a +4.00% grade at station 27+00 and elevation 466.80 ft. Length of first curve is 200 ft, second curve 600 ft.

23–15. Explain why the second differences of the curve elevations are equal for a parabolic curve.

23–16. Why is a parabola rather than a circular arc used for vertical curves?

23–17. What is meant by the rate of change on vertical curves?

23–18. When is it advantageous to use an unequal-tangent vertical curve instead of an equal tangent one?

23–19. In laying out preliminary grades on a highway line, what consideration must be given to the later introduction of vertical curves?

23–20. Write a computer program for the vertical curve of Illustration 23–2.

23–21. Why are parabolic curves not generally used for horizontal highway curves?

23–22. What factors influence the required minimal distances (tangent lengths) between a series of reversed vertical curves?

23–23. Why are parabolic curves eminently suited for landscaping work ?

23–24. Check the elevations in Fig. 23–3 by the method of second differences and explain the results.

23–25. In determining sight distances on vertical curves, how does the designer determine whether the cars or objects are on the curve or tangent ?

23–26. Compute the sight distance available in problem 23–3.

23–27. What sight distance does a driver have in problem 23–9 ?

23–28. Determine the low point of the curve in problem 23–4.

23–29. Calculate the high point of the curve in problem 23–6.

What is the minimum length of vertical curve to provide a required sight distance under the conditions given in problems 23–30 through 23–32 ?

23–30. Grades of +3.40% and −2.86%. Sight distance of 700 ft.

23–31. A summit curve with grades of +5.20% and −3.60%. Sight distance 900 ft.

23–32. Sight distance of 1200 ft, grades of +2.50% and −4.10%.

24
VOLUMES

24-1. GENERAL. Surveyors are often called upon to measure volumes of earthwork and concrete for various types of construction projects. Volume computations are also required to determine the capacity of bins, tanks, reservoirs, and buildings, and to check quantities in stockpiles.

Much of the field work formerly involved in running preliminary center lines, getting cross-section data, and making slope-stake and other measurements on long route surveys is now being done more efficiently by photogrammetry. Computation of earthwork for route surveys of more than a few stations is frequently carried out on electronic computers. It is not intended to discuss photogrammetric or electronic computer methods in this chapter. Rather, basic field and office procedures for determining and calculating volumes will be presented briefly.

The unit of volume is a cube having edges of unit length. Cubic feet, cubic yards, and cubic meters are used in surveying calculations, although the cubic yard is most common for earthwork: $1 \text{ yd}^3 = 27 \text{ ft}^3$; $1 \text{ m}^3 = 35.315 \text{ ft}^3$.

24-2. METHODS OF MEASUREMENT. Direct measurement of volumes is rarely made in surveying, since it is difficult to actually apply a unit of the material involved. Indirect measurements are obtained by measuring lines and areas which have a relation to the volume desired.

Three principal methods are used: (1) the cross-section method, (2) the unit-area, or borrow-pit, method, and (3) the contour-area method.

24-3. THE CROSS-SECTION METHOD. When the cross-section method is employed for computing volumes, ground profiles called cross sections are taken (at right angles to the center line) usually at intervals of 50 or 100 ft. Areas of these sections can be determined by calculation from the field data, or by planimetering the plotted cross sections. Volume is computed by the *average-end-area formula* or the *prismoidal formula*.

24-4. TYPES OF CROSS SECTIONS. The types of cross sections commonly used on route surveys are shown in Fig. 24-1. In flat terrain the *level section* in (a) is suitable. The *three-level section* in (b) is generally employed where ordinary ground conditions prevail. Rough topography may require a *five-level section*, (c), or more practically an *irregular section*, (d). A *transition section*, (e), and a *side-hill section*, (f), occur in passing from *cut* (excavation) to *fill* (embankment), and on side-hill locations.

The width of base b or finished roadway is fixed by project requirements. It is usually wider in cuts than on fills to provide for drainage ditches. The side slope s (horizontal dimension required for a unit vertical rise) depends upon the type of soil encountered. Side slopes in fill usually are flatter than those in cuts since the soil remains in its natural state.

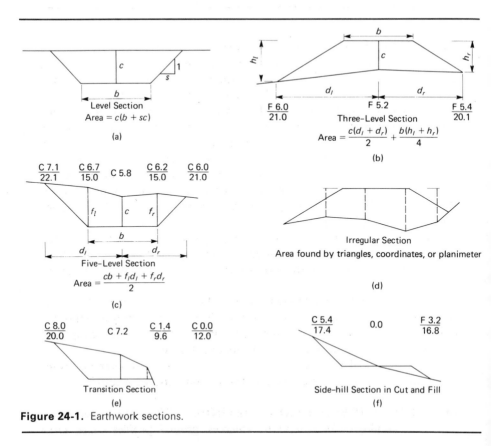

Level Section
Area $= c(b + sc)$

(a)

Three-Level Section

Area $= \dfrac{c(d_l + d_r)}{2} + \dfrac{b(h_l + h_r)}{4}$

(b)

Five-Level Section

Area $= \dfrac{cb + f_l d_l + f_r d_r}{2}$

(c)

Irregular Section
Area found by triangles, coordinates, or planimeter

(d)

Transition Section

(e)

Side-hill Section in Cut and Fill

(f)

Figure 24-1. Earthwork sections.

Cut slopes of one horizontal to one vertical, and fill slopes of $1\frac{1}{2}$ to 1 might be satisfactory for ordinary loam soils, but $1\frac{1}{2}$ to 1 in excavation, and 2 to 1 in embankment are common. Even flatter proportions may be required —one cut in the Panama Canal area was 13 to 1—depending upon type of soil, rainfall, and other factors.

Formulas for areas of the different sections are readily derived and listed beside some of the sketches in Fig. 24-1.

24-5. AVERAGE-END-AREA FORMULA.   The volume between two verti-cal cross sections A_1 and A_2 is equal to the average of the end areas multiplied by the horizontal distance L between them. Thus

$$V_e = \frac{L(A_1 + A_2)}{2} \times \frac{100}{27} \text{ yd}^3 \qquad (24\text{-}1)$$

In Eq. (24-1), V_e is in cubic yards if L is in feet and A_1 and A_2 are in square feet. This formula is approximate and gives answers which generally are slightly larger than the true prismoidal volumes. It is used in practice because of its simplicity. Increased accuracy is obtained by decreasing the distance L between the sections. When the ground is irregular, cross sections must be taken close together.

24-6. CALCULATING END AREAS.   To illustrate computation of area for the section shown in Fig. 24-2, assume the following set of notes was obtained in the field (letters A, B, C, D, E, K, and G, and the values at A and G, were not recorded in the field; they are added for this discussion), or compiled from the contours on a suitable-scale topographic map.

Station	A	B	C	D	E	K	G
24 + 00	$\frac{0}{15}$	$\frac{C\,8}{27}$	$\frac{C\,16}{20}$	$\frac{C\,18}{0}$	$\frac{C\,10}{14}$	$\frac{C\,12}{33}$	$\frac{0}{15}$

Numerators (preceded by the letter C) are cuts, in feet, and the de-nominators are distances out from the center line. Fills are denoted by the

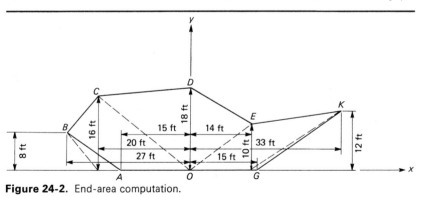

Figure 24-2. End-area computation.

letter F. Using C instead of plus for cut, and F instead of minus for fill, eliminates confusion. On many projects the measurements are carried out to tenths of a foot.

Area of the cross section in Fig. 24-2 will be found in two ways: (1) by dividing the area into simple figures (triangles and trapezoids), and (2) by coordinates.

AREA BY SIMPLE FIGURES

Figure	Computation	Area
$ODCC'$	$\frac{1}{2}(18 + 16)20$	340
$C'CB$	$\frac{1}{2}(16)7$	56
ABC'	$-\frac{1}{2}(5)8$	-20
$ODEE'$	$\frac{1}{2}(18 + 10)14$	196
$EE'F$	$\frac{1}{2}(10)19$	95
$E'FG$	$\frac{1}{2}(12)1$	6

$$\text{Area} = 673 \text{ ft}^2$$

AREA BY COORDINATES

The coordinate method for computing end areas can be used for any type of section and has many engineering applications. The procedure was described in Section 11-6 as a means for determining the area contained within a closed polygon traverse. Using notes obtained in the field for points B, C, D, E, and K, and considering the base width, coordinates of each point of Fig. 24-2 are calculated with respect to a coordinate system having point O as its origin. In computing coordinates, distances to the right of center line and cut values are considered plus; to the left and fill values are minus. Beginning with point O and proceeding clockwise around the figure, coordinates of each point are listed in sequence. Point O is repeated at the end. Then Eq. (11-7) is applied, in which products of diagonals downward to the right (solid arrows) are considered plus, and diagonal products down to the left (dashed arrows) are minus. Algebraic signs of the coordinates must be accounted for, and thus a positive product (solid arrow) having a negative coordinate will actually be minus. Total area is obtained by dividing the absolute value of the algebraic summation of all products by 2. The calculations are as illustrated at the top of page 465.

It is necessary to make separate computations for cut and fill when they occur in the same section, since they must always be tabulated independently for pay purposes. Payment is normally made only for excavation (its unit price includes making and shaping the fills) except on projects consisting primarily of embankment such as levees, earth dams, some military fortifications, and highways built up by continuous fill in flat areas.

To find the volume between this section at station 24, and another at the next station, 25, 100-ft distant, assume the section area at station 25 is 515 ft^2. Then the volume in yd^3, by the average-end-area formula, is

$$V = \frac{100}{2 \times 27}(A_1 + A_2) = \frac{100}{54}(673 + 515) = 2200 \text{ yd}^3$$

Point	X	Y	Plus	Minus
O	0	0		
A	−15	0	0	0
B	−27	8	−120	0
C	−20	16	−432	160
D	0	18	−360	0
E	14	10	0	−252
F	33	12	168	−330
G	15	0	0	−180
O	0	0	0	0
			−744	−602

$$-744$$
$$-602$$
$$\text{Area} = -\overline{1346}/2 = 673 \text{ ft}^2$$

24-7. PRISMOIDAL FORMULA. The prismoidal formula applies to volumes of all geometric solids which can be considered prismoids. Most earthwork volumes fit this classification, but relatively few of them warrant the precision of the prismoidal formula. The ground is not uniform from cross section to cross section, and right angles turned from the center line using a pentagonal prism or by the "arm" method (see Section 13-16) introduce errors.

One arrangement of the prismoidal formula is

$$V_p = \frac{L(A_1 + 4A_m + A_2)}{6} \tag{24-2}$$

where V_p is the volume, A_1 and A_2 are areas of successive cross sections taken in the field, A_m is the area of a section midway between A_1 and A_2, and L the horizontal distance between A_1 and A_2.

To use this formula it is necessary to know the area of the section half-way between stations. This area is found by the usual computation *after averaging the heights* and *widths* of *the end sections.* Obviously the middle area is *not* the average of the end areas, since there would then be no difference between the results of the end-area formula and the prismoidal formula.

The prismoidal formula generally gives a volume less than that found by the end-area formula. For example, the volume of a pyramid by the prismoidal formula is $Ah/3$, whereas by the average-end-area method it is $Ah/2$. An exception occurs when the center height is great but the width narrow at one station, and the center height is small but the width large at the adjacent station. Figure 24-3 illustrates this condition. The difference between the volume obtained by the average-end-area formula and that by the prismoidal formula is called the *prismoidal correction, C_p.*

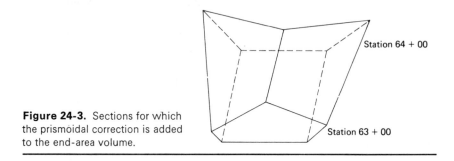

Figure 24-3. Sections for which the prismoidal correction is added to the end-area volume.

Various books on route surveying give formulas and tables for computing prismoidal corrections which can be applied to average-end-area volumes to get prismoidal volumes. Except in rock-excavation and concrete work, use of the prismoidal formula is not normally justified by the low precision of field data. Frequently it is easier to compute the end-area volume and the prismoidal correction than to calculate the prismoidal volume directly.

A prismoidal correction formula, accurate for three-level sections and close enough for most others, is

$$C_p = \frac{L}{12 \times 27} (c_1 - c_2)(w_1 - w_2) \tag{24-3}$$

where C_p is the prismoidal correction, c_1 and c_2 are center heights in cut (or in fill), and w_1 and w_2 are widths of sections (from slope stake to slope stake) at adjacent sections.

If the product of $(c_1 - c_2)(w_1 - w_2)$ is minus, as in Fig. 24-3, the prismoidal correction is added rather than subtracted from the end-area volume.

For projects with more than a few cross sections, computer programs are available and generally used, but a surveyor and engineer still must understand the method of computation. Earthwork calculations from photogrammetric data should check good field survey results within 1% in open country free of big trees or high brush. The method has received legal and contractor acceptance.

Mass diagrams are used to analyze the movement of earthwork quantities. Total mass (cut minus fill up to the station) is plotted at each station starting at the project's beginning. Horizontal (balance) lines then determine the limit of economic haul and direction of movement of material.

If there is insufficient material from cuts to make the required fills, the difference must be *borrowed* (obtained from borrow pits or other sources such as by "daylighting" curves). If there is excess cut, it is *wasted* or perhaps used to extend and flatten the fills.

24-8. UNIT-AREA, OR BORROW-PIT, METHOD. Calculations of volumes by the unit-area, or borrow-pit, method were discussed in Section 5-27.

Greater accuracy can be obtained in rough terrain by using triangular areas instead of rectangular blocks. The volume is then equal to A, the area of each triangle times the average of its three corner heights. Thus

$$V = \frac{A(a + b + c)}{3} \text{ ft}^3 \qquad (24\text{-}4)$$

24-9. CONTOUR-AREA METHOD.   Volumes based on contours can be obtained from contour maps by planimetering the area enclosed by each contour and multiplying the average of areas for adjacent contours by the contour interval, using Eq. (24-1). For example, if in the plan view of Fig. 13-5, the area within the 10-ft contour is 19,650 ft^2 and that within the 20-ft contour is 12,720 ft^2, the average end-area volume is $10(19,650 + 12,720)/2(27) =$ 5994 yd^3. Use of the prismoidal formula is seldom, if ever, justified on this type of computation.

24-10. SOURCES OF ERROR.   Some common errors in computing areas of sections and volumes of earthwork are:

1. Carrying out areas of cross sections beyond the nearest square foot, or beyond the limit justified by the field data.
2. Carrying out volumes beyond the nearest cubic yard.
3. Failing to correct for the effect of curvature when a section on a horizontal curve has cut on one side of the center line and fill on the other.

24-11. MISTAKES.   Typical mistakes made in earthwork calculations include:

1. Mistakes in arithmetic.
2. Using the prismoidal formula when end-area volumes are sufficiently accurate.
3. Using end-area volumes for pyramidal or wedge-shaped solids.
4. Mixing cut and fill quantities.
5. Not considering transition sections when passing from cut to fill, or from fill to cut.

PROBLEMS

24–1. Why must cut and fill volumes be totaled separately?
24–2. Discuss comparative side slopes in cut and fill.
24–3. Why is a roadway in cut normally wider than the same roadway in fill?

Draw the cross sections and compute V_e for the data in problems 24–4 through 24–8.

24–4. Two level sections at 100-ft stations with center heights of 3.6 and 4.8 ft in cut. Base width = 44 ft, side slopes are $1^1/_2$ to 1.

24–5. Two level sections at 70-ft stations with center heights 2.8 and 6.2 ft in fill. Base width = 28 ft, side slopes are 2 to 1.

24–6. The end area at station 33+00 is 182 ft². Field notes for station 33+60 are C 3.2/13.2, C 4.6, C 5.8/15.8. Base = 20 ft.

24–7. An irrigation ditch with $b = 14$ ft and side slopes of $1^1/2$ to 1. Field notes are station 52 : C 1.6/9.4, C 2.1, C 2.4/10.6 ; station 53 : C 2.8/11.2, C 3.3, C 3.6/12.4.

24–8. Same cuts as problem 24–7 but base = 16 ft and side slopes are 2 to 1.

24–9. Compute the section areas in problem 24–5 by the coordinate method.

24–10. Calculate the section area in problem 24–6 by the coordinate method.

24–11. Determine the section areas in problem 24–7 by the coordinate method.

24–12. Compute C_p and V_p for problem 24–4. Is the C_p significant ?

24–13. Calculate C_p and V_p for problem 24–7. Would C_p be significant in rock cut ?

24–14. Find the base width and side slopes for Fig. 24–1 (e) and calculate the section area by several different methods.

24–15. Rewrite the field notes and compute the section area by coordinates for Fig. 24–1 (c) using the same cuts but a base width of 40 ft and side slopes of $1^3/4$ to 1.

24–16. Calculate C_p and V_p for problem 24–8.

24–17. Complete the following notes and compute V_e and V_p. Base = 28 ft. Side slopes are $1^1/4$ to 1.

$$\text{Station } 90+00 \quad \frac{\text{C 6.6}}{\quad} \quad \text{C 3.2} \quad \frac{\text{C 5.3}}{\quad}$$

$$\text{Station } 89+00 \quad \frac{\text{C 2.8}}{\quad} \quad \text{C 5.1} \quad \frac{\text{C 3.4}}{\quad}$$

24–18. Similar to problem 24–17 except the base is 36 ft, the side slopes $1^1/2$ to 1.

Calculate V_e, C_p, and V_p for the slope stake notes of problems 24–19 through problem 24–22.

24–19. Base in fill = 16 ft. Base in cut = 24 ft. Side slopes are $1^1/2$ to 1.

	24–19			
12+80	$\dfrac{\text{C 2.4}}{15.6}$	C 1.0	$\dfrac{0.0}{6.0}$	$\dfrac{\text{F 2.0}}{11.0}$
12+50	$\dfrac{\text{C 1.2}}{13.8}$	0.0		$\dfrac{\text{F 4.0}}{14.0}$

	24–20			
27+00	$\dfrac{\text{C 4.2}}{19.2}$	C 2.0	$\dfrac{\text{C 3.6}}{18.6}$	
26+00	$\dfrac{\text{C 2.4}}{17.4}$	C 3.0	$\dfrac{0.0}{15.0}$	

24–20. Base in cut = 30 ft, side slopes are 1 to 1.

24–21. Base in cut 32 ft ; in fill 40 ft. Side slopes 1 to 1 in cut, $1^1/2$ to 1 in fill.

	24–21		
7+00	$\dfrac{0.0}{20.0}$	F 4.5	$\dfrac{\text{F 5.6}}{28.4}$
6+70	$\dfrac{\text{C 0.8}}{16.8}\ \dfrac{0.0}{9.0}$	F 4.0	$\dfrac{\text{F 3.2}}{24.8}$

	24–22		
43+52	$\dfrac{\text{C 3.6}}{16.4}$	C 2.1	$\dfrac{0.0}{11.0}$
43+38	$\dfrac{\text{C 1.8}}{13.7}$	C 1.2	$\dfrac{0.0}{5.0}\ \dfrac{\text{F 1.2}}{8.8}$

	24–21 (cont.)				24–22 (cont.)		
$6+50$	$\dfrac{C\ 1.6}{17.6}$	0.0	$\dfrac{F\ 4.6}{26.9}$	$43+26$	$\dfrac{C\ 1.2}{12.8}$	0.0	$\dfrac{F\ 2.6}{10.9}$
$6+40$	$\dfrac{C\ 3.0}{19.0}$	$C\ 2.0\ \dfrac{0.0}{12.0}$	$\dfrac{F\ 1.2}{21.8}$	$43+10$	$\dfrac{0.0}{7.0}$	$F\ 2.5$	$\dfrac{F\ 4.0}{13.0}$

24–22. Base $= 22$ ft in cut, 14 ft in fill. Side slopes $1\frac{1}{2}$ to 1.

For problems 24–23 and 24–24 compute the reservoir capacity between highest and lowest contours for planimetered areas from a topographic map.

24–23. Elevation (m)	320	325	330	335	340	345
Area in m²	1834	1976	2020	2185	2360	2704
24–24. Elevation (ft)	570	580	590	600	610	620
Area in ft²	832	1005	1329	1788	2146	2790

24–25. A calibrated polar planimeter gives an average reading of 1.476 revolutions of the roller over a 4-in.-diameter circle. Twenty-foot contours planimetered on a reservoir site map to a scale of $1'' = 200$ ft give the values tabulated. Calculate the reservoir volume in acre-ft.

Contour	440	460	480	500	520
Planimeter reading	0.000	0.752	1.216	3.004	5.450

24–26. Why is it often easier to compute prismoidal volume by means of $V_e - C_p$ instead of computing V_p directly?

24–27. List several things that can be learned from a mass diagram.

24–28. State two situations where prismoidal corrections are most significant.

24–29. What type of soil (not rock) that occurs in some states, China, and elsewhere appears to stand up better in vertical cuts than on sloped ones?

24–30. In your state can "borrow" come from the right-of-way, perhaps by reducing side slopes in highway cuts?

24–31. Do your state highway department construction contracts contain a provision covering free haul and overhaul? If so, list the details.

25
PHOTOGRAMMETRY

25-1. INTRODUCTION. Photogrammetry may be defined as the science, art, and technology of obtaining reliable quantitative and qualitative information from photographs. As indicated by this definition, photogrammetry encompasses two major areas of specialization: (1) *metrical* and (2) *interpretative*. The first area is applied primarily in determining distances and elevations, and compiling topographic maps. *Aerial* photographs (exposed from airborne vehicles) are usually used, although for certain special work, *terrestrial* photos (taken from earth-based cameras) are sometimes employed.

Interpretative photogrammetry applies to recognizing objects from their photographic images and judging their significance. Critical factors considered in identifying objects are the shapes, sizes, patterns, shadows, tones, and textures of their images. In general, interpretative photogrammetry consists of two branches: *photographic interpretation* (the systematic and careful study of conventional aerial photos), and *remote sensing* (a relatively new discipline that applies not only to the study of photographic imagery, but also to data obtained from nonphotographic instruments such as infrared sensors, thermal scanners, and side-looking radar).

In this chapter, metrical photogrammetry, using aerial photographs, will be emphasized because it is the phase most frequently applied in surveying work.

25-2. USES OF PHOTOGRAMMETRY. Photography dates back to 1839, and the first attempt to use photogrammetry to prepare a topographic map occurred a year later. Photogrammetry is now the chief method of topo-graphic mapping. The U.S. Geological Survey, for example, employs the procedure almost exclusively in compiling its quadrangle maps. Cameras, films, plotting instruments, and techniques have been continually improved so that photogrammetrically-prepared maps today meet very high accuracy standards. Other advantages of this method of mapping include (a) speed of coverage of an area, (b) relatively low cost, (c) ease of obtaining topographic details, especially in inaccessible areas, and (d) reduced likelihood of omitting data due to the tremendous amount of detail shown in the photographs.

Photogrammetry is presently being used for many applications in surveying and engineering. In the field of highway engineering, for example, it is employed extensively to prepare the necessary maps and cross sections for reconnaissance, preliminary planning, route selection, and final design including computation of contract quantities. Another significant application is determining precise ground-point coordinates for engineering, land, and control surveys. Photogrammetry is expected to play an important role in developing the necessary information for modern land data systems.

Photogrammetry is also being successfully applied in many non-engineering fields, for example, geology, archeology, forestry, agriculture, conservation, planning, military intelligence, medicine, dentistry, traffic management, and accident investigation. It is beyond the scope of this chapter to describe all the varied applications of photogrammetry. Use of the science has increased dramatically in recent years, and its future growth for solving measurement and mapping problems seems assured.

25-3. AERIAL CAMERAS. Aerial mapping cameras are precision in-struments designed to take photographs from aircraft. They must be capable of exposing a large number of photographs in rapid succession, while moving in an aircraft at high speed, so a short cycling time, fast lens, efficient shutter, and large-capacity magazine are required.

Aerial cameras are commonly classified by "type"—*single-lens frame, multi-lens frame, strip,* and *panoramic.* Of these, the single-lens camera is the most prevalent. Single-lens cameras are classified by "angular field of view": *normal angle* for fields of view up to 75°, *wide angle* from 75° to 100°, and *super-wide angle* when greater than 100°. These cameras generally have focal lengths of 6 in., although $3\frac{1}{2}$-, $8\frac{1}{4}$-, and 12-in. lengths are common; the frame or format size is usually 9 × 9 in. A single-lens frame camera is pictured in Fig. 25-1.

A frame aerial camera, the type most widely used, exposes the entire format simultaneously through a lens held at a fixed distance from the focal plane. Principal components of the camera are the *lens* (most important part); *shutter* to control the interval of time that light passes through the lens; *diaphragm* to regulate the size of lens opening; *filter* to reduce the effect of haze and distribute light uniformly over the format; *camera cone* to support

Figure 25-1. Aerial camera. (Courtesy Carl Zeiss, Oberkochen.)

the lens-shutter-diaphragm assembly and prevent stray light from striking the film; *focal plane* formed by the upper surface of the fiducial marks and focal-plane frame; *fiducial marks,* four or eight in number to define the photographic principal point; *drive mechanism* to cock and trip the shutter, flatten the film, and advance it between exposures; *camera body* to house the drive mechanism; and *magazine* to house a film-flattening device and hold the supply of exposed and unexposed film.

An aerial camera shutter can be operated manually by an operator, or by an *intervalometer* which automatically trips the shutter at a specified time. A level vial attached to the camera helps keep the optical axis vertical in spite of any slight tip and tilt of the aircraft. More recently, gyroscopes have been developed to keep the camera axis approximately vertical. Polyester roll film is normally used with magazine capacities of 200 ft or more.

Images of the fiducial marks are printed on the photographs so that lines joining opposite pairs intersect at or very near the *principal point,* defined as the point where a perpendicular from the emergent nodal point of the camera lens strikes the focal plane. Fiducial marks may be located in the corners as shown in Fig. 25-2, on the sides, Fig. 25-3, or both places.

Aerial mapping cameras are laboratory calibrated to get precise values for the focal length and lens distortions. Flatness of the focal plane, relative position of the principal point with respect to the fiducial marks, and fiducial mark locations are also specified. These calibration data are necessary for precise photogrammetric calculations.

25-4. TYPES OF AERIAL PHOTOGRAPHS. Aerial photographs exposed with single-lens frame cameras are classified as *vertical* (taken with the

Figure 25-2. Vertical aerial photograph. (Courtesy Alster & Associates, Inc.)

camera axis aimed vertically downward, or as nearly vertically as possible), and *oblique* (made with the camera axis intentionally inclined at an angle between the horizontal and vertical). Oblique photographs are further classified as *high* if the horizon shows on the picture, and *low* if it does not. Figures 25-2 and 25-3 show examples of vertical and low oblique photographs, respectively, which completely depict all natural and cultural features within the region covered such as roads, railroads, buildings, rivers, bridges, trees, and cultivated lands.

25-5. VERTICAL AERIAL PHOTOGRAPHS. Vertical photographs are the principal mode of obtaining imagery for topographic mapping. A *truly vertical* photograph results if the axis of the camera is exactly vertical when the exposure is made. In spite of the precautions taken, small tilts, generally less than 1° and rarely greater than 3°, are invariably present. *Near-vertical*

Figure 25-3. Low oblique aerial photograph. (Courtesy Carl Zeiss, Oberkochen.)

or *tilted* photographs contain small unintentional inclinations. Photogrammetric principles and practices have been developed to handle tilted photos so that accuracy need not be sacrificed in compiling maps from them.

Although vertical photographs look like maps to laymen, they are not true orthographic projections of the earth's surface. Rather they are perspective views, and the principles of perspective geometry must be applied to prepare maps from them. Figure 25-4 illustrates the geometry of a vertical photograph taken at the exposure station L. The photograph, considered as a contact print positive, is a 180° exact reversal of the negative. The positive shown on Fig. 25-4 is used to develop photogrammetric equations in subsequent Sections.

Distance oL, Fig. 25-4, is the camera focal length. The x and y reference axis system for measuring photographic coordinates of images is defined by straight lines joining opposite side fiducial marks shown on the positive of Fig. 25-4. The x axis, arbitrarily designated as the line most nearly parallel

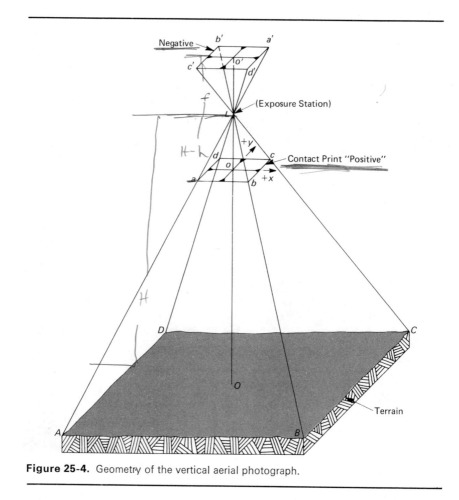

Figure 25-4. Geometry of the vertical aerial photograph.

with the direction of flight, is positive in the direction of flight. Positive y is 90° counterclockwise from positive x.

Vertical photographs for topographic mapping are taken in strips which normally run lengthwise over the area to be covered. The strips or *flight lines* generally have a *sidelap* (overlap of adjacent flight lines) of 15 to 30%. *Endlap* (overlap of adjacent photographs in the same flight line) is usually about 60% ± 5%. Figures 25-14 (a) and (b) illustrate endlap and sidelap respectively. If endlap is greater than 50%, all ground points will appear in at least two photographs and some show in three. Images common to three photographs permit extension of control through a strip of photographs using only minimal existing control.

25-6. SCALE OF A VERTICAL PHOTOGRAPH. Scale is ordinarily interpreted as the ratio of a distance on a map to that same distance on the ground, and is uniform throughout because a map is an orthographic projection. The scale of a vertical photograph is the ratio of photo distance to ground distance. Since a photograph is a perspective view, scale varies from point to point with variations in terrain elevation.

On Fig. 25-5, L is the exposure station of a vertical photograph taken at an altitude H above the datum. The camera focal length is f, and o the photographic principal point. Points A, B, C, and D, which lie at elevations above datum of h_A, h_B, h_C, and h_D, respectively, are imaged on the photograph at a, b, c, and d. The ratio ab/AB is the photo scale at the elevation of points A and B. Scale at any point can be expressed in terms of its elevation, the camera focal length, and flying height above datum. From Fig. 25-5, for similar triangles Loa and LO_AA, the following scale equation at A is written:

$$oa/O_AA = S_A = f/(H - h_A)$$

where S_A is the scale at point A. Scales at B, C, and D may be expressed similarly as

$$S_B = f/(H - h_B), \qquad S_C = f/(H - h_C), \qquad \text{and} \qquad S_D = f/(H - h_D)$$

It is apparent from the stated relationships that scale increases at higher elevations and decreases at lower ones. This concept is seen graphically on Fig. 25-5. Ground lengths AB and CD are equal but photo distances ab and cd are not, cd being longer and at larger scale than ab due to the higher eleva-

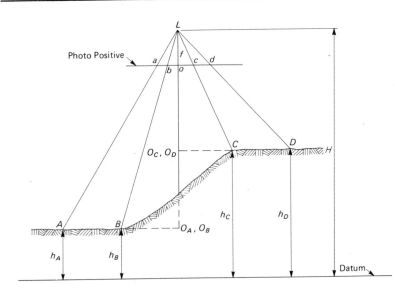

Figure 25-5. Scale of a vertical photograph.

tion of CD. In general, the scale S at any point whose elevation above datum is h may be expressed as

$$S = \frac{f}{H - h} \tag{25-1}$$

The use of an average photographic scale is frequently desirable but must be accepted with caution as an approximation. For any vertical photograph taken of terrain whose average elevation above datum is h_{av}, the average scale S_{av} is

$$S_{av} = \frac{f}{H - h_{av}} \tag{25-2}$$

Example. The photograph of Fig. 25-5 was exposed with a 6-in. focal length camera at a flying height above mean sea level of 10,000 ft. (a) What is the photo scale at point a if the elevation of point A on the ground is 2500 ft above mean sea level?

From Eq. (25-1)

$$S_A = \frac{f}{H - h_A} = \frac{6 \text{ in.}}{10,000 - 2500} = 1 : 15,000$$

(b) For the same photograph, if average terrain is 4000 ft above mean sea level, what is the average photo scale?

From Eq. (25-2)

$$S_{av} = \frac{f}{H - h_{av}} = \frac{6 \text{ in.}}{10,000 - 4000} = 1 : 12,000$$

Scale of a photograph can be determined from a map of the same area. This method does not require the focal length and flying height to be known. Rather it is necessary only to measure on the photograph a distance between two well-defined points identifiable on the map. Photo scale is then calculated from the equation

$$\text{photo scale} = \frac{\text{photo distance}}{\text{map distance}} \times \text{map scale} \tag{25-3}$$

In using Eq. (25-3), all distances must be in the same units and the answer is the scale at average elevation of the two points used.

Example. On a vertical photograph, the length of an airport runway measures 4.24 in. On a map plotted to a scale of 1 : 9600 it extends 7.92 in. What is the photo scale at the runway elevation?

From Eq. (25-3)

$$S = \frac{4.24}{7.92} \times \frac{1}{9600} = \frac{1}{17,900} \qquad \text{or} \qquad 1 \text{ in.} = 1495 \text{ ft}$$

Scale of a photograph can also be computed readily if lines whose lengths are common knowledge appear in the photograph. Section lines, a football or baseball field, and so on, can be measured on the photograph and an approximate scale at that elevation ascertained as the ratio of measured photo distance to known ground length.

25-7. GROUND COORDINATES FROM A SINGLE VERTICAL PHOTOGRAPH. Ground coordinates of points whose images appear in a vertical photograph can be determined with respect to an arbitrary ground axis system. The arbitrary X and Y ground axes are in the same vertical planes as the photographic x and y axes respectively, and origin of the system is the point in the datum plane vertically beneath the exposure station. Ground coordinates of points determined in this manner are used to calculate horizontal distances, horizontal angles, and areas.

Figure 25-6 illustrates a vertical photograph taken at flying height H above datum. Images a and b of the ground points A and B appear on the photograph. The measured photographic coordinates are x_a, y_a, x_b, and y_b;

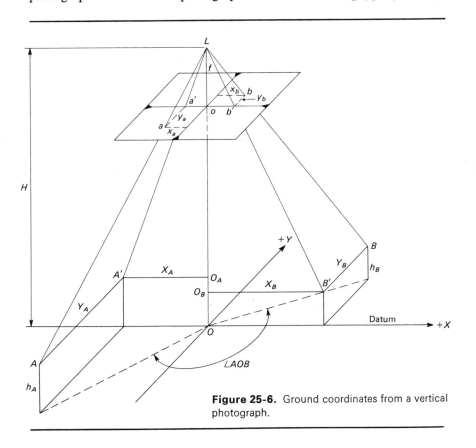

Figure 25-6. Ground coordinates from a vertical photograph.

the ground coordinates X_A, Y_A, X_B, and Y_B. From similar triangles LO_AA' and Loa'

$$\frac{oa'}{O_AA'} = \frac{f}{H - h_A} = \frac{x_a}{X_A}$$

then

$$X_A = \frac{(H - h_A)x_a}{f} \tag{25-4}$$

Also from similar triangles $LA'A$ and $La'a$

$$\frac{a'a}{A'A} = \frac{f}{H - h_A} = \frac{y_a}{Y_A}$$

and

$$Y_A = \frac{(H - h_A)y_a}{f} \tag{25-5}$$

Similarly:

$$X_B = \frac{(H - h_B)x_b}{f} \tag{25-6}$$

$$Y_B = \frac{(H - h_B)y_b}{f} \tag{25-7}$$

From the X and Y coordinates of points A and B, the horizontal length of line AB can be calculated using the Pythagorean theorem:

$$AB = \sqrt{(X_B - X_A)^2 + (Y_B - Y_A)^2}$$

Also, horizontal angle AOB may be computed by

$$\text{angle } AOB = \tan^{-1}\left(\frac{X_A}{Y_A}\right) + \tan^{-1}\left(\frac{Y_B}{X_B}\right) + 90°$$

Areas are determined from X and Y coordinates by the method discussed in Chapter 11.

25-8. RELIEF DISPLACEMENT ON A VERTICAL PHOTOGRAPH.

Relief displacement on a vertical photograph is the shift or movement of the position of an image from its theoretical datum location caused by the object's relief, that is, its elevation above or below the datum. Relief displacement on a vertical photograph occurs along radial lines from the principal point and increases in magnitude with greater distance of the image from it.

The concept of relief displacement in a vertical photograph taken from a flying height H above datum is illustrated in Fig. 25-7. The camera focal length is f, the principal point o. Points B and C are the base and top respectively of a power pole with images at b and c on the photograph. A is an imaginary point on the datum plane vertically beneath B with corresponding unreal image position a on the photograph. Distance ab on the photograph is the image displacement due to h_B, the elevation of B above datum, and bc the image displacement due to height of the power pole.

From similar triangles $LO_A A$ and Loa an expression for relief displacement is formulated:

$$\frac{r_a}{R} = \frac{f}{H}$$

and rearranging,

$$r_a H = f R \tag{a}$$

Also from similar triangles $LO_B B$ and Lob

$$\frac{r_b}{R} = \frac{f}{H - h_B} \quad \text{or} \quad r_b(H - h_B) = f R \tag{b}$$

Equating Eqs. (a) and (b),

$$r_a H = r_b(H - h_B)$$

and rearranging,

$$r_b - r_a = \frac{r_b h_B}{H}$$

If $d_b = r_b - r_a =$ the relief displacement of image b, then $d_b = r_b h_b/H$ can be written in general terms as

$$d = \frac{rh}{H'} \tag{25-8}$$

where d is the relief displacement, r the photo radial distance from principal point to image of the top or high point, h the height above datum of the top or high point, and H' the flying height above that same datum.

Equation (25-8) is used to locate the datum photographic positions of images on a vertical photograph. True horizontal angles may then be taken directly from the datum images, and if the photo scale at datum is known, true horizontal lengths of the lines are obtained directly. The datum position is located by scaling the calculated relief displacement d of a point along a radial line to the principal point (inward for a point whose elevation is above datum).

Equation (25-8) can also be applied in computing heights of vertical objects such as buildings, church steeples, radio towers, and power poles. To determine heights using the equation, images of both top and bottom of the object must be visible.

Example. On Fig. 25-7, the radial distance r_b to the image of a power pole base is 75.23 mm, and the radial distance r_c to the image of its top is 76.45 mm. Flying height H is 4000 ft and point B is 450 ft, both above mean sea level. What is the height of the pole?

The relief displacement is $r_c - r_b = 76.45 - 75.23 = 1.22$ mm. Arbitrarily selecting a datum at the pole base and applying Eq. (25-8),

$$d = \frac{rh}{H'} \qquad \text{so } 1.22 = \frac{76.45h}{4000 - 450}$$

Then

$$h = \frac{3550(1.22)}{76.45} = 56.6 \text{ ft}$$

The relief displacement equation is of particular value to photo interpreters, who are usually interested in relative heights rather than absolute elevations.

Figure 25-2 vividly illustrates relief displacements. This vertical photo, taken over the national capital, shows the relief shift of Washington Monu-

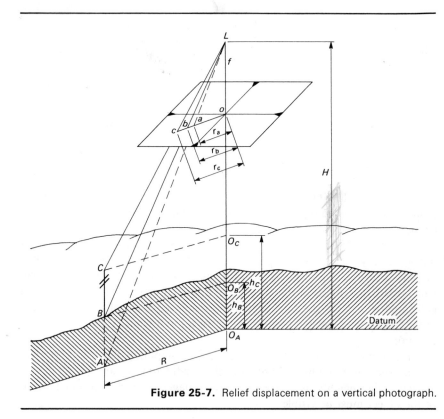

Figure 25-7. Relief displacement on a vertical photograph.

ment in the upper right-hand portion of the format. This displacement, as well as that of other buildings located throughout the photograph, occurs radially outward from the principal point.

25-9. FLYING HEIGHT OF A VERTICAL PHOTOGRAPH.

From previous Sections it is apparent that flying height above datum is an important parameter in solving basic photogrammetry equations. For rough computations, flying heights can be taken from altimeter readings if available. An approximate H can be obtained also by using Eq. (25-1) if a line of known length appears on a photograph.

Example. The length of a section line is measured on a vertical photograph as 4.15 in. Find the approximate flying height above the terrain if $f = 6$ in.

Assuming the datum at the section line elevation, Eq. (25-1) reduces to

$$\text{scale} = \frac{f}{H} \quad \text{and} \quad \frac{4.15}{5280} = \frac{6}{H}$$

from which
$$H = \frac{5280 \times 6}{4.15} = 7634 \text{ ft above the terrain}$$

If the images of two ground control points A and B appear on a vertical photograph, the flying height can be determined precisely from the Pythagorean theorem:

$$L^2 = (X_B - X_A)^2 + (Y_B - Y_A)^2$$

We can substitute Eqs. (25-4) through (25-7) in this expression:

$$L^2 = \left[\frac{(H - h_B)x_b - (H - h_A)x_a}{f}\right]^2 + \left[\frac{(H - h_B)y_b - (H - h_A)y_a}{f}\right]^2 \quad (25\text{-}9)$$

where L is the horizontal length of ground line AB, H the flying height above datum, and h the elevations of the control points above datum; and x and y are measured photo coordinates of the control points.

In Eq. (25-9), all variables except H are known; hence a direct solution can be made for the unknown flying height. The equation is a quadratic and rather time-consuming to solve directly, so it is generally expedient to find H by a trial-and-error method in which L^2 is computed based upon an estimated H. This answer is compared with the true L^2 and if the latter is too small, the first approximation of H is increased and the computations repeated until satisfactory agreement between calculated and correct L^2 is reached.

25-10. GROUND CONTROL FOR PHOTOGRAMMETRY.

Almost all phases of photogrammetry depend upon ground control (points whose positions and elevations are known, and whose images are identifiable on the photograph) for suitable results.

Ground control can be in the form of *basic control*—triangulation, trilateration, or traverse monuments and bench marks already in existence, and marked prior to photography to make them visible on the photos; or it may be *photo control*—points having images recognizable on the photographs and positions which are subsequently determined by ground surveys originating from the basic control. Ordinarily, photo control points are selected after photography to ensure their satisfactory location and positive identification. Pre-marking of points with artificial targets is sometimes necessary in areas lacking natural objects to provide definite images.

25-11. MOSAICS.   An aerial mosaic is an assembly of overlapping photographs offering a continuous representation of the terrain, contains a vast amount of detail, and is useful for many purposes. It is not the equivalent of a map which shows features on a single orthographic projection because a mosaic is a series of perspective projections.

Mosaics are generally classified as *controlled* or *uncontrolled*. The former is made from rectified photographs (corrected for tilt and brought to a common scale by a rectifier) and laid to accurate horizontal control. An uncontrolled mosaic is constructed with unrectified photographs and formed by simply matching images of objects such as roads, railroads, fence lines, and streams. A third classification, *semicontrolled* mosaic, is sometimes used to denote those mosaics which combine certain features of the other two types.

Mosaics are also grouped according to their purpose. An *index* mosaic, for example, is an assembly of all photographs of a particular flight laid so their numbers are visible. The index mosaic is photographed and prints filed for subsequent use in selecting the particular prints or negatives wanted from the flight. A *strip* mosaic is a compilation of pictures on a single flight strip and suitable for qualitative study of various proposed route locations.

25-12. STEREOSCOPIC PARALLAX.   Parallax is defined as the apparent displacement of the position of an object with respect to a frame of reference due to a shift in the point of observation. For example, a person looking through the view finder of an aerial camera in an aircraft as it moves forward sees images of objects moving across his field of view. This apparent motion (parallax) is due to the changing location of the observer. Using the focal plane of the camera as a frame of reference, parallax exists for all images appearing on successive photographs due to forward motion between exposures. The greater the elevation of any point, that is, the closer the point is to the camera, the larger will be the parallax. For 60% endlap, the parallax of images on successive photographs should average approximately 40% of the focal plane width.

The parallax of a point is a function of its relief and consequently a means of calculating elevations. It is also possible to compute X and Y ground coordinates from parallax.

Movement of an image across the focal plane between successive exposures takes place in a line parallel with the direction of flight. Thus in order to measure parallax, that direction must first be established. For a pair of overlapping photos, this is done by locating positions of the principal points and *conjugate principal points* (principal points transferred to their places in the overlap area of the other photo). The line on each print ruled through these points defines the direction of flight. It also serves as the photographic x axis for parallax measurement. The y axis for making parallax measurements is drawn perpendicular to the flight line passing through the principal point of each photo. The x coordinate of a point is scaled on each photograph with respect to the axes so constructed, and parallax of the point then calculated from the expression

$$p = x - x_1 \qquad (25\text{-}10)$$

Photographic coordinates x and x_1 are measured on the left-hand and right-hand prints, respectively, with due regard given for algebraic signs.

Figure 25-8 illustrates an overlapping pair of vertical photographs exposed at equal flight heights H above datum. The distance between exposure stations L and L_1 is called B the *air base*. The small inset figure shows the two exposure stations L and L_1 in superposition to make the similarity of triangles $La_1'a'$ and $LA'L_1$ more easily recognized Equating these two similar triangles there results

$$\frac{p}{f} = \frac{B}{H - h}$$

from which
$$H - h = \frac{Bf}{p} \qquad (25\text{-}11)$$

Also from similar triangles LOA' and Loa',

$$X = \frac{x}{f}(H - h)$$

Substituting Eq. (25-11) into the above,

$$X = \frac{B}{p} x \qquad (25\text{-}12)$$

And from triangles LAA' and Laa',

$$Y = \frac{B}{p} y \qquad (25\text{-}13)$$

In these equations, X and Y are ground coordinates of a point with respect to an origin vertically beneath the exposure station of the left photograph, positive X coinciding with the direction of flight and positive Y 90° counterclockwise to positive X. Parallax of the point is p; x and y are photo-

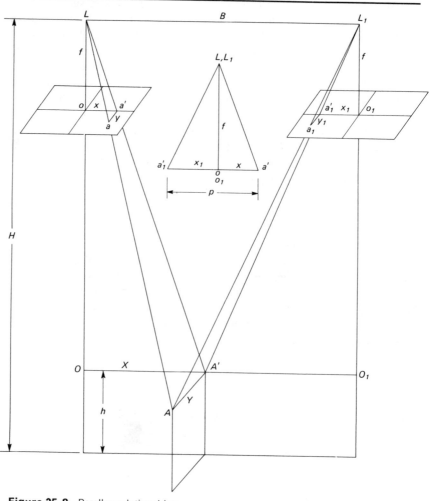

Figure 25-8. Parallax relationships.

graphic coordinates of the point on the left-hand print; H the flying height above datum; h the elevation of the point above the same datum; and f the camera lens focal length.

Equations (25-11) through (25-13) are commonly called the parallax equations and are useful for calculating horizontal lengths of lines and elevations of points. They also provide the fundamental basis for design and use of stereoscopic plotting instruments.

Example. The length of line AB and elevations of points A and B from two vertical photographs which contain the images of a and b are needed. Flying height above mean sea level was 4000 ft and air base 2000 ft. The camera had a 6-in. focal length. Measured photographic coordinates in inches on the left-hand print are $x_a = 2.10$, $x_b = 3.50$, $y_a = 2.00$, and $y_b = -1.05$; on the right-hand print $x_{1a} = -2.25$ and $x_{1b} = -1.17$.

From Eq. (25-10),

$$p_a = x_a - x_{1a} = 2.10 - (-2.25) = 4.35 \text{ in.}$$

$$p_b = x_b - x_{1b} = 3.50 - (-1.17) = 4.67 \text{ in.}$$

By Eqs. (25-12) and (25-13),

$$X_A = \frac{B}{p_a} x_a = \frac{2000 \times 2.10}{4.35} = 965.5 \text{ ft}$$

$$X_B = \frac{2000 \times 3.50}{4.67} = 1498.9 \text{ ft}$$

$$Y_A = \frac{B}{p_a} y_a = \frac{2000 \times 2.00}{4.35} = 919.5 \text{ ft}$$

$$Y_B = \frac{2000 \times (-1.05)}{4.67} = -449.7 \text{ ft}$$

From the Pythagorean theorem, length AB is

$$AB = \sqrt{(1498.9 - 965.5)^2 + (-449.7 - 919.5)^2} = 1469 \text{ ft}$$

By Eqs. (25-11), the elevations of A and B are

$$h_A = H - \frac{B}{p_a} f = 4000 - \frac{2000 \times 6}{4.35} = 1241 \text{ ft}$$

$$h_B = 4000 - \frac{2000 \times 6}{4.67} = 1430 \text{ ft}$$

25-13. STEREOSCOPIC VIEWING.   The term *stereoscopic viewing* means seeing an object in three dimensions, a process requiring a person to have normal *binocular* (two-eyed) vision. In Fig. 25-9, two eyes L and R are separated by a distance b called the *eye base*. When the eyes are focused on point A, their optical axes converge to form angle ϕ_1 and when sighting on B, ϕ_2 is produced. Angles ϕ_1 and ϕ_2 are called parallactic angles and the brain associates distances d_A and d_B with them. The depth $(d_B - d_A)$ of the object is perceived from unconscious comparison of these parallactic angles in the brain.

If two photographs of the same subject are taken from two different perspectives or camera stations, the left print viewed with the left eye and simultaneously the right print seen with the right eye, a mental impression of a three-dimensional model results. In normal stereoscopic viewing the *eye base* gives an impression of the parallactic angles. While looking at aerial

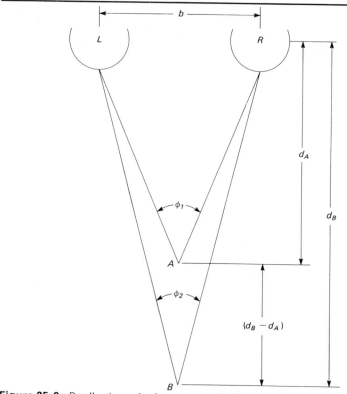

Figure 25-9. Parallactic angles in stereoscopic viewing.

photographs stereoscopically, the exposure station spacing simulates an eye base so the viewer actually sees parallactic angles comparable with having one eye at each of the two exposure stations.

The stereoscope shown in Fig. 25-10 permits viewing photographs stereo-scopically by enabling the left and right eyes to focus comfortably on the left and right prints, respectively, assuming proper orientation of the over-lapping pair of photographs under the stereoscope. Correct orientation re-quires the two photographs to be laid out in the same order they were taken, with the stereoscope so set that the line joining the lens centers is parallel with the direction of flight. Spacing of the prints is varied, carefully main-taining this parallelism, until a clear stereoscopic model is obtained.

25-14. STEREOSCOPIC MEASUREMENT OF PARALLAX. The par-allax of a point can be measured while viewing stereoscopically with the advantage of speed, and because binocular vision is used, greater accuracy. As the viewer looks through the stereoscope, two small identical marks

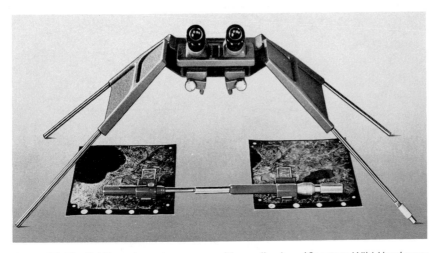

Figure 25-10. Folding mirror stereoscope with parallax bar. (Courtesy Wild Heerbrugg Instruments, Inc.)

etched on pieces of clear glass called *half marks* are placed over each photograph. The viewer simultaneously sees one mark with the left eye and the other with the right eye; then the positions of the marks are shifted until they seem to fuse together as one mark which appears to lie at a certain elevation. The height of the mark will seem to vary or " float " as the spacing of the half marks is varied; hence it is called the *floating mark*. Figure 25-11 demonstrates this principle and also illustrates that the mark can be set exactly on particular points such as A, B, and C by placing the half marks at a and a', b and b', and c and c' respectively.

Using the floating mark principle, parallax of points is measured stereoscopically with a parallax bar as shown beneath the stereoscope in Fig. 25-10. It is simply a bar to which two half marks are fastened. The right mark can be moved with respect to the left one by turning a micrometer screw and readings taken with the floating mark set stereoscopically on various points. The micrometer readings are added to the parallax bar *setup constant* to get parallax.

When a parallax bar is used, two overlapping photographs are oriented properly for viewing under a mirror stereoscope and fastened securely with respect to each other. The parallax bar constant for the setup is determined by measuring photo coordinates for a desired point and applying Eq. (25-10) to get its parallax. The floating mark is placed on the same point, the micrometer read, and the constant for the setup found by

$$C = p - r \qquad (25\text{-}14)$$

where C is the parallax bar setup constant, p the parallax of a point determined by Eq. (25-10), and r the micrometer reading obtained with the floating mark set on that same point.

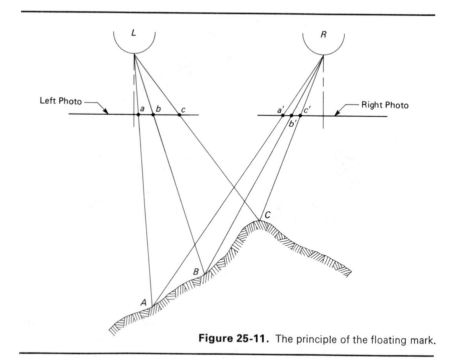

Figure 25-11. The principle of the floating mark.

Once the constant has been determined, the parallax of any other point can be computed by adding its micrometer reading to the constant. Thus a single measurement gives the parallax of a point. Each time another pair of photos is oriented for parallax measurements, a new parallax bar setup constant must be determined.

25-15. STEREOSCOPIC PLOTTERS. The primary use of stereoscopic plotters is to compile topographic maps from overlapping aerial photographs. There are two basic classifications of stereoscopic plotters: (1) *optical projection* instruments and (2) *mechanical projection* instruments. Each type consists of the following general components: (1) projection system (to create a stereomodel), (2) viewing system (which enables an operator to view the stereomodel), and (3) measuring/tracing system (for measuring or mapping, to scale, the stereomodel).

An optical projection type of stereoplotter is depicted in Fig. 25-12. With this instrument, *diapositives* (positives developed on film or glass plates) of a pair of overlapping photographs are projected so that light rays carrying images common to both intersect to form a stereomodel. Projectors used in stereoscopic plotters resemble ordinary slide projectors, except that they are much more precise and can be adjusted in angular orientation and position to re-create the exact spatial attitude of the aerial camera at the

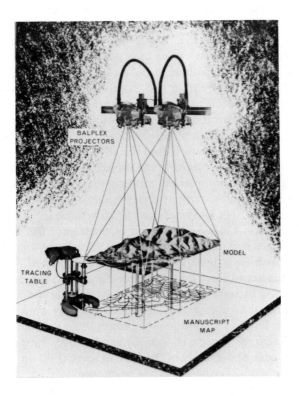

Figure 25-12. Balplex projectors and stereoscopic model. (Courtesy Bausch and Lomb, Inc.)

instants the overlapping photos were exposed. This produces a "true" model of the terrain in the overlap area, at greatly reduced scale.

Plotter viewing systems must be designed so that the left and right eye see only the projected images of the corresponding left and right diapositive. One method of accomplishing this is to place a blue filter in one projector, a red filter in the other. A pair of spectacles with one blue and one red lens is worn by the operator so that the left and right eye see only the images projected from the left and right diapositive, respectively. This system of viewing stereoscopically is called the *anaglyphic* method. A similar system, called the *polarized platen viewer* (PPV), uses filters and spectacle lenses of opposite polarity in place of red and blue filters. Another system, named the *stereo image alternator* (SIA), operates by means of rapidly rotating shutters located on the projectors, and a viewing eyepiece. The shutters are synchronized so that the left and right eye can see only the images from the corresponding left and right projector. PPV and SIA systems offer several advantages over the anaglyphic system, such as the capability of using color photographs, sharper projected images, and less light loss.

Various measuring and tracing systems have been devised for plotters. In the Balplex instrument, Fig. 25-12, light rays carrying corresponding images are intercepted on the *tracing table platen* (small white circular disk). A light emitted through a pinhole in the platen provides the floating mark which can be made to appear to rest exactly on a point of the model by raising or lowering the tracing table. A tracing pencil located directly below the floating mark permits positioning the point planimetrically. A counter linked to the tracing table responds to up-and-down motion so the elevation for any setting of the floating mark is read directly.

When diapositives are placed in the projectors and the lights turned on, corresponding rays will not intersect properly to form a clear model because of tilt in the photographs, unequal flying heights, and of course improper projector orientation. The projectors can be moved linearly along the *X, Y,* and *Z* axes and also rotated about each of them until the diapositives reproduce the exact conditions existing when the photographs were taken. This is called *relative orientation* and when accomplished, corresponding rays should intersect to form a perfect three-dimensional model.

The model is brought to required scale by making the rays of at least two ground control points intersect at their plotted positions on the manuscript map. It is leveled by adjusting the projectors so that the counter reads the correct elevations of each of a minimum of three, but preferably four, corner ground control points when the floating mark is set on them. Scaling and leveling the model is called *absolute orientation.*

When orientation is completed, measurements such as cross sections can be made from the model, or a map of it completed. Cross-section readings, used for highway design, borrow-pit and stock-pile volume determination, and flood plain mapping, have been greatly facilitated in recent years through the use of digital output systems interfaced with stereoplotters. In mapping, planimetric details are located first by bringing the floating mark into contact with objects in the model and tracing them. A pencil directly beneath the reference mark records their locations on the manuscript map below. Contours are traced by setting the elevation counter successively at each contour elevation and moving the reference mark about the model while keeping it in contact with the terrain. Again, the pencil draws contours. When a manuscript is completed, it is examined for omissions and mistakes, and field-checked. The final map is drafted or scribed by tracing from it.

Figure 25-13 shows a Kelsh (optical projection) stereoplotter having three projectors. This has the advantage of enabling two adjacent stereomodels to be oriented simultaneously.

Mechanical projection stereoplotters use two precisely made metal space rods to simulate light rays. The diapositives are viewed through binoculars via an optical train of lenses and prisms. The floating mark, com-

Figure 25-13. Kelsh three-projector stereoplotting instrument. (Courtesy Kelsh Instrument Division, Danko Arlington, Inc.)

posed of a pair of half marks superimposed in the optical train, is moved up or down by turning a hand screw or foot disk, and impelled in the X and Y directions, either manually or by means of hand wheels. Instruments equipped with a coordinatograph allow planimetry to be traced directly on the manuscript, and X and Y coordinates read.

25-16. ANALYTICAL PHOTOGRAMMETRY. In recent years, with the advent of high-speed electronic computers, much of the work done with stereoscopic plotters can now be performed economically by means of analytical photogrammetry. This science embodies precise measurements of photographic coordinates of images and construction of a mathematical model which can be solved by numerical methods. The procedures of analytical photogrammetry are particularly well adapted to establishing vertical and horizontal control through aerotriangulation.

25-17. ORTHOPHOTOS. As implied by their name, orthophotos are orthographic representations of the terrain in picture form. They are derived from aerial photos in a process called *differential rectification* which removes scale variations and image displacements due to relief and tilt. Thus the imaged features are shown in their true planimetric positions.

Instruments used for differential rectification vary considerably in design, but basically they are modified stereoscopic plotters of either optical or mechanical projection. With optical projection instruments, an orthophoto is derived by systematically *scanning* a stereomodel and photographing it in a series of adjacent narrow strips. *Rectification* (removal of tilt) is accomplished by leveling the model to ground control prior to scanning, and scale variations due to terrain relief are removed by varying the projection distance during scanning. As the instrument automatically traverses back and forth across the model, exposure is made through a narrow slit onto a negative below. An operator, viewing the model in three dimensions, continually monitors the scans and adjusts the projection distance to keep the exposure slit in contact with the model. Because the model itself has uniform scale throughout, the resulting *orthonegative* (from which the orthophoto is made) is also of uniform scale.

Orthophotos combine the advantages of both aerial photos and line maps. Like photos, they show features by their actual images rather than by lines and symbols, thus making them more easily interpreted and understood; and like maps, they show the features in their true planimetric positions. Therefore true distances, angles, and areas can be scaled directly from them. Orthophotos can generally be prepared more rapidly and economically than line and symbol planimetric maps. They are still relatively new products, but with their many significant advantages have already superseded conventional maps for many uses.

25-18. FLIGHT PLANNING. Certain factors, depending generally upon the purpose of photography, must be specified to guide a flight crew in executing its mission of taking aerial photographs. Some of them are (a) boundaries of the area to be covered, (b) required scale of the photography, (c) camera focal length and format size, (d) endlap, and (e) sidelap. Having fixed these elements, it is possible to compute the entire flight plan and prepare a flight map upon which the required flight lines have been delineated. The pilot flies the specified flight lines by choosing and correlating headings on existing natural features in the field shown on the flight map.

Purpose of the photography is the paramount consideration in flight planning. For example, in photography for mosaic construction it is desirable to minimize image displacement and scale variation due to diverse relief by increasing the flying height while maintaining photographic scale with a camera of long focal length. Conversely, photography taken for mapping purposes gains overall geometric strength and utility from flights at lower altitude using a wider-angle shorter-focal-length camera.

The *C-factor* (ratio of flight height above ground to the contour interval which is practical for any specific plotter) can be used to help select the flying height. It has been determined for various plotters and values range from approximately 800 to over 2000. By this criterion, if a plotter has a C-factor of, say, 1000 and a map is to be compiled with a 5-ft contour interval, then a flight height of not more than $1000 \times 5 = 5000$ ft above the terrain should be sustained.

Information ordinarily calculated in flight planning includes (1) flying height above mean sea level; (2) distance between exposures; (3) number of photographs per flight line; (4) distance between flight lines; (5) number of flight lines; and (6) total number of photographs. A flight plan is prepared based upon these items.

Example. A flight plan for an area 10 miles wide and 15 miles long is required. Average terrain in the area is 1500 ft above mean sea level. The camera has a 6-in. focal length with 9×9-in. format. Endlap is to be 60%, sidelap 25%. Required scale of the photography is 1 : 12,000.

a. Flying height from Eq. (25-1):

$$\text{scale} = \frac{f}{H - h_{av}} \qquad \text{so} \qquad \frac{1}{12,000} = \frac{6/12}{H - 1500} \quad \text{and } H = 7500 \text{ ft}$$

b. Distance between exposures:

Endlap is 60% so the lineal advance per photograph is 40% of the total coverage of 9 in. $\times$ 1000 ft/in. = 9000 ft. Thus the distance between exposures = $0.40 \times 9000 = 3600$ ft.

c. Total number of photographs per flight line:

length of each flight line = 15 miles $\times$ 5280 ft/mile = 79,200 ft

$$\text{number of photos per flight line} = \frac{79,200 \text{ ft}}{3560 \text{ ft/photo}} = 22.3 \text{ (say, 23)}$$

Add 4 photos on each end to ensure complete coverage, so total = $23 + 4 + 4 = 31$ photos per flight line.

d. Distance between flight lines:

Sidelap is 25% so the side advance per flight line is 75% of the total photographic coverage.

$$\text{distance between flight lines} = 0.75 \times 9000 \text{ ft} = 6750 \text{ ft}$$

e. Number of flight lines:

width of the area = 10 miles × 5280 ft/mile = 52,800 ft

$$\text{number of lines} = \frac{52,800 \text{ ft}}{6750 \text{ ft/line}} = 7.8 \text{ lines (say, 8)}$$

As a factor of safety, add one flight line so that both edges of the area are overlapped by one-half the width of one flight line coverage:

total flight lines = 8 + 1 = 9

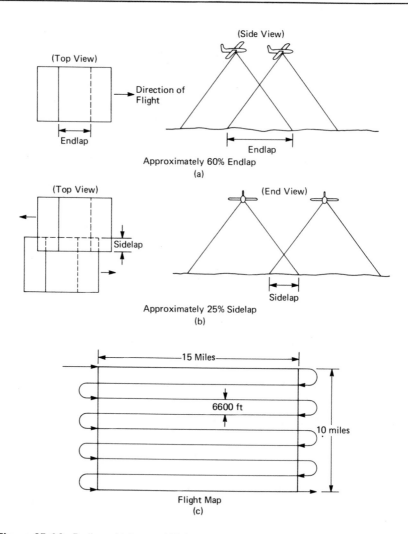

Figure 25-14. Endlap, sidelap, and flight map.

$$\text{actual spacing between flight lines} = \frac{52,800 \text{ ft}}{8 \text{ flight lines}} = 6600 \text{ ft}$$

f. Total number of photos required:

$$\text{total photos} = 31 \text{ per flight line} \times 9 \text{ flight lines} = 279 \text{ photos}$$

Figures 25-14 (a) and (b) illustrate endlap and sidelap, and (c) shows the flight map.

25-19. SOURCES OF ERROR IN PHOTOGRAMMETRY. Some sources of error in photogrammetric work are:

1. Measuring scale not standard length.
2. Inaccurate location of principal and conjugate principal points.
3. Failure to use camera calibration data.
4. Assuming vertical exposures when photographs are actually tilted.
5. Presuming equal flying heights when they were unequal.
6. Not considering differential shrinkage or expansion of the photographic prints.
7. Incorrect orientation of photographs under a stereoscope or in a stereoscopic plotter.
8. Faulty setting of the floating mark on a point.

25-20. MISTAKES. Some mistakes which occur in photogrammetry include:

1. Reading measuring scales incorrectly.
2. Mistaking units, for example inches and millimeters.
3. Confusion in identifying corresponding points on different photographs.
4. Neglect of relief displacement.
5. Failure to provide proper control or using erroneous control coordinates.
6. Attaching an incorrect sign (plus or minus) to a measured photographic coordinate.
7. Blunder in computations.
8. Misidentification of control-point images.

PROBLEMS

25–1. Define (a) photogrammetry, (b) photo interpretation, and (c) remote sensing.

The distance between two points on a vertical photograph is ab and the corresponding ground distance is AB. For the data given in problems 25–2 through 25–4 what is the photographic scale?

25–2. $ab = 2.68$ in.; $AB = 3200$ ft

25–3. $ab = 3.76$ in.; $AB = 4540$ ft
25–4. $ab = 51.28$ mm; $AB = 3810$ m

On a vertical photograph of flat terrain, section corners appear a distance X apart. If the camera focal length was f, compute the flying height above the ground for problems 25–5 and 25–6.

25–5. $X = 95.15$ mm; $f = 152.4$ mm
25–6. $X = 49.27$ mm; $f = 3^1/_2$ in.

On a vertical photograph of flat terrain, the scaled distance between two points is ab. In problems 25–7 through 25–9 find the average photographic scale along the line if the length between the same points is AB on a map plotted at a scale of S.

25–7. $ab = 3.55$ in.; $AB = 5.04$ in.; $S = 1 : 5000$
25–8. $ab = 108.71$ mm; $AB = 3.28$ in.; $S = 1 : 24{,}000$
25–9. $ab = 62.05$ mm; $AB = 74.81$ mm; $S = 1 : 14{,}400$

What are the average scales of vertical photographs for each of the values given in problems 25–10 through 25–12 for flying height above sea level H, camera focal length f, and average ground elevation AGE?

25–10. $H = 7200$ ft; $f = 6$ in.   AGE $= 1500$ ft
25–11. $H = 4500$ ft; $f = 8^1/_4$ in.;   AGE $=$ 860 ft
25–12. $H = 3000$ m; $f = 88.90$ mm; AGE $= 1150$ m

Compute the scale of a vertical photograph using the data given in problems 25–13 through 25–15.

25–13. The photographic length of a football field is 0.95 in. from goal post to goal post.
25–14. The photographic width of an interstate highway pavement is 1.08 mm.
25–15. The photographic distance between two adjacent section corners is 2.40 in.

For certain military reconnaissance it is necessary to obtain vertical aerial photography at a scale of S. In problems 25–16 and 25–17 what focal length camera would be required if the lowest safe altitude for flying over enemy defenses is H?

25–16. $S = 1 : 10{,}000$; $H = 25{,}000$ ft
25–17. $S = 1 : 24{,}000$; $H = 20{,}000$ ft

Calculate the flight height above average terrain that is required in order to obtain vertical photographs for constructing a mosaic at an average scale of S if the camera focal length is f, for problems 25–18 through 25–20.

25–18. $S = 1 : 14{,}400$; $f = 12$ in.
25–19. $S = 1 : 10{,}000$; $f = 8^1/_4$ in.
25–20. $S = 1 : 8000$; $f = 152.4$ mm

In problems 25–21 through 25–23 determine the horizontal distance between two points A and B whose elevations above datum are h_A and h_B and whose images a and b have photographic coordinates x_a, y_a, x_b, and y_b on a vertical photograph. The camera focal length was 6 in. and the flying height above datum 8000 ft.

25–21. $x_a = 2.71$ in.; $y_a = 1.95$ in.; $x_b = -1.84$ in.; $y_b = -3.30$ in.;
$h_A = 550$ ft; $h_B = 410$ ft

25–22. $x_a = 3.45$ in.; $y_a = -0.76$ in.; $x_b = -4.25$ in.; $y_b = 2.62$ in.;
$h_A = 1300$ ft; $h_B = 980$ ft

25–23. $x_a = -74.28$ mm; $y_a = -40.77$ mm; $x_b = 102.05$ mm; $y_b = -68.13$ mm; $h_A = 2400$ ft; $h_B = 760$ ft

For problems 25–21, 25–22, and 25–23, the image c of a third point C whose elevation above datum is h_c, has photographic coordinates of x_c and y_c. In problems 25–24 through 25–26 calculate the three horizontal angles in triangle ABC for the data given.

25–24. The data of problem 25–21 and $x_c = 3.65$ in., $y_c = -2.75$ in., $h_c = 200$ ft.

25–25. The data of problem 25–22 and $x_c = -2.20$ in., $y_c = -1.84$ in., $h_c = 735$ ft.

25–26. The data of problem 25–23 and $x_c = 15.25$ mm, $y_c = 78.52$ mm, $h_c = 1640$ ft.

Determine the height of radio towers from a vertical photograph for the conditions given in problems 25–27, 25–28, and 25–29 for flying height above the base of the tower H', distance on the photograph from the principal point to the base of the tower r_b, and distance from the principal point to the top of the tower r_t.

25–27. $H' = 6500$ ft; $r_b = 2.975$ in.; $r_t = 3.300$ in.

25–28. $H' = 5000$ ft; $r_b = 76.75$ mm; $r_t = 85.28$ mm

25–29. $H' = 10,000$ ft; $r_b = 53.92$ mm; $r_t = 58.03$ mm

An area has an average terrain elevation of h feet above mean sea level and the highest point in the area is Y feet above average terrain. If, in problems 25–30 through 25–32, the camera focal plane opening is 9×9 in, what flying height above mean sea level will limit relief displacement to a maximum of 0.05 in. in a vertical photograph of this area?

25–30. $h = 550$ ft; $Y = 200$ ft

25–31. $h = 1200$ ft; $Y = 50$ ft

25–32. $h = 900$ ft; $Y = 70$ ft

On a vertical photograph, images a and b of ground points A and B have photographic coordinates x_a, y_a, x_b, and y_b, respectively. The horizontal distance between A and B is L and their elevations above datum are h_A and h_B. In problems 25–33 through 25–35 calculate the flying height above datum for a camera having a focal length of 152.4 mm.

25–33. $x_a = 3.55$ in.; $y_a = 2.27$ in.; $x_b = -1.70$ in.; $y_b = -2.22$ in.; $h_A = 525$ ft; $h_B = 670$ ft; $L = 5275$ ft

25–34. $x_a = -60.05$ mm; $y_a = 94.03$ mm; $x_b = -16.54$ mm; $y_b = -87.28$ mm; $h_A = 830$ ft; $h_B = 718$ ft; $L = 4830$ ft

25–35. $x_a = 0.807$ in.; $y_a = -2.513$ in.; $x_b = 4.416$ in.; $y_b = -0.935$ in.; $h_A = 1322$ ft; $h_B = 1384$ ft; $L = 1925$ ft

25–36. Discuss the advantages and disadvantages of mosaics.

25–37. Compare an orthophoto with a conventional line-and-symbol map.

25–38. How are orthophotos prepared?

25–39. Discuss the various viewing systems utilized in optical-projection stereo-plotting instruments.

An air base of B feet exists for a pair of overlapping photographs taken at a flying height of H feet above MSL with a camera having a focal length f. The photo coordinates of points A and B on the left photograph are $x_a = 40.00$ mm, $y_a = 48.00$ mm, $x_b = 23.00$ mm, and $y_b = -29.00$ mm. The x photo coordinates on the right photograph are $x_a = -60.00$ mm and $x_b = -72.00$ mm. Calculate the horizontal length of the line AB for problems 25–40 through 25–42.

25–40. $B = 3200$ ft; $H = 9000$ ft; $f = 8^1/_4$ in.

25–41. $B = 7500$ ft; $H = 15,000$ ft; $f = 152.4$ mm

25–42. $B = 4500$ ft; $H = 6000$ ft; $f = 88$ mm

In problems 25–43 through 25–45 calculate the elevations above datum of points A and B from the overlapping photographs.

25–43. For problem 25–40.

25–44. For problem 25–41.

25–45. For problem 25–42.

A pair of overlapping vertical photographs is oriented and secured under a mirror stereoscope and a parallax bar reading is obtained on point a of $r_a = 14.23$ mm. The x photo coordinate of point a is 2.38 in. on the left photograph and -1.20 in. on the right photograph. The camera focal length is 152.4 mm, flying height is 10,500 ft above datum, and the air base 4200 ft. In problems 25–46 through 25–48 what is the difference in elevation between points B and C if their parallax bar readings are r_b and r_c, respectively?

25–46. $r_b = 15.75$ mm; $r_c = 14.98$ mm

25–47. $r_b = 14.63$ mm; $r_c = 16.95$ mm

25–48. $r_b = 13.94$ mm; $r_c = 17.91$ mm

Aerial photography is to be taken of a tract that is X miles square. Flying height will be H' feet above average terrain and the camera will have a focal length f. If the focal plane opening is 9 × 9 in. and minimum sidelap is 30%, how many flight lines will be needed to cover the tract for the data given in problems 25–49 through 25–51?

25–49. $X = 12$; $H' = 6500$; $f = 6$ in.

25–50. $X = 20$; $H' = 15,000$; $f = 8^1/_4$ in.

25–51. $X = 210$; $H' = 10,000$; $f = 88.2$ mm

Aerial photography was taken at a flying height H' feet above average terrain. If the camera focal plane dimensions were 9 × 9 in., the focal length f, and the spacing between adjacent flight lines X feet, what is the percent sidelap for the data given in problems 25–52 through 25–54?

25–52. $H' = 4200$; $f = 152.4$ mm; $X = 4600$

25–53. $H' = 6600$; $f = 3^1/_2$ in.; $X = 12,200$

25–54. $H' = 10,800$; $f = 210$ mm; $X = 7000$

Photographs at a scale of S are required to cover an area X miles square. The camera has a focal length f and focal plane dimensions 9 × 9 in. If endlap is 60% and sidelap 30%, how many pictures will be required to cover the area for the data given in problems 25–55 through 25–57?

25–55. $S = 1:12,000$; $X = 12$; $f = 152.4$ mm

25–56. $S = 1:14,400$; $X = 25$; $f = 3^1/_2$ in.

25–57. $S = 1:7200$; $X = 38$; $f = 8^1/_4$ in.

25–58. Discuss the advantages of orthophotos as compared to maps and mosaics.

SUGGESTED ORDER OF FIELD ASSIGNMENTS

ADJUSTMENT OF INSTRUMENTS

EXAMPLE FIELD NOTES

APPENDIX A

SUGGESTED ORDER OF FIELD ASSIGNMENTS

(BASED ON THREE-HOUR PERIODS AND THREE-PERSON PARTIES)

Period   *Problem*

1. Measuring distances with a steel tape. Pacing.
2. Measuring distances with a steel tape. Tying in hubs.
3. Differential leveling between two bench marks.
4. Differential leveling. Reciprocal leveling.
5. Profile levels.
6. Closing the horizon. Measurement and layout of angles with a tape.
7. Double direct angles, and bearings, of a closed traverse.
8. Prolonging a line by double centering. Prolonging a line past an obstacle.
9. Double-deflection angles of a closed traverse (same traverse as in period 7).
10. Azimuth stadia traverse.
11, 12. Topographic details by transit stadia (planimetric).
13, 14. Mapping.
15. Trigonometric leveling.
16. Staking out a building.
17. Borrow-pit leveling.
18. Layout of simple circular curve.
19. Contours by transit stadia.
20. Topographic details by planetable.

21. Topographic details and three-point location by planetable.
22. Property survey.
23. Observation on the sun for azimuth. Observation on Polaris for azimuth.
24. Field test on use of equipment.
25, 26. Special problems.

NOTES

a. This list of field problems covers sufficient material for a two-quarter or one-semester program. Assignments 1 through 14 are adequate for the typical first course in surveying given to civil and non-civil engineering students. A few deletions may be desirable to fit the particular group involved.

b. The suggested order permits a quick start on drafting-room computations and mapping if inclement weather is experienced early in the school term.

c. Many of the assignments can be carried out on the traverse used during the first field period and thus provide a sustained project rather than a series of unrelated problems.

d. Pacing, and closing the horizon, are done individually while the other two persons in the party are taping.

e. A compass and pacing survey is appropriate for certain students.

ADJUSTMENT OF INSTRUMENTS

A-1. INTRODUCTION. Surveying instruments are designed and constructed to give correct horizontal and vertical measurements. A good instrument, properly handled, may stay in adjustment for months, or longer, and last a lifetime. Nevertheless, temperature changes, jarring, and undue tension on adjusting screws can cause instruments to go out of adjustment. Therefore they should be tested periodically and adjusted when necessary to maintain accuracy. A level, for example, should be checked each day it is used on important work.

Proper field procedures, such as double centering and keeping backsights and foresights equal, permit accurate work to be done even though an instrument is out of adjustment. Frequently, however, a few minutes spent in making adjustments reduce the time and effort required to operate equipment efficiently. Furthermore, some errors may be introduced that can be eliminated only by adjusting the instrument.

Before making adjustments, *careful* tests should be made to ensure that any apparent lack of adjustment is actually caused by the condition of the instrument and not by deficiencies of the test. To properly test and adjust instruments in the field, the following rules should be followed:

1. Choose terrain that permits solid setups in a nearly level area enabling sights of at least 200 ft in opposite directions. Three permanent points set approximately 200 ft apart in a straight line, on nearly level ground, and

preferably at the same elevation, expedite adjustments. Organizations having a number of instruments in use, and surveyors working in an area over a long period of time, find it profitable to set such permanent marks.

2. Perform adjustments when good atmospheric conditions prevail, preferably on cloudy days free of heat waves. No sight line should pass through alternate sun and shadow, or be directed into the sun.

3. Place the instrument in shade, or shield it from direct rays of the sun.

4. Make sure the tripod shoes are tight and the instrument is firmly screwed onto the tripod. Spread the tripod feet well apart and position them so that the tripod plate is nearly level. Press the shoes firmly into the ground. With conventional tripods, loosen the three tripod hinge screws to relieve stresses and then tighten again.

Standard methods and a prescribed order must be followed in making adjustments. Correct positioning of parts is attained by loosening or tightening the proper adjusting nuts and screws with special pins. Time is wasted if each adjustment is perfected on the first trial, since some adjustments affect others. The complete series of tests may have to be repeated several times if the instrument is badly off. A final check of all adjustments should be made to ensure that none has been disturbed. The simplest adjustment of all, removal of parallax by careful focusing of the objective lens and eyepiece, must be kept in mind at all times.

Straight, strong adjusting pins that fit the capstans should be used, and the capstans handled with care to avoid damaging the soft metal. Adjustment screws have been properly set when an instrument is shipped from the factory. Tightening them too much (or not enough) nullifies otherwise correct adjustment procedures and may leave the instrument in worse condition than it was before testing.

Except for bull's-eye level vials, optical plummets, and some instrument plate bubbles, adjustment of automatic levels and theodolites should be left to experts. Dismantling either type of instrument can result in serious damage. If tests reveal that adjustments are required, the equipment should be carefully packaged and shipped to the manufacturer or a laboratory where specialists are available.

Surveyors and engineers can perform routine adjustments of wye and dumpy levels, and transits. Sections of this appendix describe standard techniques.

A-2. PRINCIPLE OF REVERSION. Most adjustments of surveying instruments are checked by the method of reversion, which consists of inverting the instrument in position to double the error and make it more apparent. Assume that in Fig. A-1 the angular error between the correct and unadjusted lines, ϵ, is caused by the difference in length of a and b (for example, the

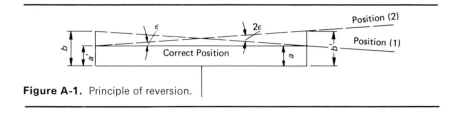

Figure A-1. Principle of reversion.

heights of the two ends of a level vial or the telescope) as shown in position 1. After the telescope is turned 180° in azimuth, the unadjusted line occupies position 2 because *a* and *b* have changed places.

Since the angle between positions 1 and 2 is 2ϵ, it follows that single reversion doubles the error. The correction adjustment is secured by making *a* equal to *b*.

A-3. ADJUSTMENT OF THE WYE LEVEL.   The purpose of a level is to establish a horizontal plane of sight when the telescope is revolved about a vertical axis. The level requires periodic adjustment. The principal lines of a level (Fig. A-2) which must be adjusted to maintain this condition are:

1. Axis of sight (line of sight). The line from the optical center of the objective lens to the intersection of the cross hairs.
2. Axis of the collars. The line joining the centers of the collars.
3. Axis of the level bubble. The line tangent to the circular arc of the level vial at its midpoint.
4. Axis of the bottom of the wyes. The line tangent to the inner surfaces of both wyes at the supporting (lowest) points for the telescope.
5. Axis of the level bar. The lengthwise reference line or axis of the level bar which is perpendicular to the vertical axis.
6. Vertical axis. The line through the spindle about which rotation takes place.

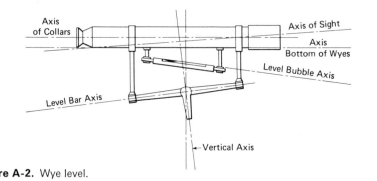

Figure A-2. Wye level.

For perfect adjustment, the axis of sight and axis of the collars have to coincide. The first five axes listed above must be parallel to each other and at right angles to the vertical axis. To provide this relationship in a wye level, the cross hairs, level vial, and wyes are adjustable. The three adjustments required will be described.

ADJUSTMENT OF CROSS HAIRS

a. *Purpose.* To make the horizontal cross hair truly horizontal when the instrument is leveled.

Test. Set up the level and sight a sharply defined point with one end of the horizontal cross hair. Turn the telescope slowly on its vertical axis so that the cross hair moves across the point. If it does not remain on the point for the full length of the cross hair, the instrument is out of adjustment.

Correction. Loosen the four capstan screws holding the reticle. Rotate the reticle in the telescope tube until the horizontal hair is in a position where it will remain on the point as the telescope is turned. The screws should be carefully tightened in their final position.

b. *Purpose.* To make the axis of sight coincide with the axis of the collars.

Test. Level the instrument and sight the intersection of the cross hairs upon some sharply defined point. Clamp the vertical axis. Unfasten the wye clips. Revolve the telescope 180° in the wyes and note whether the intersection of the cross hairs remains on this point. If a displacement occurs with the telescope inverted, an adjustment is necessary; mark a second point beside the first one.

Correction. Bring the intersection of the cross hairs halfway back to the original point by means of the capstan screws which hold the reticle in the telescope tube. Repeat the operation until the intersection remains on the original point during a complete revolution of the telescope.

ADJUSTMENT OF LEVEL VIAL

Purpose. To make the axis of the level bubble parallel to the axis of sight.

Test. Level the instrument over two opposite leveling screws. Clamp the vertical axis. Open the wyes, lift the telescope, turn it end for end, and replace it in the wyes. The distance the bubble moves off center represents double the error.

Correction. Turn the capstan nut at one end of the level vial to move it up or down until the bubble is brought halfway back to the central position. Level the instrument and retest.

NOTE: If the wyes or collars are worn, or have not been properly manufactured, the peg adjustment described in Section A-4 must be used instead of reversing the telescope in the wyes. It is performed in the same way as for the dumpy level except that the error is first corrected by moving the axis of sight to the proper rod reading by turning the leveling screws, and then centering the bubble with the wye adjustment nuts.

ADJUSTMENT OF WYES

Purpose. To make the axis of the level bubble perpendicular to the vertical axis. The axis of sight, axis of the level vial, and axis of the collars are in correct relation following the previous adjustments. The axis of the level bar and the vertical axis are fixed by the manufacturer and not adjustable. To bring the axis of sight parallel to the level bar it is necessary to make the axis of the wyes parallel to the level bar. The wyes must be of equal height.

Test. Level the instrument with the telescope directly over two opposite leveling screws. Then revolve it 180° about its vertical axis. The distance the bubble has moved off center represents double the error.

Correction. Change the height of one wye by means of the adjusting screws on it to bring the bubble halfway back toward the centered position. Level the instrument with the leveling screws and repeat the test until the level bubble remains centered as the telescope is revolved about the vertical axis.

A-4. ADJUSTMENT OF THE DUMPY LEVEL. In the dumpy level, Fig. A-3, the standards are not adjustable and the telescope tube cannot be revolved or reversed in them. Accordingly there are fewer adjustable parts. The principal lines, defined as for the wye level, are the following:

1. Axis of sight.
2. Axis of the level bubble.
3. Axis of the level bar.
4. Vertical axis.

For perfect adjustment, it is necessary that the axis of sight, axis of the level bubble, and axis of the level bar be parallel to each other and perpendicular to the vertical axis. There are two adjustable parts: the cross hairs and the level vial.

ADJUSTMENT OF LEVEL VIAL

Purpose. To make the axis of the level bubble perpendicular to the vertical axis.

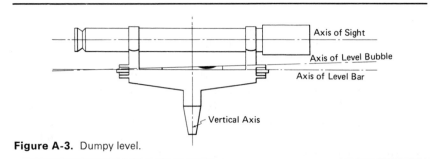

Figure A-3. Dumpy level.

Test. Set up the level, center the bubble, and revolve the telescope 180° about the vertical axis. The distance the bubble moves off the central position is double the error.

Correction. Turn the capstan nuts at one end of the level vial to move the bubble halfway back to the centered position. Level the instrument using the leveling screws. Repeat the test until the bubble remains centered during a complete revolution of the telescope.

PRELIMINARY ADJUSTMENT OF HORIZONTAL CROSS HAIR

Purpose. To make the horizontal cross hair truly horizontal when the instrument is leveled.

Test and Correction. Same as (a), first adjustment of cross hairs for the wye level.

PEG ADJUSTMENT

Purpose. To make the axis of sight perpendicular to the vertical axis and thus parallel to the axis of the level bubble. This adjustment is also called the *two-peg method* and the *direct adjustment.*

Test. Level the instrument over a point C halfway between two stakes A and B about 200 ft apart. See Fig. A-4. Determine the difference in rod readings a_1 and b_1 on A and B, respectively. Since the distance to the two points is the same, the true difference in elevation is obtained even though the axis of sight is not exactly horizontal.

Then set up the instrument at D on line with the stakes and close to one of them—A in this case—and level. With the eyepiece only a few inches from the rod, the reading on A is taken by sighting through the objective-lens end of the telescope. Usually a pencil is centered in the small field of view. A rod reading b_2 is taken on B.

If the axis of sight is parallel to the axis of the level bubble (that is, horizontal), the rod reading b_2 should equal the rod reading at A plus the difference in elevation between A and B, or $(b_1 - a_1) + a_2$. The difference, if any, between the computed and actual readings is the error to be corrected by adjustment.

Correction. Loosen the top (or bottom) capstan screw holding the reticle, and tighten the bottom (or top) screw to move the horizontal hair up or down

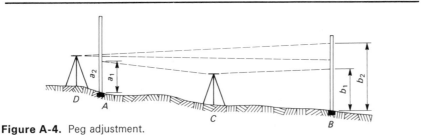

Figure A-4. Peg adjustment.

and give the required reading on the rod at B. Several trials may be necessary to get an exact setting.

An alternative method of testing the adjustment is by reciprocal leveling. A setup is made close to A and readings are taken on A and B. The level is moved to a position near B and similar sights are taken. The difference in elevation is computed and the reticle is shifted to give a reading on the distant rod equal to the reading on the near point plus the difference in elevation of the hubs.

If the difference in elevation of A and B is known, only one setup is required near either point for the adjustment.

A-5. ADJUSTMENT OF A TRANSIT.   Transits are designed to measure the vertical and horizontal projections of angles, and to serve as levels, so certain lines and axes must be precisely positioned. Principal lines of a transit, illustrated previously in Fig. 8-28, are:

1. Axis of the plate bubble. The line tangent to the upper circular arc of the level vial at its midpoint.
2. Vertical axis. Same as for the level.
3. Horizontal axis. The line through the center of rotation of the telescope axle and its bearings in the standards.
4. Axis of sight. Same as for the level.
5. Axis of telescope bubble. Same as for the level.

For correct adjustment, the axis of the plate bubble must be perpendicular to the vertical axis; the horizontal axis parallel to the plate-bubble axis; the axis of sight perpendicular to the horizontal axis; and the axis of the telescope bubble parallel to the axis of sight. To maintain these relationships, plate-level vials, cross hairs, standards, telescope-level vial, and vertical-circle vernier are adjustable.

ADJUSTMENT OF PLATE-LEVEL VIALS

Purpose. To make the axis of each plate-level bubble perpendicular to the vertical axis.

Test. Set up the instrument, bring one plate-level vial over two opposite leveling screws, and center it. Revolve the instrument 180° about the vertical axis to place that level vial, turned end for end, over the same leveling screws. The distance the bubble moves from its central position is double the error.

Correction. Turn the capstan screws at one end of the level vial to move the bubble halfway back to the centered position. Level the instrument with the leveling screws. Repeat the test until the bubble remains centered during a complete revolution of the instrument.

Adjust the other bubble in the same manner.

ADJUSTMENT OF AXIS OF SIGHT—PART I

PRELIMINARY ADJUSTMENT OF VERTICAL CROSS HAIR

Purpose. To place the vertical cross hair in a plane perpendicular to the horizontal axis of the instrument.

Test. Set up the transit and sight on a well-defined point with one end of the vertical cross hair. Turn the telescope on its horizontal axis so that the cross hair moves along the point. If it departs, the cross hair is not perpendicular to the horizontal axis.

Correction. Loosen all four capstan screws holding the reticle, and turn the reticle slightly until the vertical hair remains on the fixed point during rotation of the telescope. Tighten the capstan screws and recheck the adjustment.

ADJUSTMENT OF VERTICAL CROSS HAIR

Purpose. To make the axis of sight perpendicular to the horizontal axis.

Test. This test applies the double-centering procedure for prolonging a straight line. Level the transit and backsight carefully on a well-defined distant point *A*, Fig. A-5, clamping the plates. Plunge the telescope and set a foresight point *B* at approximately the same elevation as *A*, and at least 400 ft away if possible. With the telescope still in the inverted position, unclamp either plate, turn the instrument on the vertical axis, backsight on the first point *A* again, and clamp the plate. Plunge the telescope back to its normal position and set a point *C* beside the first foresight point *B*. The distance between *B* and *C* is four times the error of adjustment because of the double reversion.

Correction. Loosen one of the side capstan screws which hold the reticle to the telescope tube and tighten the opposite screw to move the vertical hair one-fourth of the distance *CB* to point *D*. Repeat the test until the telescope sights the same point *A'* after reversing from the backsight *A*.

ADJUSTMENT OF AXIS OF SIGHT—PART II

ADJUSTMENT OF HORIZONTAL CROSS HAIR

Purpose. To bring the horizontal cross hair into the optical axis of the telescope. This is necessary if the transit is to be used for leveling or measuring vertical angles.

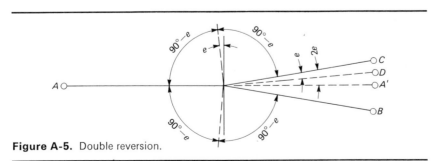

Figure A-5. Double reversion.

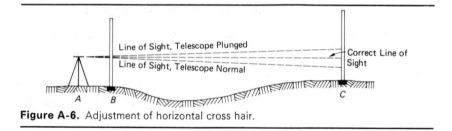

Figure A-6. Adjustment of horizontal cross hair.

Test. Set up and level the transit over point *A*, Fig. A-6. Line in two stakes *B* and *C* at approximately the same elevation. Stake *B* should be at minimum focusing distance from *A*, perhaps 5 or 10 ft, and stake *C* at least 300 ft away.

Take readings of the horizontal cross hair upon a rod held first on *B*, then on *C*. Plunge the telescope, turn the instrument about its vertical axis, and sight *B* again, setting the horizontal hair on the first rod reading. Then with vertical and horizontal axes clamped, read the rod held on far stake *C*. Any discrepancy between the two readings on the rod at *C* is approximately double the error.

Correction. By means of the top and bottom capstan screws holding the reticle, move the horizontal hair until it intercepts the rod halfway between the two readings on *C*. Repeat the test and adjustment until the horizontal-hair reading does not change for normal and plunged sights on the far point.

ADJUSTMENT OF STANDARDS

Purpose. To make the horizontal axis of the telescope perpendicular to the transit's vertical axis.

Test. With the transit carefully leveled parallel to the horizontal axis, sight a well-defined high point *A*, Fig. A-7, at a vertical angle of at least 30°, and clamp the plates. Depress the telescope and mark a point *B* near the ground. Plunge the telescope, unclamp either plate, turn the instrument about the vertical axis, sight point *A* again, and clamp the plate. Now depress the telescope and set another point, *C*, near *B*. Any discrepancy between *B* and *C* is the result of unequal standards heights and represents approximately twice the error.

Correction. Set a point *D* approximately halfway between *B* and *C*, and sight on it. With the plates clamped, elevate the telescope and bring the line of sight on point *A* by raising or lowering the movable block in one standard. To raise the horizontal axis, first loosen the friction screws holding the trunnion cap on the standard, then tighten the capstan screw below the block. To lower the axis, reverse the procedure. The friction screws holding the trunnion cap must be set carefully to prevent the telescope from being too loose, or binding.

Repeat the test and adjustment until the high and low points remain in the line of sight with the telescope in both the normal and inverted positions.

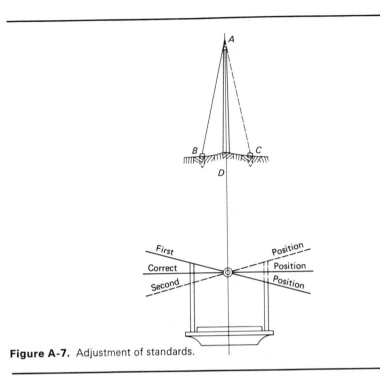

Figure A-7. Adjustment of standards.

ADJUSTMENT OF TELESCOPE-LEVEL VIAL

Purpose. To make the axis of the level bubble perpendicular to the vertical axis and parallel to the telescope axis of sight.

Test. Same as for the peg adjustment of the dumpy level.

Correction. If rod reading b_2, Fig A-4, indicates that an adjustment is necessary, the correct rod reading required to produce a horizontal axis of sight is set on the rod by means of the vertical-circle slow-motion screw. The telescope bubble is then centered by turning the capstan screws at one end of the level vial.

ADJUSTMENT OF VERTICAL-CIRCLE VERNIER

Purpose. To make the vernier of the vertical circle read zero when the telescope-level bubble is centered, thereby producing a zero index error.

Test. Level the instrument with both plate-level bubbles. Revolve the telescope about the horizontal axis until the telescope bubble is centered. The angle on the vertical-circle vernier is an index error.

Correction. Loosen the capstan screws holding the vernier plate and move it so the vertical circle and vernier zero marks coincide. Tighten the capstan screws. Avoid leaving a gap between the vernier and vertical circle since such a space introduces errors in reading angles.

A-6. ADJUSTMENT OF AN OPTICAL PLUMMET. The line of sight of an optical plummet should coincide with the instrument's vertical axis. To adjust, set the transit or theodolite over a fine point and aim the line of sight exactly at it by turning the leveling screws. Rotate the instrument 180° in azimuth. If the optical plummet reticle moves off the point, bring it halfway back by means of the adjusting screws provided. Center the reticle on the point again with the leveling screws, and repeat the test.

A-7. ADJUSTMENT OF BULL'S-EYE BUBBLES. If the bull's-eye bubble of an automatic or tilting level does not remain centered when an instrument is rotated in azimuth, an adjustment is required but need not be extremely precise because it does not control fine leveling of the sight axis. Carefully center the bubble using the leveling screws and turn the instrument 180° in azimuth. Half of the bubble run is corrected by manipulating the vial adjusting screws, the bubble centered by operating the leveling screws, and the test repeated.

A-8. ADJUSTMENT OF A HAND LEVEL. The only adjustable part of a Locke hand level is the horizontal cross hair.

Purpose. To make the axis of sight horizontal when the bubble is centered.

Test. With the hand level on a solid support at elevation *A*, and with the bubble centered, mark a point *B* on a post or building corner (Fig. A-8). The distance *AB* should not be greater than 100 ft. Support the level at *B*, center the bubble, and note whether the line of sight strikes point *A*. If it does not, mark another point, *C*.

Correction. Bisect the distance *AC* and set point *D*. With the level at *B* and bubble centered, move the cross hair to *D* by means of the adjusting screws.

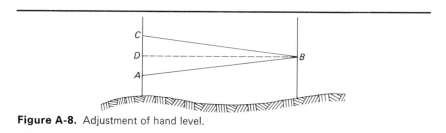

Figure A-8. Adjustment of hand level.

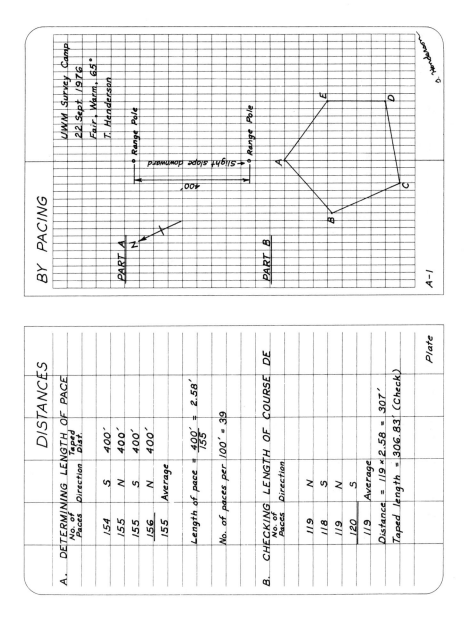

BY PACING

UWM Survey Camp
22 Sept 1976
Fair, Warm, 65°
T. Henderson

PART A

N

° Range Pole

←Slight slope downward→

° Range Pole

400'

PART B

A

B

C

D

E

D. Henderson

A-1

DISTANCES

A. DETERMINING LENGTH OF PACE

No. of Paces	Direction	Taped Dist.
154	S	400'
155	N	400'
155	S	400'
156	N	400'
155	Average	

$$\text{Length of pace} = \frac{400'}{155} = 2.58'$$

No. of paces per 100' = 39

B. CHECKING LENGTH OF COURSE DE

No. of Paces	Direction
119	N
118	S
119	N
120	S
119	Average

Distance = 119 × 2.58 = 307'

Taped length = 306.83' (Check)

Plate

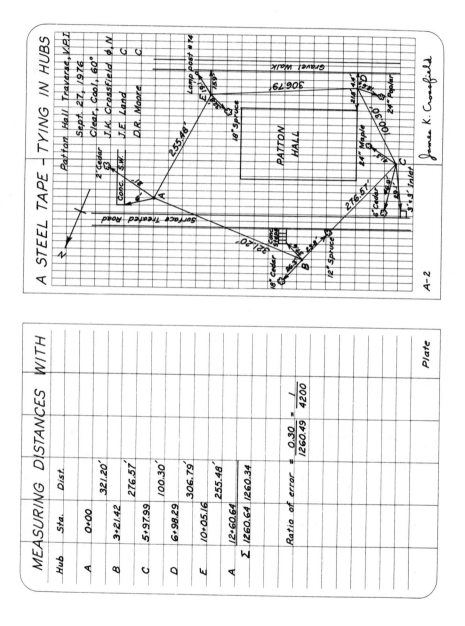

A STEEL TAPE — TYING IN HUBS

Patton Hall Traverse, VPI
Sept. 27, 1976
Clear, Cool, 60°
J.K. Crossfield ⌀, N
J.E. Land — C
D.R. Moore — C

James K. Crossfield

A-2

MEASURING DISTANCES WITH

Hub	Sta.	Dist.
A	0+00	
		321.20'
B	3+21.42	
		276.57'
C	5+97.99	
		100.30'
D	6+98.29	
		306.79'
E	10+05.16	
		255.48'
A	12+60.64	
Σ	1260.64	1260.34

Ratio of error = $\dfrac{0.30}{1260.49} = \dfrac{1}{4200}$

Plate

DIFFERENTIAL LEVELS

Sta.	+Sight	HI	−Sight	Elev.	Dist.
BM Mil.				100.00	
	1.33	101.33			150
TP 1			8.37	92.96	150
	0.22	93.18			135
TP 2			7.91 / 8.91+	85.27	135
	0.96	86.23			160
TP 3			11.72	74.51	160
	0.46	74.97			160
BM Rutgers			8.71	66.26	160
	2.97		36.71		1210
BM Rutgers				66.26	
	11.95	78.21			180
TP 1			2.61	75.60	180
	12.55	88.15			180
TP 2			0.68	87.47	180
	12.77	100.24			155
BM Mil.			0.21	100.03	155
	37.27		3.50		1030
BM Rutgers	True elev. above MSL			2053.18	
	Elev. diff.			33.75	
BM Mil.	MSL elev.			2086.93	

Plate

V.P.I. CAMPUS

BM Mil. to BM Rutgers
29 Sept. 1976
Clear, Warm, 70°

BM Mil. on V.P.I. Campus   S.D. Johnson N
SW of Old Military Bldg.   J.F. King ∅
9.4 ft north of sidewalk   D.R. Moore ⊼
to instrument room and   Gurley Level #6
1.6 ft from bldg. Bronze
disc in pipe flush with
ground.

BM Rutgers SE of Patton Hall
opposite main entrance and
8 ft from curb around drill
field. Bronze disc flush with
ground set in 6" concrete
cylinder and stamped "Rutgers".

Rod Sums		Elev. Checks	
−36.71	+37.27	+100.00	+66.26
+ 2.97	− 3.50	− 33.74	+33.77
−33.74	+33.77	+66.26	+100.03
	−33.74		

Loop closure 0.03

Permissible closure $= 0.05\sqrt{M}$

$= 0.05\sqrt{2240/5280} = 0.03'$

S. Johnson

A-3

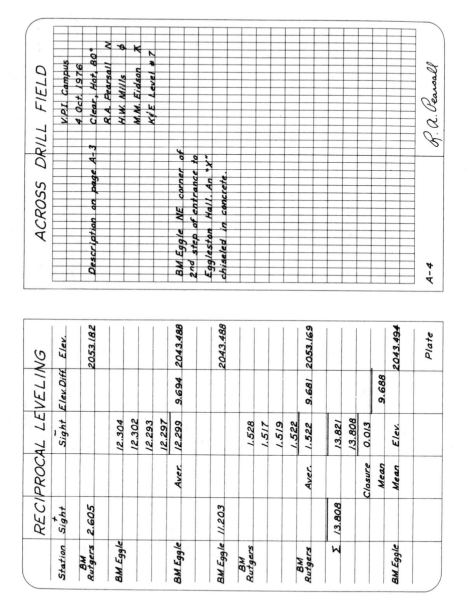

ACROSS DRILL FIELD

V.P.I. Campus
4 Oct. 1976
Clear, Hot, 80°
R.A. Pearsall N
H.W. Mills Φ
M.M. Eidson λ
K&E Level #7

Description on page A-3

BM Eggle NE corner of
2nd step of entrance to
Eggleston Hall. An "X"
chiseled in concrete.

R. A. Pearsall

A-4

RECIPROCAL LEVELING

Station	+ Sight	– Sight	Elev. Diff.	Elev.
BM Rutgers	2.605			2053.182
BM Eggle		12.304		
		12.302		
		12.293		
		12.297		
BM Eggle		Aver. 12.299	9.694	2043.488
BM Eggle	11.203			2043.488
BM Rutgers		1.528		
		1.517		
		1.519		
		1.522		
BM Rutgers		Aver. 1.522	9.681	2053.169
Σ	13.808	13.821		
		13.808		
		Closure 0.013		
		Mean	9.688	
BM Eggle		Mean Elev.		2043.494

Plate

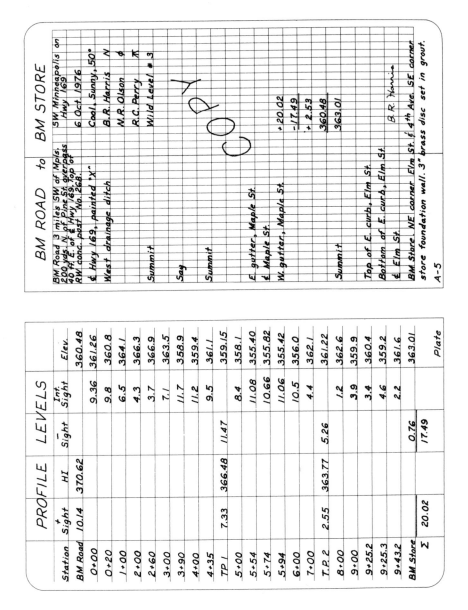

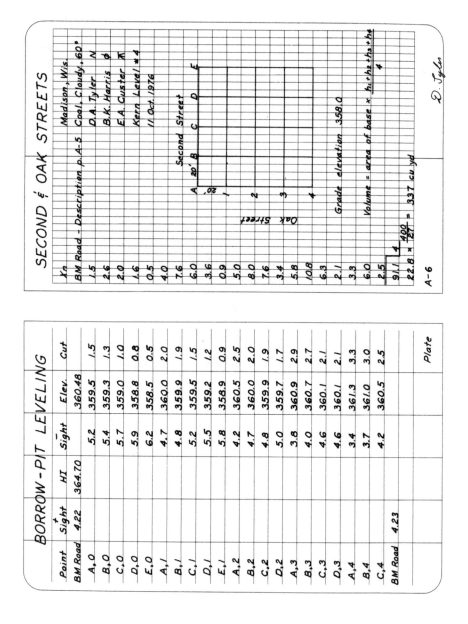

BORROW-PIT LEVELING

Point	+Sight	HI	-Sight	Elev.	Cut
BM Road	4.22	364.70		360.48	
A,0			5.2	359.5	1.5
B,0			5.4	359.3	1.3
C,0			5.7	359.0	1.0
D,0			5.9	358.8	0.8
E,0			6.2	358.5	0.5
A,1			4.7	360.0	2.0
B,1			4.8	359.9	1.9
C,1			5.2	359.5	1.5
D,1			5.5	359.2	1.2
E,1			5.8	358.9	0.9
A,2			4.2	360.5	2.5
B,2			4.7	360.0	2.0
C,2			4.8	359.9	1.9
D,2			5.0	359.7	1.7
A,3			3.8	360.9	2.9
B,3			4.0	360.7	2.7
C,3			4.6	360.1	2.1
D,3			4.6	360.1	2.1
A,4			3.4	361.3	3.3
B,4			3.7	361.0	3.0
C,4			4.2	360.5	2.5
BM Road	4.23				

Plate

SECOND & OAK STREETS

Madison, Wis.

BM Road - Description p.A-5   Cool, Cloudy, 60°

D.A. Tyler N
B.K. Harris ø
E.A. Custer π
Kern Level #4
11 Oct. 1976

Second Street

Oak Street

X_n
1.5
2.6
2.0
1.6
0.5
4.0
7.6
6.0
3.6
0.9
5.0
8.0
7.6
3.4
5.8
10.8
6.3
2.1
3.3
6.0
2.5
91.1

Grade elevation 358.0

Volume = area of base × $\frac{h_1+h_2+h_3+h_4}{4}$

$22.8 \times \frac{400}{27} = 337$ cu yd

A-6

D. Tyler

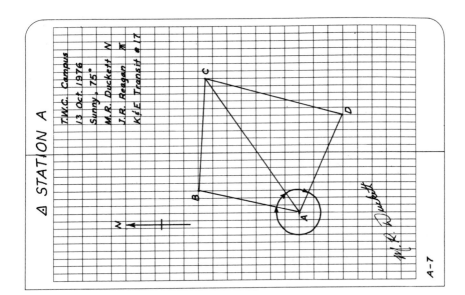

Δ STATION A

T.W.C. Campus
13 Oct. 1976
Sunny, 75°
M.R. Duckett N
J.R. Reagan ⚲
K&E Transit #17

M.R. Duckett

A-7

CLOSING THE HORIZON

⚲ at ΔA

All angles read clockwise

Object	Vern.A	Vern.B	Mean	Unadj. Angle	Sta. Adj. Angle

Reading AB to AC

ΔB	0°00'00"	180°00'00"	0°00'00"		
3 Rep N	126°36'20"	306°36'20"	(Read for prelim. check)		
3 Rep P	253°13'00"	73°13'00"	253°13'00"	42°12'10"	42°12'09"

Reading AC to AD

3 Rep N (Reading not required)
(61°2')

| 3 Rep P | 252°53'40" | 72°54'00" | 252°53'50" | 59°56'48" | 59°56'47" |

Reading AD to AB

3 Rep N (Reading not required)
(216°0')

| 3 Rep P | 0°00'20" | 180°00'20" | 0°00'20" | 257°51'05" | 257°51'04" |
| | | | | 360°00'03" | 360°00'00" |

Vernier closure   0°00'20"
Horizon closure   0°00'03"
Sta. adjustment   0°00'01"

Plate

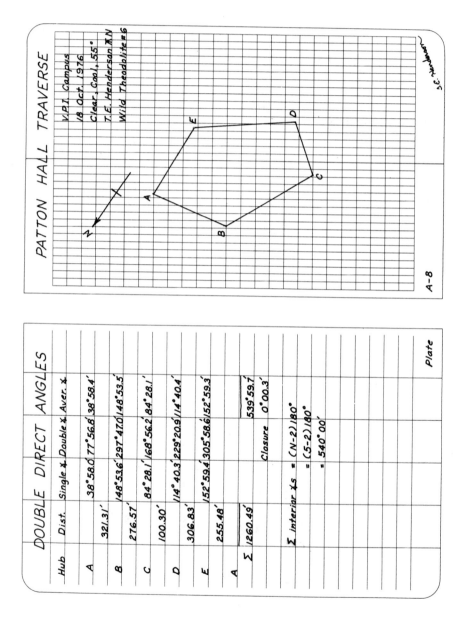

PATTON HALL TRAVERSE

V.P.I. Campus
18 Oct. 1976
Clear, Cool, 55°
T.E. Henderson XN
Wild Theodolite #6

J.E. Henderson

A-8

DOUBLE DIRECT ANGLES

Hub	Dist.	Single ∡	Double ∡	Aver. ∡
A		38°58.0′	77°56.8′	38°58.4′
	321.31′			
B		148°53.6′	297°47.0′	148°53.5′
	276.57′			
C		84°28.1′	168°56.2′	84°28.1′
	100.30′			
D		114°40.3′	229°20.9′	114°40.4′
	306.83′			
E		152°59.4′	305°58.6′	152°59.3′
	255.48′			
A				
Σ	1260.49′			539°59.7′

Closure   0′00.3′

Σ interior ∡s = (N-2)180°
              = (5-2)180°
              = 540°00′

Plate

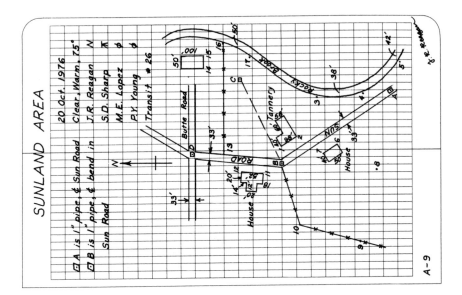

SUNLAND AREA   20 Oct. 1976. Clear, Warm, 75°

□A is 1" pipe, ₵ Sun Road   J.R. Reagan   N
□B is 1" pipe, ₵ bend in   S.D. Sharp   ⊼
Sun Road   M.E. Lopez   ϕ
    P.Y. Young   ϕ
    Transit #26

A-9

STADIA SURVEY

Station	Stadia Interval	Azimuth	Vert. ⚥ or Rod R.	Horiz. Dist.	Elev.
⊼@□B, Elev. 177.42, h.i.=5.0					
□A	6.74	148°04'	-0°34'	675	170.7
□C	4.21	60°12'	-1°35'	422	165.8
1	0.91	90°45'	8.3	92	174.1
2	1.66	120°20'	-2°12'	167	171.0
3	3.15	126°30'	-2°06'	316	165.9
4	4.60	143°45'	-1°23'	461	166.0
5	7.85	141°30'	-0°38'	786	168.7
6	2.47	167°20'	8.6	248	173.8
7	1.97	172°20'	9.6	198	172.8
8	4.99	181°15'	3.2	500	179.2
9	5.79	221°45'	+1°02'	580	187.8
10	3.47	256°00'	+1°50'	348	188.5
11	1.17	342°05'	2.4	118	180.0
12	1.71	350°15'	2.4	172	180.0
□D	4.49	6°10'	5.2	450	177.2
□A	6.74	148°04'	-0°34'	675	170.7
⊼@□C, Elev. 165.77, h.i. = 5.2					
□B	4.20	240°12'	+1°34'	421	177.3
13	3.21	286°00'	+2°01'	322	177.1
14	2.36	32°05'	8.5	237	162.5
15	2.60	41°50'	10.0	261	161.0
16	4.59	68°30'	-1°22'	460	154.8

Plate

CROSS-SECTION LEVELING

Sta.	+Sight	HI	−Sight	Elev.
5+00			9.5	
4+00			12.6	
TP 1	10.25	106.61	1.87	96.36
3+00			2.1	
2+50			5.8	
2+00			7.4	
1+35			9.7	
1+00			5.6	
0+50			7.6	
0+00			8.5	
BM Pod	8.51	98.23		89.72

Plate

HONOLULU-KAILUA HIGHWAY

Diamond Highway
25 Oct. 1976
Warm, Sunny, 70°

A.C. Chun 丌
J.E. Kaawa N
S.R. Smith ∅ C
M.L. Hagawa C
Lietz level #10

29.2 / 7.4 / 52	101.5 / 5.1 / 30	97.4 / 9.2 / 10	97.1 / 9.5 / 12	95.8 / 10.8 / 18	97.0 / 9.6 / 28	103.8 / 2.6 / 45
102.3 / 6.3 / 48	99.9 / 6.7 / 32	98.4 / 8.2 / 8	94.0 / 12.6 / 8	100.1 / 6.5 / 10	101.5 / 5.1 / 25	98.7 / 7.9 / 50
95.2 / 5.0 / 50	95.8 / 2.4 / 25	96.6 / 1.6 / 10	96.1 / 3.8 / 8	94.4 / 3.8 / 8	94.1 / 7.1 / 3	95.7 / 2.5 / 40
95.1 / 9.1 / 46	92.8 / 5.4 / 32	89.5 / 8.7 / 15	93.8 / 4.4 / 8	92.4 / 5.8 / 10	90.7 / 7.5 / 10	93.4 / 4.8 / 25	96.6 / 1.6 / 50
92.3 / 5.9 / 54	90.0 / 8.2 / 30	90.8 / 7.4 / 10	90.8 / 7.4 / 9	91.3 / 6.9 / 9	93.2 / 5.0 / 25	95.9 / 2.3 / 40
85.4 / 12.8 / 48	86.9 / 9.1 / 25	85.7 / 12.5 / 10	88.5 / 9.7 / 8	89.8 / 8.4 / 8	91.7 / 6.5 / 15	94.1 / 4.1 / 45
88.6 / 9.6 / 52	97.2 / 4.0 / 28	92.2 / 6.0 / 12	92.6 / 5.6 / 9	95.8 / 2.4 / 10	93.6 / 1.6 / 28	95.4 / 2.8 / 50
90.0 / 8.2 / 50	97.0 / 1.3 / 25	92.7 / 5.5 / 8	90.5 / 7.6 / 9	94.4 / 3.8 / 24	95.4 / 1.2 / 42	85.5 / 12.7 / 42
88.6 / 9.6 / 30	94.1 / 2.1 / 25	92.0 / 6.2 / 10	89.7 / 8.5 / 8	93.5 / 4.7 / 25	97.0 / 1.2 / 50	97.5 / 6.7 / 50

BM Pod – Kalini Valley, Oahu, Ewa-makai corner Hibiscus and Kiawe Drives. Spike in 30″ monkey pod tree, 2 ft above ground.

A-10

G. C. Kaawa

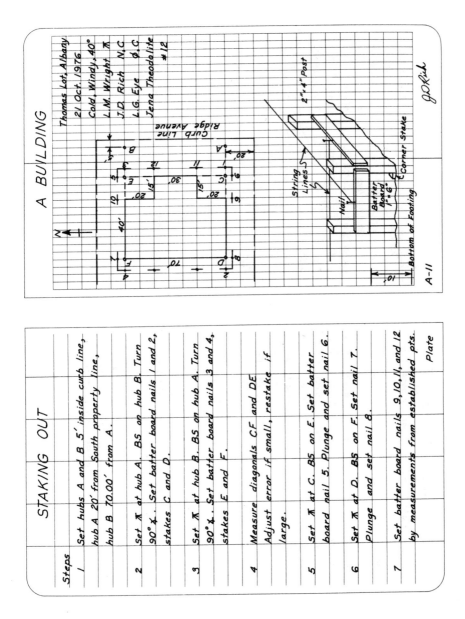

A BUILDING

Thomas Lot, Albany
21 Oct. 1976
Cold, Windy, 40°
L.M. Wright ⚹
J.D. Rich N.C.
L.G. Eye ∅.C.
Jena Theodolite #12

Curb Line
Ridge Avenue

2"x 4" Post
String Lines
Nail
Batter Board 1"x 6"
Corner Stake
Bottom of Footing

J.D.Rich

A-11

STAKING OUT

Steps	
1	Set hubs A and B 5' inside curb line, hub A 20' from South property line, hub B 70.00' from A.
2	Set ⚹ at hub A. BS on hub B. Turn 90°⚹. Set batter board nails 1 and 2, stakes C and D.
3	Set ⚹ at hub B. BS on hub A. Turn 90°⚹. Set batter board nails 3 and 4, stakes E and F.
4	Measure diagonals CF and DE. Adjust error if small, restake if large.
5	Set ⚹ at C. BS on E. Set batter board nail 5. Plunge and set nail 6.
6	Set ⚹ at D. BS on F. Set nail 7. Plunge and set nail 8.
7	Set batter board nails 9,10,11, and 12 by measurements from established pts.

Plate

8" SEWER STAKEOUT

(1) Station +Sight	(2) +Sight	(3) HI	(4) -Sight	(5) Ground Elev.	(6) Pipe Flow Line
BM 16	2.11	102.76		100.65	
0+00			6.21	96.55	96.55
+00 ₡			3.20	99.56	96.55
+50 ₡			3.91	98.85	95.95
1+00 ₡			4.07	98.69	95.34
+31 ₡			8.22	94.54	94.97
+50 ₡			4.01	98.75	94.74
2+00 ₡			4.52	98.24	94.14
+33.7 ₡			5.03	97.73	93.73
+33.7			9.03	93.73	93.73
BM 16			2.11″	100.65	

Flowline Calculations

Line drops $50'(1.206\%) = 0.60'$ per 50'

Example
Sta. $0+50 = 96.55 - 0.60 = 95.95$
$1+00 = 96.55 - 1.21 = 95.35$
$1+31 = 96.55 - 1.31(1.0267) = 94.97$

Plate

(7) Cut/Fill	
	Third Street, Statesboro, GA
	1 Nov. 1976
See page 23, Book 67 for	Cool, Clear, 65°
description.	Barnes ⊕
Floor of Existing Catch Basin	Mayer N
C 3.01	Jones φ
C 2.90	K&E # 14325
C 3.35	
F 0.43	Existing Catch Basin
C 4.02	New 8" Sewer
C 4.09	Existing Manhole
C 4.00	
Floor of Existing Manhole	

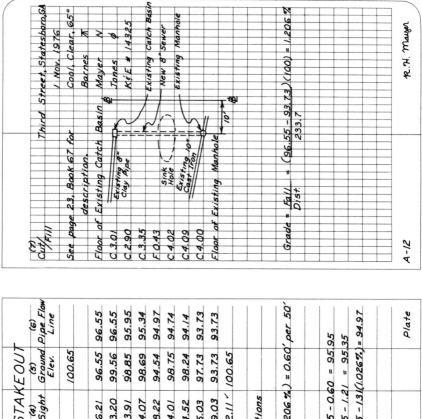

$$\text{Grade} = \text{Fall} = \frac{(96.55 - 93.73)(100)}{233.7} = 1.206\,\%$$

R.H. Mayer

A-12

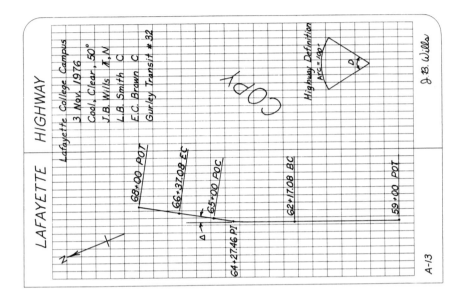

LAFAYETTE   HIGHWAY

Lafayette College Campus
3 Nov. 1976
Cool, Clear, 50°
J.B. Wills ⚲, N
L.B. Smith C
E.C. Brown C
Gurley Transit # 32

COPY

68+00 POT

66+37.08 EC

65+00 POC

64+27.46 PT

62+17.08 BC

Highway Definition
ARC = 100'

59+00 POT

J. B. Wills

A-13

ALIGNMENT   OF

Station	Chord	Total Def.	Calc. Bearing	Mag. Bearing	Curve Data
POT 68	100.00				
67	62.92			N24°42'E N24°45'E	
EC 66+37.08	37.08	4°12'00"			Δ=8°24'
		3°49'45"			R=2864.79'
66	100.00	3°49'45"			D=2°00'
POC 65	100.00	2°49'45"			L=420.00'
					T=210.38'
64	100.00	1°49'45"			E=7.71'
					M=7.69'
63	82.92	0°49'45"			Defl./ft.= 0.6 min.
BC 62+17.08	17.08	0°00'00"		N16°18'E N16°30'E	
62	100.00				
61	100.00				
60	100.00				
POT 59					

Plate

REFERENCES

TABLES

ANSWERS TO SELECTED PROBLEMS

APPENDIX B

REFERENCES

AMERICAN SOCIETY OF CIVIL ENGINEERS and AMERICAN CONGRESS ON SURVEYING AND MAPPING, Joint Committee on *Definitions of Surveying and Associated Terms*. Manual No. 34, 1972.

BARRY, BROTHER B. AUSTIN. *Construction Measurements*. New York: John Wiley & Sons, Inc., 1973.

BRINKER, RUSSELL C. *4444 Review Questions for Surveyors*, 10th ed. Published by the author (Box 1399, Sun City, Arizona 85351), 1976.

BRINKER, RUSSELL C., and BROTHER B. AUSTIN BARRY. *Noteforms for Surveying Measurements*. New York: IEP, A Dun-Donnelley Publisher, 1957.

BROWN, CURTIS M. *Boundary Control and Legal Principles*, 2d ed. New York: John Wiley & Sons, Inc., 1969.

BROWN, CURTIS M., and WINFIELD H. ELDRIDGE. *Evidence and Procedures for Boundary Location*. New York: John Wiley & Sons, Inc., 1962,

CLARK, FRANK E. *Law of Surveying and Boundaries*. Indianapolis: The Bobbs-Merrill Co., Inc., 1939.

DAVIS, RAYMOND E., FRANCIS S. FOOTE, and JOE W. KELLY. *Surveying: Theory and Practice*, 5th ed. New York: McGraw-Hill Book Company, 1966.

Ephemeris. (Ephemerides are published annually by instrument manufacturers.)

EWING, CLAIR E., and MICHAEL M. MITCHELL. *Introduction to Geodesy*. New York: American Elsevier Publishing Co., Inc., 1970.

HICKERSON, THOMAS F. *Route Location and Design*, 5th ed. New York: McGraw-Hill Book Company, 1967.

KISSAM, PHILIP. *Surveying for Civil Engineers*, New York: McGraw-Hill Book Company, 1956.

MEYER, CARL F. *Route Surveying*, 4th ed. New York: IEP, A Dun-Donnelley Publisher, 1969.

MIKHAIL, EDWARD M. *Observations and Least Squares*. New York: IEP, A Dun-Donnelley Publisher, 1976.

MOFFITT, FRANCIS H. *Photogrammetry*, 2d ed. New York: IEP, A Dun-Donnelley Publisher, 1967.

MOFFITT, FRANCIS H., and HARRY BOUCHARD. *Surveying*, 6th ed. New York: IEP, A Dun-Donnelley Publisher, 1975.

SKELTON, RAYMOND. *Boundaries and Adjacent Properties*. Indianapolis: The Bobbs-Merrill Co., Inc., 1930.

Surveying and Mapping. The quarterly journal of the American Congress on Surveying and Mapping.

UNITED STATES BUREAU OF LAND MANAGEMENT. *Manual of Instructions for the Survey of the Public Lands of the United States*. Washington, D.C.: Government Printing Office, 1973.

WOLF, PAUL R. *Elements of Photogrammetry*. New York: McGraw-Hill Book Company, 1974.

TABLE B-1. TABLE OF DISTANCES FOR SUBTENSE BAR (IN FEET)*
(Sample Pages, for Interval 0° 30' to 0° 38' Only)

0°	0''	1''	2''	3''	4''	5''	6''	7''	8''	9''
30'00"	**751.9**	**751.5**	**751.1**	**750.7**	**750.2**	**749.8**	**749.4**	**749.0**	**748.6**	**748.2**
10	747.7	747.3	746.9	746.5	746.1	745.7	745.3	744.9	744.5	744.0
20	743.6	743.2	742.8	742.4	742.0	741.6	741.2	740.8	740.4	740.0
30	739.6	739.2	738.8	738.4	738.0	737.6	737.2	736.8	736.4	736.0
40	735.6	735.2	734.8	734.4	734.0	733.6	733.2	732.8	732.4	732.0
50	731.6	731.2	730.8	730.4	730.0	729.6	729.2	728.9	728.5	728.1
31'00"	**727.7**	**727.3**	**726.9**	**726.5**	**726.1**	**725.7**	**725.3**	**724.9**	**724.6**	**724.2**
10	723.8	723.4	723.0	722.6	722.2	721.8	721.5	721.1	720.7	720.3
20	719.9	719.5	719.2	718.8	718.4	718.0	717.6	717.2	716.9	716.5
30	716.1	715.7	715.4	715.0	714.6	714.2	713.9	713.5	713.1	712.7
40	712.3	712.0	711.6	711.2	710.8	710.5	710.1	709.7	709.4	709.0
50	708.6	708.2	707.9	707.5	707.1	706.8	706.4	706.0	705.7	705.3
32'00"	**704.9**	**704.5**	**704.2**	**703.8**	**703.5**	**703.1**	**702.7**	**702.4**	**702.0**	**701.6**
10	701.3	700.9	700.5	700.2	699.8	699.5	699.1	698.7	698.4	698.0
20	697.7	697.3	696.9	696.6	696.2	695.9	695.5	695.2	694.8	694.4
30	694.1	693.7	693.4	693.0	692.7	692.3	691.9	691.6	691.3	690.9
40	690.5	690.2	689.8	689.5	689.1	688.8	688.4	688.1	687.7	687.4
50	687.0	686.7	686.3	686.0	685.6	685.3	685.0	684.6	684.3	683.9
33'00"	**683.6**	**683.2**	**682.9**	**682.5**	**682.2**	**681.8**	**681.5**	**681.1**	**680.8**	**680.5**
10	680.1	679.8	679.4	679.1	678.8	678.4	678.1	677.7	677.4	677.0
20	676.7	676.4	676.0	675.7	675.3	675.0	674.7	674.4	674.0	673.7
30	673.4	673.0	672.7	672.4	672.0	671.7	671.4	671.0	670.7	670.4
40	670.0	669.7	669.4	669.0	668.7	668.4	668.1	667.7	667.4	667.0
50	666.7	666.4	666.1	665.7	665.4	665.1	664.8	664.4	664.1	663.8

* Courtesy of Kern Instruments, Inc. The original of this page and the next also includes values for 39' and 40'.

TABLE B-1. TABLE OF DISTANCES FOR SUBTENSE BAR (IN FEET)*
(Sample Pages, for Interval 0° 30' to 0° 38' Only)

		663.5	663.1	662.8	662.5	662.2	661.8	661.5	661.2	660.9	660.5
34'00"	10	660.2	659.9	659.6	659.3	658.9	658.6	658.3	658.0	657.7	657.3
	20	657.0	656.7	656.4	656.1	655.8	655.4	655.1	654.8	654.5	654.2
	30	653.9	653.5	653.2	652.9	652.6	652.3	651.9	651.6	651.3	651.0
	40	650.7	650.4	650.1	649.7	649.4	649.1	648.8	648.5	648.2	647.9
	50	647.6	647.3	647.0	646.6	646.3	646.0	645.7	645.4	645.1	644.8
35'00"		644.5	644.2	643.9	643.6	643.3	643.0	642.7	642.4	642.1	641.7
	10	641.4	641.1	640.8	640.5	640.2	639.9	639.6	639.3	639.0	638.7
	20	638.4	638.1	637.8	637.5	637.2	636.9	636.6	636.3	636.0	635.7
	30	635.4	635.1	634.8	634.5	634.2	633.9	633.6	633.3	633.0	632.8
	40	632.5	632.2	631.9	631.6	631.3	631.0	630.7	630.4	630.1	629.8
	50	629.5	629.2	628.9	628.6	628.4	628.1	627.8	627.5	627.2	626.9
36'00"		626.6	626.3	626.0	625.7	625.4	625.1	624.9	624.6	624.3	624.0
	10	623.7	623.4	623.1	622.8	622.6	622.3	622.0	621.7	621.4	621.1
	20	620.8	620.5	620.3	620.0	619.7	619.4	619.1	618.8	618.6	618.3
	30	618.0	617.7	617.5	617.2	616.9	616.6	616.3	616.1	615.8	615.5
	40	615.2	614.9	614.6	614.3	614.1	613.8	613.5	613.2	613.0	612.7
	50	612.4	612.1	611.9	611.6	611.3	611.0	610.8	610.5	610.2	609.9
37'00"		609.7	609.4	609.1	608.8	608.6	608.3	608.0	607.8	607.5	607.2
	10	606.9	606.6	606.4	606.1	605.8	605.6	605.3	605.0	604.8	604.5
	20	604.2	603.9	603.7	603.4	603.1	602.9	602.6	602.3	602.1	601.8
	30	601.5	601.3	601.0	600.7	600.5	600.2	599.9	599.7	599.4	599.1
	40	598.9	598.6	598.3	598.1	597.8	597.6	597.3	597.0	596.8	596.5
	50	596.2	596.0	595.7	595.5	595.2	594.9	594.7	594.4	594.1	593.9
38'00"		593.6	593.4	593.1	592.8	592.6	592.3	592.1	591.8	591.5	591.3
0°		0"	1"	2"	3"	4"	5"	6"	7"	8"	9"

* Courtesy of Kern Instruments, Inc. The original of this page and the preceding also includes values for 39' and 40'.

TABLE B-2. STADIA REDUCTIONS

Minutes	0°		1°		2°		3°	
	Hor. Dist.	Diff. Elev.	Hor. Dist.	Diff. Elev.	Hor. Dist.	Diff. Elev.	Hor. Dist.	Diff. Elev.
0	100.00	.00	99.97	1.74	99.88	3.49	99.73	5.23
2	100.00	.06	99.97	1.80	99.87	3.55	99.72	5.28
4	100.00	.12	99.97	1.86	99.87	3.60	99.71	5.34
6	100.00	.17	99.96	1.92	99.87	3.66	99.71	5.40
8	100.00	.23	99.96	1.98	99.86	3.72	99.70	5.46
10	100.00	.29	99.96	2.04	99.86	3.78	99.69	5.52
12	100.00	.35	99.96	2.09	99.85	3.84	99.69	5.57
14	100.00	.41	99.95	2.15	99.85	3.89	99.68	5.63
16	100.00	.47	99.95	2.21	99.84	3.95	99.68	5.69
18	100.00	.52	99.95	2.27	99.84	4.01	99.67	5.75
20	100.00	.58	99.95	2.33	99.83	4.07	99.66	5.80
22	100.00	.64	99.94	2.38	99.83	4.13	99.66	5.86
24	100.00	.70	99.94	2.44	99.82	4.18	99.65	5.92
26	99.99	.76	99.94	2.50	99.82	4.24	99.64	5.98
28	99.99	.81	99.93	2.56	99.81	4.30	99.63	6.04
30	99.99	.87	99.93	2.62	99.81	4.36	99.63	6.09
32	99.99	.93	99.93	2.67	99.80	4.42	99.62	6.15
34	99.99	.99	99.93	2.73	99.80	4.47	99.61	6.21
36	99.99	1.05	99.92	2.79	99.79	4.53	99.61	6.27
38	99.99	1.11	99.92	2.85	99.79	4.59	99.60	6.32
40	99.99	1.16	99.92	2.91	99.78	4.65	99.59	6.38
42	99.99	1.22	99.91	2.97	99.78	4.71	99.58	6.44
44	99.98	1.28	99.91	3.02	99.77	4.76	99.58	6.50
46	99.98	1.34	99.90	3.08	99.77	4.82	99.57	6.56
48	99.98	1.40	99.90	3.14	99.76	4.88	99.56	6.61
50	99.98	1.45	99.90	3.20	99.76	4.94	99.55	6.67
52	99.98	1.51	99.89	3.26	99.75	4.99	99.55	6.73
54	99.98	1.57	99.89	3.31	99.74	5.05	99.54	6.79
56	99.97	1.63	99.89	3.37	99.74	5.11	99.53	6.84
58	99.97	1.69	99.88	3.43	99.73	5.17	99.52	6.90
60	99.97	1.74	99.88	3.49	99.73	5.23	99.51	6.96
$C = .75$	.75	.01	.75	.02	.75	.03	.75	.05
$C = 1.00$	1.00	.01	1.00	.03	1.00	.04	1.00	.06
$C = 1.25$	1.25	.02	1.25	.03	1.25	.05	1.25	.08

Minutes	4°		5°		6°		7°	
	Hor. Dist.	Diff. Elev.	Hor. Dist.	Diff. Elev.	Hor. Dist.	Diff. Elev.	Hor. Dist.	Diff. Elev.
0	99.51	6.96	99.24	8.68	98.91	10.40	98.51	12.10
2	99.51	7.02	99.23	8.74	98.90	10.45	98.50	12.15
4	99.50	7.07	99.22	8.80	98.88	10.51	98.49	12.21
6	99.49	7.13	99.21	8.85	98.87	10.57	98.47	12.27
8	99.48	7.19	99.20	8.91	98.86	10.62	98.46	12.32
10	99.47	7.25	99.19	8.97	98.85	10.68	98.44	12.38
12	99.46	7.30	99.18	9.03	98.83	10.74	98.43	12.43
14	99.46	7.36	99.17	9.08	98.82	10.79	98.41	12.49
16	99.45	7.42	99.16	9.14	98.81	10.85	98.40	12.55
18	99.44	7.48	99.15	9.20	98.80	10.91	98.39	12.60
20	99.43	7.53	99.14	9.25	98.78	10.96	98.37	12.66
22	99.42	7.59	99.13	9.31	98.77	11.02	98.36	12.72
24	99.41	7.65	99.11	9.37	98.76	11.08	98.34	12.77
26	99.40	7.71	99.10	9.43	98.74	11.13	98.33	12.83
28	99.39	7.76	99.09	9.48	98.73	11.19	98.31	12.88
30	99.38	7.82	99.08	9.54	98.72	11.25	98.30	12.94
32	99.38	7.88	99.07	9.60	98.71	11.30	98.28	13.00
34	99.37	7.94	99.06	9.65	98.69	11.36	98.27	13.05
36	99.36	7.99	99.05	9.71	98.68	11.42	98.25	13.11
38	99.35	8.05	99.04	9.77	98.67	11.47	98.24	13.17
40	99.34	8.11	99.03	9.83	98.65	11.53	98.22	13.22
42	99.33	8.17	99.01	9.88	98.64	11.59	98.20	13.28
44	99.32	8.22	99.00	9.94	98.63	11.64	98.19	13.33
46	99.31	8.28	98.99	10.00	98.61	11.70	98.17	13.39
48	99.30	8.34	98.98	10.05	98.60	11.76	98.16	13.45
50	99.29	8.40	98.97	10.11	98.58	11.81	98.14	13.50
52	99.28	8.45	98.96	10.17	98.57	11.87	98.13	13.56
54	99.27	8.51	98.94	10.22	98.56	11.93	98.11	13.61
56	99.26	8.57	98.93	10.28	98.54	11.98	98.10	13.67
58	99.25	8.63	98.92	10.34	98.53	12.04	98.08	13.73
60	99.24	8.68	98.91	10.40	98.51	12.10	98.06	13.78
$C = .75$	.75	.06	.75	.07	.75	.08	.74	.10
$C = 1.00$	1.00	.08	1.00	.10	.99	.11	.99	.13
$C = 1.25$	1.25	.10	1.24	.12	1.24	.14	1.24	.16

TABLE B-2. STADIA REDUCTIONS

Minutes	8°		9°		10°		11°	
	Hor. Dist.	Diff. Elev.	Hor. Dist.	Diff. Elev.	Hor. Dist.	Diff. Elev.	Hor. Dist.	Diff. Elev.
0	98.06	13.78	97.55	15.45	96.98	17.10	96.36	18.73
2	98.05	13.84	97.53	15.51	96.96	17.16	96.34	18.78
4	98.03	13.89	97.52	15.56	96.94	17.21	96.32	18.84
6	98.01	13.95	97.50	15.62	96.92	17.26	96.29	18.89
8	98.00	14.01	97.48	15.67	96.90	17.32	96.27	18.95
10	97.98	14.06	97.46	15.73	96.88	17.37	96.25	19.00
12	97.97	14.12	97.44	15.78	96.86	17.43	96.23	19.05
14	97.95	14.17	97.43	15.84	96.84	17.48	96.21	19.11
16	97.93	14.23	97.41	15.89	96.82	17.54	96.18	19.16
18	97.92	14.28	97.39	15.95	96.80	17.59	96.16	19.21
20	97.90	14.34	97.37	16.00	96.78	17.65	96.14	19.27
22	97.88	14.40	97.35	16.06	96.76	17.70	96.12	19.32
24	97.87	14.45	97.33	16.11	96.74	17.76	96.09	19.38
26	97.85	14.51	97.31	16.17	96.72	17.81	96.07	19.43
28	97.83	14.56	97.29	16.22	96.70	17.86	96.05	19.48
30	97.82	14.62	97.28	16.28	96.68	17.92	96.03	19.54
32	97.80	14.67	97.26	16.33	96.66	17.97	96.00	19.59
34	97.78	14.73	97.24	16.39	96.64	18.03	95.98	19.64
36	97.76	14.79	97.22	16.44	96.62	18.08	95.96	19.70
38	97.75	14.84	97.20	16.50	96.60	18.14	95.93	19.75
40	97.73	14.90	97.18	16.55	96.57	18.19	95.91	19.80
42	97.71	14.95	97.16	16.61	96.55	18.24	95.89	19.86
44	97.69	15.01	97.14	16.66	96.53	18.30	95.86	19.91
46	97.68	15.06	97.12	16.72	96.51	18.35	95.84	19.96
48	97.66	15.12	97.10	16.77	96.49	18.41	95.82	20.02
50	97.64	15.17	97.08	16.83	96.47	18.46	95.79	20.07
52	97.62	15.23	97.06	16.88	96.45	18.51	95.77	20.12
54	97.61	15.28	97.04	16.94	96.42	18.57	95.75	20.18
56	97.59	15.34	97.02	16.99	96.40	18.62	95.72	20.23
58	97.57	15.40	97.00	17.05	96.38	18.68	95.70	20.28
60	97.55	15.45	96.98	17.10	96.36	18.73	95.68	20.34
$C = .75$	.74	.11	.74	.12	.74	.14	.73	.15
$C = 1.00$	.99	.15	.99	.17	.98	.18	.98	.20
$C = 1.25$	1.24	.18	1.23	.21	1.23	.23	1.22	.25

TABLE B-2. STADIA REDUCTIONS

Minutes	12°		13°		14°		15°	
	Hor. Dist.	Diff. Elev.	Hor. Dist.	Diff. Elev.	Hor. Dist.	Diff. Elev.	Hor. Dist.	Diff. Elev.
0	95.68	20.34	94.94	21.92	94.15	23.47	93.30	25.00
2	95.65	20.39	94.91	21.97	94.12	23.52	93.27	25.05
4	95.63	20.44	94.89	22.02	94.09	23.58	93.24	25.10
6	95.61	20.50	94.86	22.08	94.07	23.63	93.21	25.15
8	95.58	20.55	94.84	22.13	94.04	23.68	93.18	25.20
10	95.56	20.60	94.81	22.18	94.01	23.73	93.16	25.25
12	95.53	20.66	94.79	22.23	93.98	23.78	93.13	25.30
14	95.51	20.71	94.76	22.28	93.95	23.83	93.10	25.35
16	95.49	20.76	94.73	22.34	93.93	23.88	93.07	25.40
18	95.46	20.81	94.71	22.39	93.90	23.93	93.04	25.45
20	95.44	20.87	94.68	22.44	93.87	23.99	93.01	25.50
22	95.41	20.92	94.66	22.49	93.84	24.04	92.98	25.55
24	95.39	20.97	94.63	22.54	93.82	24.09	92.95	25.60
26	95.36	21.03	94.60	22.60	93.79	24.14	92.92	25.65
28	95.34	21.08	94.58	22.65	93.76	24.19	92.89	25.70
30	95.32	21.13	94.55	22.70	93.73	24.24	92.86	25.75
32	95.29	21.18	94.52	22.75	93.70	24.29	92.83	25.80
34	95.27	21.24	94.50	22.80	93.67	24.34	92.80	25.85
36	95.24	21.29	94.47	22.85	93.65	24.39	92.77	25.90
38	95.22	21.34	94.44	22.91	93.62	24.44	92.74	25.95
40	95.19	21.39	94.42	22.96	93.59	24.49	92.71	26.00
42	95.17	21.45	94.39	23.01	93.56	24.55	92.68	26.05
44	95.14	21.50	94.36	23.06	93.53	24.60	92.65	26.10
46	95.12	21.55	94.34	23.11	93.50	24.65	92.62	26.15
48	95.09	21.60	94.31	23.16	93.47	24.70	92.59	26.20
50	95.07	21.66	94.28	23.22	93.45	24.75	92.56	26.25
52	95.04	21.71	94.26	23.27	93.42	24.80	92.53	26.30
54	95.02	21.76	94.23	23.32	93.39	24.85	92.49	26.35
56	94.99	21.81	94.20	23.37	93.36	24.90	92.46	26.40
58	94.97	21.87	94.17	23.42	93.33	24.95	92.43	26.45
60	94.94	21.92	94.15	23.47	93.30	25.00	92.40	26.50
$C = .75$	.73	.16	.73	.18	.73	.19	.72	.20
$C = 1.00$	.98	.22	.97	.23	.97	.25	.96	.27
$C = 1.25$	1.22	.27	1.22	.29	1.21	.31	1.20	.33

TABLE B-3. CONVERGENCY OF RANGE LINES

Latitude Degrees	Difference Between South and North Boundaries of Township Links	Angle of Convergency of Adjacent Range Lines ′ ″	Difference of Longitude per Range		Difference of Latitude, in Minutes of Arc, for	
			Arc ′ ″	Time Seconds	1 Mile in Arc	6 Miles in Arc
25	33.9	2 25	5 44.34	22.96		
26	35.4	2 32	5 47.20	23.15		
27	37.0	2 39	5 50.22	23.35	0.871	5.229
28	38.6	2 46	5 53.40	23.56		
29	40.2	2 53	5 56.74	23.78		
30	41.9	3 0	6 0.36	24.02		
31	43.6	3 7	6 4.02	24.27		
32	45.4	3 15	6 7.93	24.53	0.871	5.225
33	47.2	3 23	6 12.00	24.80		
34	49.1	3 30	6 16.31	25.09		
35	50.9	3 38	6 20.95	25.40		
36	52.7	3 46	6 25.60	25.71		
37	54.7	3 55	6 30.59	26.04	0.870	5.221
38	56.8	4 4	6 35.81	26.39		
39	58.8	4 13	6 41.34	26.76		
40	60.9	4 22	6 47.13	27.14		
41	63.1	4 31	6 53.22	27.55		
42	65.4	4 41	6 59.62	27.97	0.869	5.217
43	67.7	4 51	7 6.27	28.42		
44	70.1	5 1	7 13.44	28.90		
45	72.6	5 12	7 20.93	29.39		
46	75.2	5 23	7 28.81	29.92		
47	77.8	5 34	7 37.10	30.47	0.869	5.212
48	80.6	5 46	7 45.79	31.05		
49	83.5	5 59	7 55.12	31.67		
50	86.4	6 12	8 4.83	32.32		
51	89.6	6 25	8 15.17	33.01		
52	92.8	6 39	8 26.13	33.74	0.868	5.207
53	96.2	6 54	8 37.75	34.52		
54	99.8	7 9	8 50.07	35.34		
55	103.5	7 25	9 3.18	36.22		
56	107.5	7 42	9 17.12	37.14		
57	111.6	8 0	9 31.97	38.13	0.867	5.202
58	116.0	8 19	9 47.83	39.19		
59	120.6	8 38	10 4.78	40.32		
60	125.5	8 59	10 22.94	41.52		
61	130.8	9 22	10 42.42	42.83		
62	136.3	9 46	11 3.38	44.22	0.866	5.198
63	142.2	10 11	11 25.97	45.73		
64	148.6	10 38	11 50.37	47.36		
65	155.0	11 8	12 16.82	49.12		
66	162.8	11 39	12 45.55	51.04		
67	170.7	12 13	13 16.88	53.12	0.866	5.195
68	179.3	12 51	13 51.15	55.41		
69	188.7	13 31	14 28.77	57.92		
70	199.1	14 15	15 10.26	60.68	0.866	5.193

TABLE B-4. AZIMUTHS OF THE SECANT*

Lat.	0 mi.	1 mi.	2 mi.	3 mi.	Deflection angle 6 mi.
°	° ′	° ′	° ′		′ ″
25	89 58.8	89 59.2	89 59.6	90°	2 25
26	58.7	59.2	59.6	E or W.	2 32
27	58.7	59.1	59.6	" " "	2 39
28	58.6	59.1	59.5	" " "	2 46
29	58.6	59.0	59.5	" " "	2 53
30	58.5	59.0	59.5	" " "	3 0
31	58.4	59.0	59.5	" " "	3 7
32	58.4	58.9	59.5	" " "	3 15
33	58.3	58.9	59.4	" " "	3 23
34	58.2	58.8	59.4	" " "	3 30
35	58.2	58.8	59.4	" " "	3 38
36	58.1	58.7	59.4	" " "	3 46
37	58.0	58.7	59.3	" " "	3 55
38	58.0	58.6	59.3	" " "	4 4
39	57.9	58.6	59.3	" " "	4 13
40	57.8	58.5	59.3	" " "	4 22
41	57.7	58.5	59.2	" " "	4 31
42	57.7	58.4	59.2	" " "	4 41
43	57.6	58.4	59.2	" " "	4 51
44	57.5	58.3	59.2	" " "	5 1
45	57.4	58.3	59.1	" " "	5 12
46	57.3	58.2	59.1	" " "	5 23
47	57.2	58.1	59.1	" " "	5 34
48	57.1	58.1	59.0	" " "	5 46
49	57.0	58.0	59.0	" " "	5 59
50	56.9	57.9	59.0	" " "	6 12
51	56.8	57.9	58.9	" " "	6 25
52	56.7	57.8	58.9	" " "	6 39
53	56.6	57.7	58.8	" " "	6 54
54	56.4	57.6	58.8	" " "	7 9
55	56.3	57.5	58.8	" " "	7 25
56	56.2	57.4	58.7	" " "	7 42
57	56.0	57.3	58.7	" " "	8 0
58	55.8	57.2	58.6	" " "	8 19
59	55.7	57.1	58.6	" " "	8 38
60	55.5	57.0	58.5	" " "	8 59
61	55.3	56.9	58.4	" " "	9 22
62	55.1	56.7	58.4	" " "	9 46
63	54.9	56.6	58.3	" " "	10 11
64	54.7	56.5	58.2	" " "	10 38
65	54.4	56.3	58.1	" " "	11 8
66	54.2	56.1	58.1	" " "	11 39
67	53.9	55.9	58.0	" " "	12 13
68	53.6	55.7	57.9	" " "	12 51
69	53.2	55.5	57.8	" " "	13 31
70	89 52.9	89 55.3	89 57.6	" " "	14 15
	6 mi.	5 mi.	4 mi.	3 mi.	

* From U.S. Department of the Interior, *Standard Field Tables and Trigonometric Formulas*, 8th ed. Washington, D.C.: Government Printing Office, 1950.

TABLE B-5. OFFSETS, IN LINKS, FROM THE SECANT TO THE PARALLEL*

Lat.	0 mi.	½ mi.	1 mi.	1½ mi.	2 mi.	2½ mi.	3 mi.
°							
25	2 N.	1 N.	0	1 S.	1 S.	2 S.	2 S.
26	2	1	0	1	1	2	2
27	3	1	0	1	2	2	2
28	3	1	0	1	2	2	2
29	3	1	0	1	2	2	2
30	3	1	0	1	2	2	2
31	3	1	0	1	2	2	2
32	3	1	0	1	2	2	3
33	3	1	0	1	2	2	3
34	3	2	0	1	2	3	3
35	4	2	0	1	2	3	3
36	4	2	0	1	2	3	3
37	4	2	0	1	2	3	3
38	4	2	0	1	2	3	3
39	4	2	0	1	2	3	3
40	4	2	0	1	3	3	3
41	4	2	0	2	3	3	4
42	5	2	0	2	3	3	4
43	5	2	0	2	3	4	4
44	5	2	0	2	3	4	4
45	5	2	0	2	3	4	4
46	5	2	0	2	3	4	4
47	5	2	0	2	3	4	4
48	6	3	0	2	3	4	4
49	6	3	0	2	3	4	5
50	6	3	0	2	4	4	5
51	6	3	0	2	4	5	5
52	6	3	0	2	4	5	5
53	7	3	0	2	4	5	5
54	7	3	0	2	4	5	6
55	7	3	0	3	4	5	6
56	7	3	0	3	4	6	6
57	8	3	0	3	5	6	6
58	8	4	0	3	5	6	6
59	8	4	0	3	5	6	7
60	9	4	0	3	5	7	7
61	9	4	0	3	5	7	7
62	9	4	0	3	6	7	8
63	10	4	0	3	6	7	8
64	10	5	0	4	6	8	8
65	11	5	0	4	6	8	9
66	11	5	0	4	7	8	9
67	12	5	0	4	7	9	9
68	12	6	0	4	7	9	10
69	13	6	0	5	8	10	10
70	14 N.	6 N.	0	5 S.	8 S.	10 S.	11 S.
	6 mi.	5½ mi.	5 mi.	4½ mi.	4 mi.	3½ mi.	3 mi.

* From U.S. Department of the Interior, *Standard Field Tables and Trigonometric Formulas*, 8th ed. Washington, D.C.: Government Printing Office, 1950.

TABLE B-6. FUNCTIONS OF CIRCULAR CURVES

Degree of Curve D	Defl. Per Ft of Sta. (Min)	Chord Definition			Arc Definition	
		Radius R	log R	C.O. 1 Sta.	Radius R	log R
0° 0'		Infinite	Infin.		Infinite	Infin.
1'	0.005	343775.	5.536274	0.03	343775.	5.536274
2'	0.01	171887.	5.235244	0.06	171887.	5.235244
3'	0.015	114592.	5.059153	0.09	114592.	5.059153
4'	0.02	85943.7	4.934214	0.12	85943.7	4.934214
5'	0.025	68754.9	4.837304	0.15	68754.9	4.837304
6'	0.03	57295.8	4.758123	0.17	57295.8	4.758123
7'	0.035	49110.7	4.691176	0.20	49110.7	4.691176
8'	0.04	42971.8	4.633184	0.23	42971.8	4.633184
9'	0.045	38197.2	4.582031	0.26	38197.2	4.582031
10'	0.05	34377.5	4.536274	0.29	34377.5	4.536274
11'	0.055	31252.3	4.494881	0.32	31252.2	4.494881
12'	0.06	28647.8	4.457093	0.35	28647.8	4.457093
13'	0.065	26444.2	4.422331	0.38	26444.2	4.422331
14'	0.07	24555.4	4.390146	0.41	24555.3	4.390146
15'	0.075	22918.3	4.360183	0.44	22918.3	4.360183
16'	0.08	21485.9	4.332154	0.47	21485.9	4.332154
17'	0.085	20222.1	4.305825	0.49	20222.0	4.305825
18'	0.09	19098.6	4.281002	0.52	19098.6	4.281001
19'	0.095	18093.4	4.257521	0.55	18093.4	4.257520
20'	0.1	17188.8	4.235244	0.58	17188.7	4.235244
21'	0.105	16370.2	4.214055	0.61	16370.2	4.214055
22'	0.11	15626.1	4.193852	0.64	15626.1	4.193851
23'	0.115	14946.8	4.174547	0.67	14946.7	4.174546
24'	0.12	14324.0	4.156064	0.70	14323.9	4.156063
25'	0.125	13751.0	4.138335	0.73	13751.0	4.138334
26'	0.13	13222.1	4.121302	0.76	13222.1	4.121300
27'	0.135	12732.4	4.104911	0.79	12732.4	4.104910
28'	0.14	12277.7	4.089117	0.81	12277.7	4.089116
29'	0.145	11854.3	4.073877	0.84	11854.3	4.073876
30'	0.15	11459.2	4.059154	0.87	11459.2	4.059153
31'	0.155	11089.6	4.044914	0.90	11089.5	4.044912
32'	0.16	10743.0	4.031125	0.93	10743.0	4.031124
33'	0.165	10417.5	4.017762	0.96	10417.4	4.017760
34'	0.17	10111.1	4.004797	0.99	10111.0	4.004795
35'	0.175	9822.18	3.992206	1.02	9822.13	3.992206
36'	0.18	9549.34	3.979973	1.05	9549.29	3.979971
37'	0.185	9291.25	3.968074	1.07	9291.21	3.968072
38'	0.19	9046.75	3.956493	1.11	9046.70	3.956490
39'	0.195	8814.78	3.945212	1.13	8814.73	3.945209
40'	0.2	8594.42	3.934216	1.16	8594.37	3.934214
41'	0.205	8384.80	3.923493	1.19	8384.75	3.923490
42'	0.21	8185.16	3.913027	1.21	8185.11	3.913025
43'	0.215	7994.81	3.902808	1.25	7994.76	3.902805
44'	0.22	7813.11	3.892824	1.28	7813.06	3.892821
45'	0.225	7639.49	3.883065	1.31	7639.44	3.883061
46'	0.23	7473.42	3.873519	1.34	7473.36	3.873516
47'	0.235	7314.41	3.864179	1.37	7314.35	3.864176
48'	0.24	7162.03	3.855036	1.39	7161.97	3.855033
49'	0.245	7015.87	3.846082	1.43	7015.81	3.846078
50'	0.25	6875.55	3.837308	1.45	6875.49	3.837304
51'	0.255	6740.74	3.828708	1.48	6740.68	3.828704
52'	0.26	6611.12	3.820275	1.51	6611.05	3.820270
53'	0.265	6486.38	3.812002	1.54	6486.31	3.811998
54'	0.27	6366.26	3.803885	1.57	6366.20	3.803880
55'	0.275	6250.51	3.795916	1.60	6250.45	3.795911
56'	0.28	6138.90	3.788091	1.63	6138.83	3.788086
57'	0.285	6031.20	3.780404	1.66	6031.14	3.780399
58'	0.29	5927.22	3.772851	1.69	5927.15	3.772846
59'	0.295	5826.76	3.765427	1.72	5826.69	3.765422

TABLE B-6. FUNCTIONS OF CIRCULAR CURVES

Degree of Curve D	Defl. Per Ft of Sta. (Min)	Chord Definition			Arc Definition	
		Radius R	log R	C.O. 1 Sta.	Radius R	log R
1° 0'	0.3	5729.65	3.758128	1.75	5729.58	3.758123
1'	0.305	5635.72	3.750950	1.77	5635.65	3.750944
2'	0.31	5544.83	3.743888	1.80	5544.75	3.743882
3'	0.315	5456.82	3.736939	1.83	5456.74	3.736933
4'	0.32	5371.56	3.730100	1.86	5371.48	3.730094
5'	0.325	5288.92	3.723367	1.89	5288.84	3.723360
6'	0.33	5208.79	3.716737	1.92	5208.71	3.716730
7'	0.335	5131.05	3.710206	1.95	5130.97	3.710199
8'	0.34	5055.59	3.703772	1.98	5055.51	3.703765
9'	0.345	4982.33	3.697432	2.01	4982.24	3.697425
10'	0.35	4911.15	3.691183	2.03	4911.07	3.691176
11'	0.355	4841.98	3.685023	2.07	4841.90	3.685015
12'	0.36	4774.74	3.678949	2.09	4774.65	3.678941
13'	0.365	4709.33	3.672959	2.12	4709.24	3.672951
14'	0.37	4645.69	3.667051	2.15	4645.60	3.667042
15'	0.375	4583.75	3.661221	2.18	4583.66	3.661213
16'	0.38	4523.44	3.655469	2.21	4523.35	3.655460
17'	0.385	4464.70	3.649792	2.24	4464.61	3.649783
18'	0.39	4407.46	3.644189	2.27	4407.37	3.644179
19'	0.395	4351.67	3.638656	2.30	4351.58	3.638647
20'	0.4	4297.28	3.633194	2.33	4297.18	3.633184
21'	0.405	4244.23	3.627799	2.35	4244.13	3.627789
22'	0.41	4192.47	3.622470	2.39	4192.37	3.622460
23'	0.415	4141.96	3.617206	2.41	4141.86	3.617196
24'	0.42	4092.66	3.612005	2.44	4092.56	3.611995
25'	0.425	4044.51	3.606866	2.47	4044.41	3.606855
26'	0.43	3997.49	3.601787	2.50	3997.38	3.601775
27'	0.435	3951.54	3.596766	2.53	3951.43	3.596755
28'	0.44	3906.64	3.591803	2.56	3906.53	3.591791
29'	0.445	3862.74	3.586896	2.59	3862.64	3.586884
30'	0.45	3819.83	3.582044	2.62	3819.71	3.582031
31'	0.455	3777.85	3.577245	2.65	3777.74	3.577232
32'	0.46	3736.79	3.572499	2.68	3736.68	3.572486
33'	0.465	3696.61	3.567804	2.71	3696.50	3.567791
34'	0.47	3657.29	3.563160	2.73	3657.18	3.563146
35'	0.475	3618.80	3.558564	2.76	3618.68	3.558550
36'	0.48	3581.10	3.554017	2.79	3580.99	3.554003
37'	0.485	3544.19	3.549517	2.82	3544.07	3.549502
38'	0.49	3508.02	3.545063	2.85	3507.91	3.545048
39'	0.495	3472.59	3.540654	2.88	3472.47	3.540638
40'	0.5	3437.87	3.536289	2.91	3437.75	3.536274
41'	0.505	3403.83	3.531968	2.94	3403.71	3.531952
42'	0.51	3370.46	3.527690	2.97	3370.34	3.527673
43'	0.515	3337.74	3.523453	3.00	3337.62	3.523437
44'	0.52	3305.65	3.519257	3.03	3305.53	3.519241
45'	0.525	3274.17	3.515101	3.05	3274.04	3.515085
46'	0.53	3243.29	3.510985	3.08	3243.16	3.510968
47'	0.535	3212.98	3.506908	3.11	3212.85	3.506890
48'	0.54	3183.23	3.502868	3.14	3183.10	3.502850
49'	0.545	3154.03	3.498866	3.17	3153.90	3.498847
50'	0.55	3125.36	3.494900	3.20	3125.22	3.494881
51'	0.555	3097.20	3.490970	3.23	3097.07	3.490951
52'	0.56	3069.55	3.487075	3.26	3069.42	3.487056
53'	0.565	3042.39	3.483215	3.29	3042.25	3.483195
54'	0.57	3015.71	3.479389	3.32	3015.57	3.479369
55'	0.575	2989.48	3.475596	3.35	2989.34	3.475576
56'	0.58	2963.72	3.471836	3.37	2963.58	3.471816
57'	0.585	2938.39	3.468109	3.40	2938.25	3.468087
58'	0.59	2913.49	3.464413	3.43	2913.34	3.464392
59'	0.595	2889.01	3.460749	3.46	2888.86	3.460727

TABLE B-6. FUNCTIONS OF CIRCULAR CURVES

Degree of Curve D	Defl. Per Ft of Sta. (Min)	Chord Definition			Arc Definition	
		Radius R	log R	C.O. 1 Sta.	Radius R	log R
2° 0'	0.6	2864.93	3.457115	3.49	2864.79	3.457093
1'	0.605	2841.26	3.453511	3.52	2841.11	3.453488
2'	0.61	2817.97	3.449937	3.55	2817.83	3.449914
3'	0.615	2795.06	3.446392	3.58	2794.92	3.446369
4'	0.62	2772.53	3.442876	3.61	2772.38	3.442852
5'	0.625	2750.35	3.439388	3.64	2750.20	3.439364
6'	0.63	2728.52	3.435928	3.66	2728.37	3.435903
7'	0.635	2707.04	3.432495	3.69	2706.89	3.432470
8'	0.64	2685.89	3.429089	3.72	2685.74	3.429064
9'	0.645	2665.08	3.425710	3.75	2664.92	3.425684
10'	0.65	2644.58	3.422356	3.78	2644.42	3.422330
11'	0.655	2624.39	3.419029	3.81	2624.23	3.419002
12'	0.66	2604.51	3.415727	3.84	2604.35	3.415700
13'	0.665	2584.93	3.412449	3.87	2584.77	3.412422
14'	0.67	2565.65	3.409197	3.90	2565.48	3.409169
15'	0.675	2546.64	3.405968	3.93	2546.48	3.405940
16'	0.68	2527.92	3.402763	3.96	2527.75	3.402735
17'	0.685	2509.47	3.399582	3.98	2509.30	3.399553
18'	0.69	2491.29	3.396424	4.01	2491.12	3.396395
19'	0.695	2473.37	3.393289	4.04	2473.20	3.393259
20'	0.7	2455.70	3.390176	4.07	2455.53	3.390145
21'	0.705	2438.29	3.387085	4.10	2438.12	3.387055
22'	0.71	2421.12	3.384016	4.13	2420.95	3.383985
23'	0.715	2404.19	3.380969	4.16	2404.02	3.380938
24'	0.72	2387.50	3.377943	4.19	2387.32	3.377911
25'	0.725	2371.04	3.374938	4.22	2370.86	3.374905
26'	0.73	2354.80	3.371954	4.25	2354.62	3.371921
27'	0.735	2338.78	3.368990	4.28	2338.60	3.368956
28'	0.74	2322.98	3.366046	4.30	2322.80	3.366012
29'	0.745	2307.39	3.363122	4.33	2307.21	3.363087
30'	0.75	2292.01	3.360217	4.36	2291.83	3.360183
31'	0.755	2276.84	3.357332	4.39	2276.65	3.357297
32'	0.76	2261.86	3.354466	4.42	2261.68	3.354430
33'	0.765	2247.08	3.351618	4.45	2246.89	3.351582
34'	0.77	2232.49	3.348789	4.48	2232.30	3.348753
35'	0.775	2218.09	3.345797	4.51	2217.90	3.345942
36'	0.78	2203.87	3.343187	4.54	2203.68	3.343149
37'	0.785	2189.84	3.340412	4.57	2189.65	3.340374
38'	0.79	2175.98	3.337655	4.60	2175.79	3.337617
39'	0.795	2162.30	3.334916	4.62	2162.10	3.334877
40'	0.8	2148.79	3.332193	4.65	2148.59	3.332154
41'	0.805	2135.44	3.329488	4.68	2135.25	3.329488
42'	0.81	2122.26	3.326799	4.71	2122.07	3.326759
43'	0.815	2109.24	3.324127	4.74	2109.05	3.324086
44'	0.82	2096.39	3.321471	4.77	2096.19	3.321430
45'	0.825	2083.68	3.318832	4.80	2083.48	3.318790
46'	0.83	2071.13	3.316208	4.83	2070.93	3.316166
47'	0.835	2058.73	3.313600	4.86	2058.53	3.313557
48'	0.84	2046.48	3.311008	4.89	2046.28	3.310964
49'	0.845	2034.37	3.308431	4.92	2034.17	3.308387
50'	0.85	2022.41	3.305869	4.94	2022.20	3.305825
51'	0.855	2010.59	3.303323	4.97	2010.38	3.303278
52'	0.86	1998.90	3.300791	5.00	1998.69	3.300745
53'	0.865	1987.35	3.298274	5.03	1987.14	3.298228
54'	0.87	1975.93	3.295771	5.06	1975.72	3.295725
55'	0.875	1964.64	3.293283	5.09	1964.43	3.293236
56'	0.88	1953.48	3.290809	5.12	1953.27	3.290761
57'	0.885	1942.44	3.288349	5.15	1942.23	3.288301
58'	0.89	1931.53	3.285902	5.18	1931.32	3.285854
59'	0.895	1920.75	3.283470	5.21	1920.53	3.283421

TABLE B-6. FUNCTIONS OF CIRCULAR CURVES

Degree of Curve D	Defl. Per Ft of Sta. (Min)	Chord Definition			Arc Definition	
		Radius R	log R	C.O. 1 Sta.	Radius R	log R
3° 0'	0.9	1910.08	3.281051	5.24	1909.86	3.281001
1'	0.905	1899.53	3.278646	5.26	1899.31	3.278595
2'	0.91	1889.09	3.276253	5.29	1888.87	3.276203
3'	0.915	1878.77	3.273874	5.32	1878.55	3.273823
4'	0.92	1868.56	3.271508	5.35	1868.34	3.271456
5'	0.925	1858.47	3.269155	5.38	1858.24	3.269102
6'	0.93	1848.48	3.266814	5.41	1848.25	3.266761
7'	0.935	1838.59	3.264486	5.44	1838.37	3.264432
8'	0.94	1828.82	3.262170	5.47	1828.59	3.262116
9'	0.945	1819.14	3.259867	5.50	1818.91	3.259812
10'	0.95	1809.57	3.257576	5.53	1809.34	3.257520
11'	0.955	1800.10	3.255296	5.56	1799.87	3.255240
12'	0.96	1790.73	3.253029	5.58	1790.49	3.252973
13'	0.965	1781.45	3.250774	5.61	1781.22	3.250716
14'	0.97	1772.27	3.248530	5.64	1772.03	3.248472
15'	0.975	1763.18	3.246297	5.67	1762.95	3.246239
16'	0.98	1754.19	3.244077	5.70	1753.95	3.244018
17'	0.985	1745.29	3.241867	5.73	1745.05	3.241808
18'	0.99	1736.48	3.239669	5.76	1736.24	3.239609
19'	0.995	1727.75	3.237481	5.79	1727.51	3.237421
20'	1.0	1719.12	3.235305	5.82	1718.87	3.235244
21'	1.005	1710.57	3.233140	5.85	1710.32	3.233078
22'	1.01	1702.10	3.230985	5.88	1701.85	3.230922
23'	1.015	1693.72	3.228841	5.90	1693.47	3.228778
24'	1.02	1685.42	3.226707	5.93	1685.17	3.226644
25'	1.025	1677.20	3.224584	5.96	1676.95	3.224520
26'	1.03	1669.06	3.222472	5.99	1668.81	3.222407
27'	1.035	1661.00	3.220369	6.02	1660.75	3.220303
28'	1.04	1653.01	3.218277	6.05	1652.76	3.218210
29'	1.045	1645.11	3.216195	6.08	1644.85	3.216128
30'	1.05	1637.28	3.214122	6.11	1637.02	3.214055
31'	1.055	1629.52	3.212060	6.14	1629.26	3.211991
32'	1.06	1621.84	3.210007	6.17	1621.58	3.209938
33'	1.065	1614.22	3.207964	6.19	1613.96	3.207894
34'	1.07	1606.68	3.205930	6.22	1606.42	3.205860
35'	1.075	1599.21	3.203906	6.25	1598.95	3.203835
36'	1.08	1591.81	3.201892	6.28	1591.55	3.201820
37'	1.085	1584.48	3.199886	6.31	1584.21	3.199814
38'	1.09	1577.21	3.197890	6.34	1576.95	3.197817
39'	1.095	1570.01	3.195903	6.37	1569.75	3.195830
40'	1.1	1562.88	3.193925	6.40	1562.61	3.193851
41'	1.105	1555.81	3.191956	6.43	1555.54	3.191881
42'	1.11	1548.80	3.189996	6.46	1548.53	3.189921
43'	1.115	1541.86	3.188045	6.49	1541.59	3.187969
44'	1.12	1534.98	3.186103	6.51	1534.71	3.186026
45'	1.125	1528.16	3.184169	6.54	1527.89	3.184091
46'	1.13	1521.40	3.182244	6.57	1521.13	3.182165
47'	1.135	1514.17	3.180327	6.60	1514.43	3.180248
48'	1.14	1508.06	3.178419	6.63	1507.78	3.178339
49'	1.145	1501.48	3.176519	6.66	1501.20	3.176438
50'	1.15	1494.95	3.174627	6.69	1494.67	3.174546
51'	1.155	1488.48	3.172744	6.72	1488.20	3.172661
52'	1.16	1482.07	3.170868	6.75	1481.79	3.170786
53'	1.165	1475.71	3.169001	6.78	1475.43	3.168918
54'	1.17	1469.41	3.167142	6.81	1469.12	3.167058
55'	1.175	1463.16	3.165291	6.83	1462.87	3.165206
56'	1.18	1456.96	3.163447	6.86	1456.67	3.163362
57'	1.185	1450.81	3.161612	6.89	1450.53	3.161526
58'	1.19	1444.72	3.159784	6.92	1444.43	3.159697
59'	1.195	1438.68	3.157963	6.95	1438.39	3.157876

TABLE B-6. FUNCTIONS OF CIRCULAR CURVES

Degree of Curve D	Defl. Per Ft of Sta. (Min)	Chord Definition			Arc Definition	
		Radius R	log R	C.O. 1 Sta.	Radius R	log R
4° 0'	1.2	1432.69	3.156151	6.98	1432.39	3.156063
1'	1.205	1426.74	3.154346	7.01	1426.45	3.154257
2'	1.21	1420.85	3.152548	7.04	1420.56	3.152458
3'	1.215	1415.01	3.150758	7.07	1414.71	3.150667
4'	1.22	1409.21	3.148975	7.10	1408.91	3.148884
5'	1.225	1403.46	3.147200	7.13	1403.16	3.147108
6'	1.23	1397.76	3.145431	7.15	1397.46	3.145339
7'	1.235	1392.10	3.143670	7.18	1391.80	3.143577
8'	1.24	1386.49	3.141916	7.21	1386.19	3.141822
9'	1.245	1380.92	3.140170	7.24	1380.62	3.140074
10'	1.25	1375.40	3.138430	7.27	1375.10	3.138334
11'	1.255	1369.92	3.136697	7.30	1369.62	3.136600
12'	1.26	1364.49	3.134971	7.33	1364.19	3.134873
13'	1.265	1359.10	3.133251	7.36	1358.79	3.133153
14'	1.27	1353.75	3.131539	7.39	1353.44	3.131440
15'	1.275	1348.45	3.129833	7.42	1348.14	3.129734
16'	1.28	1343.18	3.128134	7.45	1342.87	3.128034
17'	1.285	1337.96	3.126442	7.47	1337.64	3.126341
18'	1.29	1332.77	3.124756	7.50	1332.46	3.124654
19'	1.295	1327.63	3.123077	7.53	1327.32	3.122974
20'	1.3	1322.53	3.121404	7.56	1322.21	3.121300
21'	1.305	1317.46	3.119738	7.59	1317.14	3.119633
22'	1.31	1312.43	3.118078	7.62	1312.12	3.117972
23'	1.315	1307.45	3.116424	7.65	1307.23	3.116318
24'	1.32	1302.50	3.114777	7.68	1302.18	3.114669
25'	1.325	1297.58	3.113136	7.71	1297.26	3.113028
26'	1.33	1292.71	3.111501	7.74	1292.39	3.111392
27'	1.335	1287.87	3.109872	7.76	1287.55	3.109762
28'	1.34	1283.07	3.108249	7.79	1282.74	3.108139
29'	1.345	1278.30	3.106632	7.82	1277.97	3.106521
30'	1.35	1273.57	3.105022	7.85	1273.24	3.104910
31'	1.355	1268.87	3.103417	7.88	1268.54	3.103304
32'	1.36	1264.21	3.101818	7.91	1263.88	3.101705
33'	1.365	1259.58	3.100225	7.94	1259.25	3.100111
34'	1.37	1254.98	3.098638	7.97	1254.65	3.098523
35'	1.375	1250.42	3.097057	8.00	1250.09	3.096941
36'	1.38	1245.89	3.095481	8.03	1245.56	3.095365
37'	1.385	1241.40	3.093912	8.06	1241.06	3.093974
38'	1.39	1236.94	3.092347	8.08	1236.60	3.092229
39'	1.395	1232.51	3.090789	8.11	1232.17	3.090670
40'	1.4	1228.11	3.089236	8.14	1227.77	3.089116
41'	1.405	1223.74	3.087689	8.17	1223.40	3.087566
42'	1.41	1219.40	3.086147	8.20	1219.06	3.086025
43'	1.415	1215.09	3.084610	8.23	1214.75	3.084487
44'	1.42	1210.82	3.083079	8.26	1210.47	3.082955
45'	1.425	1206.57	3.081553	8.29	1206.23	3.081429
46'	1.43	1202.36	3.080033	8.32	1202.01	3.079908
47'	1.435	1198.17	3.078518	8.35	1197.82	3.078392
48'	1.44	1194.01	3.077008	8.38	1193.66	3.076881
49'	1.445	1189.88	3.075504	8.40	1189.53	3.075376
50'	1.45	1185.78	3.074005	8.43	1185.43	3.073876
51'	1.455	1181.71	3.072511	8.46	1181.36	3.072381
52'	1.46	1177.66	3.071022	8.49	1177.31	3.070891
53'	1.465	1173.65	3.069538	8.52	1173.29	3.069406
54'	1.47	1169.66	3.068059	8.55	1169.30	3.067927
55'	1.475	1165.70	3.066585	8.58	1165.34	3.066452
56'	1.48	1161.76	3.065116	8.61	1161.40	3.064982
57'	1.485	1157.85	3.063653	8.64	1157.49	3.063517
58'	1.49	1153.97	3.062194	8.67	1153.61	3.062057
59'	1.495	1150.11	3.060740	8.69	1149.75	3.060603

TABLE B-7. LENGTHS OF CIRCULAR ARCS FOR RADIUS = 1

Deg.	Length	Deg.	Length	Min.	Length	Sec.	Length
1	0.017 45 329	61	1.064 65 084	1	.000 29 089	1	.000 00 485
2	.034 90 659	62	.082 10 414	2	0 58 178	2	00 970
3	.052 35 988	63	.099 55 743	3	0 87 266	3	01 454
4	.069 81 317	64	.117 01 072	4	1 16 355	4	01 939
5	0.087 26 646	65	1.134 46 401	5	.001 45 444	5	.000 02 424
6	.104 71 976	66	.151 91 731	6	1 74 533	6	02 909
7	.122 17 305	67	.169 37 060	7	2 03 622	7	03 394
8	.139 62 634	68	.186 82 389	8	2 32 711	8	03 879
9	.157 07 963	69	.204 27 718	9	2 61 799	9	04 363
10	0.174 53 293	70	1.221 73 048	10	.002 90 888	10	.000 04 848
11	.191 98 622	71	.239 18 377	11	3 19 977	11	05 333
12	.209 43 951	72	.256 63 706	12	3 49 066	12	05 818
13	.226 89 280	73	.274 09 035	13	3 78 155	13	06 303
14	.244 34 610	74	.291 54 365	14	4 07 243	14	06 787
15	0.261 79 939	75	1.308 99 694	15	.004 36 332	15	.000 07 272
16	.279 25 268	76	.326 45 023	16	4 65 421	16	07 757
17	.296 70 597	77	.343 90 352	17	4 94 510	17	08 242
18	.314 15 927	78	.361 35 682	18	5 23 599	18	08 727
19	.331 61 256	79	.378 81 011	19	5 52 688	19	09 211
20	0.349 06 585	80	1.396 26 340	20	.005 81 776	20	.000 09 696
21	.366 51 914	81	.413 71 669	21	6 10 865	21	10 181
22	.383 97 244	82	.431 16 999	22	6 39 954	22	10 666
23	.401 42 573	83	.448 62 328	23	6 69 043	23	11 151
24	.418 87 902	84	.466 07 657	24	6 98 132	24	11 636
25	0.436 33 231	85	1.483 52 986	25	.007 27 221	25	.000 12 120
26	.453 78 561	86	.500 98 316	26	7 56 309	26	12 605
27	.471 23 890	87	.518 43 645	27	7 85 398	27	13 090
28	.488 69 219	88	.535 88 974	28	8 14 487	28	13 575
29	.506 14 548	89	.553 34 303	29	8 43 576	29	14 060
30	0.523 59 878	90	1.570 79 633	30	.008 72 665	30	.000 14 544
31	.541 05 207	91	.588 24 962	31	9 01 753	31	15 029
32	.558 50 536	92	.605 70 291	32	9 30 842	32	15 514
33	.575 95 865	93	.623 15 620	33	9 59 931	33	15 999
34	.593 41 195	94	.640 60 950	34	9 89 020	34	16 484
35	0.610 86 524	95	1.658 06 279	35	.010 18 109	35	.000 16 969
36	.628 31 853	96	.675 51 608	36	10 47 198	36	17 453
37	.645 77 182	97	.692 96 937	37	10 76 286	37	17 938
38	.663 22 512	98	.710 42 267	38	11 05 375	38	18 423
39	.680 67 841	99	.727 87 596	39	11 34 464	39	18 908
40	0.698 13 170	100	1.745 32 925	40	.011 63 553	40	.000 19 393
41	.715 58 499	101	.762 78 254	41	11 92 642	41	19 877
42	.733 03 829	102	.780 23 584	42	12 21 730	42	20 362
43	.750 49 158	103	.797 68 913	43	12 50 819	43	20 847
44	.767 94 487	104	.815 14 242	44	12 79 908	44	21 332
45	0.785 39 816	105	1.832 59 571	45	.013 08 997	45	.000 21 817
46	.802 85 146	106	.850 04 901	46	13 38 086	46	22 301
47	.820 30 475	107	.867 50 230	47	13 67 175	47	22 786
48	.837 75 804	108	.884 95 559	48	13 96 263	48	23 271
49	.855 21 133	109	.902 40 888	49	14 25 352	49	23 756
50	0.872 66 463	110	1.919 86 218	50	.014 54 441	50	.000 24 241
51	.890 11 792	111	.937 31 547	51	14 83 530	51	24 726
52	.907 57 121	112	.954 76 876	52	15 12 619	52	25 210
53	.925 02 450	113	.972 22 205	53	15 41 708	53	25 695
54	.942 47 780	114	.989 67 535	54	15 70 796	54	26 180
55	0.959 93 109	115	2.007 12 864	55	.015 99 885	55	.000 26 665
56	0.977 38 438	116	.024 58 193	56	16 28 974	56	27 150
57	0.994 83 767	117	.042 03 522	57	16 58 063	57	27 634
58	1.012 29 097	118	.059 48 852	58	16 87 152	58	28 119
59	1.029 74 426	119	.076 94 181	59	17 16 240	59	28 604
60	1.047 19 755	120	.094 39 510	60	17 45 329	60	29 089

TABLE B-8. TRIGONOMETRIC FORMULAS FOR THE SOLUTION OF RIGHT TRIANGLES

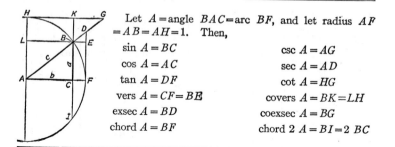

Let A = angle BAC = arc BF, and let radius AF = AB = AH = 1. Then,

$\sin A = BC$	$\csc A = AG$
$\cos A = AC$	$\sec A = AD$
$\tan A = DF$	$\cot A = HG$
vers $A = CF = BE$	covers $A = BK = LH$
exsec $A = BD$	coexsec $A = BG$
chord $A = BF$	chord 2 $A = BI = 2\ BC$

In the right-angled triangle ABC, let $AB = c$, $BC = a$, $CA = b$. Then,

1. $\sin A = \dfrac{a}{c}$

2. $\cos A = \dfrac{b}{c}$

3. $\tan A = \dfrac{a}{b}$

4. $\cot A = \dfrac{b}{a}$

5. $\sec A = \dfrac{c}{b}$

6. $\csc A = \dfrac{c}{a}$

7. vers $A = 1 - \cos A = \dfrac{c-b}{c}$ = covers B

8. exsec $A = \sec A - 1 = \dfrac{c-b}{b}$ = coexsec B

9. covers $A = \dfrac{c-a}{c}$ = vers B

10. coexsec $A = \dfrac{c-a}{a}$ = exsec B

11. $a = c \sin A = b \tan A$

12. $b = c \cos A = a \cot A$

13. $c = \dfrac{a}{\sin A} = \dfrac{b}{\cos A}$

14. $a = c \cos B = b \cot B$

15. $b = c \sin B = a \tan B$

16. $c = \dfrac{a}{\cos B} = \dfrac{b}{\sin B}$

17. $a = \sqrt{c^2 - b^2} = \sqrt{(c-b)(c+b)}$

18. $b = \sqrt{c^2 - a^2} = \sqrt{(c-a)(c+a)}$

19. $c = \sqrt{a^2 + b^2}$

20. $C = 90° = A + B$

21. Area = $\tfrac{1}{2}ab$

142.6224

TABLE B-9. TRIGONOMETRIC FORMULAS FOR THE SOLUTION OF OBLIQUE TRIANGLES

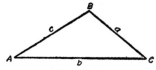

No.	Given	Sought	Formula
22	A, B, a	C, b, c	$C=180°-(A+B)$
			$b=\dfrac{a}{\sin A}\times\sin B$
			$c=\dfrac{a}{\sin A}\times\sin (A+B)=\dfrac{a}{\sin A}\times\sin C$
		Area	$\text{Area}=\tfrac{1}{2}ab\sin C=\dfrac{a^2\sin B\sin C}{2\sin A}$
23	A, a, b	B, C, c	$\sin B=\dfrac{\sin A}{a}\times b$
			$C=180°-(A+B)$
			$c=\dfrac{a}{\sin A}\times\sin C$
		Area	$\text{Area}=\tfrac{1}{2}ab\sin C$
24	$C, a, b,$	c	$c=\sqrt{a^2+b^2-2ab\cos C}$
25		$\tfrac{1}{2}(A+B)$	$\tfrac{1}{2}(A+B)=90°-\tfrac{1}{2}C$
26		$\tfrac{1}{2}(A-B)$	$\tan\tfrac{1}{2}(A-B)=\dfrac{a-b}{a+b}\times\tan\tfrac{1}{2}(A+B)$
27		A, B	$A=\tfrac{1}{2}(A+B)+\tfrac{1}{2}(A-B)$
			$B=\tfrac{1}{2}(A+B)-\tfrac{1}{2}(A-B)$
28		c	$c=(a+b)\times\dfrac{\cos\tfrac{1}{2}(A+B)}{\cos\tfrac{1}{2}(A-B)}=(a-b)\times\dfrac{\sin\tfrac{1}{2}(A+B)}{\sin\tfrac{1}{2}(A-B)}$
29		Area	$\text{Area}=\tfrac{1}{2}ab\sin C$
30	a, b, c	A	Let $s=\dfrac{a+b+c}{2}$
31			$\sin\tfrac{1}{2}A=\sqrt{\dfrac{(s-b)(s-c)}{bc}}$
			$\cos\tfrac{1}{2}A=\sqrt{\dfrac{s(s-a)}{bc}}$
			$\tan\tfrac{1}{2}A=\sqrt{\dfrac{(s-b)(s-c)}{s(s-a)}}$
32			$\sin A=\dfrac{2\sqrt{s(s-a)(s-b)(s-c)}}{bc}$
			$\cos A=\dfrac{b^2+c^2-a^2}{2bc}$
33		Area	$\text{Area}=\sqrt{s(s-a)(s-b)(s-c)}$

TABLE B-10. RELATIONS BETWEEN LINEAR AND ANGULAR ERRORS

Allowable Angular Error for Given Linear Precision		Allowable Linear Error for Given Angular Precision					
Precision of Linear Measurements	Allowable Angular Error	Least Reading in Angular Measurements	Allowable Linear Error in				Ratio
			100'	500'	1000'	5000'	
$\frac{1}{500}$	6'53"	5'	.145	.727	1.454	7.272	$\frac{1}{688}$
$\frac{1}{1000}$	3 26	1'	.029	.145	.291	1.454	$\frac{1}{3440}$
$\frac{1}{5000}$	0 41	30"	.015	.073	.145	.727	$\frac{1}{6880}$
$\frac{1}{10,000}$	0 21	20"	.010	.049	.097	.485	$\frac{1}{10,300}$
$\frac{1}{50,000}$	0 04	10"	.005	.024	.049	.242	$\frac{1}{20,600}$
$\frac{1}{100,000}$	0 02	5"	.002	.012	.024	.121	$\frac{1}{41,200}$
$\frac{1}{1,000,000}$	0 00.2	2"	.001	.005	.010	.048	$\frac{1}{103,100}$
		1"		.002	.005	.024	$\frac{1}{206,300}$

TABLE B-11. PRECISION OF COMPUTED VALUES

SIZE OF ANGLE AND FUNCTION		ANGULAR ERROR				
		1'	30"	20"	10"	5"
		Precision of computed value using sine or cosine				
sin 5° or cos 85°		$\frac{1}{300}$	$\frac{1}{600}$	$\frac{1}{900}$	$\frac{1}{1800}$	$\frac{1}{3600}$
10	80	$\frac{1}{610}$	$\frac{1}{1210}$	$\frac{1}{1820}$	$\frac{1}{3640}$	$\frac{1}{7280}$
20	70	$\frac{1}{1250}$	$\frac{1}{2500}$	$\frac{1}{3750}$	$\frac{1}{7500}$	$\frac{1}{15,000}$
30	60	$\frac{1}{1990}$	$\frac{1}{3970}$	$\frac{1}{5960}$	$\frac{1}{11,970}$	$\frac{1}{23,940}$
40	50	$\frac{1}{2890}$	$\frac{1}{5770}$	$\frac{1}{8660}$	$\frac{1}{17,310}$	$\frac{1}{34,620}$
50	40	$\frac{1}{4100}$	$\frac{1}{8190}$	$\frac{1}{12,290}$	$\frac{1}{24,580}$	$\frac{1}{49,160}$
60	30	$\frac{1}{5950}$	$\frac{1}{11,900}$	$\frac{1}{17,860}$	$\frac{1}{35,720}$	$\frac{1}{71,440}$
70	20	$\frac{1}{9450}$	$\frac{1}{18,900}$	$\frac{1}{28,330}$	$\frac{1}{56,670}$	$\frac{1}{113,340}$
80	10	$\frac{1}{19,500}$	$\frac{1}{39,000}$	$\frac{1}{58,500}$	$\frac{1}{117,000}$	$\frac{1}{234,000}$
		Precision of computed value using tan or cot				
tan or cot 5°		$\frac{1}{300}$	$\frac{1}{600}$	$\frac{1}{900}$	$\frac{1}{1790}$	$\frac{1}{3580}$
10		$\frac{1}{590}$	$\frac{1}{1180}$	$\frac{1}{1760}$	$\frac{1}{3530}$	$\frac{1}{7050}$
20		$\frac{1}{1100}$	$\frac{1}{2210}$	$\frac{1}{3310}$	$\frac{1}{6620}$	$\frac{1}{13,250}$
30		$\frac{1}{1490}$	$\frac{1}{2980}$	$\frac{1}{4470}$	$\frac{1}{8930}$	$\frac{1}{17,870}$
40		$\frac{1}{1690}$	$\frac{1}{3390}$	$\frac{1}{5080}$	$\frac{1}{10,160}$	$\frac{1}{20,320}$
45		$\frac{1}{1720}$	$\frac{1}{3440}$	$\frac{1}{5160}$	$\frac{1}{10,310}$	$\frac{1}{20,630}$
50		$\frac{1}{1690}$	$\frac{1}{3390}$	$\frac{1}{5080}$	$\frac{1}{10,160}$	$\frac{1}{20,320}$
60		$\frac{1}{1490}$	$\frac{1}{2980}$	$\frac{1}{4470}$	$\frac{1}{8930}$	$\frac{1}{17,870}$
70		$\frac{1}{1100}$	$\frac{1}{2210}$	$\frac{1}{3310}$	$\frac{1}{6620}$	$\frac{1}{13,250}$
80		$\frac{1}{590}$	$\frac{1}{1180}$	$\frac{1}{1760}$	$\frac{1}{3530}$	$\frac{1}{7050}$
85		$\frac{1}{300}$	$\frac{1}{600}$	$\frac{1}{900}$	$\frac{1}{1790}$	$\frac{1}{3580}$

ANSWERS TO SELECTED PROBLEMS

CHAPTER 2

2-3. 17,213.8 ft

2-6. 2566.7 ft

2-9. 34.604 ft

2-12. 43.99 acres

2-17. 2.971 acres

2-20. 156°53'16.8″
2.7382 rad

2-23. 156

2-27. 5.13×10^3

2-32. 0.722227
1.209077
1.210289
$\overline{3.141593} = \pi$ (check)

2-39. MPV = 942.97 ft
$\sigma = \pm 0.049$ ft
$\sigma_m = \pm 0.017$ ft

2-45. $E_{50} = \pm 0.04$ ft (5 of 11)
$E_{90} = \pm 0.09$ ft (11 of 11)

2-48. $\sigma_A = \pm 0.019$; $\sigma_B = \pm 0.021$
(set A is better)

2-52. MPV = 43°29'05″
$\sigma = \pm 48.2″$
$\sigma_m = \pm 17.0″$

2-56. $\sigma = \pm 0.15$ ft
$E_{90} = \pm 0.25$ ft

2-60. ± 0.24 ft

2-65. 48°21'58.7″

2-69. 11,673 m² $\pm$ 1.95 m²

2-73. 70°24'17.4″
52°04'33.7″
57°31'08.9″
$\overline{180°00'00.0″}$ (check)

CHAPTER 4

4-5. 671.84 ft

4-10. 561.00 ft

4-14. 462.695 ft

4-17. 752.282 ft

4-23. 87.083 ft

4-31. 2806.35 ft; 2805.57 ft

4-34. 17¾ lb

4-40. 0.030 ft

4-44. Triangle $GAB = 63,031$ ft²

4-48. ± 0.155 ft

4-52. 0.070 ft

4-63. 0.528 ft

4-66. 1402.374 m

CHAPTER 5

5-3. 6.60 miles

5-7. -0.00044 ft

5-9. 10.0 m

5-12. 1206.69 ft

5-15. 16.9″

5-27. 7.75 cm

5-30. Elev. BM 2 = 95.98 ft

5-36. Diff. in elev. = 0.4575 m
Reading on $A = 1.365$ m

5-41. 564.71 ft

5-44. Elev. $C = 781.141$ ft
2nd order—class II

5-49. 493 ft

5-65. 30 mm

5-69. ± 0.03 ft

CHAPTER 6

6-4. N 42°54' E; S 9°55' E;
S 37°22' W; N 57°45' W

6-7. Angles = 64°44'; 177°54'; 81°54'

6-11. 337°05'

6-16. N 73°01' W

6-20. Bearing $DE = $ S 85°59' W

6-25. Bearing $CD = $ N 9°16' W

6-29. Bearing $EF = $ S 33°21' W

6-35. Azimuth $AB = 238°42'$

6-39. 40°12'37.1″

CHAPTER 7

7-5. True South = S 4°50' W
7-7. 15°15' westward
7-9. N 1°10' W in 1800
7-12. S 19°15' E
7-18. S 85°58' W

7-25. 3°05' E
7-28. Local attraction at $C = 2°$ W;
  bearing $CD = $ S 29° W
7-38. Angle $BCD = 102°45'$

CHAPTER 8

8-3. 13.8"
8-9. 7.2"
8-12. 2'17.5"
8-15. $n = 30$
8-27. 272°42.5'
8-30. $x = 126°43.2'$; $y = 233°16.8'$
8-32. Angle $BAC = 80°41'34''$

8-35. 0.036 ft
8-42. 10.6"
8-46. Index error = $-0°02'$
  Correct angle = $-4°15'$
8-50. 1'04.8"
8-54. 4.2"
8-59. For $\frac{1}{2000}$, angle = 1'43"

CHAPTER 9

9-11. For 20-sided traverse,
  Σ interior angles = 3240°
9-17. Closure error = 5'

9-19. 1 part in 4340
9-22. Angle D is incorrect.

CHAPTER 10

10-4. Closure = 06'
  Balanced angle at $D = 157°21'$
  Bearing $DE = $ N 84°55' W
10-5. Lat. DE = $+72.14$ ft; dep. DE = -811.00 ft
  Linear error of closure = 12.6 ft
  Precision = $\frac{1}{3930}$
10-6. Balanced lat. $DE = +72.32$ ft; dep. $DE = -810.89$ ft
  Coordinates of D are: $X = 11,466.22$ ft; $y = 9410.57$ ft
  Length $AD = 1580.26$ ft; bearing $AD = $ S 68°06' E
10-14. Linear error of closure = 0.32 ft
  Precision = $\frac{1}{2310}$
10-22. Length $FC = 1438.83$ ft; bearing $FC = $ N 80°20.6' W
10-25. Course BC too short, probably by 10 ft
10-28. Length $CD = 221.36$; azimuth $CD = 288°26.1'$
10-41. Angle $C = 72°43.8'$; angle $D = 153°27.0'$

CHAPTER 11

11-2. 6.447 acres
11-5. 15.63 ch^2 = 1.563 acres
11-7. 0.573 acre

11-12. 6.957 acres
11-14. 26.608 acres
11-19. 142,850 ft^2 = 3.279 acres

11-25. Lat. GA = +300 ft;
dep. GA = +1000 ft;
area = 14.578 acres
11-32. Area = 26,298 ft^2 = 0.604 acre

11-34. Area = 2.838 acres
11-38. 87.29 ft
11-40. 4.190 acres

CHAPTER 12

12-3. 0.00003 in.
12-14. 470 ft
12-17. 212 ft, +12.1 ft
12-21. 1.24 ft
12-33. 524.2 ft
12-37. H = 247 ft; V = 348.0 ft

12-40. AB = 252 ft;
elev. B = 1007.5 ft
12-44. About 2½′
12-50. A = 425.7; B = 445.0;
C = 457.3; D = 446.0 ft

CHAPTER 13

13-8. 0.10 in.

CHAPTER 14

14-2. 2 ft (assuming 0.01 in. as smallest possible scaling division)
14-21. 1000 ft/in. (assuming 0.01 in. as smallest plotting error)
14-28. Heavied contours are 870, 880, 890, and 900 ft

CHAPTER 15

15-21. Elev. 1 to 2 ft, distance 10 ft
15-22. 0.0033 in., insignificant

15-27. $\frac{1}{320}$

CHAPTER 16

16-19. 2 AM
16-32. 9 May 2^{h}05^{m}11^s AM
16-44. 20^{h}06.7^m

16-48. 0^{h}30.8^m
16-51. S 12°05.5′ E
16-65. Az = 68°54.5′ from N

CHAPTER 17

17-4. Factor @ 6000 ft = 0.99971308
17-8. Length = 1973.84 ft; bearing = S 36°41′59.3″ W
17-11. X = 1,448,499.47 ft; Y = 1,763,620.03 ft
17-12. Length = 9795.95 ft; bearing = N 32°57′06.421″ E
17-16. BC = 2127.32 ft
17-17. BC = 2127.17 ft
17-18. Azimuth BC = 117°23′13″
17-19. Precision = $\frac{1}{6860}$
17-20. Coords. sta. C are X = 1,518,881.92 ft; Y = 484,490.47 ft

CHAPTER 18

18-19. Closure of 5 mm exceeds 3 mm allowable for this circuit
18-20. Elev. BM $y = 161.266$ m

CHAPTER 19

73, 37

19-30. $x = 299.79$ ft   **19-34.** Area $= 11,776$ ft^2
19-33. Area $= 10,595$ ft^2

CHAPTER 20

20-5. 3N, 1N, 0, 1S, 2S, 2S, 2S   **20-22.** 3200 rods
20-9. 823.6 ft   **20-38.** Single, single
20-12. 132 miles   **20-46.** Over 50 acres must be
20-18. 40 acres   meandered

CHAPTER 21

21-9. Yes, reentrant corners   **21-27.** For drainage, runoff

CHAPTER 22

22-4. $R = 1432.69$, $T = 252.62$, $L = 500.00$, $BC = 69 + 95.98$
22-8. $E = 22.10$, $M = 21.77$ ft
22-11. $D = 4°00'$, $T = 447.5$, $L = 867.5$, $E = 68.3$, $M = 65.2$ ft
22-21. $D = 3°20'$, $R = 1718.87$, $T = 180.66$, $L = 360.00$, $E = 9.47$ ft
22-24. $AV = 189.93$, $R = 1145.92$, $D = 5°00'$, $T = 417.08$, $L = 800.00$,
          $E = 73.54$ ft, $BC = 34 + 19.93$
22-27. $R_x = 1350$ ft
22-43. $C = 454$ ft
22-46. $L = 500$ ft (each)
22-49. $R = 2106$ ft

CHAPTER 23

23-2. $1\frac{1}{8}$ in.
23-4. Elev. sta. 33 $= 551.50$, sta. 36 $= 549.70$, sta. 39 $= 549.10$
23-8. $L = 800$ ft; elev. sta. 60 $= 407.00$, sta. 64 $= 403.00$
23-11. Elev. sta. 47 $= 189.50$, sta. 52 $= 194.50$
23-26. 775 ft
23-30. 1100 ft

CHAPTER 24

24-4. 784 yd^3
24-6. 326 yd^3
24-12. $C_p = 1.33$ yd^3, $V_p = 783.1$ yd^3 (carried beyond nearest yd^3 for your
          checking purposes only)
24-19. V_p in cut $= 17.28$ yd^3, in fill $= 8.89$ yd^3

CHAPTER 25

25-3. 1210 ft/in. = 1 : 14,520
25-8. 1530 ft/in. = 1 : 18,360
25-12. 1 : 20,810
25-17. 10 in.
25-20. 4000 ft
25-23. 7770 ft
25-26. Angle $ABC = 44°11.4'$
25-29. 708 ft

25-32. 9800 ft
25-35. 4310 ft
25-41. 6007 ft
25-44. $h_A = 3570$ ft
25-47. 173.6 ft
25-50. 11
25-53. 28.1%
25-56. 741

INDEX

Measurement (Cont.)
  of lengths, 77, 214, 257
  linear, 51
  precision of, 71, 89
  proportionate, 416
  by repetition, 191
  slope, 62
  by taping, 58
  types of, 15
  units of, 15
  of vertical angles, 202
  of volumes, 461
  weights of, 37
Measuring wheel, 52
Mercator projection, 360
Meridian, 325, 365
  arrow, 302
  assumed, 145
  celestial, 330
  central, 352
  convergence of, 412
  determination of, 325
  distance, 245
  by equal altitudes of the sun, 327
  geodetic, 353, 355
  geographic, 145
  grid, 146
  magnetic, 145
  from Polaris observations, 328
  principal, 405
  reference, 145
  by shadow method, 327
  true, 145
Metallic tape, 56
Meter, 16, 17, 51, 387, 436
Metes and bounds, 387
Microclimate, 66
Micrometer, 185, 187, 188, 380, 381
Microwave instruments, 86
Middle ordinate, 438
Mil, 17
Military grid, 237
Minimum focus, 180
Minus sight, 101
Mistakes in surveying, 22, 72, 137, 153,
  167, 179, 207, 219, 237, 254, 287, 304,
  345, 397, 432, 448, 454, 467, 497
Modern Land Data Systems (MOLDS),
  386
Modulated, 79
Modulus of elasticity, 66
Monuments, 274, 286, 371, 385, 388, 395,
  416
Mosaic, 484
Most probable value, 29
Movable stadia lines, 264
Mylar, 303, 313

Nadir, 329
National Bureau of Standards (NBS), 56,
  65, 74
National Cartographic Information Cen-
  ter, 290
National Control Networks, horizontal,
  vertical, 10, 13, 368, 369, 376
National Defense Mapping Agency
  (DMA), 11, 289
National Geodetic Survey (NGS), 7, 11,
  98, 132, 147, 158, 218, 236, 290, 349,
  355, 370, 376, 378, 388
National Map Standards of Accuracy,
  286, 295
National Vertical Geodetic Datum
  (NVGD), 10, 366
Natural error, 22
Needle, magnetic, 146
Negative lens, 105
Nodal point, 258, 473
Normal density curve, 25
Normal error distribution curve, 25
Normal tension, 68
Northing, 223
North-seeking gyroscope, 7, 317, 325
Note check, 125
Notebooks, 44
Notes; see Field notes

Objective lens, 105
Oblique Mercator projection, 360
Oblique photograph, 474
Obliterated corner, 416
Observations, 387
  on Polaris, 334
  on sun, 340
  weighted, 37
Obstacle, prolonging straight line past,
  200
Odometer, 52
Offset lines, 423, 426
Offset traverse, 215, 395
Offsets, 201, 215, 423, 442
  area by, 244
  chord, 423
  details by, 276
  in links, 537
  right-angle method, 210, 276
  tangent, 423, 451
Omitted measurement, 235
Open traverse, 149, 211, 218
Optical axis, 105, 509
Optical micrometer, 185, 187, 188
Optical plumbing, 52, 181, 184, 189, 512
Optics, 107
Orders of accuracy, 367

77 78 79 80 81 7 6 5 4 3 2

ABBREVIATIONS

CONSTRUCTION SURVEYS

b.b.	batterboards
B.L.	building line
C.B.	catch basin
C.G.	center line of grade
₵	center line
const.	construction
C	cut
esmt.	easement
F	fill
F.G.	finish grade, Fin. Gr.
F.H.	fire hydrant
₤	fence line
F.L.	flow line (invert)
F.S.	finished surface
G.C.	grade change
G.P.	grade point
G.R.	grade rod (s.s. notes)
L	left (x-sect. notes)
M.H.	manhole
₤	property line
P.P.	power pole
pvmt.	pavement
R	right (x-sect. notes)
R/W	right-of-way
S.D.	storm drain
S.G.	subgrade
S.L.	spring line
spec.	specifications
Sq.	square
s.s.	slope stake, side slope
Std.	standard
Str. Gr.	straight grade
X-sect.	cross-section

PROPERTY SURVEYS

A	area
C.F.	curb face
ch "X"	chiseled X cross
C.I.	cast iron
diam.	diameter
Dr.	drive
ER	end of return
Ex.	existing

H & T	hub and tack
H.C.	house connection sewer
I.B.	iron bolt (bar)
I.P.	iron pipe; iron pin (confusing)
L & T	lead and tack
max.	maximum
min.	minimum
M.H.W.	mean high water
M.L.L.W.	mean low low water
M.L.W.	mean low water
Mon.	monument
No.	number
P	pipe; pin (confusing)
Rec.	record
St.	street
Std. Surv. Mon.	standard survey monument
Std. Trav. Mon.	standard traverse monument
2″ × 2″	two- × two-inch stake
X	cross cut in stone
yd	yard

PUBLIC LANDS SURVEYS

ac	acres
AMC	auxiliary meander corner
bdy., bdys.	boundary, boundaries
BT	bearing tree
CC	closing corner
ch, chs	chain, chains
cor., cors.	corner, corners
corr.	correction
decl.	declination
dist.	distance
frac.	fractional (sec., etc.)
Gr.	Greenwich
G.M.	guide meridian
lk, lks	link, links
meas.	measurement
mer.	meridian
mkd.	marked
Mi. Cor.	mile corner
MC	meander corner
M.S.	mineral survey